AIP Conference Proceedings

Series Editor: Hugh C. Wolfe

Number 14

Particles and Fields Subseries No.6

Particles and Fields – 1973

(APS/DPF Berkeley)

Editors

H. H. Bingham, M. Davier, G. R. Lynch,
University of California, Berkeley

American Institute of Physics

New York   1973

L. C. Catalog Card No. 73-91923
ISBN 0-88318-113-4
AEC CONF-730837

American Institute of Physics
335 East 45th Street
New York, N. Y. 10017

Printed in the United States of America

EDITORS' FOREWORD

The Berkeley Meeting of the Division of Particles and Fields of the American Physical Society was held at the University of California, Berkeley, California, August 13-17, 1973. This meeting is the third of the biennial "odd year" meetings of the DPF; the previous ones were held in Boulder, Colorado (1969) and Rochester, New York (1971). The proceedings of the 1971 meeting were published with the title "Particles and Fields - 1971" in this AIP Conference Proceedings series.

Some 350 physicists attended the meeting. Parallel and plenary sessions were held as detailed in the conference program. The editors were also the organizing committee and, to a large extent, the program committee. However, the program for each parallel session, as well as the choice of which papers from the parallel sessions were included in these proceedings, was the responsibility of the session chairmen, some of whom put in considerable effort to plan their sessions and organize review talks and panel discussions. These proceedings were intended to contain all of the talks from the plenary sessions and some of the talks from the parallel sessions, primarily those that were of review nature.

These pages, unfortunately, convey little of the excitement with which news of evidence for neutral currents in the CERN neutrino experiments was received, for example, nor of the enthusiasm generated by early glimpses into the physics of the NAL and ISR energy domains.

We are indebted to our conference secretary, Ann McLellen, for keeping things organized before the conference. We thank Ted Kirksey, Howard Smith, Mabel Smith, and Loretta Lizama from the LBL Technical Information Division for helping with preparations for the conference and Bill Kimley from the UCB physics department for taking charge of the conference operations. The editing of Charles Pezzotti was very helpful both before the conference and in the preparation of this volume.

Harry H. Bingham
Michel Davier
Gerald R. Lynch

Berkeley, California
1973-10-19

Contents

Chapter I
Weak and Electromagnetic Interactions and Gauge Theories

Gauge Theories

Deep Inelastic

NEUTRAL CURRENTS

SPEAR

W

Higgs Particles

Bj Scaling

R

$K_L^0 \to \mu^+ \mu^-$

νW_2

AUG. 1973 - REVIEW OF LATEST RESULTS FROM

HIGH ENERGY NEUTRINO EXPERIMENTS

H. Wachsmuth[*] - CERN

I)   INTRODUCTION

II) BRIEF DESCRIPTION OF THE EXPERIMENTS AT ANL, CERN
     AND NAL

III) RESULTS OF CHARGED WEAK CURRENT STUDIES

   III.1 With Muonic Neutrinos

   a) $\nu_\mu + N \to \mu + $ anything, σ_{tot}, scaling

   b) $\nu_\mu + n \to \mu^- + p$, $\bar{\nu}_\mu + p \to \mu^+ + n$

   c)   W-mass limit

   III.2 With Electronic Neutrinos

   a) $\nu_e + N \to e + $ anything, σ_{tot}, μ-e universality

   b)   Muon number conservation law multiplicative ?

IV) NEUTRAL CURRENT SEARCH

   IV.1 Leptonic : $\nu_\mu + e^- \to \nu_\mu + e^-$

   IV.2 Hadronic : $\nu_\mu + N \to \nu_\mu + $ hadrons

V)   HEAVY LEPTON SEARCH

VI) CONCLUSION

     FOOTNOTES AND REFERENCES

I. INTRODUCTION

Since the last reviews of neutrino experiments [1,2], the following new results have been obtained :

1) Neutral hadronic weak currents as the most probable interpretation of muonless events, which cannot be attributed to neutron background [3], and a more precise analysis of the leptonic neutral current reactions $\bar\nu_\mu e^- \to \bar\nu_\mu e^-$ [4].
2) First quantitative measurements of high energy ν_e-N scattering [5].
3) First results of ν_μ-N scattering in the energy region 10 to 150 GeV coming from the two NAL experiments [6,7] and results for $1 < E < 10$ GeV from the Gargamelle experiment [8].
4) First measurement of the elastic $\bar\nu$ and re-measurement of the elastic ν cross section [8,9].
5) A new W mass limit [10].
6) Heavy lepton (Georgi-Glashow type) mass limits [11].

Earlier results are summarized in the conclusions.

II. BRIEF DESCRIPTION OF THE EXPERIMENTS AT ANL, CERN AND NAL-NB AND NAL-WB

The main features of the four experiments reported here are summarized in table 1.

Table I Experimental characteristics

	ANL	CERN	NAL EX.21 (NB in fig. 1)	NAL EX.1A (WB in fig. 1)
Proton momentum (GeV/c)	12.4	26.3	300	300 AND 400
Average proton intensity per pulse	1.2×10^{12}	1.1×10^{12}	$\sim 10^{12}$	$\sim 10^{12}$
Spill length	$\sim$ 20 μs	2.1 μs	$\sim$ 300 ms	100 μs
π,K focusing	HORN (250 kA)	HORN (340 kA) & R2 (400 kA)	QUADRU-POLES (160–18)+ GeV/c	NONE
Decay path length (m)	40 m	70 m	400 m	400 m
Shielding	10 m Fe	22 m Fe	530 m Fe + earth	1000 m Fe + earth
Detector	H/D Bubble chamber (12 foot) filling: D_2	Heavy liquid bubble chamber (Gargamelle) filling: CF_3Br	Fe-plates + spark chambers +toroidal magnet	liqu. scint. + spark chambers + toroidal magnets
Total (fiducial) mass of detector	3 (1.2) tons	18 (4.5) tons	160 tons	120 (60) tons

The two NAL experiments use the same decay tunnel and have a common ν beam axis (see Fig. 1). NAL-NB (for Narrow Band beam experiment) obtains ν's from a sign-and momentum selected secondary hadron beam, NAL-WB (for Wide Band beam experiment) temporarily from unfocused pions and kaons emerging from a Fe-target (1 λ) bombarded by 300 and 400 GeV protons by-passing the NB focusing system. Later on a horn focusing system will provide the WB beam. The present versions of the NAL ν-detectors are sketched in Fig. 1. At CERN the detector (Gargamelle) is a beam parallel cylindrical heavy liquid bubble chamber of length 4.8 m and diameter 1.85 m with a visible volume of 7 m^3 and a magnetic field of 20 kG. The ANL-12 ft-H_2/D_2 bubble chamber is a cylinder perpendicular to the beam and has 16 m^3 visible volume. The ν and $\bar{\nu}$ spectra for all 4 experiments are shown in Fig. 2.

III. RESULTS OF CHARGED WEAK CURRENT STUDIES
III.1 With Muonic Neutrinos
a) $\nu + N \rightarrow \mu^- + $ anything, σ_{tot}, scaling

The Gargamelle results [8] are based on an analysis of 95'000 and 175'000 pictures exposed to ν and $\bar{\nu}$ beams, respectively, yielding samples of 2500 ν and 950 $\bar{\nu}$ events. ν ($\bar{\nu}$) events are signalled by at least one μ^- (μ^+) candidate in the final state (particle with no strong interaction within visible volume, mean potential length 150 cm). The ν ($\bar{\nu}$) energy is taken to be the sum of energies carried away by all charged and neutral secondaries. The average energy correction due to missing neutron energy (75 % detection efficiency, 1/3 of n energy visibly deposited), missing gammas (average e^+e^- pair energy 230 MeV), and unmeasurable hadrons ($\sim$ 7 %) amounts to $\sim + (5 \frac{+}{-} 2.5)$ % of the visible energy. Cuts were applied on the total longitudinal momentum along the ν beam axis (> 0.6 GeV/c), on the total visible energy (> 1 GeV), on the four-momentum transfer < maximum allowed in a νN collision), and on the total energy measurement error (< 30 %, excludes 4 %; mean energy error for muons is 8 %, for total hadron energy 15 %, for γ energy 30 %). 23 % (15 %) of ν ($\bar{\nu}$) events are ambiguous between ν and $\bar{\nu}$ (having also a muon candidate of the wrong sign); 6 % do not show lepton candidates. Corrections for these contaminations have been applied. The total cross sections for ν and $\bar{\nu}$ are shown in Fig. 3, best linear fits in table 2 (taking account of the distortion expected for a linearly

Table 2

		one parameter fit	two parameter fit
E > 1 GeV	ν	$(.74 \frac{+}{-} .02)$ E	$(.70 \frac{+}{-} .07)$E + $(.14 \frac{+}{-} .18)$
	$\bar{\nu}$	$(.28 \frac{+}{-} .01)$ E	$(.26 \frac{+}{-} .04)$E + $(.05 \frac{+}{-} .09)$
E > 2 GeV	ν	$(.74 \frac{+}{-} .03)$ E	$(.77 \frac{+}{-} .09)$E - $(.11 \frac{+}{-} .25)$
	$\bar{\nu}$	$(.27 \frac{+}{-} .01)$ E	$(.32 \frac{+}{-} .06)$E - $(.13 \frac{+}{-} .17)$

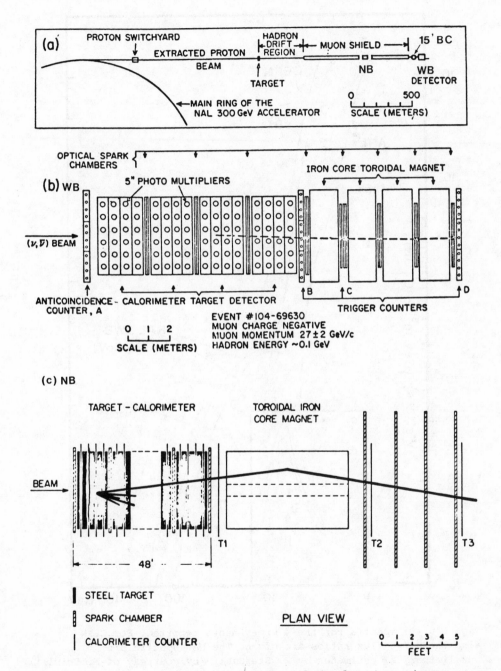

Fig. 1 NAL - ν - layout (a) and sketches of the detector set-ups in the wide band beam (b, WB) and narrow band beam (c, NB) experiments.

6

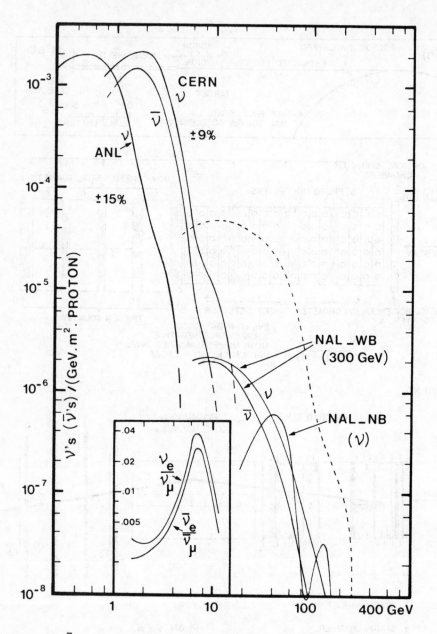

Fig. 2 ν (ν̄) spectra for the 4 experiments reported. For CERN also the ν_e/ν_μ flux ratios are given. The NAL spectra are (preliminary ?) estimates by R. Stefanski (by courtesy of F. Sciulli). A 70 % ideal 400 GeV spectrum is shown (----------) to indicate future possibilities of the NAL-WB experiment.

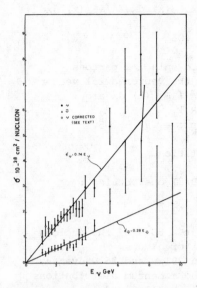

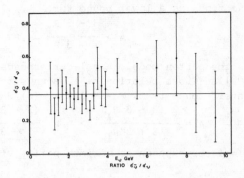

Fig. 4 Ratio of total cross sections

← Fig. 3 Total cross sections (CERN)

rising cross section due to measurement error and steeply falling ν spectra). Fig. 4 shows the ratio $R_1 = \sigma(\bar{\nu})/\sigma_+(\nu)$ as a function of energy. R_1 is compatible with a constant $= .37 \pm .02$ (E > 1 GeV) or $= .38 \pm .02$ (E > 2 GeV). Figs. 5 and 6 show the mean four-momentum transfer squared $\langle q^2 \rangle$ as a function of energy for ν and $\bar{\nu}$ events, respectively. The straight line fits are suggested by the hypothesis of scale invariance (structure functions depend only on dimensionless variables, if $q^2 \gg M^2$, $\nu \gg M$), which was confirmed experimentally by the SLAC-ep-scattering results in the "true" scaling region : q^2, $\nu > 2 - 3$ GeV. Most of the events are not in the "true" scaling region ($\langle q^2 \rangle = .56$ (.27) GeV^2/c^2 at 2 GeV, 1.3 (.8) GeV^2/c^2 at 5 GeV for ν ($\bar{\nu}$), $\langle\nu\rangle = .9$ (.7) GeV at 2 GeV, 2.1 (1.8) GeV at 5 GeV for ν ($\bar{\nu}$)). However, since the straight line fits are compatible with the ν ($\bar{\nu}$) total cross sections and $\langle q^2 \rangle$ distributions, the results are discussed further using the cross section formula in the scaling region (with $x = q^2/2M\nu$, $y = \nu/E$) :

$$\frac{\pi}{G^2 ME} \frac{d^2\sigma^{\nu \cdot \bar{\nu}}}{dxdy} = (1-y) F_2(x) + \frac{y^2}{2} (2xF_1(x)) \mp y \left(1 - \frac{y}{2}\right) x F_3(x)$$

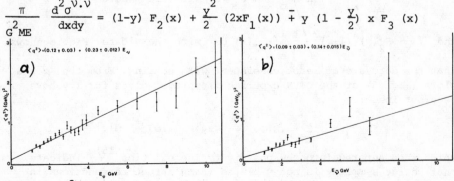

Fig. 5 $\langle q^2 \rangle$-E plots for ν's (a) and $\bar{\nu}$'s (b) from Gargamelle experim.

One finds as a lower bound for $A = \int 2 \, x \, F_1(x) \, dx \, / \int F_2(x) \, dx$

$$A > \frac{3 - 3R_1}{1 + 3R_1} = .87 \overset{+}{-} .05$$

In the parton model, $A = 1$ corresponds to spin 1/2 partons (Callan-Gross relation [12]). Bounds for the vector-axial vector interference term, $B = - \int x \, F_3(x) \, dx \, / \int F_2(x) \, dx$ are :

$$.9 \overset{+}{-} .04 = \frac{2 \, (3 - 3R_1)}{3 + 3R_1} > B > \frac{(3 - 3R_1)}{1 + 3R_1} = .87 \overset{+}{-} .05.$$

$B = 1$ corresponds to maximum parity violation.

From $\sigma^{\nu} - \sigma^{\bar{\nu}} = (G^2 ME/\pi) \int F_2(x) \, dx \, (2B/3)$ one obtains :

$$.49 \overset{+}{-} .03 < \int F_2(x) \, dx < .51 \overset{+}{-} .03,$$

which - in the parton model - means, that ~ 50 % of the nucleon momentum is carried by isoscalar partons or gluons.

The NAL-WB [9] analysis is based on 391 ν and 95 $\bar{\nu}$ events, from 300 and 400 GeV runs. Muon angle and momentum distributions agree with Monte Carlo calculations using scaling-model production formulae and a best estimate for the ν spectrum. 136 ν and 31 $\bar{\nu}$ events with 65 and 40 GeV average energy, respectively, could be fully reconstructed (muon and hadron energy measured) and also they agree with Monte Carlo predictions. They have been used to determine $\sigma^{\bar{\nu}}/\sigma^{\nu}$ yielding

$$R_1 = \sigma^{\bar{\nu}}/\sigma^{\nu} = .36 \overset{+}{-} .08$$

assuming a weighted $\nu/\bar{\nu}$ flux ratio of 1.8. The absolute cross sections are consistent with rising linearly with energy with the same slope as found in the CERN experiment [13]. Since the invariant quantity $x.y = 2 \, (E_\mu/m_p) \cdot \sin^2 (\theta_\mu/2)$ is an observable depending only on muon quantities, all events can be used [14] to test scaling by comparing

$$\frac{1}{N} \frac{dN}{d(xy)} \sim \int_{xy}^{1} \frac{dx}{x} \, F_2(x) \bigg/ \int_{o}^{} dx \, F_2(x) \quad \text{with the } \nu \text{ data}$$

and $\int_{xy}^{1} \frac{dx}{x} \, F_2(x) \, (1-y)^2 \bigg/ \frac{1}{3} \int_{o}^{1} F_2(x) \, dx$ with the $\bar{\nu}$ data. Fig. 6 shows that the data are at least consistent with scaling. From the $<q^2>$-E plots (Fig. 5) of the CERN experiment, average values for $x.y$ have been obtained :

$$<xy>_\nu = .12 \overset{+}{-} .01, \qquad <xy>_{\bar{\nu}} = .07 \overset{+}{-} .01,$$

which when entered into the positivity inequalities [15], indicate that charge symmetry is not violated (same structure functions in

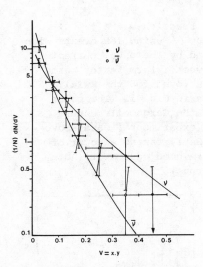

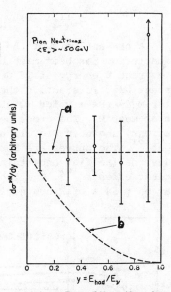

Fig. 6 (x.y)-distribution
of the NAL-WB events

Fig. 7 y-distribution
of the NAL-NB ν events.
a) prediction for ν's,
b) for ν̄'s

ν and ν̄ interactions).

    NAL-NB reported the result [6] of a first run (using $2.7 \cdot 10^{16}$ protons) yielding 167 ν events, 112 of which were reconstructable : 94 with <E> ~50, 18 with <E> ~145 GeV, in agreement with the dichromaticity of the narrow band ν beam. In fig. 7 - 9 the data are compared with the simplest quark parton model predictions (A = B = 1, $F_2(x) = F_2^{ed}(x)$) and found to be consistent with these.

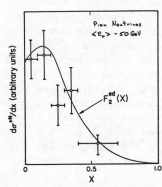

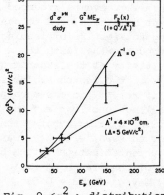

Fig. 8 X-distribution of
NAL-NB events

Fig. 9 $<q^2>$ distribution as
function E. The predicted curves take account of the limited
kinematic range of the detector

$$\text{III.1 (b) } \nu_\mu + n \rightarrow \mu^- + p, \quad \bar{\nu}_\mu + p \rightarrow \mu^+ + n$$

A new analysis of the quasi-elastic reaction $\nu + n \rightarrow \mu^- + p$ in deuterium has been made by the ANL group[9] using 166 events with an average ν energy of .7 GeV. If described by the usual current-current weak interaction theory with the vector form factor parameter $M_V = .84$, a value $(0.95 \pm .12)$ GeV is found for the axial vector mass M_A. The cross section is shown in Fig. 10. The cross sections, shown in Fig. 11 are results of the Gargamelle experiment[8]. The curves are best fits to the experimental data above 2 GeV (due to flux uncertainties below 2 GeV), taking account of nuclear effects[16]. The two results are in good agreement (note, that only 54 % of Freon nucleons are neutrons).

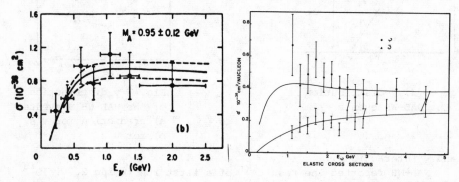

Fig. 10 Cross section for $\nu n \rightarrow \mu^- p$ measured in deuterium

Fig. 11 Cross section for $\nu n \rightarrow \mu^- p$ and $\bar{\nu} p \rightarrow \mu^+ n$ measured in Freon

III.1 (c) W-mass limit [10]

The 112 ν events produced in the first run of the NAL-NB experiment have been used to search for direct W-boson production according to Fig. 12 (b) leading to a clear signal of a low energy μ^- produced together with the W, and a higher energy μ^+ from W-decay. The sensitivity of the experiment has been determined by calculating the ratio of two lepton production using the W production cross section of ref. 17 to one-muon-production (Fig. 12 (a)) assuming the above scaling functions and the W-propagator as a function of E and M_W (Fig. 12 (a)). No events with a pair of muons were found (the one observed event with a μ^+ was not accompanied by a μ^-, and attributed to $\bar{\nu}$ contamination in the beam). The 90 % confidence limit as a function of the branching ratio B, as shown in Fig. 13, gives e.g. $M_W > 4.4$ GeV/c^2 for B = 0.5.

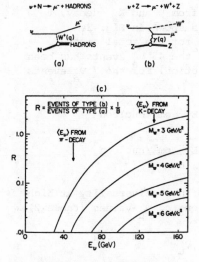

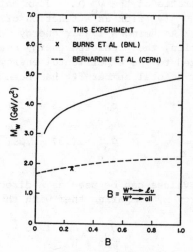

Fig. 12 Predicted ratio of
$\mu^+\mu^-$ events to μ^- events
as a function of E, M_W

Fig. 13 Lower limit
(90 % CL) on W-mass

III.2 With electronic Neutrinos
a) $\nu_e + N \to e^-$ anything, σ_{tot}; μ-e universality

For the first time quantitative results are available on
high energy ν_e nucleon scattering [5]. The analysis is based on
230'000 ν and 260'000 $\bar{\nu}$ photos in Gargamelle. The films were double
scanned for events with identified e^-, e^+ or $e^\pm$ (detection
efficiency 100 %). The electron energy was measured using the total
track length method ($\sim$ 30 % error). Cuts were applied to the electron
energy (> 300 MeV) to exclude most Dalitz pairs and to the total
energy (> 1 GeV). 48 events in the ν film were accepted. Three events
were removed, because their electrons were consistent with being
asymmetric Dalitz pairs (combined with a single γ pointing to the
vertex they fitted the π^0 mass). The remaining events are classified
in table 3 according to e-charge and hadrons observed in the final
state. All $e^\pm$ events in the ν film have been taken as ν_e-events
(only 5 % of the ν-flux is $\bar{\nu}_e$), the one e^- event in the $\bar{\nu}$ film has
been taken as an $\bar{\nu}_e$ event.

Table 3 Classification of the ν_e and $\bar{\nu}_e$ events

ν film	e^- +protons	e^- +protons and pions	$e^\pm$ +protons	$e^\pm$ + protons and pions	e^+ + hadrons
	15	13	7	10	0
$\bar{\nu}$ film	e^+ +protons	e^+ +protons and pions	$e^\pm$ +protons	$e^\pm$ + protons and pions	e^- + hadrons
	0	6	0	1	3

The ratio of the ν_e ($\bar{\nu}_e$) flux calculated from μ and K_{e3} decay, to the ν_μ ($\bar{\nu}_\mu$) flux as a function of energy is shown in Fig. 2.

Assuming a linear energy dependence for the total cross-section, the predicted energy spectrum of the 45 ν_e events has been fitted to the experimental energy distribution. For the 7 $\bar{\nu}_e$ events only a total number fit has been made :

$$\sigma_{\nu_e} = (.93 \overset{+}{-} .17) \times 10^{-38} \, E_{\nu_e} \, cm^2/nucleon$$

$$\sigma_{\bar{\nu}_e} = (.37 \overset{+}{-} .09) \times 10^{-38} \, E_{\bar{\nu}_e} \, cm^2/nucleon$$

The values can be used as a direct test of μ-e universality at high energy by comparing them with the corresponding ν_μ-values (table 2) :

$$\sigma_{\nu_e}/\sigma_{\nu_\mu} = 1.26 \overset{+}{-} .23, \quad \sigma_{\bar{\nu}_e}/\sigma_{\bar{\nu}_\mu} = 1.32 \overset{+}{-} .32$$

The $\bar{\nu}_e$, ν_e cross section ratio is $\sigma^{\bar{\nu}_e}/\sigma^{\nu_e} = .4 \overset{+}{-} .12$.

b) Muon number conservation law multiplicative ?

A multiplicative lepton conservation law [18] allows in addition to the μ decay mode $\mu^+ \rightarrow e^+ + \nu_e + \bar{\nu}_\mu$ the decay mode $\mu^+ \rightarrow e^+ + \bar{\nu}_e + \nu_\mu$, i.e.

$$r = \frac{\mu^+ \rightarrow e^+ + \nu_e + \bar{\nu}_\mu}{all \ \mu^+ \ decay \ modes} = \begin{cases} .5, \ multiplicative \\ 0, \ additive \end{cases}$$

The relative magnitude of ν_e and $\bar{\nu}_e$ fluxes below 3 GeV is sensitive to r, which consequently can be determined from the relative number of e^- and e^+ events in the ν film.

From the fact that no unambiguous e^+ event was observed the probability to determine the e charge taken to be 70 %, and the cross-section ratio $\sigma_{\bar{\nu}}/\sigma_\nu = .4 \overset{+}{-} 12$, a flux ratio $\bar{\nu}_e/\nu_e < 20$ % is obtained. This yields $r < .25$ (90 % confidence level) favouring the additive law.

IV. NEUTRAL CURRENT SEARCH

IV.1 Leptonic: $\overset{(-)}{\nu}_\mu + e^- \rightarrow \overset{(-)}{\nu}_\mu + e^-$

The existence of these processes is required as a consequence of the simplest model renormalising the intermediate vector boson (IVB) weak interaction theory by introducing new particles in the S-channel and "unifying" weak and electromagnetic interactions [19]. The cross sections of the above interactions depend on the ratio of electromagnetic to (isotriplet) IVB coupling $e^2/g^2 = \sin^2\theta$ and have been calculated by t'Hooft [20].

A search for these processes has been carried out in the Gargamelle experiment [4], 375'000 ν and 360'000 $\bar{\nu}$ pictures were double scanned for single electrons inside a useful volume of 6.2 m^3. A cut on the electron energy (> 300 MeV) excludes low energy background from ν interactions around the chamber and ensures that all electrons from the above processes have angles < 5° with respect to the ν beam direction.

One single electron event fulfilling these criteria was found in the $\bar{\nu}$ film (no event in the ν film). Its charge is negative, its energy 385 $\pm$ 100 MeV and its angle to the beam axis (1.4 $^{+1.6}_{-1.4}$) degr.. Background analysis. (a) Background due to Compton electrons or asymmetric e^+e^- pairs has been estimated from 2 isolated e^+e^- pairs (with $E_+ >$ 300 MeV, $\theta < 5^{\circ}$) in the ν film and none in the $\bar{\nu}$ film to be .04 $\pm$ .02 events in the ν film and zero in the $\bar{\nu}$ film). (b) Background from the "diagonal" V-A interactions $\overset{(-)}{\nu}_e + e \rightarrow e + \overset{(-)}{\nu}_e$ with cross sections of the same order as the processes searched for is negligible due to the small ν_e flux (cf. Fig. 2). (c) Background from the purely electromagnetic interaction n + e $\rightarrow$ n + e is absent due to the lack of high energy (> 16 GeV) neutrons. (d) The main source of background comes from ν_e + n $\rightarrow$ e$^-$ ($\theta < 5^{\circ}$) + p (invisible). It has been determined from the kinematically equivalent ν_μ events : ν_μ + n $\rightarrow$ μ ($\theta < 5^{\circ}$) + p (invisible), which were found to be (1.3 $^{+}_{-}$ .7) % of the (μ^- + protons)-events. From the 15 ν_e events (Table 3) with e$^-$ + protons which is in agreement with the calculated ν_e/ν_μ flux ratio a background of 0.3 $\pm$ 0.2 events in the ν film and 0.03 $^{+}_{-}$ 0.02 events in the $\bar{\nu}$ film (10 times less ν_e flux, no e$^-$ proton event) is estimated.

As a result of this search the following 90 % confidence upper limits are (with 87 % detection efficiency) :

for ν_μ + e$^-$ $\rightarrow$ ν_μ + e$^-$: $\sigma <$ 0.26 E_ν x 10^{-41} cm^2/electron,

for $\bar{\nu}_\mu$ + e$^-$ $\rightarrow$ $\bar{\nu}_\mu$ + e$^-$: $\sigma <$ 0.88 E_ν x 10^{-41} cm^2/electron.

A maximum likelihood analysis combining the ν and $\bar{\nu}$ results and taking account of fluxes and backgrounds gives the following limits (90 % c.l.) for the above mentioned model parameter :
0.1 < $\sin^2\theta$ < 0.6.

IV.2 Hadronic : ν_μ + N $\rightarrow$ ν_μ + hadrons

In all high energy neutrino experiments over the last decade events were observed which had no muon candidate. Due to lack of statistics and/or detector limitations these events were simply attributed to neutron background and only used as upper limits for possible neutral current interaction cross sections [21]. The size of

the present detectors and the higher energies at NAL allow to
study distributions of these events (called NC) in space and
energy and to compare them with those of equivalent events with
lepton candidate (called CC), and to estimate - from the rate of
neutral stars (called AS) associated with CC events- the fraction of
NC events which could be ν $(\bar{\nu})$ induced neutral hadron background.

A first detailed study based on 80'000 ν and 200'000 $\bar{\nu}$ [3]
pictures has been reported by the Gargamelle group . 102 events in
ν film and 64 in $\bar{\nu}$ film were observed with no lepton candidate and
> 1 GeV total energy. These have to be compared with 428 ν and 148 $\bar{\nu}$
events with only one μ candidate of the correct sign and > 1 GeV
total hadron energy. In the same ν $(\bar{\nu})$ sample were 15 (12) AS events.
The distributions of the NC events in space (parallel (Fig. 14) and
perpendicular (Fig. 15) to the beam direction), in total energy
(Fig. 16), and in cosθ (Fig. 17, θ being the direction of the total
visible momentum of the secondaries with respect to the ν beam), are
found to be similar to the equivalent distributions of the CC events
taking for E and θ the hadronic secondaries only).

Neutrals from cosmic rays or from the primary beam as the only
background source can be excluded on the basis of rates per picture
and essentially zero up-down asymmetry of the NC events. The most
important background source is neutral hadrons produced by ν's $(\bar{\nu}$'s)
in the material around the visible volume. Detailed Monte Carlo calculations using best estimates for the energy and angular distributions
of the neutrons and for their cascading behaviour show that only of
the order of 10 to 15 events can be attributed to this background
source, and that only with inconsistent assumptions about the neutrons'
angular and energy distribution the observed NC distributions in
space and energy can be reproduced. In addition, a flight path analysis of the NC spatial distribution in terms of an apparent interaction length (Fig. 18) shows that the NC are inconsistent with
neutrons.

Hence it is concluded, that - after background subtraction and
accounting for ν $(\bar{\nu})$ contamination in the CC samples -

$$\frac{NC}{CC}_{\nu} = .21 \overset{+}{-} .03$$

$$\frac{NC}{CC}_{\bar{\nu}} = .45 \overset{+}{-} .09$$

(these numbers might still change within 10 % due to further corrections under study), are the relative rates of ν $(\bar{\nu})$ interactions
without charge exchange (neutral currents) or of interactions of
penetrating particles other than ν_μ, ν_e, produced by ν's and in
equilibrium with the ν beam, or of heavy leptons decaying immediately [22]
into hadrons and no charged leptons (see section V). If interpreted
in terms of Salam-Weinberg neutral currents, the parameter $\sin^2\theta$

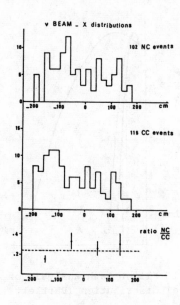

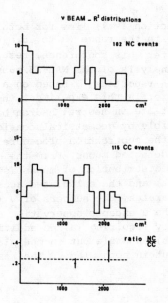

Fig. 14 along ν beam axis

Fig. 15 Radial distribution

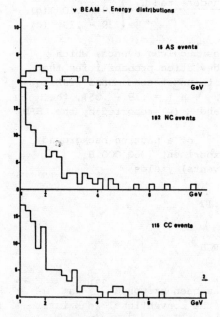

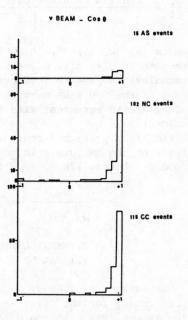

Fig. 16 Energy distribution

Fig. 17 Cosθ distribution

Fig. 14 - 17. Distribution in space and energy of muonless events observed in the Gargamelle experiment ν film compared with 1-μ-events. Similar agreement between NC and CC is found in the ν̄ film.

(see section IV.1) lies for both ν and $\bar{\nu}$ results in the range .3 to .5.

After this conference, results of a refined analysis of the NAL-WB muonless events has been reported [3], based on a larger sample of events. In this experiment the difficulty does not lie in neutral hadron background (negligible by geometrical considerations), but in the subtraction procedure for events with undetected muons. From the experimental angular distribution of muons (see section III.1 (a) and the calculated acceptance of the apparatus, the numbers of ν $(\bar{\nu})$ events where the μ escapes observation has been calculated by requiring (a) no additional angle cuts, (b) an angle cut in one plane, (c) an angle cut in both planes. The results are

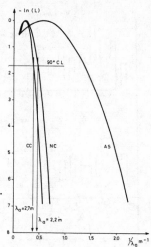

Fig. 18 Flight path analysis of spatial distribution (Bartlett method)

$$R = \frac{NC}{CC} = \frac{\text{muonless events-events with undetected }\mu}{\mu \text{ events}} = \begin{cases} .28 \pm .09 & \text{(a)} \\ .29 \pm .10 & \text{(b)} \\ .39 \pm .19 & \text{(c)} \end{cases}$$

based on (a) 38, (b) 30, (c) 9.1 excess muonless events, which correspond to 5.2, 5.1, 6.7 standard deviation probabilities that all muonless events are just events with undetected muons. Taking account of the $\bar{\nu}$-ν beam mixture $(\mu^+/(\mu^+ + \mu^-) = .19 \pm .05)$, the R values are in agreement with R (ν) and R $(\bar{\nu})$ reported by the CERN experiment.

Finally a post-conference result [3] of a neutron background analysis by the ANL group in the N* experiment (360'000 H_2, 250'000 D_2 photos, 176 $\nu p \rightarrow \mu^- \pi^+ p$ events) yields

$$\frac{\nu p \rightarrow \nu \Delta^+}{\nu p \rightarrow \mu^- \Delta^{++}} = .22 \pm .17$$

V. HEAVY LEPTON SEARCH
V.1 NAL-NB

The existence of heavy leptons has been proposed [23] as another remedy for the divergences in the conventional weak interaction theory. The conjectured production process would be $\nu_\mu + N \rightarrow y^+ + $ hadrons. Assuming $y^+ \rightarrow \mu^+ + \nu + \bar{\nu}_\mu$ to be 1/3 of all decay modes and using the calculation by Bjorken and Llewellyn-Smith [24] of the ratio of y^+ to μ^+ production as a function of m_{y^+} and the ν energy, a lower bound of $m_{y^+} > 2$ GeV/c^2 (90 % c.l.) has been reported [11] on the basis of the 112 analysed

NAL-NB events and $m_y + > 4 - 5$ GeV/c^2 using the bigger sample currently under study.

V.2 Gargamelle experiment

From the facts that no e$^+$ event has been observed in the ν film (see table 3) and the $\bar{\nu}_e$ flux is only $\sim 3 \times 10^{-4}$ of the ν_μ flux and assuming y$^+ \to$ e$^+ + \nu_e + \bar{\nu}_\mu$ to be 15 % of all decay modes, one finds : $m_y + > 2.4$ GeV (90 % c.l.).

VI. CONCLUSION

Fig. 19 shows a summary of ν cross sections : measured (ν_ℓ N $\to \ell$ + hadrons, $\ell = \mu$,e, ν_μN $\to \mu$N), measured and energy dependence conjectured from Fig. 16 (ν_μN $\to \nu_\mu$ + hadrons), [25)] predicted and found to be compatible with measurements [26)] (νp $\to \mu^+ \Lambda$), upper limits ($\bar{\nu}_\mu$ e $\to \bar{\nu}_\mu$ e, $\bar{\nu}_e$ e $\to \bar{\nu}_e$ e) [27)], or only predicted and not yet verified: inverse μ decay (ν_μ e $\to \mu \nu_e$), diagonal interactions ($\nu_\mu \to \nu_\mu \mu\mu$), νn $\to \mu^+ \Sigma^-$ [28)]. σ (ν_μp $\to \mu^- N^{*)}$) [29,3)] (not shown) has been measured in propane and deuterium and saturates above ~ 2 GeV at a value of $\sim 10^{-38}$ cm^2/proton.

1. Scaling ? Although the ν data do not prove the validity of the scaling hypothesis (the CERN data are too low in energy, the NAL data in statistics), they certainly are remarkably consistent with it up to energies of close to 200 GeV: the total ν and $\bar{\nu}$ cross sections seem to rise linearly with energy, their relative values correspond to nearly maximum vector-axial vector interference. In terms of the parton model neutrinos seem to mostly scatter off spin 1/2 partons.

2. μ-e universality has been confirmed at high energy by the equality of ν_e and ν_μ cross sections within $\sim$ 25 %. The muon number conservation law is rather additive than multiplicative.

3. Baryon-baryon transistions. Also the pn transition in the quasi elastic $\bar{\nu}$ interactions seems to agree with the theoretical predictions, at least up to 4 $\pm$ 5 GeV. From νn $\to \mu^- p$, the value of M_A has been remeasured : $(.95 \pm .12)$ GeV.

4. Neutral currents ? Neutrino-like events without lepton candidates have been observed and shown not to be neutral hadron background. Their explanation in terms of heavy leptons is improbable since no evidence has been found for the leptonic decay mode of heavy leptons. If they are due to heavy leptons decaying into hadrons only, then (1) the hadrons' total transverse momentum distribution should be different in NC and CC events (which does not seem to be the case) and (2) the production rate should be larger at NAL than at CERN, unless the CERN ν energies are already well above threshold, which is unlikely. New types of "ν's" produced in the target are ruled out (rates per proton are different in ν and $\bar{\nu}$ runs).

If interpreted in terms of Salam-Weinberg neutral weak currents and the quark parton model [30] which appears to be the simplest explanation, then the parameter e^2/g^2 (ratio between electromagnetic and weak coupling) lies in the same range for ν's and $\bar{\nu}$'s (.3 - .5) and also for $\overset{(-)}{\nu}_\mu\, e \to \overset{(-)}{\nu}_\mu\, e$ (.1 - .6).

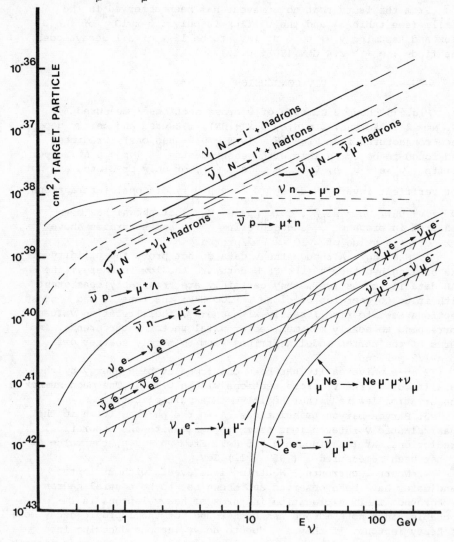

Fig. 19 Summary of ν cross sections (see text). Slopes of σ_{tot} for $\nu N \to \ell$ + hadrons are .74, .28, .17, .11 for $\ell = \ell^-$, ℓ^+, ν_μ, $\bar{\nu}_\mu$, respectively.

FOOTNOTES AND REFERENCES

*) The talk was given during a short visit to the Physics Department
of the University of Wisconsin whose hospitality (especially that
of Profs. W.F. Fry, U. Camerini, D. Reeder) is gratefully
acknowledged.

1) D. Perkins, XVI. Intern. High Energy Conf.., Batavia (Sep. 1972).
2) C. Baltay, Los Angeles Meeting of the American Phys. Soc.
(Dec. 1972).
3) F.J. Hasert, et.al., to be published in Phys. Letters and
(announced after this conference):
A. Benvenuti et al., Harvard-Pennsylvania-Wisconsin-NAL-preprint,
(Aug. 1973).
S. Barish et al., (ANL), paper submitted to Int. Symp. on
Electron and Photon Interactions, Bonn, 27.8.1973.
4) H. Faissner et al., to be published in Phys. Letters.
5) H. Deden et al., to be published in Phys. Letters.
6) B.C. Barish et al., Phys. Rev. Lett. 31 (1973) 565.
7) A. Mann, paper submitted to this conference and
A. Benvenuti et al., Phys. Rev, Lett. 30 (1973) 1084.
8) T. Eichten et al., to be published in Phys. Letters.
9) W.A. Mann et al., ANL preprint, July 1973.
10) B.C. Barish et al., CALT-68-394 (May 1973).
11) B.C. Barish et al., Phys. Rev. Lett. 31 (1973) 410.
12) C.G. Callan and D.G. Gross, Phys. Rev. Lett. 22 (1969) 156.
13) Result announced after this conference.
14) J. Bjorken, D. Cline, A. Mann, SLAC-PUB 1244 (1973).
15) A. de Rujula and S.L. Glashow - Harvard Preprint (May 1973).
16) J. Løvseth, Nuovo Cimento 57 A (1968) 382.
17) R.W. Brown and J. Smith, Phys. Rev. D 3 (1971) 207.
18) G. Feinberg and S. Weinberg, Phys. Rev. Lett. 6 (1961) 381.
G. Kalbfleisch, Nucl. Phys. B 25 (1970) 197.
19) A. Salam and J.G. Ward, Phys. Lett. 13 (1964) 168.
S. Weinberg, Phys. Rev. Lett. 19 (1967) 1264.
20) G. t'Hooft, Phys. Lett. 37 B (1971) 195 .
21) D.C. Cundy et al., Phys. Lett. 31 B (1970) 479 .
Y. Cho et al., XVI. Int. Conf. on High Energy Physics, Batavia,
1972.
W.Y. Lee, Phys. Lett. 40 B (1972) 423.
22) A. Pais and S.B. Treiman, Phys. Rev. D6 (1972) 2700.
E.A. Paschos and L. Wolfenstein, Phys. Rev. D7 (1973) 91.
23) H. Georgi and S.L. Glashow, Phys. Rev. Lett. 28 (1972) 1494.
24) J.D. Bjorken and C.H. Llewellyn-Smith, Phys. Rev. 7D (1973) 887.
25) N. Cabibbo, F. Chilton, Phys. Rev. 137 B (1965) 1628.
26) T. Eichten et al.,Phys. Lett. 40 B (1972) 593.
27) H. Gurr, F. Reines, H. Sobel, Trieste Conf. (1973) and PRL 28
(1972) 1406 .
28) I. Budagov et al., Phys. Lett. 29 B (1969) 524.
29) J. Campbell et al., Phys. Rev. Lett. 30 (1973) 335.
30) R.B. Palmer, BNL 18059, NG-258 (May 1973).

REVIEW OF K° DECAYS*

David R. Nygren
Lawrence Berkeley Laboratory, Berkeley, California 94720

ABSTRACT

A review is given of selected topics in K^o decays for which recent results have led to substantial progress and/or controversy.

I.   INTRODUCTION

Since the last review by Pondrom in 1971[1], new experimental results have significantly affected the status of the following topics of K^o decays:

1. Form factors in the decay $K_L^o \to \pi \ell \nu$;
2. CP Violation and $K_{S,L}^o$ decay parameters;
3. The $K_L^o \to \mu^+ \mu^-$ puzzle.

In the case of the $K_{\ell 3}^o$ form factors, new results from two very precise experiments are in good agreement with expectations. On the other hand, some parameters relevant to CP violation have changed by many standard deviations according to recent results, and the origin of the discrepancies with the older data remains unknown. Finally, a pair of related experiments have provided evidence that the decay $K_L^o \to \mu^+ \mu^-$ does exist at an appropriate rate, in contradiction with the negative result of a Berkeley group.

II. $K_L^o \to \pi \ell \nu$ FORM FACTORS

In the Cabibbo theory of the V-A weak interaction, the matrix element for the decay $K^o \to \pi^- \ell^+ \nu$ can be written in a Lorentz-covariant form as

$$M = \frac{G}{\sqrt{2}} \sin \theta_c \left[\bar{u}_\ell \gamma_\mu (1-\gamma_5) \, u_\nu \right] x \left\langle \pi^- \mid V^\mu \mid K^o \right\rangle.$$

The hadronic part is customarily expressed as

$$\left\langle \pi^- \mid V^\mu \mid K^o \right\rangle = F_+(t) \, (P_k + P_\pi)^\mu + F_-(t) \, (P_k - P_\pi)^\mu \, , \tag{1}$$

where the scalar functions $F_\pm(t)$ describe the dependence of the strangeness-changing weak hadronic vector current on convenient combinations of the two independent four vectors P_k and P_π. $F_\pm(t)$ are functions only of the invariant four momentum transfer

$$t = (P_k - P_\pi)^2 = M_k^2 + M_\pi^2 - 2M_k E_\pi^* \tag{2}$$

where E_π^* is the pion energy in the K^o rest frame. The rather limited range of t available in K^o decay is

$$M_\ell^2 \leq t \leq (M_k - M_\pi)^2 = 0.128 \; (\text{GeV}/c)^2 \tag{3}$$

In the rate, terms involving $F_-(t)$ are proportional to M_ℓ^2, with the consequence that only $F_+(t)$ contributes to K_{e3} decays. Furthermore, the Cabibbo formulation is invariant under time reversal, leading to the requirement that $F_-(t)$ and $F_+(t)$ must be relatively real. Finally, $\Delta S=-\Delta Q$ transitions are forbidden in lowest order.

Violations of the $\Delta S=+\Delta Q$ rule are customarily described by the introduction of new form factors $g\pm(t)$ defined in an analogous way:

$$\left\langle \pi^+ \middle| V^\mu \middle| K^o \right\rangle = g_+(t) \, (P_K+P_\pi)^\mu + g_-(t) \, (P_K-P_\pi)^\mu$$

$$\left\langle \pi^- \middle| V^\mu \middle| \bar{K}^o \right\rangle = g_+^*(t) \, (P_K+P_\pi)^\mu + g_-^*(t) \, (P_K-P_\pi)^\mu$$

and the ratio $X \equiv g/F$ must be zero if the $\Delta S=\Delta Q$ rule is satisfied. Non-zero values of $\mathrm{Im}X$ imply time-reversal violation, of special interest as a possible connection to the phenomenon of CP violation in K_L^o decays.

Most of the experimental work on the search of $\Delta S=\Delta Q$ amplitudes has employed the study of the time dependence of the semileptonic decays of an initially produced K^o state. The essential complication in such experiments is the natural development of a $\bar{K}^o$ component in the evolution of the state as the K_S^o and K_L^o amplitudes decay:

$$\left| K^o \right\rangle \rightarrow \left| K_S^o \right\rangle e^{-iM_S\tau} + \left| K_L^o \right\rangle e^{-iM_L\tau}$$

$$= \left| K^o \right\rangle (e^{-iM_S\tau} + e^{-iM_L\tau}) + \left| \bar{K}^o \right\rangle (e^{-iM_S\tau} - e^{-iM_L\tau}) \tag{5}$$

where $M_{L,S} = m_{L,S} - i\Gamma_{L,S}/2$ and M_L and M_S are the masses, and Γ_L and Γ_S are the total decay rates of the long- and short-lived states. The decay rate into positive and negative leptons is easily found to be

$$N^\pm(\tau) \propto \left|1+x\right|^2 e^{-\Gamma_S\tau} + \left|1-x\right|^2 e^{-\Gamma_L\tau}$$

$$+ \left[\pm 2(1-\left|x\right|^2) \cos (\Delta m \, \tau) - 4\mathrm{Im}X \sin (\Delta m \, \tau)\right] e^{-\bar{\Gamma}\tau} \tag{6}$$

where $\Delta m = m_L - m_S$ and $\bar{\Gamma} = (\Gamma_S + \Gamma_L)/2$.

An MIT contribution to this conference[2] describes an experiment which employed the reaction sequence

$$K^+ + \text{Platinum} \rightarrow K^o + \text{neutrals}$$
$$\hookrightarrow \pi^\pm \cdot e^\pm \nu$$

The decays were observed by optical spark chambers embedded in a magnetic field of 14.5 Kilogauss. Electrons were identified by shower production in a 2.8 radiation length lead-plate spark chamber, followed by lead-lucite cerenkov counters. Approximately 1700 K_{e3} decays survived cuts, with a small background due to the relatively copious $K_S^0 \rightarrow \pi^+ \pi^-$ mode. The analysis gives

$$
\begin{aligned}
\text{ReX} &= -0.008 \pm 0.044 \\
\text{ImX} &= -0.017 \pm 0.060
\end{aligned}
\tag{7}
$$

in good agreement with the $\Delta S = \Delta Q$ rule. In this case $X = g_+/f_+$ since just K_{e3} decays are being studied. Adding this result to the world average one obtains[3]

$$
\begin{aligned}
\text{ReX} &= +0.0016 \pm 0.025 \\
\text{ImX} &= +0.0002 \pm 0.024
\end{aligned}
\tag{8}
$$

shown in Fig. 1 along with recent results of comparable accuracy. For the remaining purposes of this review X can safely be assumed to equal zero.

In the t region available in K^0 decays it is reasonable to assume that a linear approximation will adequately describe the t dependence of $F\pm(t)$:

$$
F+(t) \simeq F+(0) \left[1 + \lambda_+ (t/M_\pi^2) \right]
\tag{9}
$$

$$
F-(t) \simeq F-(0) \left[1 + \lambda_- (t/M_\pi^2) \right]
\tag{10}
$$

Frequently, the ratio $\xi(t) \equiv F_-(t)/F_+(t)$ has also been used to characterize experimental data, but it is theoretically advantageous to use instead $F_+(t)$ and another variable $F_0(t)$, given by

$$
F_0(t) = F_+(t) + \frac{t}{M_K^2 - M_\pi^2} F_-(t);
\tag{11}
$$

F_+ and F_0 correspond respectively to 1^- and 0^+ amplitudes for the lepton pair.[4] The expansion of $F_0(t)$ as a linear function of t

$$
F_0(t) = F_0(o) \left[1 + \lambda_o \frac{t}{M_\pi^2} \right],
\tag{12}
$$

implicitly assumes that λ_- is negligibly small. In this approximation,

$$
\xi(0) = \frac{M_K^2 - M_\pi^2}{M_\pi^2} (\lambda_o - \lambda_+)
\tag{13}
$$

The form factors F_+ and F_o are also expected to be adequately described by simple pole forms with masses appropriate to the 1^- and 0^+ intermediate states. If $F_+(t) = F_+(0)M^2/(M^2-t)$ is assumed to be dominated by the $K^*(892)$ state then $\lambda_+ = 0.024$ around t=0; averaged over the physical region λ_+ is about 0.030.

The assumptions of chiral $SU_3 \otimes SU_3$ algebra, soft pions and PCAC lead to the Callan-Treiman relation, essentially a statement about F_o at the unphysical t value of M_K^2:

$$F_o(M_K^2) = F_+(0)x(1.27 \pm 0.03)$$

(14)

In the linear approximation (12), this fixes λ_o to be

$$\lambda_o = 0.021 \pm 0.002$$

(15)

Experimentally, the shape of the Dalitz plot density, the branching ratio $\Gamma(K_{\mu 3})/\Gamma(K_{e3})$, and the polarization variation within the $K_{\mu 3}$ Dalitz plot can be measured to determine the form factors. The results for λ_+ from studies of K_{e3}^+ and K_{e3}^o are reasonably consistent and in good agreement with the pole approximation (Fig. 2). A contribution to this conference by a CERN-Heidelberg group[5] and a recent result by a SLAC-Santa Cruz group[6] have reduced the error on this parameter by a very substantial factor, and merit special attention here.

The apparatus of the CERN-Heidelberg experiment is shown in Figure 3. $K_{S,L}^o$ decays are observed in a short neutral beam with a magnetic spectrometer employing multiwire proportional chambers, a hydrogen gas cerenkov counter for electron identification, and a thick concrete absorber-hodoscope combination for muon identification. The Dalitz plot was studied for 5×10^5 K_{e3}^o decays and three different methods were employed to overcome the ambiguity problem arising from backward or forward neutrino emission. The first is to weight the two solutions with an a priori probability that is proportional to the Jacobian of the Lorentz transformation. The second is to select events for which the two solutions give pion energies differing by less than 10 MeV. The third consists of a fit to the matrix defined by entering each event according to the two solutions for t.

The three methods give consistent results, shown in Fig. 4. The curves are the prediction of the K^* dominance model, not fits to the data; pole form fits to the data give $M^* = 840 \pm 35$ MeV. A linear parametrization describes the data sufficiently well and gives the result $\lambda_+ = 0.031 \pm 0.0025$, substantially more accurate than the previous world average of 0.032 ± 0.004.

In the SLAC-Santa Cruz experiment, the Dalitz plot distribution of 1.6×10^6 $K_L \rightarrow \pi \mu \nu$ decays was studied to measure both F_+ and F_o. A wire spark chamber spectrometer was followed by 7.7 interaction lengths of lead to identify muons, and time of flight information was used to determine the K_L^o momentum. The Monte Carlo results for the detection efficiency over the Dalitz plot were studied in detail by very high statistics comparisons with experimental distributions. Radiative corrections were introduced in such a way that the effects of the detection efficiency were correctly included. Good fits to the data are obtained in both unparametrized and 2-parameter linear fits (Fig. 5). The results for the 2-parameter fit give λ_+=0.030 ± 0.003 and λ_o=0.019 ± 0.004. This value for λ_+ is in excellent agreement with λ_+ from K_{e3}^o decays, and with $K^*(892)$ dominance of the vector form factor. The result λ_o=0.019 ± 0.004 is in excellent agreement with the Callan-Treiman prediction (14) yielding $F_+(M_K^2)$ = (1.25 ± 0.04) $F_+(0)$. A separate unparametrized fit for $\xi(t)$ gives -0.11 ± 0.04 with no apparent t dependence. Using (13), with λ_+ given by K^* dominance and λ_o by (15), $\xi(0)$ is predicted to be -0.02 ± 0.03, in good agreement with the SLAC-Santa Cruz experiment.

An important new aspect of these two experiments is that no significant limitation from statistics exists in the comparison of data and Monte Carlo distributions, with the consequence that systematic effects are more readily discovered and dealt with. The excellent agreement of these results with the theoretical expectations noted above contrasts sharply with the situation heretofore; based on an analysis in 1971 of the available data,[4] Chounet, Gaillard, and Gaillard concluded that quadratic terms were needed for F_+ and that λ_o = - 0.11 ± 0.03, four standard deviations away from (15).

These new values increase the discrepancy between Dalitz plot results and muon polarization results. In the past, the experimental studies of the muon polarization have given large negative $\xi(0)$ values, and an average of $\xi(0)$ = - 2.0 ± 0.7 was obtained in the analysis of Chounet et al.[4] Recently, an experiment by a Yale-Argonne group[7] gave the result $\xi(0)$ = - 0.51 ± 0.11 (for λ_+=0.031), increasing the average substantially, but still in disagreement with the SLAC-Santa Cruz K^o Dalitz plot result at about the four standard deviation level.[13]

III.   CP VIOLATION AND $K_{S,L}^o$ DECAY PARAMETERS

The customary phenomenological description of CP violation defines the following quantities:[8]

$$\eta_{+-} \equiv \frac{\left\langle \pi^+ \pi^- \mid H_{wk} \mid K_L^o \right\rangle}{\left\langle \pi^+ \pi^- \mid H_{wk} \mid K_S^o \right\rangle} = \left| \eta_{+-} \right| e^{i\phi^{+-}} = \varepsilon + \varepsilon', \tag{16}$$

$$\eta_{00} \equiv \frac{\left\langle \pi^0\pi^0 \left| H_{wk} \right| K_L^0 \right\rangle}{\left\langle \pi^0\pi^0 \left| H_{wk} \right| K_S^0 \right\rangle} = \left| \eta_{00} \right| e^{i\phi_{00}} = \varepsilon - 2\varepsilon'. \tag{17}$$

The parameter ε describes the nonorthogonality of K_L^0 and K_S^0:

$$K_L^0 = \frac{1}{\sqrt{2(1+|\varepsilon|^2)}} \left[(1+\varepsilon) \left| K^0 \right\rangle - (1-\varepsilon) \left| \bar{K}^0 \right\rangle \right] \tag{18}$$

$$K_S^0 = \frac{1}{\sqrt{2(1+|\varepsilon|^2)}} \left[(1+\varepsilon) \left| K^0 \right\rangle + (1-\varepsilon) \left| \bar{K}^0 \right\rangle \right] \tag{19}$$

and ε' describes CP violation in $K^0 \to 2\pi$:

$$\varepsilon' = \frac{i}{\sqrt{2}} \, \mathrm{Im} \, \frac{A_2}{A_0} \, e^{i(\delta_2 - \delta_0)} \, , \text{ where}$$

$$A_0 e^{i\delta_0} = \left\langle 2\pi(I=0) \left| H_{wk} \right| K^0 \right\rangle , \text{ and}$$

$$A_2 e^{i\delta_2} = \left\langle 2\pi(I=2) \left| H_{wk} \right| K^0 \right\rangle .$$

There are six experimentally measurable quantities, namely, the magnitudes and phases of η_{+-} and η_{00}, and the leptonic charge asymmetries δ_μ and δ_e in $K_L^0 \to \pi^{\pm} \ell^{\mp} \nu$ decays:

$$\delta_\ell \equiv \frac{\Gamma(\ell^+) - \Gamma(\ell^-)}{\Gamma(\ell^+) + \Gamma(\ell^-)} = \frac{1 - |x|^2}{|1 - x|^2} \, 2\mathrm{Re} \, \varepsilon \tag{20}$$

A. Status of $\left| \eta_{+-} \right|$

Five optical spark chamber experiments from 1964–1967 gave results of excellent consistency (Fig. 6) and an average value of

$$\left| \eta_{+-} \right| = (1.96 \pm 0.03) \times 10^{-3}. \tag{21}$$

Pondrom justifiably concluded in 1971[1] that $\left| \eta_{+-} \right|$ was the best known parameter in the topic of CP violation. Recently, four new measurements have become available, also quite consistent among themselves, but their average differing from the old value by 11 standard deviations!

Typically, the determination of $\left| \eta_{+-} \right|$ involves the following quantities:

$$\left|n_{+-}\right|^2 = \frac{\text{Rate } (K_L^0 \to \pi^+\pi^-)}{\text{Rate } (K_L^0 \to \text{charged})} \quad x \quad \frac{\text{Rate } (K_L^0 \to \text{charged})}{\text{Rate } (K_L^0 \to \text{all})}$$

$$x \quad \frac{\text{Rate } (K_S^0 \to \text{all})}{\text{Rate } (K_S^0 \to \pi^+\pi^-)} \quad x \quad \frac{\Gamma_L}{\Gamma_S} \tag{23}$$

where just the first ratio is measured, the rest being obtained from available data. The noteworthy exception to this is a determination of $\left|n_{+-}\right|$ by a CERN-Heidelberg group who analysed the time dependence of the $\pi^+\pi^-$ intensity produced from an initial (predominantly) K^0 state. In this case, the observed intensity is

$$I_{\pi^+\pi^-}(\tau) \propto \epsilon\,(\tau,P)S(P)\left[e^{-\Gamma_S\tau} + \left|n_{+-}\right|^2 e^{-\Gamma_L\tau}\right.$$

$$\left. +2D(P)\left|n_{+-}\right|e^{-\overline{\Gamma}\tau}\cos(\Delta m\tau+\phi_{+-})\right] \tag{24}$$

Here ϵ expresses the dependence of the detection efficiency on the K^0 momentum and proper time, $S(P)$ is the $K_{S,L}^0$ momentum spectrum, and $D(p)$ is a "dilution" factor accounting for the intensity contribution from a $\overline{K}^0$ initial state. Here K^0 and $\overline{K}^0$ decay incoherently but give an interference term of the opposite sign:

$$D(P) = \frac{I(P) - \overline{I}(P)}{I(P) + \overline{I}(P)}, \quad .5 < D(p) < .85 \tag{25}$$

The data comprise some 6×10^6 $K_{S,L}^0$ decays, about 100 times that of previous experiments, and permit the simultaneous determination of $\left|n_{+-}\right|$, Γ_S, and ϕ_{+-}. The result from the fit is $\left|n_{+-}\right| = (2.30 \pm 0.035)\times10^{-3}$. A conventional measurement by the same group using (23) and K_{e3} decays for normalization gives the same result, $\left|n_{+-}\right| = (2.30 \pm 0.06)\times10^{-3}$.

The CERN-Heidelberg group[5] also reported a value for the K_S^0 decay rate, $\Gamma_S = (1.119 \pm 0.006)\times10^{10}$ sec^{-1} in good agreement with the value 1.116 ± 0.006 from a recent high-statistics bubble chamber experiment.[9] The previous world average, $\Gamma_S = 1.160 \pm 0.008$, is five standard deviations from the average of these two results, $\Gamma_S = 1.1175 \pm 0.004$. The impact, however, of the change in Γ_S on measurements of $\left|n_{+-}\right|$ is small, increasing $\left|n_{+-}\right|$ by $\simeq 2\%$.

Taking the average of the four recent results, one obtains

$$\left|n_{+-}\right| = (2.29 \pm 0.026)\times10^{-3} \tag{26}$$

corresponding to an increase in the rate of 36% relative to (21). A plausible explanation for this dramatic shift is lacking, and if one shies away from the profound implications of a time-dependent η_{+-} (and/or Γ_S), the remaining alternative would seem to be a substantial embarrassment for experimentalists.

B.   Status of ϕ_{+-}

Generally, measurements of ϕ_{+-} suffer from a sensitivity to the value of the K_L^0-K_S^0 mass difference Δm. In turn, most measurements of Δm depend somewhat on the Γ_S value assumed in the analysis of those data. If the new value of $\Gamma_S = (1.1175 \pm 0.004) \times 10^{10}$ sec^{-1} is utilized to correct the three most accurate results, $\Delta m/\hbar$ increases by $\approx 0.6\%$ to $(0.5436 \pm 0.004) \times 10^{10}$ sec^{-1}, a shift of about one standard deviation. The world average value $\phi_{+-} = (41.8 \pm 2.8)°$ then becomes

$$\phi_{+-} \approx (42.6 \pm 2.8)° \qquad (27)$$

This adjusted value is still suspect because some experiments have obtained results with Γ_S fixed at the old value, and the correlation of ϕ_{+-} and Γ_S is not negligible.

The CERN-Heidelberg group[5] have presented a new value for ϕ_{+-}, obtained from the fit to (24). The efficiency-corrected $\pi^+\pi^-$ intensity versus $K_{S,L}^0$ proper time is shown in figure 7, and the interference term isolated in the fit is shown in figure 8. The accuracy of the result is dominated at present by the dependence of the result on Δm:

$$\phi_{+-} = (48.3 \pm 1.0)° + 300° \times \frac{(\Delta m - 0.540)}{\Delta m} \qquad (28)$$

Introducing the adusted Δm value and propagating the error, one obtains

$$\phi_{+-} = (50.3 \pm 2.4)° \qquad (29)$$

The lack of agreement between (27) and (29) is somewhat disturbing, but the χ^2 sum for the combined results of the relevant experiments is acceptable, and the best estimate is

$$\phi_{+-} \approx (49.2 \pm 2.8)°, \qquad (30)$$

where the error has been increased by 20% to account for the discrepancies, and includes the Δm uncertainty.

C. Status of $|\eta_{oo}|$

Several measurements of $|\eta_{oo}|$ exist, with scattered results, and none has been reported recently. The average of these experiments, the neutral analogues of (23), is

$$|\eta_{oo}| = (2.26 \pm 0.20) \times 10^{-3} \tag{31}$$

where a scale factor of 1.5 has been applied to the error by the Particle Data Group (see fig. 6).

Two measurements of the ratio $|\eta_{oo}/\eta_{+-}|$ have also been reported,[11] in good agreement with each other and together yielding

$$|\eta_{oo}/\eta_{+-}| = 1.013 \pm 0.046 . \tag{32}$$

This value is in good agreement with the ratio of (31) and (26)

$$|\eta_{oo}/\eta_{+-}| = 0.987 \pm 0.088 \tag{33}$$

combining (33) and (32) gives finally

$$|\eta_{oo}/\eta_{+-}| = 1.007 \pm 0.040 \tag{34}$$

D. Status of ϕ_{oo}

A new result measuring the phase difference $\phi_{oo} - \phi_{+-}$ has been reported:[12]

$$\phi_{oo} - \phi_{+-} = (7.6 \pm 18)^{\circ} . \tag{35}$$

This value is obtained by combining results from separate regenerator studies for $K_{L,S}^{o} \to \pi^{+}\pi^{-}$ and $K_{L,S}^{o} \to \pi^{o}\pi^{o}$ decays. Combined with (30) and the previous world average (uncorrected for Δm),

$$\phi_{oo} = (43.3 \pm 19.2)^{\circ} \tag{36}$$

the new average is

$$\phi_{oo} = (50.4 \pm 13.2)^{\circ} . \tag{37}$$

E. Charge Asymmetries

Three new values have been reported recently, two at this conference. The same CERN-Heidelberg group[5] who have presented results for Γ_S, η_{+-}, ϕ_{+-}, and λ_{+}, have also presented definitive results for the $K_{\mu 3}$ and K_{e3} asymmetries.[13] A BNL-Yale group[13] have measured the combined asymmetry using a new technique, and final results have become available for a measurement by a Princeton group.[14]

The CERN-Heidelberg group study the region at large proper time where interference effects have diminished sufficiently, and are left with 2×10^7 $K_{\mu 3}$ and 4×10^7 K_{e3} decays after cuts. The "raw" asymmetries are

$$\delta_e = (3.65 \pm 0.17) \times 10^{-3},$$
$$\delta_\mu = (3.23 \pm 0.26) \times 10^{-3}, \tag{38}$$

to which a number of very tiny corrections are made, yielding

$$\delta_e = (3.51 \pm 0.18) \times 10^{-3},$$
$$\delta_\mu = (3.47 \pm 0.28) \times 10^{-3}. \tag{39}$$

These are the most accurate results to date by a considerable margin. No difference in the corrected asymmetries at any proper time is observed, providing evidence that $X_e = X_\mu$ (see (20), and removing the possibility that discrepancies between previously reported K_{e3} and $K_{\mu 3}$ decays could be explained in this fashion.

The BNL-Yale group used a magnetic spectrometer employing multi-wire proportional chambers, but no conventional particle identification. Instead, they employed a novel approach to the problem, identifying leptons statistically, noting that the decay pion characteristically carries more transverse momentum than the charged lepton. The price is a reduction of statistical sensitivity, but is offset by the advantage of a simpler apparatus and different systematics. The result,

$$\delta_\ell = (3.33 \pm 0.50) \times 10^{-3} \tag{40}$$

while of moderate precision, is very useful because all measurements of the charge asymmetry suffer from the absence of a means to "calibrate" the apparatus with adequate accuracy.

The Princeton group also employed a magnetic spectrometer with multiwire proportional chambers, but utilized a cerenkov counter to label electrons in a conventional way. A reanalysis of the data, removing a bias arising from the acceptance boundaries of the cerenkov yields a result in good agreement with the other experiments:

$$\delta_e = (3.18 \pm 0.38) \times 10^{-3} \tag{41}$$

All results for K_{e3} and $K_{\mu 3}$ experiments are shown in figure 9. The averages of the electron and muon modes are

$$\delta_e = (3.39 \pm 0.14) \times 10^{-3}$$
$$\delta_\mu = (3.42 \pm 0.24) \times 10^{-3} \tag{42}$$

in good agreement with each other and with (40). The overall result for δ_ℓ, including (40), is then

$$\delta_\ell = (3.39 \pm 0.12) \times 10^{-3} \tag{43}$$

F.   Conclusions

The graphical representation of the results (26), (30), (34), and (37), known as the Wu-Yang diagram, is given in figure 10. There is no evidence for a non-zero value of the parameter $\varepsilon' = (\eta_{+-} - \eta_{oo})/3$. The predicted phase of the superweak model, for which $\eta_{+-} \cong \eta_{oo} = \varepsilon$ and $\phi\varepsilon = \tan^{-1}(2\Delta m/\Gamma_S)$,

$$\phi_{s\omega} = (44.0 \pm 0.3)^\circ \tag{44}$$

is also shown, indicating a disagreement with (30) at the 2-standard deviation level.

The charge asymmetry δ_ℓ provides a check of the consistency of other results. Taking the real part of (17), and setting $X = 0$ in (20), one obtains

$$-\text{Re}\,\varepsilon' = \frac{\delta}{2} - \left|\eta_{+-}\right|\cos(\phi_{+-}) = (0.21 \pm 0.10) \times 10^{-3} \tag{45}$$

suggesting a non-zero $R_e\varepsilon'$. On the other hand, if $\phi_{s\omega}$ is used to predict the charge asymmetry,

$$\delta = 2\left|\eta_{+-}\right| \cos(\phi_{s\omega}) = (3.30 \pm 0.04) \times 10^{-3} \tag{46}$$

then the agreement with (43) is good.

When confronted with irreconciliable conflicts between results bearing on the CP violation parameters, the author has taken the liberty of rejecting the older data. This viewpoint leads to a fairly consistent picture, but nevertheless, additional results of improved reliability and accuracy are badly needed, in particular for Δm and ϕ_{oo}. The physical basis of the phenomenon, after a decade of experimental effort, remains unknown.

IV.   THE $K_L^o \to \mu^+ \mu^-$ PROBLEM

This decay, which could occur as a direct manifestion of weak neutral currents, can also be generated by the combined effects of conventional first-order weak plus second-order electromagnetic interactions. The consequence of the latter process is to place a lower bound on the decay rate.

$$\frac{\Gamma(K_L^o \to \mu^+ \mu^-)}{\Gamma(K_L^o \to \text{All})} \geq 5.3 \times 10^{-9}, \tag{47}$$

known as the Primitive Unitarity Limit.

The limit (47) is derived with the assumptions of unitarity, CP and CPT conservation, conventional quantum electrodynamics for the coupling $\gamma\gamma \to \ell^+\ell^-$, a negligible absorptive part of the amplitude for $K_L^o \to \gamma\gamma$, and dominance of the two-photon intermediate state in the unitarity sum. Finally, the experimental result for the rate $K_L^o \to \gamma\gamma$ is needed.

A very surprising result, contradicting (47), was published in 1971 by a Berkeley group[15] placing a 90% confidence level upper bound

$$\frac{\Gamma(K_L^o \to \mu^+\mu^-)}{\Gamma(K_L^o \to All)} < 1.8 \times 10^{-9} \tag{48}$$

with no observed events.

As this result is very difficult to accomodate theoretically without new particles or interaction mechanisms, the experiment has been repeated by a Columbia-CERN-NYU group[16] at the BNL AGS, and is being undertaken by other groups as well. The Columbia-CERN-NYU experiment yielded six events satisfying their criteria for the decay, with background contribution 0.25 ± 0.15 events, and a branching ratio compatible with (47):

$$\frac{\Gamma(K_L^o \to \mu^+\mu^-)}{\Gamma(K_L^o \to All)} = 11 \, ^{+10}_{-5} \times 10^{-9} \ (90\% \ C. \ L.) \tag{49}$$

Both experiments utilize the kinematically similar decay $K_L^o \to \pi^+\pi^-$ to determine the K_L^o flux, and both values (48) and (49) are based on the old value (21) for $|\eta_{+-}|$. A subsequent reanalysis of the Berkeley data, correcting some errors, yields a higher limit (no events discovered)[17]:

$$\frac{\Gamma(K_L^o \to \mu^+\mu^-)}{\Gamma(K_L^o \to All)} < 2.5 \times 10^{-9} \ (90\% \ C. \ L.) \tag{50}$$

Adjusting (49) and (50) for the newer $|\eta_{+-}|$ (26), one has finally

$$\frac{\Gamma(K_L^o \to \mu^+\mu^-)}{\Gamma(K_L^o \to All)} < 3.4 \times 10^{-9} \ (Berkeley) \tag{51}$$

$$\frac{\Gamma(K_L^o \to \mu^+\mu^-)}{\Gamma(K_L^o \to All)} = 14 \, ^{+13}_{-7} \times 10^{-9} \ (Columbia) \tag{52}$$

According the Columbia value, the Berkeley data should have contained 9 events, a result which is independent of $|\eta_{+-}|$. As the work on these experiments is completed, the discrepancy between these two experiments has little chance of alleviation.

A new experimental result, however, has been reported at this conference supporting the existence of the decay at an appropriate rate[18]. This work is an extension of the technique employed by the Columbia-CERN-NYU group, and is designed to meet some criticisms applicable to the first result.

The modified apparatus of the Columbia-CERN-BNL experiment is shown in Fig. 11. An additional muon hodoscope has been installed to improve background rejection, and a different spectrometer setting, corresponding to 240 MeV/c rather than the 210.6 MeV/c of the previous experiment, has been employed. The latter change guarantees that any possible geometric pecularities of the apparatus creating a "background to $K_L^0 \to \mu\mu$" leakage channel cannot lead to the same event distribution.

The data are shown in figure 12, displayed versus invariant mass and the angle defined by the incident K_L^0 direction and the visible momentum. The background is understood in terms of $K_L^0 \to \pi\mu\nu$ decays in which the second muon signature is completed by π decay or by penetration of the concrete and steel. Three events survive the 2-standard deviation cuts in mass and angle, and correspond to a branching ratio (using (26))

$$\frac{\Gamma(K_L^0 \to \mu^+\mu^-)}{\Gamma(K_L^0 \to All)} = 9 \, ^{+13}_{-7} \times 10^{-9} \; (90\% \; C. \; L.) \tag{53}$$

with a background level similar to that of the Columbia-CERN-NYU result.

The two experiments can be combined, with the resulting mass distribution shown in Fig. 13. The final averaged branching ratio for the 9 events is

$$\frac{\Gamma(K_L^0 \to \mu^+\mu^-)}{\Gamma(K_L^0 \to All)} = 12 \, ^{+8}_{-4} \times 10^{-9} \; (90\% \; C. \; L.) \tag{54}$$

in good agreement with (47).

One of the most interesting suggestions to deal with the problems raised by the Berkeley result is that of Christ and Lee[19], who propose that a cancellation of the amplitude leading to (47) can be arranged if an anomalously large $K_S^0 \to \mu^+\mu^-$ rate exists.

The required interference necessarily involves CP violation in at least one of the amplitudes $K_S^0 \to \mu^+ \mu^-$, or $K_{S,L}^0 \to \gamma\gamma$. The most economical realization of the Christ-Lee mechanism is that of Dass and Wolfenstein[20], who propose a model incorporating the anomalous rate and the CP violation in a direct $K_S^0 \to \mu^+ \mu^-$ coupling. The anomalously large rate is a consequence of the smallness of ε, which couples K_L^0 and K_S^0 and permits interference to occur. To give the Berkeley result, the $K_S^0 \to \mu^+ \mu^-$ rate is bounded by

$$\Gamma(K_S^0 \to \mu^+ \mu^-) \geq \frac{[A \text{ (Unitarity)} - A \text{ (Berkeley)}]^2}{(\text{Re}\varepsilon)^2} \tag{55}$$

where A(unitarity) corresponds to the amplitude leading to (47), and A(Berkeley) corresponds to the amplitude limit implied by the Berkeley result. In 1971, using (48) and (21), (55) yielded

$$\frac{\Gamma(K_S^0 \to \mu^+ \mu^-)}{\Gamma_S} \geq 10.0 \times 10^{-7} \tag{56}$$

At present, using (51) and (26), (55) gives

$$\frac{\Gamma(K_S^0 \to \mu^+ \mu^-)}{\Gamma_S} \geq 1.7 \times 10^{-7}. \tag{57}$$

Consequently, an upper bound reported recently by the CERN-Heidelberg group,[21]

$$\frac{\Gamma(K_S^0 \to \mu^+ \mu^-)}{\Gamma_S} > 3.1 \times 10^{-7} \text{ (90\% C. L.)} \tag{58}$$

no longer rules out this possiblity as an explanation of the Berkeley result. On the other hand, the present discrepancy between (47) and (41) is now much smaller than before, implying only a 20% cancellation of the unitarity amplitude. The significance of the effect is consequently of the same order as the validity of the assumption that the unitarity sum is dominated completely by the $\gamma\gamma$ intermediate state, for which some authors have calculated as much as a 10% uncertainty due to other real intermediate states such as $\pi\pi\gamma$.[21] The likelihood that an exotic possibility such as $K_S^0 \to \mu\mu$ is responsible seems therefore somewhat diminished, but the new experiments underway will hopefully settle the controversy.

*Work supported by the U. S. Atomic Energy Commission.

REFERENCES

1. Lee G. Pondrom, "Experimental Review of Weak Interactions", in AIP Conference Proceedings, No. 2, Particles and Fields - 1971, p. 151-180 (1971).

2. O. Fackler, D. Frisch, J. Martin, G. Smoot, and L. Sompayrac, Conference Contribution #8, and Phys. Rev. Letters, 31, 847 (1973).

3. World averages are those compiled by the Particle Data Group, as presented in Rev. Mod. Phys. 45 Supplement, April (1973).

4. L-M. Chounet, J-M. Gaillard, and M. K. Gaillard, Physics Reports 4, 199-324 (1972).

5. G. Geweniger, S. Gjesdal, T. Kamae, G. Presser, P. Steffen, J. Steinberger, F. Vanucci, H. Wahl, F. Eisele, H. Filthuth, K. Kleinknecht. V. Lüth, G. Zech, Conference Contributions #151-153. The authors emphasize that the values given here must be considered preliminary as the analysis is continuing; final results when published may accordingly differ slightly from those quoted in this report.

6. G. Donaldson, D. Fryberger, D. Hitlin, J. Lin, B. Meyer, R. Piccioni, A. Rothenberg, D. Uggla, S. Wojcicki, and D. Dorfan, Phys. Rev. Letters 31, 325 (1973).

7. J. Sandweiss, J. Sunderland, W. Turner, W. Willis, and L. Keller, Phys. Rev. Letters 30, 1002 (1973). The result given by these authors is Re $\xi(o) = -0.385 \pm 0.105 - 6.0\lambda_+$.

8. T. T. Wu and C. N. Yang, Phys. Rev. Letters 13, 380 (1964).

9. O. Skjeggestad, F. James, L. Montanet, E. Paul, P. Saetre, D. M. Sendall, G. Burgun, E. Lesquoy, A. Muller, E. Paul, S. Zylberajch, Nuc, Phys. B48, 343 (1972).

10. The stated correlations of Δm and τ_S are: $+1/2$ for the result $\Delta m = 0.542 \pm 0.006$ of Aronson et al., Phys. Rev. Letters 25, 1057 (1970); $-1/30$ for the result $\Delta m - 0.534 \pm 0.007$ of Carnegie et al., Phys. Rev. D6, 2335 (1971), and Ph.D thesis of L. Sulak, Princeton University, 1971; 0.0 for the result $\Delta m = 0.542 \pm 0.006$ of Cullen et al., Physics Letters 32B, 523 (1970).

11. M. Banner, J. W. Cronin, C. H. Hoffman, B. C. Kanpp, and M. J. Shochet, Phys. Rev. Letters 28, 1597 (1972); and H. Holder, E. Radermacher, A. Staude, P. Darriulat, J. Deutsch, M. Hansroul, S. Orito, J. Pilcher, C. Rubbia, P. Strolin, K. Tittel, A. Fainberg, C. Grosso-Pilcher, and M. Scire, Physics Letters 40B, 141 (1972).

12. G. Barbiellini, P. Darriulat, A. Fainberg, M. Holder, G. Maderni, S. Orito, E. Radermacher, C. Rubbia, A. Staude, P. Strolin, and K. Tittel, Physics Letters 43B, 529 (1973).

13. H. H. Williams, R. C. Larsen, L. B. Leipuner, W. W. Sapp, A. L. Sessoms, L. W. Smith, R. K. Adair, and R. C. Turner, Conference Contribution #58.

14. V. Fitch, V. Hepp, D. Jensen, M. Strovink, and R. C. Webb, Abstract submitted to Rochester 1971 Conference, and for final result, M. Strovink, private communication.

15. A. R. Clark, T. Elioff, R. C. Field, H. J. Frisch, R. P. Johnson, L. T. Kerth, and W. A. Wenzel Phys. Rev. Letters 26, 1667 (1971).

16. W. C. Carithers, T. Modis, D. R. Nygren, T. P. Pun, E. L. Schwartz, H. Sticker, J. Steinberger, P. Weilhammer, and J. H. Christenson, Phys. Rev. Letters 30, 1336 (1973).

17. Priviate communication from R. C. Field and L. T. Kerth; also reported at APS meeting in Washington, D. C. April 30 - May 2, 1973.

18. W. C. Carithers, D. R. Nygren, H. A. Gordon, M. L. Ioffredo, Kwan-Wu Lai, and Peter Weilhammer, submitted to Phys. Rev. Letters.

19. N. Christ and T. D. Lee, Phys. Rev. D4, 209 (1971).

20. G. V. Dass and L. Wolfenstein, Physical Letters 38B, 435 (1972).

21. M. K. Gaillard, Phys. Letters 35B, 431 (1971) See also H. Stern and M. K. Gaillard, Annals of Physics 76, 580 (1973) for a review of the theoretical implications.

REFERENCES FOR λ_+ FROM $K_L^0 \to \pi e \nu$

1. Geweniger et al., Conference contribution #153

2. Brandenburg et al., Conference contribution #73

3. Buchanan et al., Conference contribution #169

4. Neuhofer et al., Physics Letters 41B, 642 (1972)

5. Dally et al., Physics Letters 41B, 647 (1972)

6. Bisi _et al._, Physics Letters 36B, 533 (1971)

7. Basile _et al._, Physics Letters 26B, 542 (1968)

8. Aronson _et al._, Phys. Rev. Letters 20, 287 (1968)

9. Kadyk _et al._, Phys. Rev. Letters 19, 597 (1967)

10. Firestone _et al._, Phys. Rev. Letters 18, 176 (1967)

REFERENCES FOR $\left| \eta_{+-} \right|$

1. Geweniger _et al._, Conference contribution #151 $\left| \eta_{+-} \right|$ = (2.30 ± 0.06)x10^{-3}, measured by conventional ratio method, eq. 23.

2. Geweniger _et al._, Conference contribution #151 $\left| \eta_{+-} \right|$ = (2.30 ± 0.035)x10^{-3}, obtained from the fit to eq. 24.

3. S. Aronson, private communication. A preliminary result by conventional ratio method: $\left| \eta_{+-} \right|$ = (2.38 ± 0.15)x10^{-3}

4. R. Messner _et al._, Phys. Rev. Letters 30, 876 (1973).
$\left| \eta_{+-} \right|$ = (2.25 ± 0.05)x10^{-3}

5. V. Fitch _et al._, Phys. Rev. 164, 1711 (1967) $\left| \eta_{+-} \right|$ = (1.91 ± 0.06)x10^{-3}

6. M. Bott-Bodenhausen _et al._, Physics Letters 23, 277 (1966),
$\left| \eta_{+-} \right|$ = (1.87 ± 0.08)X10^{-3}

7. M. Bott-Bodenhausen _et al._, Physics Letters 23, 277 (1966)
$\left| \eta_{+-} \right|$ = (1.93 ± 0.04)x10^{-3}

8. Basile _et al._, Balaton Conference, $\left| \eta_{+-} \right|$ = (1.86 ± 0.20)x10^{-3}

9. W. Galbraith _et al._, Phys. Rev. Letters 14, 383 (1965).
$\left| \eta_{+-} \right|$ = (2.02 ± 0.17)x10^{-3}

10. J. H. Christenson _et al._, Phys. Rev. Letters 13, 138 (1964)
$\left| \eta_{+-} \right|$ = (1.94 ± 0.20)x10^{-3}

REFERENCES FOR $K_L^0 \rightarrow \pi\ell\nu$ CHARGE ASYMMETRY

1. Geweniger et al., Conference contribution #152 $\delta = (3.51 \pm 0.18)$ x10^{-3} see ref. 5.

2. Fitch et al., see ref. 14
   $\delta = (3.18 \pm 0.38)$x10^{-3}

3. Ashford et al., Physics Letters 38B, 47 (1972)
   $\delta = (3.6 \pm 1.8)$x10^{-3}

4. Marx et al., Physics Letters 32B, 219 (1970)
   $\delta = (3.46 \pm 0.33)$x10^{-3}

5. Bennett et al., Phys. Rev. Letters 19, 993 (1967) and H. Saal, Ph.D thesis, Columbia University
   $\delta = (2.46 \pm 0.59)$x10^{-3}

6. Williams et al., Conference contribution #58
   $\delta = (3.33 \pm 0.50)$x10^{-3}

7. Geweniger et al., Conference contribution #152
   $\delta = (3.47 \pm 0.28)$x10^{-3}

8. Piccioni et al., Phys. Rev. Letters 29, 1412 (1972)
   $\delta = (2.78 \pm 0.51)$x10^{-3}

9. McCarthy et al., Phys. Rev. D7, 687 (1973)
   $\delta = (6.0 \pm 1.4)$x10^{-3}

10. M. A. Paciotti, Ph.D thesis, UCRL-19446, Lawrence Berkeley Laboratory, Dec. 1969 (unpublished)
    $\delta = (5.8 \pm 1.7)$x10^{-3}

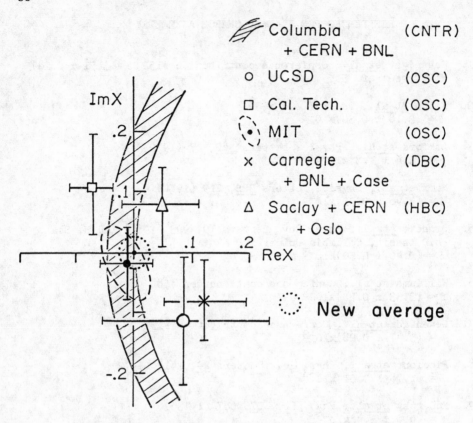

Fig. 1. Recent results for ΔS=-ΔQ amplitudes including the new
MIT result. Also shown is a new world average incorporating the MIT result.

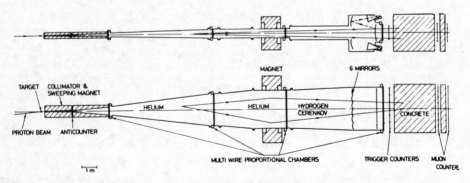

Fig. 3. View of the CERN-Heidelberg apparatus.

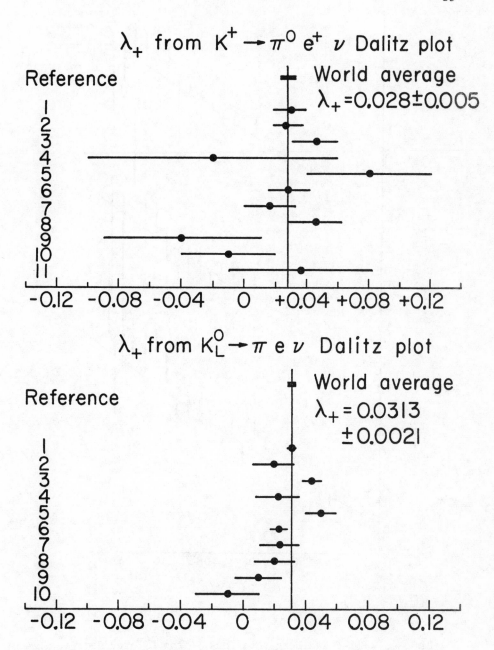

Fig. 2. Comparison of λ_+ results for K^0 and K^+ decays.

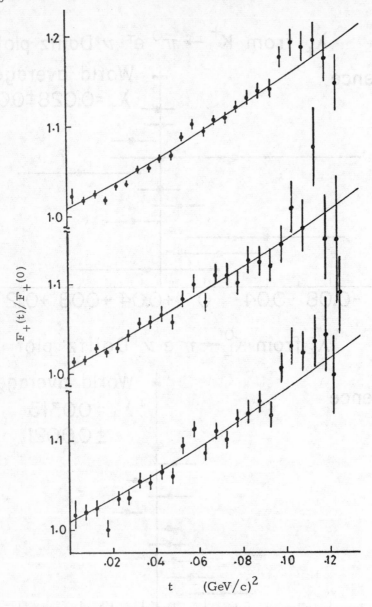

Fig. 4. CERN-Heidelberg data for λ_+ from $K_L^0 \to \pi e \nu$ decays.
Top curve-weighted solutions; middle curve –
$|\Delta T_\pi| < 10$ MeV; bottom curve – fit of matrix. The
curves are the prediction of the $K^*(892)$ dominance
model.

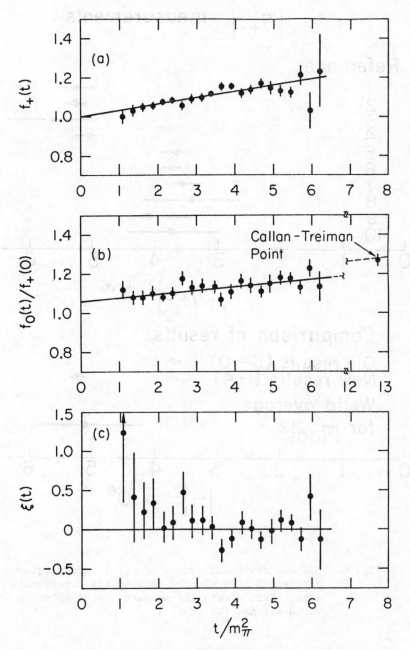

Fig. 5. SLAC-Santa Cruz results for $F_+(t)$, $F_0(t)$, and $\xi(t)$.

42

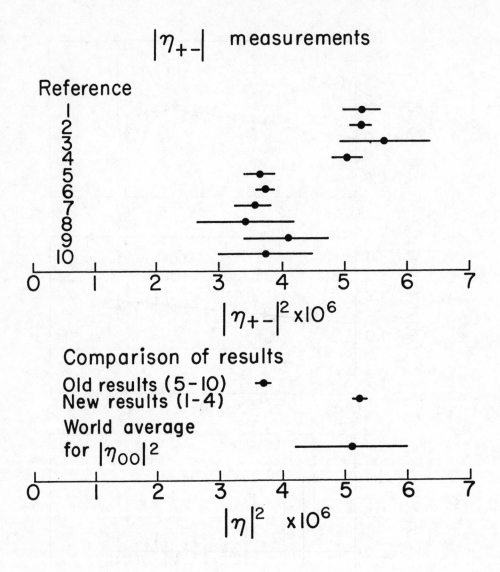

Fig. 6. Old and new measurements of $|\eta+-|$, shown squared to correspond more closely to what all experiments except Ref. 2 actually measure. Also shown is the world average for $|\eta_{00}|^2$,

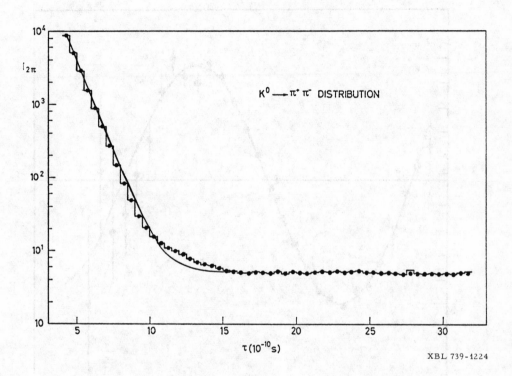

Fig. 7. $K^0 \to \pi^+ \pi^-$ intensity versus proper time, corrected for efficiency, and showing prominent constructive interference around $\tau \approx 12 \times 10^{-10}$ sec. Data is from CERN-Heidelberg group contribution, Ref. 5.

44

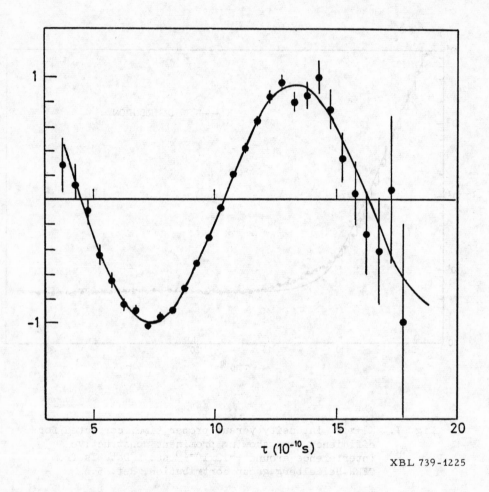

Fig. 8. Isolated interference term of the data shown in Fig. 7.

XBL 739-1225

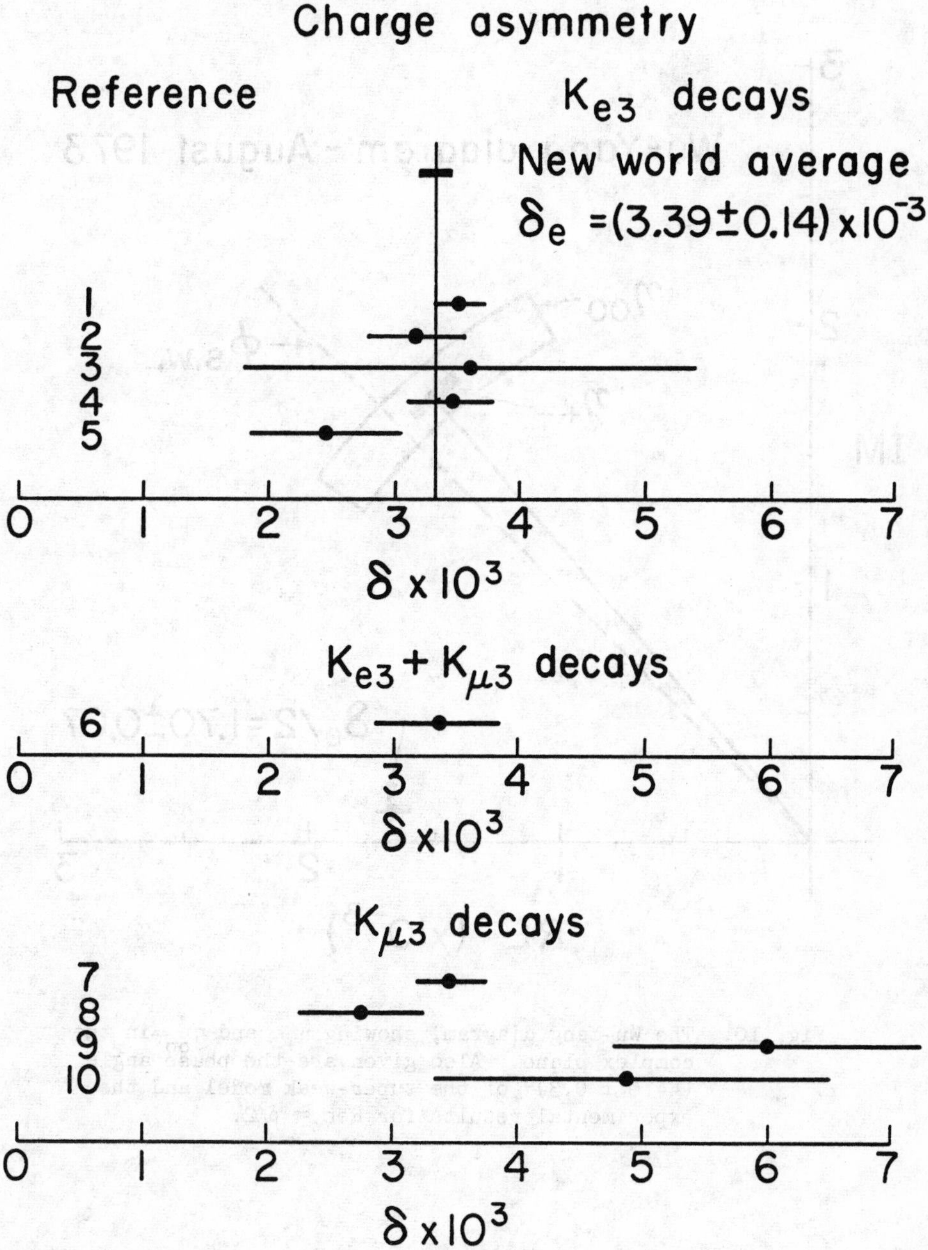

Fig. 9. Results for the charge asymmetry in $K_L^0 \rightarrow \pi \ell \nu$ decays.

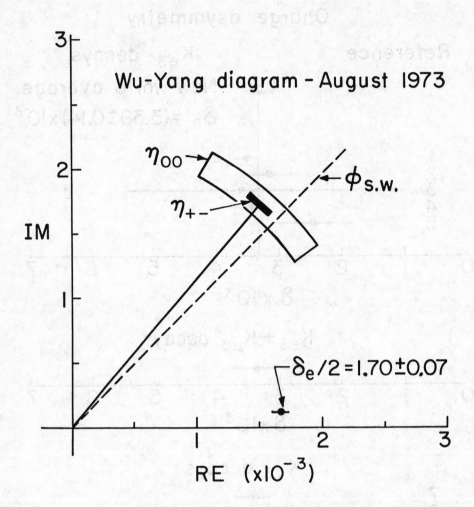

Fig. 10. The Wu-Yang diagram, showing η_{+-} and η_{oo} in the complex plane. Also given are the phase angle $(44.0 \pm 0.3)^{o}$ of the super-weak model and the experimental results for $\mathrm{Re}\epsilon = \delta/2$.

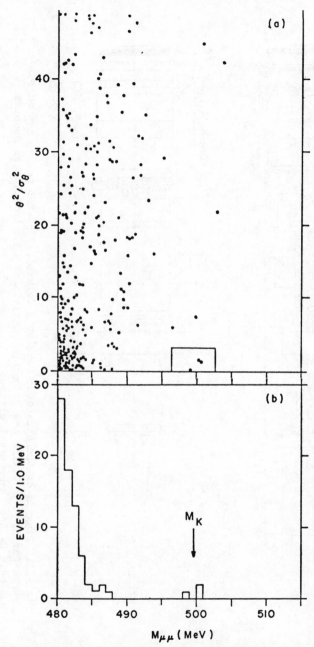

Fig. 12. Data obtained by the Columbia-CERN-BNL collaboration.
9) Mμμ versus K_L^0 angle scatter plot, showing three
events within the accepted region, b) Projection
of the data on the Mμμ axis, for angles smaller
than 3 (units of θ^2/σ^2).

48

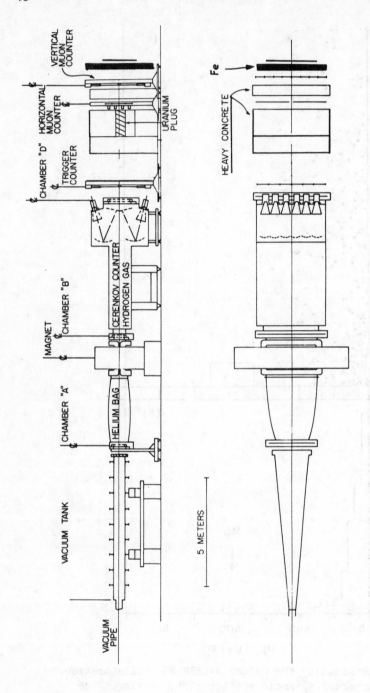

Fig. 11. Diagram of the apparatus used by a Columbia–CERN–BNL collaboration to search for $K_L^0 \rightarrow \mu^+ \mu^-$. The new hodoscope consists of 23 scintillators mounted behind a 2-inch thick steel plate.

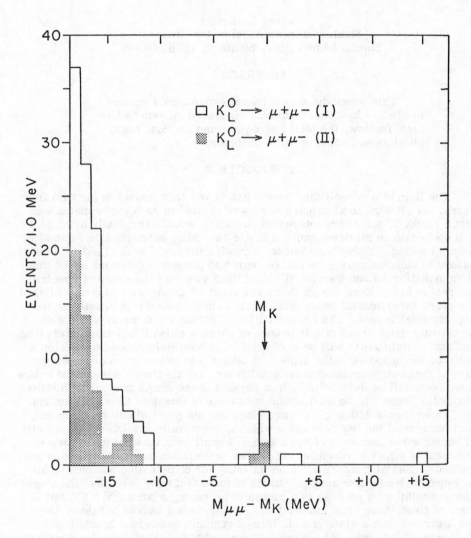

Fig. 13. Combined data of the Columbia-CERN-NYU (I)
and Columbia-CERN-BNL (II) experiments
showing nine events at the K⁰ mass.

SUMMARY OF e^+e^- COLLIDING BEAM EXPERIMENTS*

Harvey L. Lynch
Stanford Linear Accelerator Center
Stanford University, Stanford, Calif. 94305

ABSTRACT

This paper discusses recent experiments related to $e^+e^- \rightarrow$ hadrons. Subjects discussed include hadron form factors, the total hadronic cross section, multiplicities and some specific channels.

INTRODUCTION

The field of e^+e^- colliding beams has grown enormously in the past five years. In 1968 the total number of papers related to such experiments was just a handfull, and every interested physicist could very easily bring himself up to date on all developments in e^+e^- colliding beam physics in an afternoon's reading. Today for someone already immersed in the field it is necessary to launch a major literature search to present a coherent set of timely information. Even then he will be obliged to select the areas of special interest to him. Even though there are about 10 theoretical papers published for every experimental paper in the field I shall concentrate heavily on the experimental issues. Thus it is that in delivering my summary I have selected only those areas of this branch of physics which I find most interesting, and that certain areas will be neglected. I deliberately choose to develop a selected set of topics to the neglect of others just to present a coherent picture of the controversial experimental issues at this time. Almost the entire discussion will be devoted to hadron physics in the single photon annihilation channel. There will be no discussion of tests of Quantum Electrodynamics.

Experiments with e^+e^- storage rings are not particularly easy, in large part because of the low data rates which are generally available. At the risk of boring some members of the audience I shall indicate what makes the investment of effort worthwhile. First, an annihilation process is the cleanest method of obtaining information on the behavior of time-like photons. This fact opens a whole new area to studies of form factors. Secondly, the single photon annihilation process is a means of preparing a pure $J^{PC} = 1^{--}$ initial state of fixed energy and momentum. Rarely does a hadron physicist have the luxury of such a state of well defined quantum numbers. In addition to the purity of the state, its richness is somewhat overwhelming, because any particles which even indirectly couple to a photon may be produced. Nevertheless, there are limitations; for example any final state consisting entirely of π^0's cannot be produced because such a state has even charge conjugation. There is no way to investigate $c = +1$ states with a single photon initial state. It has been pointed out, however, that a two photon initial state can be prepared with colliding beams; such a state would have $c = +1$ but lacks a definite angular momentum, energy, or momentum. The branch of two photon physics has been much admired and discussed, but mainly as a novelty. Unfortunately because of its novelty it has been subjected to a great

* Work supported by the U.S. Atomic Energy Commission.

excess of calculation per unit thought by theoreticians and experimentalists alike. There is much room for creative work in the physics connected to the two photons rather than the QED or approximations thereto to calculate the equivalent photon fluxes.

FORM FACTORS

Since the early days of high energy physics people have studied electromagnetic form factors, and by now very extensive studies have been made in the space-like region. With few exceptions the other half of the world, the time like region, was inaccessible. Historically the first study of form factors was for nucleons and only with much difficulty and through indirect means were any meson form factors studied. For several reasons this order was reversed when the time like region became accessible. The pion form factor was studied first in some elegant but difficult experiments at Orsay[1,2] and Novosibirsk.[3] The strong coupling of the two pions to the ρ, which, being a 1^{--} state, has the same quantum numbers as a photon, produces a spectacular peak in the pion form factor, as shown in Fig. 1. The same experiment[2] allowed a study of ρ-ω interference via the G-parity violating amplitude $\omega \to \pi^+\pi^-$. A dramatic peak in the K form factor[4,5] is a reflection of the existence of the ϕ vector meson; see Fig. 2. However, away from these well known vector mesons no dramatic structure has been found in the pion form factor. Figure 3 shows a compilation of existing data[2,6-8] on the pion form factor for $s \geq 1$ GeV^2. The figure does not show all the world's data; a few datum points having very large estimated errors have been discarded in the interest of a tidy picture. The fall off of the square of the form factor is consistent with s^{-2}. This smooth fall is a disappointment to those who would seek another vector meson coupling to $\pi^+\pi^-$. The rate of fall is also somewhat disappointing to people planning such measurements at higher energies. If this rate continues to $s = 27$ GeV^2, the highest energy available at SPEAR, this process will be all but lost in the noise. Nevertheless, one must look and perhaps there could be a surprise. A word of caution should be injected here about this figure. The data for

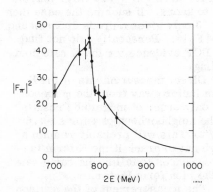

FIG. 1--Measurements of pion form factors in the region of the ρ (Ref. 2).

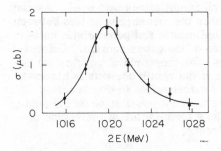

FIG. 2--Representative measurements of kaon form factors in the region of the ϕ (Ref. 5).

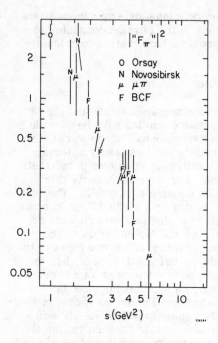

FIG. 3--Measurements of pion form factor at high energies. Data selected from Refs. 2, 6-8.

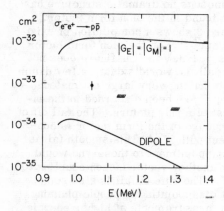

FIG. 4--Total cross section for $e^+e^- \to p\bar{p}$ (Ref. 9) compared with upper limits obtained for $p\bar{p} \to e^+e^-$ by Refs. 10 and 11.

$s < 2.25$ GeV^2 are unambiguously identified as being pionic events. Above this region the situation is not so clear, since no compelling separation of pions from kaons has been made. Simplest arguments based on SU$_3$ would indicate that the number of K's should be the same as the number of π's. A perhaps more realistic scheme of SU$_3$ breaking would have the number of K's only one third the number of π's. Experimentally the situation is somewhat murky; the BCF group[8] has presented some data indicating that perhaps half of their data for $2.25 \leq s \leq 2.9$ GeV^2 may be due to kaons. If such be the case then Fig. 3 only gives a crude upper bound for $|F_\pi|^2$. Personally I do not find the BCF evidence for the K rate compelling.

Direct measurements of the K form factor away from the ϕ meson are only order of magnitude results[6] in the neighborhood of 1 for $s \sim 1.6$ GeV^2. This will probably remain a tough nut to crack if the K form factor continues to fall at the same rate as the pion form factor.

The measurement of the nucleon form factor in the time like region has had to wait for some rather recent results from Frascati-Naples.[9] Figure 4 shows the result of their measurement, $\sigma(e^+e^- \to p\bar{p}) = 0.91 \pm 0.22$ nb. This measurement is shown along with some upper limits set by searches[10,11] for $p\bar{p}$ annihilations into e^+e^-. As can be seen the measurement lies between the optimistic and pessimistic estimates of the cross section. Unfortunately for the world of physics the region of the vector mesons is kinematically inaccessible to this reaction. Thus it is not possible to do the analog of the π form factor in the region of interest.

MULTIHADRON PRODUCTION

The study of multihadron production has produced great stimulation to theoretical thought on parton or quark models. The cross sections turned out to be remarkably large and none of the first generation experiments were properly instrumented to handle the process. Nevertheless people went ahead and did the best they could with the data. Figure 5 shows a compilation of the world's data[12-17] on the total cross section for producing multihadrons. It should be emphasized that the commonly used description of total cross section is somewhat of a misnomer. What is meant here is a final state having at least two charged hadrons plus something else. This figure shows the ratio of σ_{tot} to the cross section for producing a pair of massless, ideal Dirac particles, generically called $\sigma_{\mu\mu}$. This ratio is useful first because it removes some expected kinematic factors, and second it emphasizes the magnitude of the cross section; thirdly note the dramatic difference of character from the s dependence of the pion form factor squared (which is $\approx 4\sigma_{\pi\pi}/\sigma_{\mu\mu}$). The ratio $\sigma_{tot}/\sigma_{\mu\mu}$ is at worst a constant with s and more likely is increasing. G. Tarnopolsky has reported to this conference the latest result from CEA at $s = 25$ GeV^2; $\sigma_{tot}/\sigma_{\mu\mu} = 5.4 \pm 1.3(\pm 0.6)$. Such a large cross section gives much trouble to quark model builders, who say that $R = \sigma_{tot}/\sigma_{\mu\mu} = \sum_i Q_i^2$, where Q_i are to the charges of the constituents. The idea is that a pair of quarks are produced and they dress themselves as multihadrons. The model is simple and thus appealing. Unfortunately "old fashioned" quarks predict

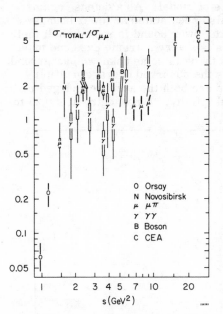

FIG. 5--Measurements of "total" hadronic annihilation cross section divided by point-like pair cross section. Data derived from Ref. 12-17. Note, the data from Ref. 12 represent only $e^+e^- \rightarrow \pi^+\pi^-\pi^0\pi^0$ data.

that R = 2/3, which lies far below the data. The suggestion of introducing three different kinds of quarks having color allows one to triple R. This is a big help and such a result would satisfy all the Frascati data, but is inconsistent with both the CEA points at higher s. There are other variations, for example adding charm, which allows R = 10/3. Frankly I find such maneuvering rather unconvincing. The idea is attractive, but one must be honest too and recognize the weakness of extreme simplicity, where all but the most rudimentary kinematics have been discarded. There is no compelling reason to believe that we have reached the asymptotic region where we can afford such luxuries. There is, for example, no prohibition against the ratio peaking and then falling. In fact if one looked only at the data below $s = 9$ GeV^2 this is a consistent statement. A large part of these data are

54

represented by what has been advertized as the ρ', which is certainly not part
of an asymptotic region. This should raise a feeling of caution to the model
builders: these experiments are hard, and not all experiments agree on the
results. For example, the points by the $\gamma\gamma$ group at Frascati are consistently lower than the other two Frascati groups represented by published or
preprint data. In addition all experiments must make rather large corrections for detection efficiency. To a greater or lesser extent all of these
results are dependent upon the models used to calculate these efficiencies.
Generally a pure phase space model has been used, and various models have
been used to test sensitivity to the choice of model. As a defense against
this problem both the CEA points have also been stated as lower bounds
defined by assuming unit efficiency. This lower bound is roughly half their
best estimate for the ratio R. Since this is a very extreme case one must
take seriously the fact that $R \geq 2$ unless there is some unknown background.

Also of interest to model builders is the observed average multiplicity[17, 18] shown on Fig. 6. Plotted here are both the average charged multiplicity as well as the estimated total multiplicity. A new entry at s = 25 to

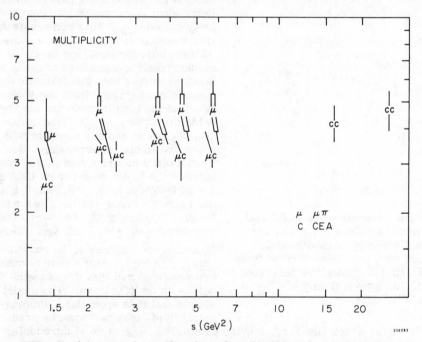

FIG. 6--Average charged and total multiplicity for multihadron
production. Data from Ref. 17, 18. Charged multiplicity points
have a "c" appended to the experiment legend.

this plot has been reported by CEA at this conference. It is clear that the
total multiplicity exceeds the charged multiplicity by about one and that both
multiplicities vary only slowly with s. A simple statistical model[19] of en-
ergy limiting would lead one to expect $\langle n \rangle \sim \sqrt{s} / \langle E_\pi \rangle$. Other models would
predict a logarithmic increase similar to that observed in ordinary hadronic
reactions. The existing data do not clearly distinguish between the two alternatives if an arbitrary additative constant is allowed.

One of the clear predictions of quark models of multihadron production is the appearance of jets of hadrons along the path of the pair produced quark. Unfortunately at present no such jets have been found, but none are really expected at the energies available. The average particle momentum even at CEA energies is of the order of 1 GeV; transverse momenta of several hundred MeV characteristic of hadronic interactions would make any such jets rather diffuse in nature. It was suggested some time ago by Bjorken and Brodsky[19] that a statistical test for jets might be useful even though the visual impression may not be clear. The technique is to look for nondegenerate eigenvalues of the tensor

$$T_{\alpha\beta} = \sum_{\text{particle-}i} \left(\frac{3}{2} p_\alpha^i p_\beta^i - \frac{1}{2} \delta_{\alpha\beta} \vec{p}^{i2} \right) \bigg/ \sum_i \vec{p}^{i2} \, .$$

Such a test seeks a nonvanishing quadrupole moment in the angular distribution of the hadrons of a single event. To my knowledge this test has not been attempted nor do I have a qualitative feeling for the sensitivity of such a test. Only experimenters having raw data can perform this test on the model, and one would hope that results could be forthcoming in the near future. In the mean time the observed multiplicity distribution speaks in favor of this model.

Another topic which has received much attention recently is the existence of a new vector meson, the ρ'. To storage ring people such an object manifests itself as a broad enhancement in the yield of four charged pions as shown in Fig. 7. The relative merits of the photoproduction data and the storage ring data indicating the existence of the ρ' have been debated elsewhere by people more closely related to the subject than myself, so I shall not enter into this discussion. Suffice it to say that in principle a colliding beam experiment could be a valuable tool for such an investigation, but considerably higher statistics are required to put the ρ' on any kind of footing like the ρ. One could also study the channel $\rho' \to \pi^+\pi^-\pi^0\pi^0$, and use this information for isotopic spin assignment. Figure 8 shows data[12,13,16] on this reaction; it is clear that the rate to $\pi^+\pi^-\pi^+\pi^-$ is about the same as the rate to $\pi^+\pi^-\pi^0\pi^0$. Under certain simplifying assumptions[20] this result favors I = 1 for the ρ'. One very clear advantage of a positive storage ring experiment is the assignment $J^{PC} = 1^{--}$.

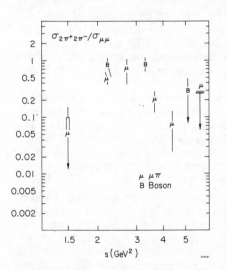

FIG. 7--Annihilation cross section for $e^+e^- \to \pi^+\pi^-\pi^+\pi^-$. Data from Refs. 15, 16.

There is a very pretty piece of physics lurking on the left edge of Fig. 8. The three Orsay points[12] are new and are nicely described by a quasi two body process $e^+e^- \to (\pi^+\pi^-\pi^0)\pi^0$, where the three pion state may be identified

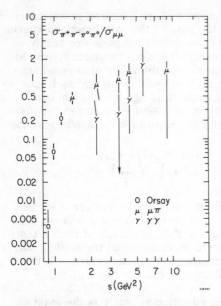

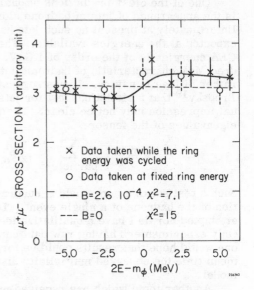

FIG. 8--Annihilation cross section for $e^+e^- \to \pi^+\pi^-\pi^0\pi^0$. Data from Refs. 12, 13 and 16.

FIG. 9--s dependence of cross section for $e^+e^- \to \mu^+\mu^-$ showing contribution of ω to vacuum polarization (Ref. 23).

with an ω meson. These data are quantitatively fit by a model of Renard.[21] One should note that this model only accounts for the threshold behavior of the reaction and accounts for only about 20% of the yield seen at higher energies. Perhaps it is worth noting that the data presented span about two decades. For experiments which are generally severely limited by data rate this is a remarkable achievement.

The very first results from SPEAR were presented at this conference by a group from UCLA,[22] whose results were obtained by parasitic running during a feasibility test. They wish to study an antinucleon spectrum. During their running on a piece of test apparatus they found one clear $\bar{p}$ event and essentially no background and two $\bar{n}$ candidates, but with substantial background. They thus place 90% confidence upper limits on the total cross sections leading to $\bar{p}$ or $\bar{n}$ final states: $\sigma_{\bar{p}} < 5 \times 10^{-34} \text{cm}^2$ and $\sigma_{\bar{n}} < 2 \times 10^{-33}$.

Generally speaking storage ring experiments to date have been rather straight forward in concept and if difficult or even heroic, not terribly imaginative. In closing, here is a plum recently offered by ORSAY[23] which is all of the above except unimaginative. By making very accurate measurements of the s dependence of $e^+e^- \to \mu^+\mu^-$ near the ϕ mass they observed the contribution to vacuum polarization due to the ϕ intermediate state. Their results are shown in Fig. 9.

REFERENCES

1. J. E. Augustin, D. Benaksas, J. Buon, F. Fulda, V. Gracco, J. Haissinski, D. Lalanne, F. Laplanche, J. Lefrancois, P. Lehmann, P. C. Marin, J. Perez-y-Jorba, F. Rumpf and E. Silva, Lett al Nuovo Cimento II, 214 (1969).

2. D. Benaksas, G. Cosme, B. Jean-Marie, S. Jullian, F. Laplanche, J. Lefrancois, A. D. Liberman, G. Parrour, J. P. Repellin and G. Sauvage, Phys. Letters 39 B, 289 (1972).

3. V. L. Auslander, G. I. Budker, E. V. Pakhtusova, Yu. N. Pestov, V. A. Sidorov, A. N. Skrinsky, and A. G. Khabakhpashev, Sov. J. Nucl. Phys. 9, 69 (1969).

4. J. C. Bizot, J. Buon, Y. Chatelus, J. Jeanjean, D. Lalane, H. Nguyen Ngoc, J. P. Perez-y-Jorba, P. Petroff, F. Richard, F. Rumpf and D. Treille, Phys. Letters 32 B, 416 (1970).

5. V. E. Balakin, G. I. Budker, E. V. Pakhtusova, V. A. Sidorov, A. N. Skrinsky, G. M. Tumaikin and A. G. Khabakhpashev, Phys. Letters 34 B, 328 (1971).

6. V. E. Balakin, G. I. Budker, L. M. Kurdadze, A. P. Onuchin, E. V. Pakhtusova, S. I. Serednyakov, V. A. Sidorov and A. N. Skrinsky, Phys. Letters 41 B, 205 (1972).

7. μ π group: G. Barbiellini, M. Grilli, E. Iarocci, P. Spillantini, V. Valente, R. Visentin, F. Ceradini, M. Conversi, S. d'Angelo, G. Giannoli, L. Paoluzi, R. Santonico, M. Nigro, L. Trasatti and G. I. Zorn, Lett. al Nuovo Cimento 6, 557 (1973).

8. BCF group: V. Alles-Borelli, M. Bernardini, D. Bollini, P. L. Brunini, E. Fiorentino, T. Massam, L. Monari, F. Palmonari, F. Rimondi, and A. Zichichi, Phys. Letters 40 B 433 (1972); M. Bernardini, D. Bollini, P. L. Brunini, E. Fiorentino, I. Massam, F. Palmonori, F. Rimondi, and A. Zichichi, Phys. Letters 44 B, 393 (1973)

9. M. Castellano, G. Di Giugno, J. W. Humphrey, E. Sassi Palmieri, G. Troise, N. Troya and S. Vitale, Nuovo Cimento 14 A, 1 (1973).

10. D. L. Hartill, B. C. Barish, D. G. Fong, R. Gomez, J. Pine and A. V. Tollestrup, Phys. Rev. 184, 1485 (1969).

11. M. Conversi, T. Massam, Th. Muller and A. Zichichi, Nuovo Cimento 40 A, 690 (1965).

12. G. Cosme, A. Courau, B. Dudelzak, B. Grelaud, B. Jean-Marie, S. Jullian, D. Lalanne, F. Laplanche, G. Parrour, R. Riskalla, P. Roy and G. Szklarz (private communication).

13. γ γ group: C. Bacci, G. Penso, G. Salvini, B. Stella, R. Baldini-Celio, G. Capon, C. Mencuccini, G. P. Murtas, A. Reale and M. Spinetti, Phys. Letters 38 B, 551 (1972) and private communication to be published in Phys. Letters.

14. L. M. Kurdadze, A. P. Onuchin, S. I. Serednyakov, V. A. Sidorov, and S. I. Eidelman, Phys. Letters 42 B, 515 (1972).

15. Boson group: B. Bartoli, F. Felicetti, H. Ogren, V. Silvestrini, G. Marini, A. Nigro and F. Vanoli, Phys. Rev. D 6, 2374 (1972).

16. μ π group: M. Grilli, E. Iarocci, P. Spillantini, V. Valente, R. Vistentin, B. Borgia, F. Ceradini, M. Conversi, L. Paoluzi, R. Santonico, M. Nigro, L. Trasatti and G. T. Zorn, Nuovo Cimento 13 A, 593 (1973) and private communication.

17. A. Litke, G. Hanson, A. Hofmann, J. Koch, L. Law, M. E. Law, J. Leong, R. Little, R. Madaras, H. Newman, J. M. Patterson, R. Pordes, K. Strauch, G. Tarnopolsky and Richard Wilson, Phys. Rev. Letters 30, 1189 (1973), Phys. Rev. Letters 30, 1349 (1973), and contribution to this conference.

18. $\mu\pi$ group: F. Ceradini, R. Santonico, M. Conversi, L. Paolugi, M. Grilli, E. Iarocci, P. Spillantini, V. Valente, R. Visentin and M. Nigro. Phys. Letters 42 B, 501 (1972).

19. James D. Bjorken and Stanley Brodsky, Phys. Rev. D 1, 1416 (1970).

20. M. Davier, Proceedings of XVIth International Conference on High Energy Physics, 1972. Vol. I, p. 104.

21. F. M. Renard, Nuovo Cimento 64, 679 (1970).

22. C. Buchanon, et al., contribution to this conference.

23. J. E. Augustin, A. Coureu, B. Dudelzak, F. Fulda, G. Grosdidier, J. Haissinski, J. L. Masnou, R. Riskalla, F. Rumpf, and E. Silva, Phys. Rev. Letters 30, 462 (1973).

Anti-Nucleon Production at SPEAR

Presented at the APS Meeting of the Division of
Particles and Fields, Berkeley, California

August, 1973

D. Berk, C. Buchanan, D. Drickey,
C. May, P. Shepard, D. Stork, R. Zdarko
University of California, Los Angeles

J. Dakin, E. Seppi
Stanford Linear Accelerator Center

We report results of an initial survey for anti-proton and anti-neutron inclusive events produced at SPEAR by colliding electron and positron beams of 5.2 GeV center-of-mass energy. This was a preliminary search leading to a major spark chamber and timed-counter experiment proposed for Summer 1974 which would collect 50-300 each of $\bar{p}$'s and $\bar{n}$'s and provide distributions in angle from 25° to 90° and in $\omega \equiv E_{\bar{N}}/E_o$.

Such inclusive nucleon events are of interest (a) because they represent the time-like reflection of the physics of deep inelastic scattering and (b) because they contribute to answering the important question of how hadronic matter created with large C.M. energy breaks up into pions, kaons, and nucleons, etc. (e.g., how often do multi-hadronic events produced by colliding e^+e^- beams contain a nucleon and what is their distribution in angle and energy.

The search was performed for anti-nucleons rather than nucleons because of the striking signature of the "explosion" which an anti-nucleon creates when it annihilates. A "timed Volume" counter array was used. (See Fig. 1.) Six 8" x 8" x 10' liquid scintillator tanks with 1" F_e plates on each side and with phototubes on each end were placed $\sim$ 10' from the interaction region to serve as anti-nucleon annihilators and counters. These subtended a range of polar angles of 90° ± 26°. Additional counters with phototubes on each end were placed $\sim$ 2 feet from the $\bar{N}$ counters to fire on the annihilation fragments. Timed counters were also placed near the e^+e^- interaction region to be fired by charged particles recoiling against the anti-nucleon in a multi-hadronic event. The relative timing of the counters was established by cosmic rays with typical resolution of ± 1.0 ns and ± 0.4 feet along the length of the counters.

The overall timing, relative to the e^+e^- interaction time as stabilized by a synchronized rf signal, was established by using elastic e^+e^- scattering events. A sub-sample of 90 wide angle Bhabha events was obtained which agreed both in number of events and angular distribution with the predictions of QED and which determined the absolute interaction time to ± 0.4 ns. (See Fig. 2.)

The signature for an anti-nucleon event demanded (a) a pulse height in an $\bar{N}$ counter of greater than twice that of a minimum ionizing particle, (b) two or more of the "fragment" counters to fire within a ± 2 ns window of the appropriate time for a particle emanating from an annihilation, (c) a properly timed Charged Recoil Counter response, (d) no early fragment counters and no late ones representing a fragment slower than $\beta = 0.5$. In addition, the fragment counter between each $\bar{N}$ counter and the e^+e^- interaction region was used as a veto or identity counter: to be an anti-neutron event, it was required not to have fired; to be an anti-proton event, it was required to have fired at the proper position (within ± 0.8 feet) and time (within ± 2.0 ns) for a charged particle coming from the interaction region.

When an event satisfied these criteria, the time of the annihilation relative to the e^+e^- interaction time was plotted. The results are shown in Fig. 3. The plots are divided into four regions: machine-induced, prompt, $\bar{N}$, and cosmic. The prompt region represents particles emanating from the e^+e^- interaction region and traveling close to the speed of light. (e^+e^- pairs, μ pairs, γ's, charged pions in multi-hadronic events.) Machine-induced backgrounds are caused by beam-gas and beam-pipe interactions. Most frequently these produce forward going particles which therefore reach the $\bar{N}$ counters before the prompts. Machine induced backscattering backgrounds can occur in the $\bar{N}$ timing region, but should be much less common than the early machine-induced events. The timing region populated by $\bar{N}$'s in theory extends to infinite time, but in practice the cross-section must become negligibly small after a few nanoseconds beyond the prompts. Finally the active timing region was extended well beyond the $\bar{N}$ region in order to monitor the rate at which cosmic showers simulate $\bar{N}$-like events.

In the $\bar{p}$ distribution, there are no "events" in the early "machine induced" region. There are several "events" in the prompt peak; these are understood and are typically pions from multi-hadronic events which have interacted in the 1" F_e annihilator.

There is one genuine candidate in the $\bar{N}$ time-of-flight region. There are no events present in the very-late "cosmic ray region." It is improbable that the one genuine candidate is (a) a cosmic shower (there are no events in the cosmic ray region), (b) a pion from a multi-hadronic event (it is 3-4 standard deviations in time from the prompt peak), or (c) a machine-induced background (there are no events in the early region).

Thus, it is probable that the one event in the $\bar{N}$-region is indeed a $\bar{p}$ inclusive event. If so, it was produced with $\omega = 0.54 \pm 0.05$ and at an angle of 69°.

A smaller sample has been searched for $\bar{n}$'s. Note that the identity counter criterion for anti-neutrons is weaker than for $\bar{p}$'s leading to a weaker signature. There are two candidates in the $\bar{N}$-region, but there are non-zero backgrounds in the cosmic ray region and the machine induced region. Thus only an upper limit can be quoted on anti-neutron production.

The probability that an anti-nucleon which aimed at an $\bar{N}$ counter would annihilate and satisfy our criteria was calculated to be about 12% from a Monte Carlo program incorporating measured $\bar{p}$ annihilation cross-sections in hydrogen.[1] The system of $\bar{N}$ counters covered 1.5% of the total solid angle. Combining these with the integrated luminosity and assuming isotropy both for the produced $\bar{N}$'s and the recoiling charged particles, we find

a) $\sigma(\bar{p}) \simeq 2 \times 10^{-34}$ cm^2 if the one good candidate is interpreted as a $\bar{p}$.

b) An upper limit with 90% confidence that $\sigma(\bar{p}) < 5 \times 10^{-34}$ cm^2.

c) An upper limit with 90% confidence that $\sigma(\bar{n}) < 2 \times 10^{-33}$ cm^2.

Bjorken and Kogut[2] have made a phenomenological prediction of the "$\bar{p}$ branching fraction for hadronic matter" (i.e., the fraction of multi-hadronic events which will contain a $\bar{p}$) based on the low momentum $\bar{p}$ production at the ISR, the Frascati measurement of $e^+e^- \to p\bar{p}$, and "correspondence" arguments which allow smooth interpolation between exclusive and inclusive channels. They estimate that $\sim$ 2-10% of the multi-hadronic events will contain a $\bar{p}$ at 5.2 GeV C.M. energy. Using σ_{Tot}(hadronic) = (1.9 ± 0.5) x 10^{-32} (i.e., 6.3 times $\sigma_{\mu\mu}$),[3] the Bjorken and Kogut model predicts $\sigma(\bar{p}) = (2.8 - 24.0) \times 10^{-34}$ cm^2.

On the other hand, assuming that the anti-nucleon production is purely an inversion of the space-like deep inelastic scattering[4] [i.e., the structure function continues analytically across $\omega = 1$ and $f(\omega) \propto (1-\omega)^3$], we find an estimate of $\sigma(\bar{p}) \simeq 0.4 \times 10^{-34}$ cm^2.

Thus our result is near the lower limit of the Bjorken-Kogut "$\bar{p}$ branching fraction" estimate and a factor of five larger than the simplest pure space-like inversion estimate.

We wish to thank the SPEAR and SLAC staff for their work and hospitality, Drs. J. Bjorken and S. Drell for several stimulating discussions, and Mr. A. Sugarman for his analysis work on the Bhabha sample.

REFERENCES

1. Particle Data group, "$\bar{N}N$ and $\bar{N}D$ Interactions--A Compilation," LBL-58 (May, 1972).
2. J. Bjorken and J. Kogut. To be published in Phys. Rev.
3. Presented by the CEA colliding beam group at the present APS meeting, Berkeley, August 1973.
4. We follow the work of S. Drell, D. Levy, and T.-M. Yan, Phys. Rev. D, 1617 (March, 1970).

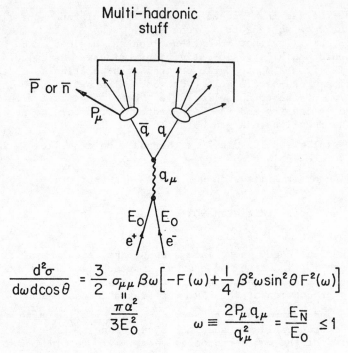

Multi-hadronic
stuff

$\overline{P}$ or $\overline{n}$

P_μ

$\overline{q}$ q

q_μ

E_0 E_0

e^+ e^-

$$\frac{d^2\sigma}{d\omega d\cos\theta} = \frac{3}{2}\underset{\underset{\frac{\pi\alpha^2}{3E_0^2}}{\parallel}}{\sigma_{\mu\mu}}\beta\omega\left[-F(\omega)+\frac{1}{4}\beta^2\omega\sin^2\theta\,F^2(\omega)\right]$$

$$\omega \equiv \frac{2P_\mu q_\mu}{q_\mu^2} = \frac{E_{\overline{N}}}{E_0} \leq 1$$

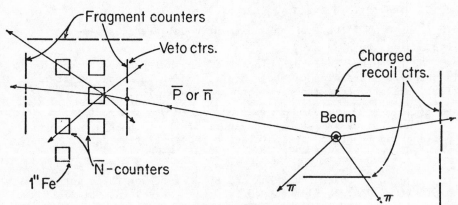

Fragment counters

Veto ctrs.

Charged
recoil ctrs.

$\overline{P}$ or $\overline{n}$

Beam

$\overline{N}$-counters

1" Fe

π

π

Signal = P.H. > 2 × min. ion. in $\overline{N}$-ctr.
- 2 or more properly timed Fragment ctrs.
- Properly timed Charged recoil ctr.
- Reasonable β for $\overline{N}$
- $\begin{cases} \overline{P} \Rightarrow \text{Proper time and position in Veto ctr.} \\ \overline{n} \Rightarrow \text{Nothing in Veto ctr.} \end{cases}$

FIGURE 1 Apparatus layout

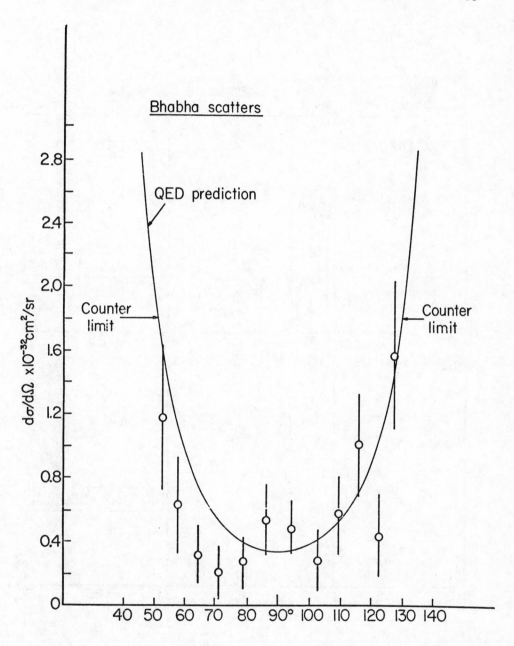

FIGURE 2. Bhabha Scattering Results

64

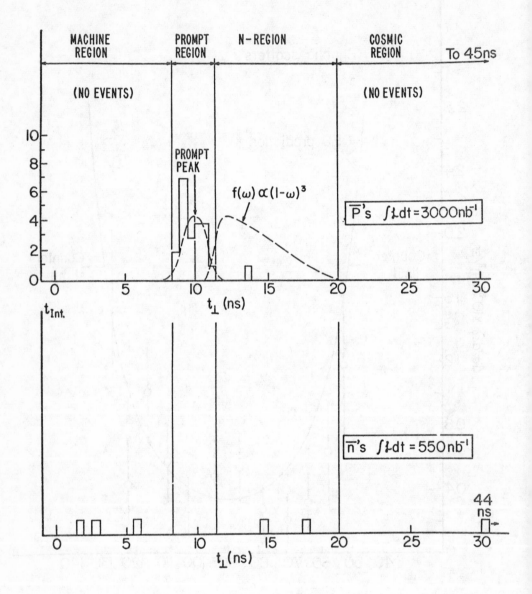

FIGURE 3   p̄ and n̄ Results from
Summer, 1973

ELECTRON-POSITRON ANNIHILATION INTO HADRONS*

Robert N. Cahn†
Stanford Linear Accelerator Center
Stanford University, Stanford, Calif. 94305

John Ellis††
California Institute of Technology, Pasadena, Calif.

ABSTRACT

Theories about the behavior of the ratio

$$\frac{\sigma(e^+e^- \rightarrow \gamma \rightarrow \text{hadrons})}{\sigma(e^+e^- \rightarrow \gamma \rightarrow \mu^+\mu^-)}$$

are reviewed, and qualitative features of the final state hadron distributions are discussed.

INTRODUCTION

The process $e^+e^- \rightarrow \gamma \rightarrow$ hadrons has long been a favorite playground of theoreticians. It is interesting because all theories which exhibit Bjorken scaling in electroproduction also make the naive scale invariant prediction[1]

$$\sigma(e^+e^- \rightarrow \gamma \rightarrow \text{hadrons}) \underset{q^2 \rightarrow \infty}{\sim} \frac{1}{q^2} \tag{1}$$

Hence if the prediction (1), or the equivalent (assuming QED) statement

$$R(q^2) \equiv \frac{\sigma(e^+e^- \rightarrow \gamma \rightarrow \text{hadrons})}{\sigma(e^+e^- \rightarrow \gamma \rightarrow \mu^+\mu^-)} \xrightarrow[q^2 \rightarrow \infty]{} R \tag{2}$$

where R is some model-dependent constant, should fail, then we would have to conclude that we really do not understand scaling in electroproduction at all.

Experimental data from CEA[2] seem to show little evidence that the asymptotic prediction (2) is being approached for $q^2 \leq 25$ GeV. In fact the hadron-muon ratio seems to be increasing, and is already large compared with many theoretical predictions. (Though this trend may not be statistically significant at the present level of accuracy of the data.) Hence it is very important:

---

*Work supported in part by the U. S. Atomic Energy Commission.
† Present address: Physics Department, Univ. of Washington, Seattle 98195.
†† Present address: Theory Division, CERN, 1211 Geneva 23, Switzerland.

1. To confirm the CEA experiments.

2. To see whether $R(q^2) \to \infty$ as $q^2 \to \infty$ could be accommodated theoretically.

3. To try to understand an increase in R over a range in q^2.

4. To understand implications elsewhere, e.g., for QED, of $R(q^2)$ being large, and

5. To see what theoretical values for R are still plausible. We leave 1. to SPEAR, and here review 2. to 5. Data either are or will shortly be available from CEA and SPEAR on topological cross section, the multiplicity and higher moments of the multiplicity distribution, and we discuss these qualitative features of the hadronic final state. Detailed data on the inclusive distributions and their scaling behavior are rather further away and we do not discuss them in detail here: there is more about them in the parallel session on partons and the light-cone.

THE ASYMPTOTIC BEHAVIOR OF $R(q^2)$

Since it has the dimensions of (length)^2, $\sigma(e^+e^- \to \gamma \to$ hadrons) would have to go as $1/q^2$ as $q^2 \to \infty$ in order to be scale invariant, and this is what is predicted in simple parton[3] and canonical short distance behavior[4] models of scaling. Since according to QED $(e^+e^- \to \gamma \to \mu^+\mu^-) \sim 1/q^2$ also, this would mean that $R(q^2)$ approaches a constant R as $q^2 \to \infty$. Setting aside oscillations, the other possibilities are that $R(q^2) \to 0$ or ∞. The former of these is not suggested by the data and is unfashionable theoretically. If $R(q^2) \to \infty$, might go as a power of $\ln q^2$ or as a power of q^2 itself. There seems to be nothing wrong in principle with $R(q^2) \sim (\ln q)^n$ for some n > 0: indeed this is what occurs in any finite order of a renormalizable field theory (except for gauge theories,[5,6] of which more later). Indeed one actually expects that the naive scaling prediction (1) will be modified by terms $0(\alpha \ln q^2/q^2)$ etc., when radiative corrections to the strong interactions are taken into account (cf. electroproduction)[7].

Could $R(q^2) \sim (q^2)^m$ for some power m > 0 as $q^2 \to \infty$? We know of no theory where this occurs, and it can be argued that such a possibility would destroy the renormalizability of QED. Consider for example the contribution of the high q^2 part of the hadron vacuum polarization to the muon (g-2) shown in Fig. 1. It is given by

$$\Delta(g-2)_\mu = \frac{m_\mu^2}{6\pi^3} \int_{Q^2}^{\infty} \frac{\sigma(e^+e^- \to \gamma \to \text{hadrons})}{q^2} \, dq^2 \tag{3}$$

where Q^2 is some lower limit $\gg m_\mu^2$. It is clear that the integral diverges if $(e^+e^- \to \gamma \to$ hadrons) goes to a constant as $q^2 \to \infty$, entailing a subtraction and a new renormalization constant. Indeed, simple Dyson power counting indicates that an infinite number of QED graphs become divergent if $(e^+e^- \to \gamma \to$ hadrons) $\sim (q^2)^m$ for any m > 0, because internal photon propagators acquire $\alpha(q^2)^{m-1}$ corrections. Actually, in such theories even an expansion in powers of α would be invalid: we can only use a photon propagator (see Fig. 2)

$$P(q^2) = \frac{1}{q^2} (1 + \Pi(q^2))$$

where

$$\frac{\Pi(q^2)}{q^2} = \frac{1}{4\pi^2 \alpha} \int ds \ \frac{\sigma_{e^+e^- \to \gamma \to hadrons}(s)}{q^2 - s + i\epsilon} \qquad (4)$$

when

$$P(q^2) = \frac{1}{q^2} \ \frac{1}{1 - \Pi(q^2)}$$

as in Fig. 3. Clearly one expects that the rise in $R(q^2)$ should cut off when $|\Pi(q^2)| \ll 1$: for $R(q^2) \sim (q^2)^{1/2}$, $\Pi \sim 0.1$ when $(q^2)^{1/2} \sim 35$ GeV.

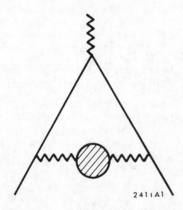

FIG. 1--Hadronic contribution to the vacuum polarization cor- to g-2 of the muon.

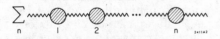

FIG. 2--Geometric series responsible for the full vacuum polarization correction to the photon propagator.

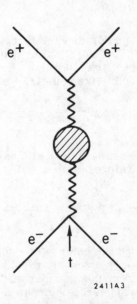

FIG. 3--Hadronic vacuum polarization correction for t-channel photon exchange in e^+e^- elastic scattering.

One major piece of recent theoretical progress has been the realization[5,6] that some renormalizable field theories have the naive scaling law (1). These are a class of non-Abelian gauge theories (i.e., theories with a non-commutative symmetry group in which a set of vector mesons are present whose transformation properties are such that the theory is invariant under "rotations" within the group even when the "rotation" is a function of x, the space-time point), which have for some time been popular among constructors[8] of renormalizable theories of weak interactions, and those trying to understand how quarks might be bound in hadrons.[9] It has been shown that these theories are "asymptotically free" which means that at short distances and near the light cone their singularity structures are almost the same as those of a free field theory. Bjorken scaling in electroproduction in such theories is violated by calculable inverse powers of $\ln q^2$.[10] The naive parton or canonical short distance model scaling prediction

$$\frac{\sigma(e^+e^- \to \gamma \to \text{hadrons})}{\sigma(e^+e^- \to \gamma \to \mu^+\mu^-)} \to R \tag{5}$$

is valid in these models. Also, sub-asymptotic inverse logarithm corrections to (5) can be calculated as discussed later.

WHAT IS R?

Let us now assume that $R(q^2)$ approaches a constant, R, as $q^2 \to \infty$ in accord with theoretical prejudice. In all theoretical models[3,4,5] this occurs because at large q^2 the electromagnetic current acts as if it is coupled to point-like spin-1/2 fields (quarks) in addition to the usual leptons:

$$J_\mu^{e.m.} \propto - \bar{e}\gamma_\mu e - \bar{\mu}\gamma_\mu \mu + \sum_i Q_i \bar{q}_i \gamma_\mu q_i \tag{6}$$

where the sum is over all quarks, q_i, with charges Q_i. Since each quark enters analogously to a muon,

$$R(q^2) \equiv \frac{\sigma(e^+e^- \to \gamma \to \text{hadrons})}{\sigma(e^+e^- \to \gamma \to \mu^+\mu^-)} \xrightarrow[q^2 \to \infty]{} \sum_i Q_i^2 \tag{7}$$

(Spin-0 quarks enter with a contribution $Q_i^2/4$.) Thus for the usual Gell-Mann-Zweig[11] scheme R = 4/9 + 1/9 + 1/9 = 2/3.

There are both experimental and theoretical reasons for considering alternative quark schemes. Early colliding beam results give $R(q^2) > 1$ and perhaps $R(q^2) > 2$-3. Theoretically, the $\pi^0 \to 2\gamma$ decay rate can be related to short distance behavior[12] where we hope the electromagnetic current has the simple form indicated in (6). Together with PCAC, the Gell-Mann-Zweig scheme gives a rate too small by a factor of about 10.

Also the Gell-Mann-Zweig scheme has well-known intrinsic problems with statistics. One solution is to invoke a new underlying symmetry by supposing there are several "colors" of each kind of quark.[13] To get the $\pi^0 \to 2\gamma$ decay rate right, one needs three colors — red, blue and yellow, say — giving a factor nine in the square of the amplitude. With three colors we can put three quarks in a symmetric 10 representation of the usual (p, n, λ) SU(3) and in an anti-symmetric $\underline{1}$ representation of color SU(3), making an overall anti-symmetric state without any further machinations.

More recently, further theoretical support has been given to "color" schemes. Lipkin,[9] following an old proposal of Nambu,[14] has pointed out that "colored gluons" i.e., vector mesons belonging to an $\underline{8}$ representation of color SU(3) can reproduce the fact that only triality zero hadrons are observed. The result follows from a simplified treatment in which the quarks are very heavy but move non-relativistically with a lighter effective mass. Lipkin finds that only color singlets are bound while color $\underline{8}$'s, $\underline{3}$'s etc., are unbound by energies of the order of the quark mass. Since all color singlets (e.g., $\overline{RR} + \overline{BB} + \overline{YY}$) have triality zero, a fundamental fact is accounted for. Whether Lipkin's analysis can be used to study exoticity (i.e., the absence of 27's of (p, n, λ) SU(3)) is less clear, as is the question of whether his vector gluons are gauge vector gluons.

The realization[5] that non-Abelian gauge theories are asymptotically free has added impetus to the study of color schemes which furnish an underlying non-Abelian symmetry. Abelian gauge theories like the original Gell-Mann-Zweig scheme with a neutral gauge vector gluon violate scaling by positive powers of $\ln q^2$.

These recent theoretical developments have increased interest in color schemes which have been around for some time. We mention here a few such schemes in the hope that if $R(q^2)$ does approach a constant $q^2 \to \infty$, then it will be an interpretable number — 2/3 for example — rather than $\pi/2$, say.

Table I Gell-Mann-Zweig with Color

	Q	I_z	Y
$p_{R,Y,B}$	2/3	1/2	1/3
$n_{R,Y,B}$	-1/3	-1/2	1/3
$\lambda_{R,Y,B}$	-1/3	0	-2/3

$$J^{em} \ \alpha \ \frac{2}{3} \left(\overline{p}_R p_R + \overline{p}_Y p_Y + \overline{p}_B p_B \right) - \frac{1}{3} \left(\overline{n}_R n_R + \overline{n}_Y n_Y + \overline{n}_B n_B \right)$$

$$- \frac{1}{3} \left(\overline{\lambda}_R \lambda_R + \overline{\lambda}_Y \lambda_Y + \overline{\lambda}_B \lambda_B \right)$$

J^{em} is a color singlet and a (p, n, λ) SU(3) octet, so that final states in $e^+ e^-$ annihilation are color singlets. $R = 3 \times 2/3 = 2$.

Table II Han-Nambu[15]

	Q	I_z	Y		Q	I_z	Y
p_R	1	1/2	1	p_B	0	0	0
n_R	0	-1/2	1	n_B	-1	-1	0
λ_R	0	0	0	λ_B	-1	-1/2	-1
p_Y	1	1	0				
n_Y	0	0	0				
λ_Y	0	1/2	-1				

$$J^{em} \; \alpha \; \bar{p}_R p_R + \bar{p}_Y p_Y - \bar{n}_B n_B - \bar{\lambda}_B \lambda_B = (\bar{p}_R p_R + \bar{p}_Y p_Y + \bar{p}_B p_B)$$

$$- (\bar{p}_B p_B + \bar{n}_B n_B + \bar{\lambda}_B \lambda_B)$$

J^{em} has singlet and octet pieces under both color and (p, n, λ) SU(3) groups. Hence the final states in $e^+ e^-$ annihilation include color octet pieces. If all final states are included, $R = 4$. If only color singlets are permitted we must calculate

$$\sum_{n \in \underset{\sim}{1}} <0|J|n> <n|J|0>$$

Inserting the contributing color singlet states

$$\frac{1}{\sqrt{3}} \; (\bar{p}_R p_R + \bar{p}_Y p_Y + \bar{p}_B p_B),$$

$$\frac{1}{\sqrt{3}} \; (\bar{n}_R n_R + \bar{n}_Y n_Y + \bar{n}_B n_B),$$

$$\frac{1}{\sqrt{3}} \; (\bar{\lambda}_R \lambda_R + \bar{\lambda}_Y \lambda_Y + \bar{\lambda}_B \lambda_B),$$

one finds that for these restricted final states, $R = 2$.

Weak interaction theorists[16] have proposed introducing a new conserved quantum number "charm" with associated quarks, which enables them to eradicate neutral strangeness changing weak currents. A prototypal scheme is shown in Table III.

In this model (Table III) we see that $R = 4/9 + 4/9 + 1/9 + 1/9 = 10/9$. Color can be added in a manner analogous to the usual Gell-Mann-Zweig model with the result $R = 10/3$. This scheme is rather complicated: hadrons may be colored (i.e., not a singlet under color SU(3)) or charmed. The charmed sector brings R to a value of 6. Of course the electromagnetic current has zero charm, and so no charmed particles need appear in the final state even if R saturates the value 6. If only color singlets are produced R is reduced to 10/3.

Table III Han-Nambu with Charm

	Q	I_z	Y	Charm
p'_R	1	0	0	1
p_R	1	1/2	1	0
n_R	0	-1/2	1	0
λ_R	0	0	0	0
p'_Y	1	1/2	-1	1
p_Y	1	1	0	0
n_Y	0	0	0	0
λ_Y	0	1/2	-1	0
p'_B	0	-1/2	-1	1
p_B	0	0	0	0
n_B	-1	-1	0	0
λ_B	-1	-1/2	-1	0

$$J^{em} = J^{em} \text{ (Han-Nambu)} + \overline{p'_R}\, p'_R + \overline{p'_Y}\, p'_Y$$

These schemes do not exhaust the possibilities but it is clear that experiments at CEA and SPEAR at $q^2 = 25$ GeV^2 and 80 GeV^2 next year (?) are of the greatest importance to quark schemes. If R is found to be a constant the many proposals may be narrowed down to a few or perhaps just one.

WHEN SHOULD ASYMPTOPIA BE REACHED?

Assuming that $R(q^2)$ does indeed approach a constant R as $q^2 \to \infty$, what sets the scale for approaching asymptopia? A first guess might be that by analogy with inelastic scattering off composite systems like atoms and nuclei, scaling should set in when q^2 >> (typical level spacing of hadrons), i.e., O ([a few hundred MeV]^2). Indeed this is apparently observed in deep inelastic electroproduction with scaling occurring for $|q^2| > (1-2)$ GeV^2. One should expect scaling in annihilation to set in later because the most striking singularities in q^2 are timelike: the vector mesons ρ, ω, ϕ

with $q^2 \sim 1$ GeV^2 (and ρ' with $q^2 \sim (2\text{-}3)$ GeV^2 ?). Presumably one needs $q^2 \gg$ these values for scaling to occur, probably when the widths of the 1^- states become comparable with their level spacing: $q^2 = O(10$ GeV$^2)$ might seem reasonable from these arguments.

However, it can be argued threshold effects might tend to make $R(q^2)$ rise appreciably over a range in q^2. These might either be those for producing conventional massive particles such as baryons, or unconventional particles such as colored or charmed hadrons. The baryon effect could in principle be non-negligible:[7] even at low q^2 $e^+e^- \to \bar{p}p$ is comparable with $e^+e^- \to \pi^+\pi^-$. Also it has been suggested[18] that the parton model may be applied to large $p_\perp$ phenomena in hadron-hadron collisions. Experiments indicate there may be relatively many baryons at large $p_\perp$ suggesting there may be many baryons produced at large q in e^+e^- annihilation. Also estimates suggest[19] that asymptopia for baryon production may set in only when $q^2 \gg 10$ GeV^2.

As mentioned in the previous section, the asymptotic cross section expected in Han-Nambu type models increases when color octet hadron states are excited because J^{em} has a color octet piece. Thus $R(q^2)$ could have a plateau in q^2 and then a rise, or else rise more gradually and continuously. Colored hadrons would presumably be rather more massive than ordinary hadrons, so asymptopia might be even later than suggested above. Detecting produced colored hadrons in e^+e^- annihilation might be very tricky: the heavier ones would decay electromagnetically and rapidly ($\tau \ll 10^{-16}$ sec probably). As also mentioned earlier, asymptopia could be reached in charmed theories even if charmed particles were not being produced, because the J^{em} is uncharmed. However threshold effects might make the approach rather slow. Charmed hadrons would have to decay weakly, and might have a distinctive experimental signature if they exist.

As mentioned earlier, asymptotically free gauge theories not only reproduce the standard prediction

$$R(q^2) \equiv \frac{\sigma(e^+e^- \to \gamma \to \text{hadrons})}{\sigma(e^+e^- \to \gamma \to \mu^+\mu^-)} \xrightarrow[q^2 \to \infty]{} R = \sum Q_i^2$$

but also predict that scaling is approached as $1/\ln q^2$ with a calculable coefficient.[6] For example in a three triplet Gell-Mann-Zweig model

$$R(q^2) \underset{q^2 \to \infty}{\widetilde{}} 2 \left(1 + \frac{4}{9} \frac{1}{\ln(q^2/Q_0^2)} + \cdots \right) \tag{8}$$

where Q_0 is some arbitrary scale of (mass)^2. The coefficient of $1/\ln(q^2/Q_0^2)$ is model dependent, but always positive. Hence if the rising trend suggested by the CEA data were correct, then one would have to conclude that asymptopia is not reached for $q^2 \leq 25$ GeV^2.

Chanowitz and Drell[20] have suggested another reason why $R(q^2)$ may increase at present colliding beam energies, though they are agnostic about what happens to $R(q^2)$ asymptotically. Motivated largely by experimental deviations[21] from a dipole form for the protons magnetic form factor at large q^2, they suggest that scaling laws may gradually break down for $|q^2| > 20$ GeV^2. They expect a breakdown of point-like behavior of the constituents (partons) of hadrons corresponding to a structure generated by gluons with masses $M_G \simeq 10$ GeV. In the region $1 \ll |q^2| \ll M_G^2$ they find the dipole form factor modified by a factor $(1 - |q^2|/M_G^2)$, violation of scaling in deep inelastic electroproduction by a factor $(1 - 2|q^2|/M_G^2)$ and in $e^+e^- \to \gamma \to$ hadrons

$$\sigma \sim \frac{1}{q^2} \left(1 + \frac{2q^2}{M_G^2}\right) \qquad \text{for } 1 \ll q^2 \ll M_G^2$$

Chanowitz and Drell are non-committal about what happens when $q^2 \gtrsim M_G^2$. If the gluon coupled directly to the photon, then it would be seen as a resonance bump in the annihilation cross section. However, if it were not so coupled (e.g., if the gluon were scalar or colored), then the behavior for $q^2 \sim M_G^2$ would not be predictable. In any case behavior in this model in the limit $q^2 \to \infty$ is unknown, as it faces the usual problem of a renormalizable theory with a large coupling constant.

It is amusing to consider the implications for purely leptonic processes of a large ratio $R(q^2)$. Bjorken and Frishman[22] have considered the effects of the hadronic corrections to the photon propagator in processes like $e^+e^- \to e^+e^-$ and $e^+e^- \to \mu^+\mu^-$ (see Figs. 3, 4). If $R(q^2)$ were as large as suggested by CEA and increased as a power of q^2 up to the unitarity limit then the t-channel Born graph cross section in $e^+e^- \to e^+e^-$ (see Fig. 3) could be affected by $O(2\%)$ at $-t \sim 12 \,\text{GeV}^2$, the maximum momentum transfer accessible at SPEAR or CEA. There could also be interesting polarization effects in $e^+e^- \to e^+e^-$ because of the phase in the time-like graph shown in Fig. 4. There would of course be no corrections to the conventional lowest order QED calculation of $e^+e^- \to \gamma\gamma$ because it contains no internal photon propagators.

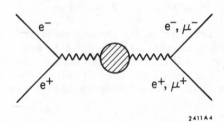

FIG. 4--Hadronic vacuum polarization correction for s-channel photon exchange in $e^+e^- \to e^+e^-$ and $e^+e^- \to \mu^+\mu^-$.

QUALITATIVE FEATURES OF THE FINAL STATE

Jets or Not?

One approach to the study of final states in e^+e^- annihilation is to build upon our experience with hadronic collisions where the final state hadrons have limited transverse momentum. If the final states in annihilation were isotropic then we might conclude that the total momentum of the final state hadrons would be similarly limited.[23] A direct consequence would be a multiplicity growing as $s^{1/2}/\langle E_\pi \rangle$ where $\langle E_\pi \rangle \sim 400$ MeV. Early data from CEA already give trouble for this picture, since at $q^2 \simeq (16-25)$ GeV^2 they show $\langle n_{ch} \rangle \sim 4$-$4.5$ suggesting $\langle n_{all} \rangle \sim 6$-$7$ and $\langle E_\pi \rangle \sim 700$ MeV.

Of course parton models do not predict isotropic final states, but jets aligned in the directions of the "produced" partons. These jets would have $(1 + \cos^2\theta)$ distribution if the partons had spin -1/2. Bjorken and Brodsky[23] suggest that jets might be searched for by considering the traceless tensor

$$T_{\alpha\beta} = \frac{\sum_i \left(\frac{3}{2} p_\alpha^i p_\beta^i - \frac{1}{2} \delta_{\alpha\beta} [p^i]^2 \right)}{\sum_i [p^i]^2}$$

where the sum over i is over all particles in any particular event. The eigenvalues of $T_{\alpha\beta}$ would be determined for each event. Isotropic events would give degenerate eigenvalues, while jets would give non-degenerate eigenvalues a, $-a/2$, $-a/2$, say. The diagonalization of $T_{\alpha\beta}$ would determine the jet axis which should have a $(1 + \cos^2\theta)$ distribution.

In the parton model momenta transverse to the jet axis are limited to $O(400 \text{ MeV})$. In this and other models[24] the one particle inclusive distributions exhibit Feynman scaling. The energy conservation sum rule

$$\sum_{\substack{\text{particle} \\ \text{types a}}} \int \frac{d^3 p_a}{E_a} \left(\frac{E_a}{\sigma_{tot}} \frac{d\sigma}{d^3 p_a} \right) E_a = \sqrt{s}$$

is satisfied by having $\frac{E}{\sigma} d\sigma/d^3 p$ become a function of $x = 2|\underline{p}|/(q^2)^{1/2}$ as $q^2 \to \infty$.

Another possibility for the hadron distribution is that the momenta are large, so that the one particle distribution scales in $x = 2|\underline{p}|/(q^2)^{1/2}$, but the momenta in individual events do not have a limit transverse to any axis. This is the analogue of having $p_\perp \sim (Q^2)^{1/2}$ in the photon fragmentation region of deep inelastic scattering.[25] Early data[26] do not support this picture in electroproduction.

MULTIPLICITIES AND TOPOLOGICAL CROSS SECTIONS

Data on the total charged multiplicity are already available from CEA: more information on the multiplicity distribution and topological cross sections will soon be available from there and from SPEAR. It is commonly expected that the multiplicity will increase $\propto \ln q^2$, as seems to be the case in hadronic collisions. A rapidity variable $y = 1/2 \ln (E + |\underline{p}|)/(E- |\underline{p}|)]$ can be introduced for particle produced in annihilation, and if the one particle inclusive rapidity distribution is flat in the central region with a height

$$\frac{1}{\sigma} \frac{d\sigma}{dy} = C_{e^+e^-}$$

then the multiplicity is $<n> = C_{e^+e^-} \ln q^2 + \text{const}$. In the parton model of Feynman and Bjorken[27] $C_{e^+e^-} \neq 0$ is favored so that the two ends of the rapidity axis can communicate and eliminate their quark-like quantum numbers from the final state hadrons. In this model the multiplicities in e^+e^- annihilation, hadron-hadron collisions and deep inelastic lepton production are closely related[28]

$$\langle n \rangle_{e^+e^-} = C_{e^+e^-} \ln q^2 + \text{const.}$$

$$\langle n \rangle_{\text{hadrons}} = C_n \ln s + \text{const.}$$

$$\langle n \rangle_{\substack{ep \\ \nu p}} = C_{e^+e^-} \ln q^2 + C_n \ln (\omega - 1) + \text{const.}$$

Preliminary data from Frascati and CEA[2] indicate that $\langle n \rangle_{e^+e^-}$ is increasing at a rate comparable with that in hadron-hadron collisions. Data on deep inelastic electroproduction also indicate that $\langle n \rangle$ increases with ω and q^2.[29]

One of the reasons why increasing hadronic multiplicities in annihilation are favored is that if the multiplicity were asymptotically finite, then at least one exclusive channel would have to scale:

$$\frac{\sigma_{\text{exch}}}{\sigma_{\text{tot}}} \xrightarrow[q^2 \to \infty]{} \text{const.}$$

(see for example, Ref. 19). Two-body channels like $e^+e^- \to \pi^+\pi^-$ or $p\bar{p}$ seem experimentally and are expected theoretically to behave as

$$\frac{1}{q^2} [F(q^2)]^2 \quad \text{as} \quad q^2 \to \infty$$

with $F(q^2)$ some form factor going to zero in the limit. Quasi-two-body channels like $e^+e^- \to \rho^+\rho^-$ and $\Delta^{++}\Delta^{--}$ are expected to exhibit similar behavior. This is analogous to the behavior of non-diffractive exclusive channels in hadronic collisions, which are expected to fall relative to the total cross section as $s^{2\alpha - 2}$ with α some Regge intercept $\lesssim 1/2$. Diffractive channels in hadronic collisions would correspond to exclusive channels which scaled so that $F(q^2) \to \text{const}$ as $q^2 \to \infty$, i.e., exclusive channels with asymptotically point-like form factors. If partons were actually types of hadrons, then their production could be "diffractive" in this sense. It is easy to show that if $\langle n \rangle$ is asymptotically finite, as for example if $C_{e^+e^-} = 0$, then the limit of the total annihilation cross-section is just the sum of the limits of the "diffractive" exclusive cross sections:

$$\lim_{q^2 \to \infty} q^2 \sigma_{\text{tot}}(q^2) = \sum_n \lim_{q^2 \to \infty} q^2 \sigma_n(q^2)$$

In most parton models, partons are not actual hadrons, but there may still be "diffractive" channels. For example in the model of Landshoff and Polkinghorne,[30] the total annihilation cross section is proportional to

$$\frac{1}{q^2} \int_1^S d\sigma \, \rho(\sigma) \int_1^T d\tau \, \rho(\tau)$$

where ρ is the spectral function of a parton propagator and S and T are upper bounds of order q^2. There is a normalization condition

$$\int_1^\infty d\sigma \; \rho(\sigma) = \text{finite}$$

In this model, one could truncate the σ and τ integrals at any finite values S_0 and T_0, and still get a contribution to the cross section which goes as $1/q^2$. If there is a mechanism adjusting the quantum numbers in the final state so that only normal hadrons appear, and if this does not substantially change the rapidity distribution in individual events, this would correspond to the production of two finite mass jets of hadrons widely separated in rapidity. Since there are only a finite number of hadronic states with masses less than any given value, this means that at least some quasi-two-body exclusive channels should be point-like or "diffractive". Partons appearing as hadrons would correspond to δ-function contributions to $\rho(\sigma)$. However, this may involve taking the details of the final state in the Landshoff-Polkinghorne model too seriously: perhaps one should only expect some of the predictions for inclusive distributions to be valid.

In the parton model of Bjorken, Feynman and others[27,28] all exclusive channels in annihilation are expected to fall relative to the total cross section, and they all conspire in a "multiperipheral" manner to build up the total cross section. Naively in the Landshoff-Polkinghorne[30] the total cross section, even if the multiplicity increases logarithmically, is completely constructed out of point-like exclusive channels asymptotically, as in diffractive excitation[31] models of hadron collisions. How can we discriminate between these two pictures? One way is to look directly for the scaling exclusive channels. Another is to look at the topological cross sections and see whether they have the "multiperipheral" structure of Fig. 5, or the "diffractive" structure of Fig. 6, or some combination of the two.

Light-cone analysis allows a logarithmically increasing multiplicity.[32] If the bilocal operator is expressible as a finite sum of factorizable terms

$$B(x, 0) \sim \sum_i \phi_i(x) \; \phi_i'(0)$$

then the final state structure must be similar to the Landshoff-Polkinghorne model.[33] However, a more general structure for the bilocal, as found for example in canonical manipulations of the quark-vector gluon model, does

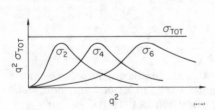

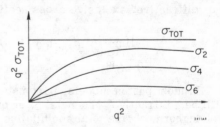

FIG. 5--Schematic representation of "multiperipheral-like" partial cross sections adding up to a scaling cross section.

FIG. 6--Schematic representation of "diffractive-like" partial cross sections adding up to a scaling cross section.

not imply any two jet structure. In the Landshoff-Polkinghorne model with logarithmic multiplicity scaling in annihilation is approached from below, and no more rapidly than $(q^2)^{-1/2}$.[34]

These various different pictures say different things about moments of the multiplicity distribution. In the Landshoff-Polkinghorne model with logarithmic multiplicity, f_2 and the higher moments grow like powers of q^2. Naively one might expect $f_2 \sim (q^2)^{1/2}$,[35] as in the simple formulation of the diffractive excitation model. But just as t_{min} effects can cut down f_2 in the diffractive excitation model,[35] f_2 in annihilation could increase more slowly. For example

$$\sigma_n \sim \frac{\theta((q^2)^\epsilon - n)}{n^2} \qquad 0 < \epsilon < 1/2$$

implies

$$\langle n \rangle = \sum_{n=1}^{(q^2)^\epsilon} \frac{1}{n} \sim \epsilon \ln q^2$$

and

$$f_2 \sim \langle n^2 \rangle \sim (q^2)^\epsilon$$

In the conventional "multiperipheral" parton model of Bjorken and Feynman,[28,29] all the multiplicity moments are expected to grow as powers of $\ln q^2$. Unfortunately experiments at CEA and SPEAR will presumably be at values of q^2 too low to discriminate between a logarithm and a small power of q^2.

ACKNOWLEDGMENTS

We thank J. D. Bjorken, M. S. Chanowitz, E. W. Colglazier, Y. Frishman, R. L. Jaffe, H. R. Quinn and J. Stack for useful conversations. One of us(J.E.) thanks SLAC for its generous hospitality while this talk was prepared.

ERRATUM

Table IV has been mislabeled "Table III." Table IV should appear on the previous page, preceeding the sentence "This scheme is rather complicated:..." Table III was inadvertantly deleted. It should have appeared following "A prototypal scheme is shown in Table III." Table III would have shown four quarks, p, n, λ and p' (Q=2/3, I_z=0, Y=-2/3, Charm = 1).

REFERENCES

1. J. D. Bjorken, Phys. Rev. 148, 1467 (1966).
   V. N. Gribov, B. L. Ioffe and I. Pomeranchuk, Yadern. Fiz. 6, 586 (1967).
2. A. Litke, et al., Phys. Rev. Letters 30, 1189 (1973) and talk presented by H. Newman at the SLAC Summer Institute in Particle Physics (1973).
3. N. Cabibbo, G. Parisi and M. Testa, Lettere al Nuovo Cimento, IV, 35 (1970).
4. K. G. Wilson, Phys. Rev. 179, 1499 (1969).
5. D. J. Gross and F. Wilczek, Phys. Rev. Letters 30, 1343 (1973).
   H. D. Politzer, Phys. Rev. Letters 30, 1346 (1973). It appears this result was also known to G. t'Hooft.
6. T. Appelquist and H. Georgi, Harvard preprint (1973). A. Zee, "Electron-Positron Annihilation in Stagnant Field Theories," Rockefeller Univ. preprint (1973).
7. R. L. Kingsley, Nucl. Phys. B 46, 615 (1972). P. M. Fishbane and R. L. Kingsley, Preprint ITP-SB-73-33 (1973).
8. S. Weinberg, Phys. Rev. Letters 19, 1264 (1967). A. Salam and J. C. Ward, Nuovo Cimento 11, 568 (1959). H. Georgi and S. L. Glashow, Phys. Rev. Letters 28, 1494 (1972).
9. H. J. Lipkin, Weizman Institute preprint (1973).
10. D. J. Gross and F. Wilczek, preprint NAL THY 73-49 (1973).
11. M. Gell-Mann, Phys. Letters 8, 214 (1964). G. Zweig, CERN reports TH-401 and TH-412, unpublished (1964).
12. K. G. Wilson, op.cit. R. J. Crewther, Phys. Rev. Letters 28, 1421 (1972).
13. H. Fritzsch and M. Gell-Mann, Proceedings of the XVI International Conference on High Energy Physics. J. D. Jackson and A. Roberts, ed. Vol. 2, p. 135 (1972) and references therein.
14. Y. Nambu, in "Preludes in Theoretical Physics," A. de-Shalit, H. Feshbach, L. Van Hove, ed. (North Holland, Amsterdam, 1966) p. 133.
15. M. Y. Han and Y. Nambu, Phys. Rev. 139, B 1006 (1965).
16. S. L. Glashow, J. Iliopoulos and L. Maiani, Phys. Rev. D 2, 1285 (1970).
17. J. D. Bjorken, private communication.
18. S. Berman, J. D. Bjorken and J. Kogut, Phys. Rev. D 4, 3388 (1971).
19. J. D. Bjorken and J. Kogut, Phys. Rev. D 8, 1341 (1973).
20. M. Chanowitz and S. D. Drell, Phys. Rev. Letters 30, 807 (1973).
21. D. Coward, et al., Phys. Rev. Letters 20, 292 (1968). T. Massam and A. Zichichi, Nuovo Cimento Letters 1, 387 (1969).
22. J. D. Bjorken and Y. Frishman, private communication.
23. J. D. Bjorken and S. J. Brodsky, Phys. Rev. D 1, 1416 (1970).
24. S. D. Drell, D. J. Levy and T.-M. Yan, Phys. Rev. D 1, 1617 (1970). J. Ellis, Phys. Letters 35 B, 537 (1971).
25. J. Stack, Phys. Rev. Letters 28, 57 (1972). M. Gonzalez and J. Weis, Univ. of Washington preprint, 1973.
26. E. Lazarus, et al., Phys. Rev. Letters 29, 743 (1972). C. J. Bebek, et al., Phys. Rev. Letters 30, 624 (1973).
27. R. P. Feynman in "Photon Hadron Interactions"(W. A. Benjamin, 1972). J. D. Bjorken, "Proceedings of the Fifth International Symposium on Electron and Photon Interactions at High Energies", at Cornell Univ.,

1971, N. B. Mistry, ed. and Phys. Rev. D 7, 282 (1973). S. Berman
J. D. Bjorken and J. Kogut, op.cit.

28. R. Cahn, J. Cleymans and E. W. Colglazier, Phys. Letters 43 B, 323 (1973).

29. K. Berkelman, et al., CLNS-240 (1973) preprint.

30. R. L. Kingsley, P. V. Landshoff, C. Nash and J. C. Polkinghorne, preprint DAMTP 73/19 (1973).

31. R. Hwa, Phys. Rev. Letters 26, 1143 (1971).

32. J. Ellis and Y. Frishman, Phys. Rev. Letters 31, 135 (1973).

33. J. Stack, Univ. of Illinois preprint, ILL-(TH)-73-4 (1973).

34. H. Osborn and G. Woo, preprint DAMTP, 73/13, April 1973.

35. D. M. Scott, preprint DAMTP 73/26 (1973).

36. R. Hwa, Phys. Rev. Letters 28, 1487 (1972).

EXPERIMENTAL RESULTS ON DEEP INELASTIC LEPTOPRODUCTION*

B. C. Barish
California Institute of Technology, Pasadena, Calif. 91109

ABSTRACT

A review of recent results for both deep inelastic electroproduction and neutrino scattering is presented.

INTRODUCTION

Particle physicists have been concerned with the "substructure" of the hadrons for more than a decade. Baryon and meson spectroscopy gave us indications that there might be an underlying substructure. A description in terms of quarks ($q+q+q$ forming baryons, and $q+\bar{q}$ forming mesons) has been remarkably successful.

Of course we do not know whether there are real quarks or whether this is just a mathematical prescription which successfully describes the particle spectra. Also, fundamental questions, such as whether "exotic" baryons (5 quark states) or mesons (4 quark states) exist, remain to be resolved.

More recently evidence of a substructure behavior has resulted from a completely different area of particle physics--lepton-hadron scattering. Deep inelastic electron scattering data show a behavior which is consistent with a picture of the nucleon being made up of point-like constituents. The well known features of the e-p data are: (1) a large point-like scattering in the deep inelastic region; (2) "scaling behavior", that is that the structure functions $\nu W_2(Q^2, \nu)$ and $W_1(Q^2, \nu)$ are non-trivial functions of only the variable $x = Q^2/2m\nu$; and (3) that the scattering is primarily transverse for the virtual photon, implying dominantly scattering off spin 1/2 constituents.

These results have prompted development of a variety of theoretical models including both the quark-parton model and alternately light cone current algebra.

There are a variety of tests which can be made to determine the nature of this substructure. So far, results are consistent with a quark model picture, but the most critical tests remain. In this review I will concentrate on the most recent electron results and the neutrino results which are beginning to test these ideas.

* Work supported in part by the U. S. Atomic Energy Commission.

DEEP INELASTIC ELECTRON SCATTERING

The cross sections for deep inelastic electron scattering exhibit a point-like behavior. This demonstrates itself by the large cross sections in the deep inelastic region with no apparent damping at large Q^2 (four-momentum transfer) characteristic of a form factor (or structure). This should be contrasted with elastic e-p scattering which exhibits the well known dipole behavior of the form factors. Point-like scattering, suggests an interpretation in terms of constituent models of the nucleon.

Scaling Behavior: The best known consequence of the point-like behavior is the so called "scaling behavior" of the structure functions.

The two structure functions that describe deep inelastic scattering are non-trivial functions of a single variable

$$x = Q^2/2M_p\nu \qquad 0 \le x \le 1$$

That is,

$$\nu W_2(Q^2,\nu) = F_2(x)$$
$$W_1(Q^2,\nu) = F_1(x)$$

Other scaling variables $\omega = 1/x$, x', ω', etc. are often used but for the purpose of this talk the differences are not important.

This general scaling behavior has been known for several years. One important question, especially when we try to compare with neutrino data, is to determine how rapidly scaling sets in. It has been shown that scaling at SLAC sets in very rapidly and is achieved by $Q^2 \sim 1$ GeV^2 and even at $Q^2 \sim .5$ GeV^2 we are within 25% of the scaling limit. [1]

Also, it is now possible with accurate SLAC data and eventually with NAL muon and neutrino data to determine how well scaling holds. As a first attempt the SLAC data has been analyzed in terms of a propagation term

$$F(x') \rightarrow \frac{F(x')}{\left(1+\dfrac{Q^2}{\Lambda^2}\right)^2}$$

(one possible form of a breakdown). Figure 1 shows this analysis not including the more recent SLAC - MIT results which, when corrected for systematic errors, will allow a better analysis. We see that even allowing $R = \sigma_s/\sigma_t$ to have different behaviors the data is inconsistent with this form of scale breaking for $\Lambda < 10$ GeV.

It should be noted that a more detailed analysis of scaling evaluating the moments of νW_2 has been presented by Bloom. [2]

Behavior of R: The virtual photon in inelastic electron scattering can have either transverse or longitudinal polarization.

An interesting parameter to determine is

$$R = \frac{\sigma_s}{\sigma_t}$$

(the ratio of longitudinal to transverse scattering). The cross-sections σ_s and σ_t can be determined by separating the structure functions $W_1(Q^2,\nu)$ and $W_2(Q^2,\nu)$ for inelastic e-p scattering.

$$W_1 = \frac{K}{4\pi^2\alpha}\,\sigma_t$$

$$K = \frac{W^2 - M^2}{2M}$$

$$W_2 = \frac{K}{4\pi^2\alpha}\frac{Q^2}{Q^2+\nu}(\sigma_t+\sigma_s)$$

The ratio R has been shown to be small ($\bar{R} = .18 \pm .10$).[3] The value R = 0 is expected in a model where the constituents are spin 1/2. This then could imply that the behavior is consistent with a quark-like behavior. Also, it has been shown by Callan and Gross that this implies a relationship between structure functions,[4]

$$2xF_1(x) = F_2(x)$$

Since the value of R is not zero at SLAC energies it is interesting and important to see whether it is approaching zero in the expected way.

For theories with a spin 1/2 substructure this behavior should be approached,

$$R = f(x)/_\nu$$

where the function $f(x)$ is model dependent.[5] A detailed analysis of R is being performed and thus far the most complete results are reported in an MIT thesis by E. M. Riordan.[6] He finds that the x dependence of R deviates from the simple form

$$\frac{Q^2}{\nu}\,\frac{1}{\nu} = R$$

only for x < 0.2, and seems to be consistent with this form for larger values of x (see Figure 2). More importantly (Figure 3) he fits νR_p = a + bν at fixed x for 13 values of x. If b $\neq$ 0 we can conclude there are spin 0 in addition to spin 1/2 constituents. He concludes that for x > 0.2 the coefficient b $\sim$ 0, however for x < 0.2 the coefficient b $\neq$ 0. The systematic errors are most important for x < 0.2; however he does not believe they account for the result.

<u>Scattering off Neutrons</u>: Using deuterium, results have been extracted for the neutron structure functions. The first result of interest is the ratio of neutron to proton structure functions,

$F_2^n(x)/F_2^p(x)$. It has been shown that this ratio is bounded in a quark-parton model,[7]

$$1/4 \leq \frac{F_2^n(x)}{F_2^p(x)} \leq 4 .$$

Experimentally, the most recent results for the ratio are shown in Figure 4. Although the ratio approaches the lower bound at large x, present data does not appear to threaten this limit.

Another interesting result concerns the evaluation of the integral

$$\int_0^1 \frac{F_2^p(x) - F_2^n(x)}{x} \, dx$$

This integral is predicted to yield a value near 1/3 for a simple quark-parton model. The most recent experimental data is shown in Figure 5 and the value of the measured integral is

$$\int_{0.05}^1 \frac{F_2^p(x) - F_2^n(x)}{x} \, dx = .18 \pm .04$$

It is extremely difficult and model dependent to evaluate the unmeasured part of the integral. However, it appears difficult to extrapolate the data from x = 0.05 → x = 0 and approach the value of 1/3.

Keeping the electron results in mind let us now proceed to the neutrino data. Since this data is still rather qualitative, we will mainly see if the general features are consistent with the picture that has emerged from the deep inelastic electron scattering experiments.

DEEP INELASTIC NEUTRINO SCATTERING

The physics with incident electrons and neutrinos is analogous. However, for neutrinos the reaction is mediated by a charged current.

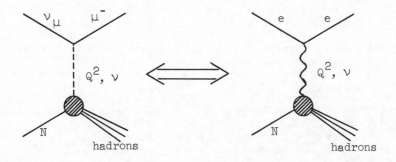

In the scaling limit, the differential cross section may be written as

$$\frac{d^2\sigma}{dxdy} = \frac{G^2ME_\nu}{\pi} \left\{ (1-y) F_2(x) + \frac{y^2}{2} \left(2xF_1(x) \mp y(1-\frac{y}{2})xF_3(x)\right)\right\}$$

where

$$x = \frac{Q^2}{2M\nu} \qquad Q^2 = -q^2 = 4EE' \sin^2 \frac{\theta}{2}$$

$$y = \nu/E_\nu = \frac{E_\nu - E'}{E_\nu}$$

It should be noted that in contrast to electron scattering the propagator is very massive (W-boson mass), therefore there is no $1/Q^4$ term in the cross section. Experimentally, this means that large Q^2 are accessible even though neutrino rates are relatively low. Also, for neutrinos there is a third structure function $F_3(x)$. This comes about since there are both vector and axial vector contributions to the structure functions $F_1(x)$ and $F_2(x)$, and $F_3(x)$ represents the vector-axial vector interference term. Also, $F_3(x)$ has opposite sign for neutrino and antineutrino scattering.

Integrating the expression for the differential cross section over x and y, we obtain

$$\sigma = \frac{G^2ME_\nu}{\pi} \int_0^1 dx \left\{ \frac{1}{2} F_2(x) + \frac{x}{3} (F_1(x) \mp F_3(x)) \right\}$$

This implies that σ rises linearly with E_ν, and the integral over the structure functions yields the slope of the rising cross section.

The value of the slope is of crucial importance when compared with the electron results. In order to make the comparison we assume (1) $2x F_1(x) = F_2(x)$, Callan-Gross relation for spin 1/2 constituents; (2) Isospin symmetry; (3) isoscalar part of $F_2^{en} < 10\%$; (4) Isotriplet current hypothesis (CVC); and (5) $|V| = |A|$. Using these assumptions and adding neutrino and antineutrino cross sections, we obtain

$$\sigma^{\nu N} + \sigma^{\bar\nu N} = \frac{G^2ME_\nu}{\pi} \frac{4}{3} \int_0^1 F_2^{\nu N}(x) \, dx$$

From the slope of the CERN neutrino data,

$$\int_0^1 F_2^{\nu N}(x) \, dx = .47 \pm .07$$

From electron scattering, we predict using the above assumption,

$$\int_0^1 F_2^{\nu N}(x) \, dx = .56 \pm .04$$

The agreement is remarkably good! It will be of fundamental importance to check this relationship at high energies.

In terms of a quark-parton model this slope requires gluons. In order to have a No gluon sum rule it can easily be shown that using the existing electron data we would predict

$$\int_0^1 F_2^{\nu N}(x) \, dx \approx .27$$

So at high energies (NAL) we would expect to observe a slope of about half that observed at CERN. Also, within the context of this model this result would require that the strange quarks carry ~ 75% of the momentum (a rather unattractive alternative).

What about the general features of the neutrino inelastic scattering data? For simplicity, again assume (1) $2x \, F_1(x) = F_2(x)$, Callan-Gross and (2) $xF_3(x) = - F_2(x)$, Pure V-A (no antiquarks). Then,

$$\frac{d^2\sigma^{\nu N}}{dxdy} \approx \frac{G^2 ME\nu}{\pi} \, F_2(x)$$

$$\frac{d^2\sigma^{\bar{\nu} N}}{dxdy} \approx \frac{G^2 ME\nu}{\pi} \, (1-y)^2 \, F_2(x)$$

We can compare this approximate expected behavior with the early qualitative results from NAL and CERN

(1) $\frac{d\sigma^{\nu}}{dy} \sim$ const.

Figure 6 shows the initial results from the Caltech ν-experiment[9] at NAL for $< E_\nu > ~ 50$ GeV, which is at least qualitatively consistent with this behavior.

(2) $\frac{d\sigma^{\bar{\nu}}}{dy} \sim (1-y)^2$

Figure 7 shows the Caltech $\bar{\nu}$ results which again agree qualitatively at $< E_\nu > ~ 50$ GeV,

(3) $\frac{\sigma^{\bar{\nu}}}{\sigma^{\nu}} \sim \frac{1}{3}$

CERN has measured R = .38 $\pm$ .02 between 1 - 10 GeV.[10] Recently, the Harvard-Pennsylvania-Wisconsin ν - experiment[11] shows a similar behavior at higher energies. This is shown in Figure 8.

(4) $F_2^{\nu N}(x) \propto F_2^{ed}(x)$

Figure 9 shows the distribution $F_2^{\nu N}$ from the Caltech ν- experiment with the $F_2^{ed}(x)$ fit superposed. Again, qualitative agreement is seen.

(5) Finally, is there any evidence for scaling behavior in the neutrino data? This can be checked by measuring the linearity of σ_t, however, this has not yet been done.

Alternately,

$$Q^2 = 2 ME_\nu \; xy$$

or

$$<Q^2> = \frac{2 ME_\nu \iint xy \; F(x,y) \; dxdy}{\iint F(x,y) \; dxdy}$$

Where $F(x,y)$ is related to the structure functions. Again, a linear dependence on E_ν is expected.

Figure 10 shows the neutrino data from the Caltech experiment compared to the expected linear behavior and also the behavior modified by a propagation term $F_2(x) \to F_2(x)/(1+\frac{Q^2}{\Lambda^2})^2$. We see that the neutrino data is consistent with "scaling" holding at least up to ~ 5 GeV for Λ.

CONCLUSIONS

Deep inelastic electron scattering data is consistent with a picture of scattering off point-like constituents. There is some evidence that the constituents behave as if they are spin 1/2 and preliminary neutrino results are consistent with this conclusion.

Early neutrino results bear out the expectation that they provide a complementary way of studying the same physics. Again, a point-like scaling behavior is emerging and the structure functions have a qualitatively similar behavior to the electron scattering structure functions.

Many of the most important tests, which will reveal information about the other quantum numbers of the constituents remain to be made. However, we can look forward to these results soon.

ACKNOWLEDGEMENTS

I would especially like to acknowledge E. Bloom for numerous discussions of the deep inelastic electron scattering results.

REFERENCES

1. E. Bloom, Caltech Report CALT-68-392 (1973). To be published in proceedings of International Conference on New Results from Experiments on High Energy Particle Collisions, Vanderbilt Univ.
2. Rapporteur talk of E. Bloom, Proceedings 1973 International Symposium on Electron and Photon Interactions at High Enegies, Bonn, Aug. 27-31, 1973.
3. J. Friedman and H. Kendall, Ann. Rev. of Nuclear Physics, Vol. 22 p. 203 (1972).
4. C. G. Callan and D. J. Gross, Phys. Rev. Lett. 22, 156 (1969).
5. R. P. Feynman, Photon Hadron Interactions, Benjamin Inc. p. 139.
6. Riordan, MIT Thesis, MIT Report No. COU-3069-176 (1973).
7. O. Nachtmann, Nucl. Phys. B38, 397 (1972).

8. C. H. Llewellyn-Smith, Phys. Reports 3C, 261 (1972).
9. B. Barish, et al, Phys. Rev. Letters, 31, 565 (1973).
10. Eichten, et al, Phys. Letters, B46, 274 (1973).
11. Harvard-Pennsylvania-Wisconsin NAL ν-experiment (presented by A. Mann, this conference).

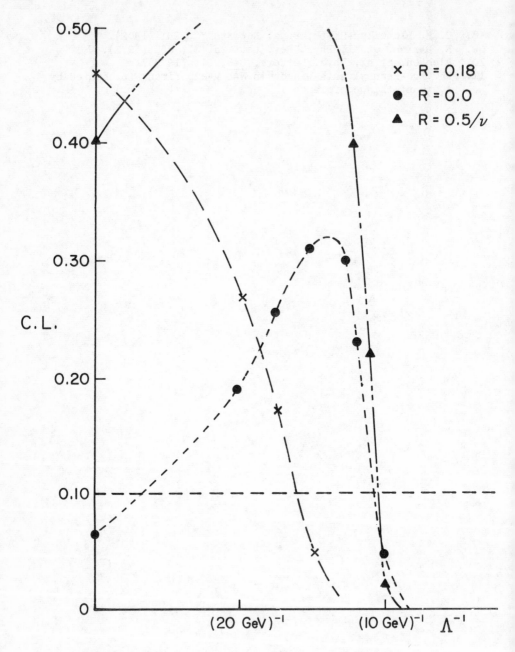

Figure 1. SLAC electron data fit to the form
$F(x', Q^2, \Lambda) = \sum\limits_{n=3}^{7} a_n (1-x')^n \left[\dfrac{1}{1+\frac{Q^2}{\Lambda^2}}\right]^2$. The plot
shows the confidence level of the fit (C.L.) vs. Λ^{-1}
using three different cases for $R = \sigma_s/\sigma_t$. Scaling
holds with 90% confidence for $\Lambda \leq 10$ GeV.

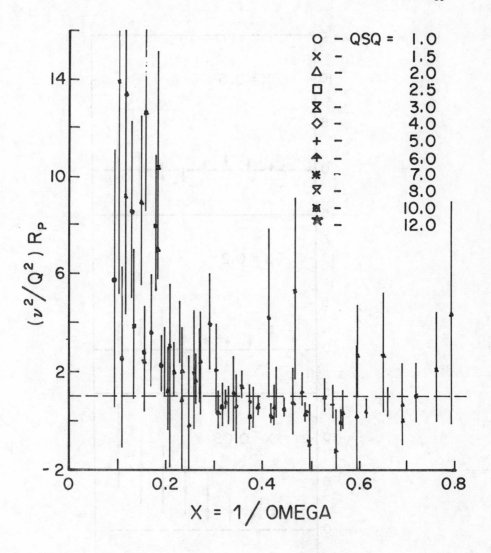

Figure 2. $\left(\dfrac{\nu^2}{Q^2}\right)$ R_p vs. x is shown from the MIT thesis of Riordan.[6]

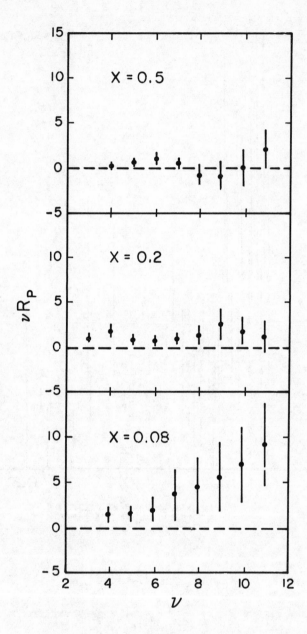

Figure 3. Representative plots of νR_p vs. ν from Riordan's MIT thesis.[6]

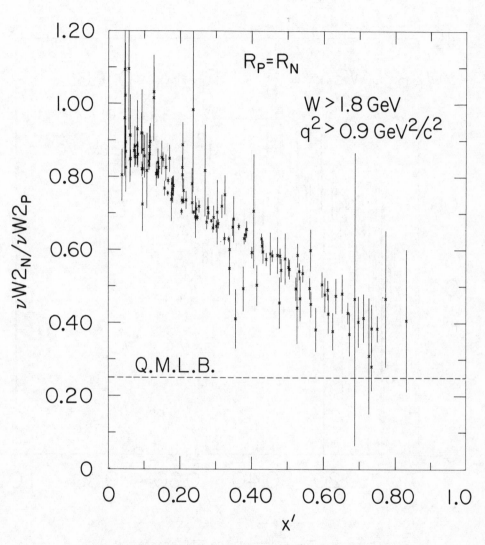

Figure 4. The ratio of the structure functions
$\nu W_2(x')$ for neutrons and protons vs. x' is
shown. Also the quark model lower bound of
1/4 is indicated.

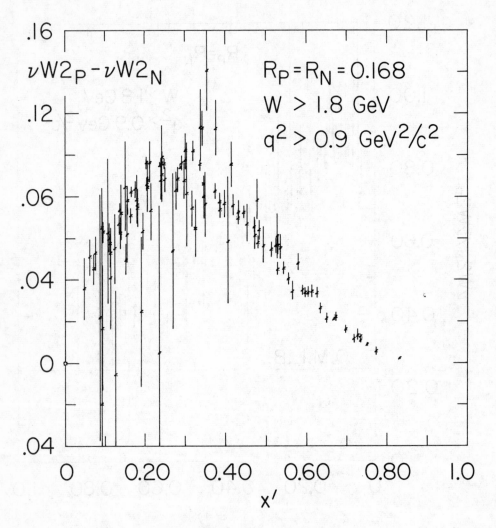

Figure 5. The value of the difference in
νW_2 for protons and neutrons is shown vs.
x'.

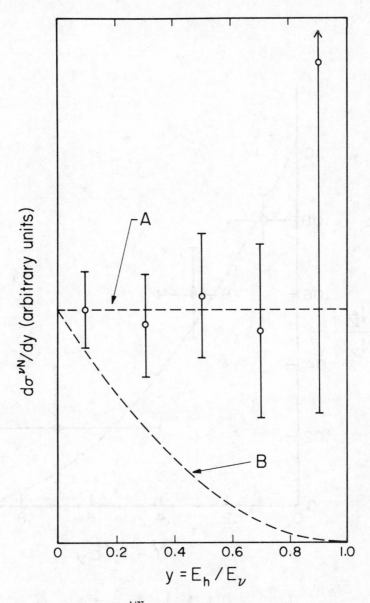

Figure 6. $\dfrac{d\sigma^{\nu N}}{dy}$ vs. y for neutrinos is shown for $< E_{\nu}> = 50$ GeV from the Caltech ν - experiment.9 A flat y dependence and a $(1-y)^2$ dependence are shown for comparison.

94

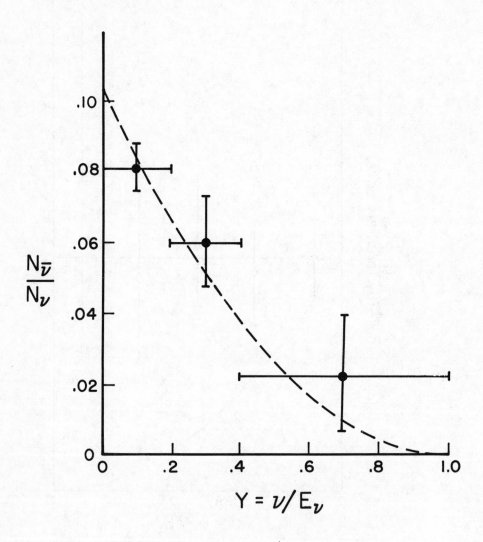

Figure 7. The ratio of $N_{\bar{\nu}}/N_{\nu}$ events vs. y are shown from recent data taken by the Caltech group at $< E_{\nu} > \sim 50$ GeV. The behavior $\frac{N_{\bar{\nu}}}{N_{\nu}} \propto (1-y)^2$ is shown for comparison.

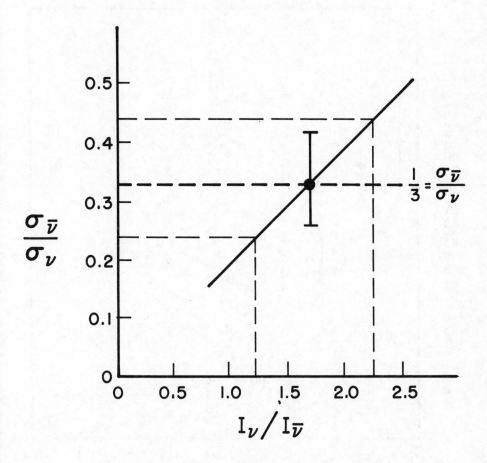

Figure 8. The ratio of $\sigma_{\bar{\nu}}/\sigma_{\nu}$ for
$< E_{\nu}> \sim$ 30 GeV is shown for the Harvard
Pennsylvania-Wisconsin Group.[10] Since the
relative flux of neutrinos to antineutrinos
is not yet well known, the dependence of the
ratio on $I_{\nu}/I_{\bar{\nu}}$ is displayed. The measured
point is for the best estimate of $I_{\nu}/I_{\bar{\nu}}$.

96

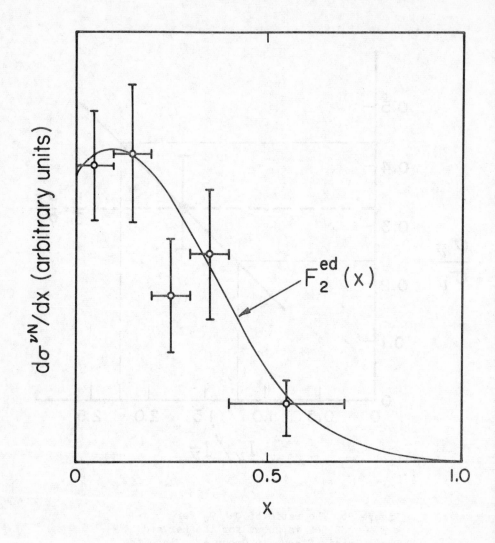

Figure 9. The structure function $F_2^{\nu N}(x)$ vs. x is shown for the Caltech ν - experiment[9] at $\langle E_\nu \rangle \sim 50$ GeV. For comparison a fit to $F_2^{ed}(x)$ vs. x is shown.

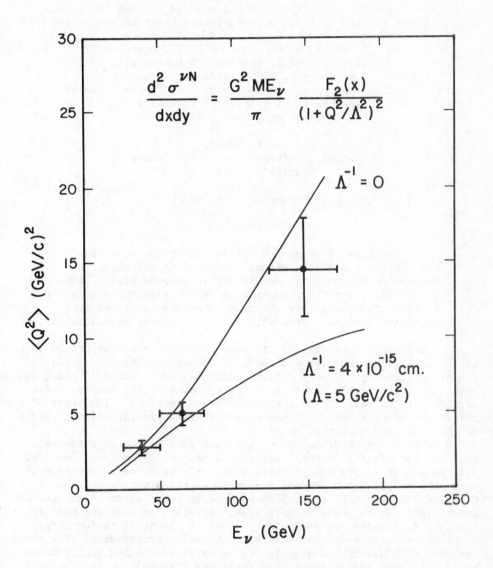

Figure 10. $< Q^2 >$ vs. E_ν is shown for the Caltech experiment.[10] For comparison the expected behavior for $F_2^{\nu N}(x) \propto F_2^{ed}(x)$ is shown. Also the expected behavior modified by a scalebreaking term of the form $F_2(x) \rightarrow \dfrac{F_2(x)}{1+Q^2/\Lambda^2}$ for $\Lambda = 5$ GeV/c^2 is indicated.

Experimental Results on Scaling and the Neutron to Proton Cross Section Ratio in Deep Inelastic Electron Scattering

A. Bodek, M. Breidenbach[*], D.L. Dubin,
J.E. Elias, J.I. Friedman, H.W. Kendall,
J.S. Poucher, E.M. Riordan, M.R. Sogard[+]
Physics Department and Laboratory for Nuclear Science
Massachusetts Institute of Technology
Cambridge, Mass. 02139[**]

D.H. Coward
Stanford Linear Accelerator Center
Stanford, Calif. 94305

Presented by A. Bodek

ABSTRACT

A review of present knowledge about the scaling of the neutron and proton structure functions and about the neutron to proton cross section ratio is presented. Emphasis is placed on the results of a recent electron scattering experiment at SLAC from which neutron cross sections were extracted from deuterium data using an impulse approximation.

The discovery of scaling[1] in deep inelastic electron proton scattering resulted in the formulation of a number of theoretical models explaining the experimental data. Additional measurements[2-5] have established that the neutron exhibits scaling, but that the neutron cross sections are different from the proton cross sections. The study of the comparison of neutron and proton cross sections provide valuable tests of those nucleon structure models.

In this presentation, we will review some of the experimental evidence for scaling in deep inelastic electron scattering. Emphasis will be placed on the results of a recent electron scattering experiment at SLAC[2] in which e-p and e-n cross sections were compared. A detailed discussion of the apparatus used in these electron scattering experiments can be found in Refs. 1-6. Briefly, an electron beam of energy E is incident on a liquid hydrogen or liquid deuterium target. Scattered electrons are detected by a magnetic spectrometer. The cross section $d^2\sigma/d\Omega dE'$ is measured for several scattering angles Θ and various initial and final electron energies E and E'.

In the one photon exchange approximation, the cross section is represented by two structure functions W_1 and W_2.

$$\frac{d^2\sigma}{d\Omega dE'} = \sigma_M \left[W_2(q^2, \nu) + 2 \tan^2\frac{\theta}{2} W_1(q^2, \nu) \right]$$

*Present address: Stanford Linear Accelerator Center
**Work supported in part by the U.S. Atomic Energy Commission under Contract #AT(11-1) 3069
+ Present address: Laboratory of Nuclear Studies, Cornell University

where
$$\sigma_M = \frac{\alpha^2 \cos^2 \frac{\theta}{2}}{4 E^2 \sin^4 \frac{\theta}{2}} \quad , \quad \nu = E - E' , \quad q^2 = 4EE' \sin^2 \frac{\theta}{2} .$$

The mass of the final hadronic state W is defined by $W^2 = M^2 + 2M\nu - q^2$ where M is the nucleon mass.

An alternate way of describing the cross section is in terms of cross sections for transverse and scalar virtual photons, σ_t and σ_s. The electron's kinematics determine the flux Γ, polarization ϵ, and effective momentum K of the virtual photon.

$$\frac{d^2\sigma}{d\Omega dE'} = \Gamma \left(\sigma_t + \epsilon \sigma_s \right)$$

$$\Gamma = \frac{\alpha K E' \, 2}{4\pi^2 q^2 E (1-\epsilon)} \quad , \quad K = \frac{W^2 - M^2}{2M} \quad , \quad \epsilon = \frac{1}{1 + 2 \tan^2 \frac{\theta}{2} \left(1 + \frac{\nu^2}{q^2} \right)}$$

Experimental separation of W_1 and W_2 is possible if data is taken at several angles for the same ν and q^2. The separated structure functions are usually given in terms of W_2 and $R = \sigma_s / \sigma_t = W_2 / W_1 (1 + \frac{\nu^2}{q^2}) - 1$

Earlier determinations[6] of R for the proton, R_p, have established that it is consistent with being a constant over the region where it was measured (2 < W < 4 GeV, $1.5 < q^2 < 11$ [GeV/c]^2). The quoted average value was 0.18 ± 0.10[6]. The assumption that R_p has this value elsewhere allowed the determination of νW_2^p over a wider kinematic range (2 < W < 5 GeV, $1.0 < q^2 < 20$ [GeV/c]^2). νW_2^p was found to be consistent with being a function of the single variable $\omega = 2M\nu/q^2$ over that wider kinematic range if only data for which W was greater than 2.6 GeV were included. If data for W < 2 GeV were also included, then νW_2^p was better represented by a function of the single variable $\omega' = \omega + M^2/q^2$.

Our analysis of data from the recent electron scattering experiment[2] and of data from an earlier small angle experiment[5] has yielded better determinations of R_p, and the first determinations of R for the neutron and the deuteron, R_n and R_d, respectively. R determinations were made for the range $3 < \nu < 12$ GeV and $0.5 < q^2 < 16$ [GeV/c]^2. The great bulk of the R values lie in the range 0.05 to 0.40. We also see indications of a possible kinematic dependence in R_p; a detailed discussion can be found in Ref. 4. We obtain an average value for R_p of 0.168 ± 0.074 in agreement with previous results. We also find that R_d is consistent with being equal to R_p with the average difference $R_d - R_p = -0.005 \pm 0.043$. As is shown in Ref. 3, the equality $R_p = R_d$ implies $R_p = R_n$.

We investigated the scaling behavior of the structure functions νW_2 and $2MW_1$ for the proton and the deuteron without making any assumptions about R, as both W_1 and W_2 were extracted from the data in the region where measurements from several angles were available. The error in the value of R extracted from each separation point was propagated into the errors in W_1 and W_2. Interpolated values of cross sections were employed in order to study the q^2 behavior of νW_2 and $2MW_1$ for several contours of constant values of ω. Plots of νW_2^p vs q^2 for a few selected values of ω are shown in Fig. 1; similar behavior is observed for $2MW_1^p$. Only W > 2 GeV data were used. Exact scaling in ω would require that νW_2^p be constant in q^2 for fixed ω. Our data indicate that small deviations from scaling in ω occur in the form of a slow fall-off in the value of νW_2^p with q^2 for $q^2 > 1.0$ [GeV/c]^2. An alternate way of looking at the data says that we observe approximate scaling in ω at around $q^2 = 1$ [GeV/c]^2 and that exact scaling might gradually set in at higher q^2. We have made least square fits of the form $2MW_1^P = a_1(1+b_1q^2)$ and $\nu W_2^P = a_2(1+b_2q^2)$ to the structure functions at each fixed ω contour. In the region $1.5 \leqslant \omega \leqslant 3.0$ we find average values $b_1 = -0.033 \pm 0.004$ [GeV/c]$^{-2}$ and $b_2 = -0.026 \pm 0.003$ [GeV/c]$^{-2}$. Similar values are obtained for fits to the deuteron structure functions. The above values for b_1 and b_2 shift by less than the quoted statistical error if the constraint $W > 2.6$ GeV is imposed. Chanowitz and Drell[7] have suggested that a fall-off of νW_2^P and $2MW_1^P$ with increasing q^2 may be interpreted as evidence of structure of possible nucleon constituents. For gluons of mass M_g the fall-off will take the form $\nu W_2^P = F(\omega)[1-2q^2/M_g^2]$. Our data indicate a value of M_g^2 in the range 60-75 GeV^2 with a statistical error of about 10 GeV^2.

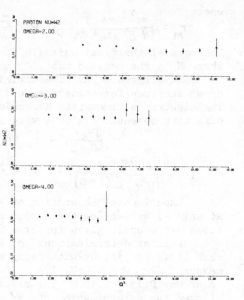

Fig. 1 νW_2^P vs q^2 for fixed ω.

A similar study was done to test scaling in ω'[8]. We have performed fits of the form $2MW_1 = g_1(\omega')(1+C_1q^2)$ and $\nu W_2 = g_2(\omega')(1+C_2q^2)$. We find C_1 and C_2 consistent with zero for the range $1.5 \leqslant \omega \leqslant 3.0$.

We conclude that an analysis of our data when no assumptions are made about R shows that νW_2 and $2MW_1$ display a statistically significant deviation from scaling in ω for $q^2 > 1$ [GeV/c]^2. A slope of νW_2 vs q^2 at constant ω could be interpreted as evidence for scaling breaking either at high q^2 ($q^2 \simeq 10$ [GeV/c]^2) or at low q^2 ($q^2 \simeq 1$ [GeV/c]^2). The indication that structure functions scale well in the variable ω' tends to support the latter view. A similar study for the range $\omega > 4$ could in principle distinguish between the two alternatives, but the range of q^2 for our data for $\omega > 4$ is too small for any significant scaling study.

The ratio of the neutron and proton cross sections[2] is shown in Fig. 2(a) as a function of the variable $x = 1/\omega$. Neutron cross sections were obtained from deuterium data using an impulse approximation[3,9]. Similarly, the difference between the proton and neutron structure functions $\nu W_2^P - \nu W_2^n$ is shown in Fig. 2(b). Within the errors, the neutron structure functions display a similar kind of scaling behavior as is seen in the proton data[3,4]. The neutron cross section is smaller than the proton cross section at small ω, indicating a significant non-diffractive component in the virtual photon-nucleon interaction. The small ratio at small ω cannot be explained in terms of a simple quark gluon model. Quark-quark correlations must be included in the model in order to explain the experimental results.

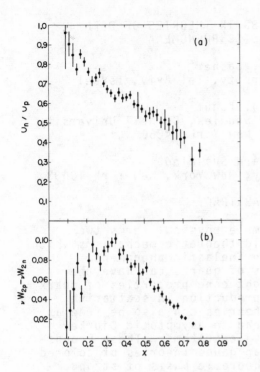

Fig. 2(a) σ_n/σ_p vs $x = 1/\omega$.

2(b) $\nu(W_2{}^p - W_2{}^n)$ vs x,

with the assumption $R_p = R_n = 0.18$. The errors

shown are statistical

only.

REFERENCES

1. M. Breidenbach et al., Phys. Rev. Lett. 23, 935 (1969),
    E.D. Bloom et al., Phys. Rev. Lett. 23, 930 (1969),
    J.I. Friedman & H.W. Kendall, Ann. Rev. of Nucl. Sci. 22, 203
    (1972).
2. A. Bodek et al., Phys. Rev. Lett. 30, 1087 (1973).
3. A. Bodek, Ph.D. Thesis, LNS-COO-3069-116, MIT (1972).
4. E.M. Riordan, Ph.D. Thesis, LNS-COO-3069-176, MIT (1973).
5. R.E. Taylor, Report to the 15th International Conference on High
    Energy Physics, Kiev (1969),
    J.S. Poucher, Ph.D. Thesis, MIT (1971).
6. G. Miller et al., Phys. Rev. D5, 528 (1972).
7. M.S. Chanowitz & S.D. Drell, Phys. Rev. Lett. 30, 807 (1973).
8. E.D. Bloom & F.J. Gilman, Phys. Rev. D4, 2901 (1971).
9. W.B. Atwood & G.B. West, Phys. Rev. D7, 773 (1973).

RECENT PROGRESS IN THEORIES OF DEEP INELASTIC PHENOMENA

A. Casher[*]
Tel Aviv University, Tel Aviv, Israel

J. Kogut[†]
Laboratory of Nuclear Studies, Cornell University
Ithaca, New York 14850

Leonard Susskind[‡]
Yeshiva University, New York, New York 10033

ABSTRACT

We discuss in simple physical terms two recently proposed field theoretic mechanisms which may shed light on deep inelastic phenomena. Certain gauge theories of quarks can have the short distance and light cone properties of quark fields without their production in scattering experiments. Gauge theories can also be free at short distances and lead to asymptotic Bjorken scaling broken only by logarithms. These proposals suggest non-abelian gauge theories of colored quarks as the field-theoretic basis of strong interactions.

The quark-parton model has experienced considerable success in describing the deep inelastic reactions explored at SLAC, CERN and NAL. The model rests on two very specific and very bold assumptions concerning strong interaction dynamics. These are,

1. <u>Large Distances</u> - the model supposes that hadrons are composed of fundamental constituents which do not exist as isolated states.

2. <u>Short Distances</u> - the forces which bind the constituents at short distances are assumed to be finite in strength.

Field-theoretic realizations of both of these properties have been proposed recently.[1,2] Although both proposals are tentative and incomplete, they point to non-abelian gauge theories as the dynamical origin of strong interactions.

Let us begin by briefly reviewing the role of assumptions 1 and 2 in the parton picture of deep inelastic scattering. Consider the process virtual photon + proton→ hadrons in an infinite momentum frame in which the proton has (infinite) momentum p in the z direction and the virtual photon momentum q is essentially transverse.[3] In such a frame the virtual photon cannot produce pairs, so the

electromagnetic current interacts directly with the charge
distribution of the proton. This is one reason why (if
the parton model is correct) deep inelastic physics is so
interesting: a fundamental feature of the hadron is being
probed in a clear, quasi-classical fashion. Furthermore,
at any instant one views the proton as consisting of bare
quanta (partons) each of which share the proton's available
infinite momentum. In a deep inelastic collision one of the
charged partons absorbs the photon. If one assumes (moviated
by the data, naturally) that parton-parton forces are always smooth and finite, then deep inelastic scattering is
impulsive and incoherent. The structure functions (νW_2,
say) can then be computed as an incoherent sum over partons
of various types (Fig. 1). As q grows larger than the
average momenta transferred by the
interparton forces, the points 1
and 2 in Fig. 1 necessarily become
relatively light-like, $(x_1 - x_2)^2 \to 0$.
The calculation of the matrix element therefore consists of two
pieces: first, the probability to
find a charged constituent at x_1 ;
and, second, the essentially free,[4]

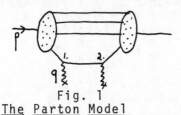

Fig. 1
The Parton Model

light-like propagation of that constituent between the
points x_1 and x_2. This simple picture then ensures Bjorken
scaling and a simple interpretation of the structure function νW_2,[5]

$$\nu W_2 = x \sum_i e_i^2 \, F_i(x) \quad , \quad x = -q^2/2q \cdot p \qquad 1.$$

where $F_i(x)$ is the probability that a constituent of type
i carries a fraction x of the proton's infinite momentum.
     Now we can return to assumptions 1 and 2 above and
discuss them more critically in the light of quantum field
theory.
     First, if parton-parton forces are indeed finite in
strength, why are the pointlike quanta not produced in deep
inelastic reactions? In fact, one can estimate the distance the struck parton travels before it loses a finite
fraction of the energy imparted to it by the virtual
photon. In the infinite momentum frame described above,
this distance is, naturally, proportional to the photon's
momentum q. If q is chosen large compared to the sizes of
typical hadrons, one would then naively think that the
quarks should be produced.
     In fact, the earliest versions of the parton model
were based on cut-off field theories[6] in which parton-
parton forces vanish near the light cone (Fig. 2). In
such models the constituents of the field theory are
necessarily produced. This follows because as q increases
the trajectory of the struck parton lies closer and
closer to the light cone. Therefore, the constituent

104

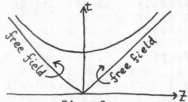

Fig. 2
Interactions in Naive
Parton Models

travels a distance q before it can interact with its surroundings at all. As $q^2 \to \infty$, the constituent becomes isolated in space-time and must be produced.[7] Furthermore, since the constituent is supposed to have a small invariant mass, these early models predicted finite multiplicities in deep inelastic reactions.[6]

Consider now the second assumption. How can it be that parton-parton forces are finite in strength for small and lightlike distances? If strong interactions are really describable by field theories, then such simplicity is very special. To understand why, recall that four dimensional quantum field theories possess dimensionless coupling constants. They do not possess a natural scale of length to distinguish high frequencies from low.[8] Therefore, one must expect a priori that the fields of the theory experience frequency fluctuations over the entire range of zero to infinity with roughly equal importance.[9] This picture contrasts sharply with the parton picture of deep inelastic scattering sketched above: in renormalizable field theory one cannot expect to be able to neglect parton-parton forces no matter how high q is simply because the field theory itself always possesses frequency fluctuations arbitrarily faster than q. This is the physics behind the logarithmic violations of canonical scaling that many authors have found in perturbation theory.[10] In light of this, can any renormalizable field theory come close to canonical scaling? The above discussion suggests that this is possible only if the _strength_ of the theory's high frequency fluctuations is in fact zero.

Recent investigations into gauge theories of strong interactions have suggested that both miracles 1 and 2 are possible field-theoretic phenomena. We shall try to discuss both topics in turn. The emphasis will be on simple physical arguments and many-body analogs to the deep field theoretic issues at hand. We shall try to convey some of the excitement generated by these tentative suggestions, point out gaps in the investigations and suggest problems for the future.

First, let us discuss the problem of avoiding quark-parton production in deep-inelastic scattering events. Is there a natural field-theoretic mechanism which builds hadrons from triality bearing fields but avoids the appearance of triality bearing asymptotic states? As a warm-up, consider a somewhat simpler and more familiar problem. Imagine placing a single charged impurity into a dielectric medium. The charge is a source for an electric field,

$$\nabla \cdot \underset{\sim}{E}(x) = \rho(x)$$

2.

where $\rho(x)$ is the total charge density in the medium. By Gauss' Theorem a long range electric field is thereby generated as long as the charge Q inside a sphere centered at x is different from zero,

$$|E| \sim Q/r^2 \qquad\qquad 3.$$

However, the medium (analogous to the vacuum of a field theory) may be so polarizable that charge flows toward the impurity until it is exactly and completely neutralized, i.e. Q = 0. Then the long range electric field of Eq. 3 disappears and the impurity only effects the medium within a finite distance ξ, say.[11] For distances much less than ξ, the system's screening length, the impurity's charge can be felt with almost full strength. For example, an experimental probe with high spatial resolution would detect a charge Q at position x. However, for distances large compared to ξ, no electric field exists. Thus, the conducting ground state of the system has dramatically altered the long distance properties of the theory, while leaving the short distance properties identical to those of a theory with a non-conducting ground state. The low energy excitations of the conducting system are chargeless and interact through short range forces, although the local, short distance degrees of freedom are pointlike, mobile charges.

Consider again the quark field theory problem. Here we wish to eliminate ("screen") fermion quarks from the physical spectrum, i.e. we seek a natural dynamical mechanism which ensures that the asymptotic states of the theory all have triality zero.[12] This suggests that we consider three triplet models because they possess color currents of SU(3)' in addition to the usual SU(3) currents. We will later discuss models for screening these color currents. Then, assuming the success of such a scheme, the only allowed stable asymptotic states of the theory would be color singlets. Since color singlets necessarily do not carry triality, the quarks will not be physical particles.

A very simple (abelian) example of the elimination of a quantum number might appear in electrodynamics. Define a quantum number f as follows: -1 for each fermion or anti-fermion and +1 for each boson. Then

$$f = (-1)^{N_f + N_{\bar{f}}} = (-1)^{N_f - N_{\bar{f}}} = (-1)^Q$$

where $N_{f(\bar{f})}$ is the number of fermions (anti-fermions) in a state. So, if we have a mechanism which completely screens charge Q, then the physical sectors of the theory necessarily have $f = +1$ (bosons). The model which we turn to now is just of this type. Later our discussion will return to model building and the difficult problems which must be surmounted in the construction of one with realistic quantum numbers and algebraic structure.

A very simple but instructive example of complete screening was offered by Schwinger in 1962.[13] The theory is simply quantum electrodynamics in 1 space - 1 time dimensions. Its familiar Lagrangian reads,

$$\mathcal{L} = \bar{\psi} i \gamma^\mu \partial_\mu \psi - \tfrac{1}{4} F_{\mu\nu} F^{\mu\nu} - g \bar{\psi} \gamma^\mu \psi A_\mu \qquad \qquad 5.$$

where we have written the coupling constant g (instead of the traditional e) to emphasize that $\mathcal{L}$ will be interpreted as the Lagrangian governing the strong interactions of quarks. Accordingly, the term "charm" will replace "charge". Observe that in a world of 1 space - 1 time dimensions g has the dimensions of mass, so the theory is super-renormalizable. This ensures that high mass fluctuations in the quark field are absent. So, the theory should have a simple parton interpretation, a canonical light cone expansion, etc. This is particularly nice because it will allow us to test many parton model ideas about the final states of deep inelastic reactions.

It is not appropriate to present the details of a solution of 2 dimensional quantum electrodynamics here. Rather, we will sketch parts of it, discuss the physics involved and refer the reader to the literature for details. The equations of motion which follow from $\mathcal{L}$ read,

$$\gamma^\mu (i \partial_\mu - g A_\mu) \psi = 0 \quad , \quad \partial_\nu F^{\nu\mu} = j^\mu \qquad \qquad 6.$$

where[14]

$$j^\mu(x) = \text{Point Split} \left[g \bar{\psi} \gamma^\mu \psi \right] \quad , \quad F^{\mu\nu} = \partial^\mu A^\nu - \partial^\nu A^\mu \qquad 7.$$

The current j^μ is, of course, conserved,

$$\partial^\mu j_\mu = 0 \qquad \qquad 8.$$

The theory also contains an axial current,

$$j_5^\mu = g \bar{\psi} \alpha \gamma^\mu \psi \quad , \quad \alpha = \gamma_0 \gamma_1 \qquad \qquad 9.$$

which one might guess (formally) should also be conserved. However, this is not true and a careful discussion shows that the conservation of axial current is spontaneously broken,[15]

$$\partial^\mu j_\mu^5 = - \frac{g^2}{2\pi} \epsilon^{\mu\nu} F_{\mu\nu} \qquad \qquad 10.$$

In two dimensions j^μ and j_5^μ are very simply related. A little excercise in Dirac algebra shows that,

$$j_5^\mu = \epsilon^{\mu\nu} j_\nu \qquad \qquad 11.$$

It then follows from Eqs. 8, 10 and 11 that,

$$(\Box + m^2)\, j^\mu = 0 \qquad \text{12.}$$

where $m^2 = g^2/\pi$, i.e. the vector current of the theory describes free, <u>massive</u> vector mesons. Therefore, the long range piece of the field $F^{\mu\nu}$ has disappeared. According to our earlier physical discussion, this leads us to expect complete screening of fermion number in this theory.

Since j^μ is conserved, it can be written as the curl of a scalar field ϕ,

$$j^\mu = \epsilon^{\mu\nu} \partial_\nu \phi \qquad \text{13.}$$

In a later illustration we shall interpret ϕ as a dipole density. This is sensible since Eq. 13 reads,

$$j^0 = \text{"charge density"} = \partial\phi/\partial z \;,\; j^1 = \text{"charge flux"} = -\partial\phi/\partial t \qquad \text{14.}$$

From Eqs. 12 and 13 it is clear that ϕ is a free, massive scalar field. Furthermore, from the equations of motion,

$$\Box A_\mu = j_\mu \qquad \text{15.}$$

in the Lorentz ($\partial^\mu A_\mu = 0$) gauge. From Eqs. 12 and 15, it is clear that $m^2 A_\mu + j_\mu$ satisfies a free, massless Klein-Gordon equation. In analogy with Eq. 13 it is convenient to introduce a free, massless (but unphysical[16]) field $\hat{\phi}$ such that,

$$m^2 A_\mu + j_\mu = \epsilon_{\mu\nu} \partial^\nu \hat{\phi} \qquad \text{16.}$$

Now turning to the Dirac equation we see that it is solved simply in terms of the auxiliary free fields ϕ and $\hat{\phi}$,

$$\psi(x) = \exp\left[-ig\alpha\, \Phi(x)\right] \cdot \chi(x) \qquad \text{17.}$$

where $\Phi(x) = (\hat{\phi} - \phi)/m^2$ and χ is a free, massless Dirac field. This completes the solution of the field theory.

To understand the complete screening of fermion number in this model, consider a 2 dimensional analog of $e^+e^- \to$ "virtual scalar photon" $\to$ hadrons. Let the external scalar current $s(x) = \bar{\psi}(x)\psi(x)$ couple weakly into the two dimensional theory of quarks.[17] The process "virtual current" $\to$ hadrons is governed by the imaginery part of the matrix element

$$S(x) = i\langle 0|\, T\, s(x)\, s(0)\, |0\rangle \qquad \text{18.}$$

From Eq. 17 we have,

$$S(x) = i \langle 0| T \, \bar{\chi}(x) \, e^{-2ig\alpha\Phi(x)} \, \chi(x) \, \bar{\chi}(0) \, e^{-2ig\alpha\Phi(0)} \, \chi(0) \, |0\rangle \qquad 19.$$

which is simple to evaluate since only free fields are involved. Doing the contractions[1] we have,

$$S(x) = i \left[t_2 G_0(x) \right]^2 e^{-4\pi i \left\{ \left[(\Delta_F(0,x^2) - \Delta_F(0,0) \right] - \left[\Delta_F(m^2,x^2) - \Delta_F(m^2,0) \right] \right\}} \qquad 20.$$

where $G_0(x)$ ($\Delta_F(m^2, x^2)$) is the free fermi (bose) propagator. First consider the light-cone properties of $S(x)$. As $x^2 \to 0$ (x^2 small compared to $m^{-2} = \pi/g^2$, say) the boson propagators in Eq. 20 cancel leaving only the square of the fermion propagator. Thus, the light-cone properties (scaling laws) of $S(x)$ are characteristic of free fermi fields (Fig. 3). It is a separate question to ask what physical particles appear in the intermediate states which build up the scaling law. Recalling that,

$$-4\pi i \left[\Delta_F(0,x^2) - \Delta_F(0,0) + \Delta_F(m^2,0) \right] = \ln(x^2 - i\epsilon) \qquad 21.$$

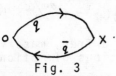

Fig. 3
Light-Cone Behavior
of S(x)

we see that the fermion singularity in $S(x)$ is cancelled and,

$$S(x) = \text{const.} \cdot e^{4\pi i \Delta_F(m^2, x^2)} \qquad 22.$$

Expanding the exponential it is clear that only massive bosons appear in the intermediate states (Fig. 4). In fact, the cancellation of fermion singularities from matrix elements of currents as illustrated here is a general property of the theory.[18]

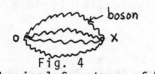

Fig. 4
Physical Spectrum of S(x)

The physics behind these results can be understood in a more transparent semi-classical discussion of $e^+e^- \to$ hadrons.

Consider an initial state of a quark and a anti-quark leaving the point $(z,t) = (0,0)$ with momenta $-q/2$ and $q/2$, respectively. Represent this state by c-number external currents,

$$j_0^{ext} = g\,\delta(z-t) \quad , \quad j_1^{ext} = g\,\delta(z-t) \qquad \text{for } z > 0$$
$$j_0^{ext} = -g\,\delta(z-t) \quad , \quad j_1^{ext} = g\,\delta(z+t) \qquad \text{for } z < 0 \qquad 23.$$

The generalizations of Eqs. 12 and 13 to incorporate an external current then lead straight-forwardly to an equation for the induced q-number dipole density,

$$(\Box + m^2)\,\phi = g\,m^2\,\theta(t+z)\,\theta(t-z) \qquad 24.$$

which is easily solved,

$$\phi(z,t) = g\,\Theta(t+z)\,\Theta(t-z) - g\,\Delta_R(m^2,x^2) \quad , \quad t^2 > z^2 \qquad 25.$$

Here $\Delta_R(m^2,x^2)$ is the familiar retarded commutator. Many crucial properties of complete screening and the parton model interpretation of this theory can be read directly off Eq. 25. Since $\Delta_R(m^2,x^2)$ is well approximated by $\Theta(t+z)\Theta(t-z)$ near the light cone ($x^2 \ll m^{-2}$) and by $\exp(-m|x|)$ for $|x|$ large, ϕ vanishes near the light cone and tends to a constant (g) when $|x| \gg m^{-1}$ (Fig. 5). The polarization

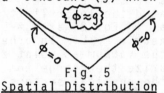

Fig. 5
Spatial Distribution
of the Dipole Density

charge $j^\circ = \partial\phi/\partial z$ is found wherever ϕ varies. Therefore, j° approaches the light-cone as $t \to \infty$ and is of just the right magnitude (g) to exactly neutralize the outgoing quarks. One can read off Eq. 25 that the polarization charge lies within a distance $(m^2 t)^{-1}$ of the light cone as soon as $t \gg m^{-1}$. Once this distance is of order q^{-1} in the center of mass frame, the polarization charge can neutralize the quarks. This occurs in a time $t \sim q/m^2$. In other words, the quark propagates as if it were free for times which grow with q - this is just as the parton model assumes and means that scaling laws in this theory will be identical to the theory of free quarks. The fact that the time till neutralization grows proportionally with q also justifies the semi-classical treatment sketched here. (The semi-classical treatment makes sense until the polarization charges catch the quarks. At this point the quarks have only lost a finite fraction of their initial energy, and are still on the light cone.) The formal discussion of S(x) provides the last link in the calculation - once the polarization charge has caught the quark, neutralization of the fermion <u>always</u> occurs.

The flow of polarization charge gives rise to a spectrum of free, massive bosons whose distribution in momentum space is easily computed. Since the equation governing ϕ is Lorentz invariant, it follows that the momentum space distribution of bosons must be boost invariant. Therefore, the boson distribution should be flat on the rapidity axis and the multiplicity of hadrons produced in $e^+e^- \to$ hadrons should grow logarithmically with the center of mass energy of the reaction. A detailed calculation confirms this argument and shows that the height of the rapidity distribution is unity[19] (as dictated by energy conservation). Final state particle distributions of this type have been guessed within the parton model.[20]

The disappearance of the fermions from this theory is so striking that it is worthwhile to consider it again before turning to other questions. It is useful to solve the model in the Coulomb gauge because then the hamiltonian

110

is positive and the theory has a sensible probability
interpretation. When this is done, the Coulomb gauge
analog of Eq. 17 becomes[1],

$$\chi_R(z,t) = \exp\left\{ ig \int_{-\infty}^{z} \psi^\dagger (1+\alpha) \psi \, dz'/m^2 \right\} \cdot \psi_R(z,t) \qquad 26.$$

where the subscript R denotes a fermion moving to the right.
This result means that a right moving normal mode (recall
that χ_R satisfies a free Dirac equation) consists of a fermion created by ψ_R plus a trail of quark-anti-quark pairs
(Fig. 6). It is also interesting to ask where the net

··x o x o x o $\overset{q}{\underset{x}{}}$ $\overset{\bar{q}}{\underset{o}{}}$ $\overset{q}{\underset{x}{}}$ charge resides in such a state.

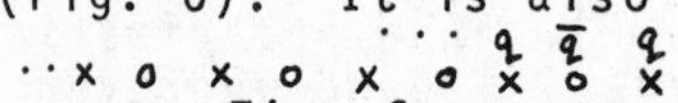

Fig. 6   If one terminated the lower limit
A "Fermion" Normal Mode of the integral in Eq. 26 at z =-L,
then, in fact, the "charge" is found near z = -L. In other
words, when a fermion is placed into the vacuum at point z,
a string of pairs materialize and polarize the charge to
infinity. This mechanism causes all the physical sectors
of the theory to be "chargeless".

Obviously many features of this simple model are
special to 2 dimensional space-time. It is not clear how
many aspects of the model will generalize to a more sensible
theory. However, one thing is for sure: complete screen-
is not special to two dimensions. For example, there are
superconducting wires, films, solids, etc. A simple four
dimensional field theory with complete screening is afforded
by the simplest Higg's model[21] which is described by the
Lagrangian,

$$\mathcal{L} = -\tfrac{1}{4} F_{\mu\nu} F^{\mu\nu} - (\partial_\mu + ig A_\mu)\varphi^*(\partial^\mu - ig A^\mu)\varphi - \mu^2 \varphi^* \varphi - \lambda(\varphi^*\varphi)^2 \qquad 27.$$

where φ is a complex scalar field and $\mu^2 < 0$. Letting $g \to 0$,
we recognize the original Goldstone model[22] in which phase
transformation symmetry ($\varphi \to e^{i\lambda}\varphi$) is spontaneously broken
and φ develops a vacuum expectation value $(-\mu^2/2\lambda)^{1/2}$. The
particle content of that theory consists of two scalar
fields of mass zero and $-2\mu^2$ each. When the long range
force is turned back on ($g \neq 0$), the spontaneous symmetry
breaking becomes physically more significant because global
phase transformations are generated by the total "charge"
operator. Since φ has developed a vacuum expectation value,
its phase is fixed and the total charge operator is forced
to vanish identically, Q=0. Therefore, it must be that
the photon dynamically acquires a mass and that the theory
can be written in terms of chargeless (gauge invariant)
fields. To see this write the scalar field in the form,

$$\varphi = (\langle 0|\varphi|0 \rangle + \tilde{\varphi})\, e^{i\theta/\langle\varphi\rangle_0} \quad , \quad \langle\tilde{\varphi}\rangle_0 = 0 \qquad 28.$$

and make a gauge transformation which maps the field θ to zero,

$$A_\mu \to \tilde{A}_\mu = A_\mu - \frac{1}{g}\frac{1}{\langle\varphi\rangle_0}\partial_\mu\theta \qquad 29.$$

When $\mathcal{L}$ is written in terms of $\tilde{\varphi}$ and $\tilde{A}_\mu$, one finds,

$$\mathcal{L} = -\frac{1}{4}F_{\mu\nu}F^{\mu\nu} - g\langle\varphi\rangle_0^2\tilde{A}_\mu\tilde{A}^\mu + \partial_\mu\tilde{\varphi}\,\partial^\mu\tilde{\varphi} + 2\mu^2\tilde{\varphi}^2$$
$$+ g^2(2\langle\varphi\rangle_0\tilde{\varphi} + \tilde{\varphi}^2)\tilde{A}_\mu\tilde{A}^\mu - \lambda(4\langle\varphi\rangle_0\tilde{\varphi}^3 + \tilde{\varphi}^4) \qquad 30.$$

Therefore, as claimed, the gauge dependent field θ has disappeared, $\tilde{A}_\mu$ has developed a mass $g\langle\varphi\rangle_0$ and the scalar field $\tilde{\varphi}$ has a mass $-2\mu^2 > 0$. Thus, we have complete screening and no total "charm" in the physical Hilbert space.

Of course, this model is not realistic (its quarks are bosons, etc.), but it does illustrate complete screening in a dimension independent fashion. One might guess that the Higg's model with charmed fermions, abelian gauge field and charmed bosons would also be the basis for a better model. However, this is not the case, i.e. the fermions are not removed from the physical spectrum of states. It is true that the gauge symmetry of the theory is spontaneously broken and the gauge fields acquire a mass. However, "charm" is carried by both the fermi and bose fields, so although the total charm in the theory vanishes, this does not force the absence of fermions from the asymptotic states. When a charmed fermion is introduced into the vacuum, its charm is completely screened by charmed bosons as well as charmed fermions. Thus, this model does not have a simple algebraic connection between fermion number and charm which forces charmless states to be fermion-free.

These considerations suggest that a realistic model should involve a multiplet of fermi quarks coupled to massless non-abelian gauge fields. The red, white and blue quark scheme[23] is one possibility - the eight SU(3)' currents would couple to the non-abelian gauge fields, complete screening of the color currents would occur dynamically and the physical spectrum would consist of only SU(3)' singlets. Three triplet models are also popular because they are thought to account for the symmetries of the hadron spectrum. Clearly the speculative model proposed here is much more sophisticated than any example of complete screening produced to date. Its study will require the development of new techniques. When Schwinger first discussed complete screening, he speculated that his mechanism would occur in four dimensional theories of fermions and gauge fields when the coupling constant exceeds a certain critical value. This speculation is eleven years old but virtually unstudied.

Now consider the second major assumption of the parton model - that the forces which bind the partons into hadrons are finite at short distances. This assumption is crucial in the establishment of the impulse approximation and, as discussed earlier, is not generally expected in four dimensional field theories. To study how the strength of interaction varies with distances in field theory one uses the modern form of the renormalization group.[24] In this approach there is a dimensionless coupling constant $g(\lambda)$ which, roughly speaking, is the strength of interactions between quanta having momenta $\lambda\hat{p}$, where $\hat{p}$ is some convenient reference space-like momentum. As λ grows large the momenta of the interacting quanta all become arbitrarily large and space-like so $g(\lambda)$ then governs the short distance interactions in the theory. If one further assumes that the masses of the field theory should not influence the short distance (very large momenta) properties of the theory, then $g(\lambda)$ should satisfy an equation of the form,[25]

$$\lambda^2 \, \partial g_\lambda^2 / \partial \lambda^2 = \Psi(g_\lambda^2)$$

31.

where Ψ is a dimensionless function.

Consider the various behaviors Ψ can have for small values of the coupling constant $g(\lambda)$. Either Ψ is positive (Fig. 7a) or negative (Fig. 7b). In the first case Eq. 31 implies that $g(\lambda)$ increases as λ increases.

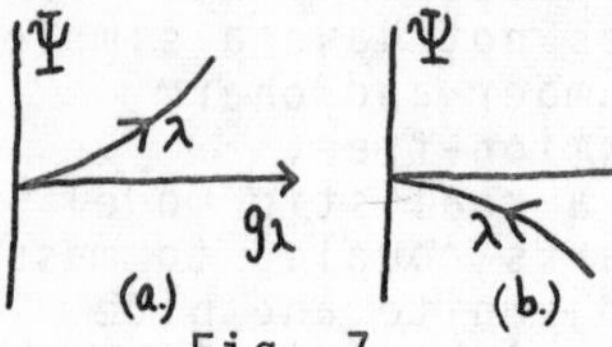

Fig. 7
Alternative Perturbative Behavior for Ψ

In other words the interaction strength grows stronger at short distances. Quantum electrodynamics in four dimensions has this property which can be understood simply in terms of screening: a positive charge when inserted into the vacuum polarizes its neighborhood thereby partially neutralizing its net charge. Thus, the interactions between charges are weaker at greater distances and stronger at shorter distances. If Ψ is negative near the origin, then interactions vanish at short distances[26]. Theories having this property but existing in less than four dimensions have been studied for some time.[27] Quantum electrodynamics in two dimensions is a simple, familiar example. Here the coupling constant g has dimensions of a mass, so one does not write a renormalization group equation for it directly. Rather, consider the dimensionless propagator for the massive vector meson,[28]

$$g^2(g^2) = -g^2 / \left(g^2 - g^2/\pi\right)$$

32.

Then $g^2(q^2)$ satisfies the renormalization group equation,

$$\lambda^2 \frac{\partial}{\partial \lambda^2} g^2(\lambda) = -g^2(\lambda)\left[1 - g^2(\lambda)/\pi\right] = \Psi(g_\lambda^2) \qquad 33.$$

and we see explicitly that Ψ is negative near the origin. In fact, Ψ has a second zero at $g^2(\lambda) = \pi$. From Eq. 32 it follows that $q^2 = 0$ at this second zero, so $g^2(\lambda=0) = \pi$ governs the long distance properties of the theory. An equivalent but perhaps physically more revealing discussion considers screening in configuration space. The "electric" field produced by an isolated charge is constant in strength in 1 space-1 time dimensions. So, the force between two charges g reads,

$$F = g^2 = \left(\frac{g^2}{r^2}\right) \cdot r^2 = g^2(r)/r^2 \qquad 34.$$

where we have identified a dimensionless interaction strength $g(r)$,

$$g(r) = g \cdot |r| \qquad 35.$$

So, $g(r)$ vanishes at small distances and grows as the charges separate in agreement with the more precise momentum space analysis. However, once r becomes large (greater than the Compton wavelength of the vector meson, $m^{-1} = \sqrt{\pi}/g$), Eqs. 34 and 35 do not capture the essential physics at work. The point is that once the charges become separated by a distance of order m^{-1}, a sizeable dipole density ϕ develops between them. Then polarization charges form around them neutralizing their net charges and eliminating their mutual long range interactions. Therefore,

$$g(r) \to 0 \quad , \quad r > m^{-1} \qquad 36.$$

as r grows large on the scale of m^{-1}, the screening length,
      Recently several authors[2] have discovered that non-abelian gauge theories can also have negative Ψ functions sufficiently close to the origin. These include theories in which a multiplet of fermions interact with non-abelian gauge mesons. As discussed earlier, such theories may be the dynamical basis of "screened" color quark models of hadrons. Needless to say this is an exciting possibility. The short distance behavior of these theories is actually quite subtle and not yet well understood. For example, the renormalizability of four dimensional gauge theories implies that $\Psi \sim \alpha g^4 + \cdots$ for small g^2. Eq. 31 then implies (when the constant α is negative) that $g^2(\lambda)$ approaches zero as $\lambda \to \infty$ only logarithmically,

$$g^2(\lambda) = g^2/(1 + b \log \lambda^2) \qquad 37.$$

where b is a constant which is model dependent and computable. Thus, only at enormous q^2 values can one really say that the interactions between constituents of field theory have vanished. This should be compared to the parton model interpretation of the "early" scaling apparently observed at SLAC - in the parton model one neglects parton-parton interactions once q^2 is greater than the "transverse momentum cutoff" ≈ 1 GeV/c^2. However, the early scaling hypothesis has never really been analyzed with much numerical care. In fact, in the parton model of spin 1/2 constituents the ratio σ_L/σ_T should behave as,

$$\sigma_L/\sigma_T \sim K^2/q^2 \qquad\qquad 38.$$

where K is the average transverse momentum fluctuation of the partons. However, the data favor $\sigma_L/\sigma_T \sim .10-.20$ over the q^2 interval from 1 to 10, so perhaps the non-abelian gauge theory estimate,

$$\sigma_L/\sigma_T \sim O\left(\ln q^2\right)^{-1} \qquad\qquad 39.$$

is not bad. Anyway, more data analysis is necessary to really decide.

The scaling properties of field theories are neatly studied via Wilson's operator product expansion.[29] In this method one finds that the most fundamental information in the scaling function νW_2 can be extracted by computing the q^2 dependences of its moments,[30]

$$\int_0^1 x^{m-2} \, \nu W_2\left(q^2, x\right) dx = f_m\left(q^2\right) \qquad\qquad 40.$$

The point is that these moments isolate individual local operators whose short distance scaling properties are simply reflected in the q^2 dependence of Eq. 40.[31] In the simple theory of fermions and non-abelian gauge fields,[32]

$$f_m\left(q^2\right) \underset{\ln q^2 \to \infty}{\sim} \left(\frac{1}{\ln q^2}\right)^{\delta_m} \qquad\qquad 41.$$

where $\{\delta_m\}$ comprises a sequence of increasing computable small numbers. In particular, $\delta_2 = 0$ and $\delta_m \to \text{const.} \cdot \log n$ as $n \to \infty$. Therefore, as q^2 grows one should expect the present $\nu W_2(q^2 \approx 10, x)$ to shift toward lower x values in such a way that the area under the curve is preserved (Fig. 8). If these theories apply to the present generation of experiments, then the change of νW_2 with q^2 will be very slow and difficult to detect. Clearly the q^2 dependence of νW_2 will be most apparent near $x = 1$, but even here the effect might be small since the constant in the relation $\delta_m \to \text{const. } \log n$ is small ($\sim 1/3$) for simple

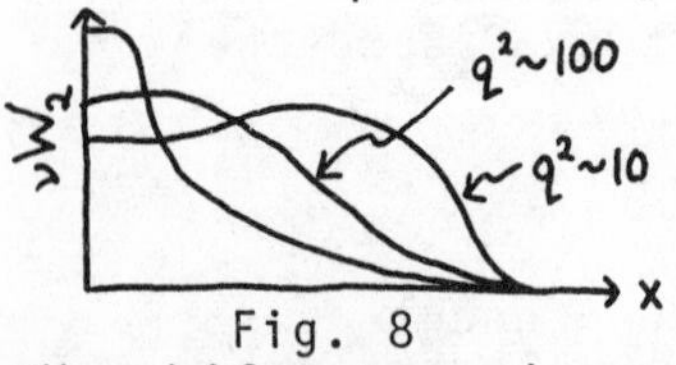

Fig. 8
νW_2 shifts toward $x=0$ as $q^2 \to \infty$.

theories.[32] Familiar parton model sum rules will also be true in these theories, however the approach to the simple parton answers will again be logarithmic. For example, the n = 2 moment of νW_2 measures the mean-squared charge of the partons up to a $(\log q^2)^{-1}$ correction. This correction term may be sizeable. It suggests that parton model sum rules may not be numerically reliable at the present values of q^2. Certainly questions of this type deserve careful experimental analysis.

It may a priori appear surprising that these theories which are free at short distances violate Bjorken scaling at all. However, the following simple considerations should motivate the result. Think in terms of the parton model and suppose for a minute that the nucleon were really a point particle. Then νW_2 would scale and be given by a Born term $\sim \delta(x-1)$. However, according to the parton model nucleons are composite and scaling sets in only once q^2 is large enough to resolve the interparton spacing. When q^2 is this large, νW_2 scales and is a smooth distribution lying between x = 0 and 1, i.e. occupying smaller x values than the $\delta(x-1)$ Born term. Suppose now that the constituents presently thought to be pointlike really are composites of smaller constituents (labelled with a prime, say). Then, when q^2 is large enough to resolve the distances between the primed constituents, νW_2 will shift to a new scaling curve, $\nu W_2'$. Since each primed constituent must share the longitudinal momentum of its parent constituent, the new scaling curve $\nu W_2'$ will be shifted toward x=0 relative to νW_2 . However, since the total longitudinal momentum carried by the primed constituents must equal the longitudinal momentum of the target nucleon, the area under $\nu W_2'$ is the same as the area under νW_2 . If smaller constituents are really uncovered in a smooth way as q^2 increases, then νW_2 should vary as depicted in Fig. 8 (although in general the q^2 dependence could be much faster than logarithmic.[33])

These ideas show that to understand the q^2 dependence of $\nu W_2(q^2,x)$ one must estimate two effects: first, the rate at which the coupling constant $g(q^2)$ goes to zero as q^2 grows; and second, the rate at which smaller constituents are resolved as q^2 increases. For the gauge theories of interest, the first rate is logarithmic. The second rate is also logarithmic. This follows because once $g(q^2)$ is small, one can use perturbation theory to calculate the distribution of primed constituents in a constituent. In practice at fixed q^2 a primed constituent appears in a graph whenever a substantial contribution occurs from the region of configuration space where two constituents are closer in transverse separation than q^{-1} Then these two constituents cannot be resolved by the external probe and are labelled with a prime.[34] But small transverse distances contribute with logarithmic

strength in simple graphs, so the rate at which primed
constituents are uncovered is logarithmic as claimed.
Since the two rates are comparable, i.e. new structure
in the theory is resolved at the same rate that the
interactions between the structures fall to zero, it is
not until q^2 is so large that νW_2 is concentrated at
the origin that interactions between the constituents are
really negligible.

This crude discussion just barely scratches the surface
of the new physics contained in non-abelian gauge theories.
The subject begs for a simple physical explanation of the
fact that $\frac{d\Psi}{d}$ is negative at short distances. Present developments and formulations of gauge theories do not seem to
help here.

It is unclear how one should interpret the work done
to date on the asymptotic short distance properties of
these theories. Since logarithms appear often, it is
hard to guess if leading asymptotic calculations should
sensibly be compared with present data. Also, near $q^2 = 0$
strong interaction coupling constants are large and it
is hard to guess how quickly they fall to small values
(assuming they do!) where the asymptotic calculations
apply. Clearly much more work remains to be done before
drawing firm conclusions. Of course, many of these calculations appear beyond our present technical ability because they involve large coupling constants.

If the gauge theory interpretations of assumptions 1.
and 2. survive their many theoretical and experimental
hurdles, then our understanding of hadrons will have improved enormously. A black cloud lingers on the horizon,
however. It appears that the total cross section for
$e^+e^- \rightarrow$ "single virtual photon" $\rightarrow$ hadrons is too large to
be accomodated by simple quark models and is not scaling.[35]
Perhaps charmed hadrons[36] are being produced and strong
interactions are strong at short distances!

ACKNOWLEDGMENT

The first draft of this talk was prepared at the
Stanford Linear Accelerator Center. The author (J.K.)
thanks Prof. Sidney Drell and the members of the SLAC
theory group for their comments and hospitality.

REFERENCES

*Supported in part by the Israeli Academy of Sciences.
†Speaker, supported in part by the National Science
Foundation.
‡Supported in part by the National Science Foundation.

1. A. Casher, J. Kogut and Leonard Susskind, Phys. Rev.
    Lett. 31, 792 (1973) and Tel Aviv University pre-
    print - 373-73, June 1973.
2. G. t'Hooft, Marseilles Conference on Gauge Theories
    June 1972. H.D. Politzer, Phys. Rev. Lett. 30, 1346
    (1973). D.J. Gross and F. Wilczek, Phys. Rev. Lett.
    30, 1343 (1973).
3. The kinematics of infinite momentum frames of this
    variety are discussed in J. Kogut and Leonard
    Susskind, Physics Reports 8C, 75 (1973).
4. In the two dimensional model to be discussed the
    light-like propagation of the struck constituent is
    modulated by a smooth eikonal phase.
5. R.P. Feynmann, Phys. Rev. Lett. 23, 1415 (1969).
6. S.D. Drell, D.J. Levy and T.-M. Yan, Phys. Rev.
    Lett. 22, 744 (1969).
7. J. Kogut, D.K. Sinclair and Leonard Susskind, Phys.
    Rev. D7, 3637 (1973), and D.K. Sinclair, unpublished.
8. Here "low" means large on the scale of masses in the
    Lagrangian, ten times a typical mass, say, while
    "high" means unbounded.
9. Strictly speaking this is the case only when the
    short distance interactions in the theory are
    characterized by a single number g*, a non-zero
    solution of the renormalization group. In general,
    more complicated behavior is expected and the rel-
    ative importance of frequency fluctuations can vary
    from one scale to the next.
10. S. Adler and W.-K. Tung, Phys. Rev. Lett. 22, 978
    (1969), and R. Jackiw and G. Preparata, Phys. Rev.
    Lett. 22, 975 (1969) and many other authors.
11. As in a superconductor in which the field falls as
    exp(-r/ξ) at large distances.
12. Following Peter A. Carruthers, Introduction to
    Unitary Symmetry (Interscience Publishers, New York,
    1966) the triality of the basic 3 of SU(3) is 1, of
    3 x 3 is 2, of 3 x 3 x 3 is 0, etc.
13. J. Schwinger, Phys. Rev. 128, 2425 (1962), and
    Theoretical Physics (International Atomic Energy
    Agency, Vienna, 1963), pg. 89.
14. A careful, point split definition of $j^{\mu}(x)$ is essen-
    tial here, J. Schwinger, Phys. Rev. Lett. 3, 296
    (1959).
15. This is the two dimensional analog of the Adler-

118

Bell-Jackiw anomaly. S.L. Adler, Phys. Rev. 177, 2426 (1969), J.S. Bell and R. Jackiw, Nuovo Cimento 60A, 47 (1969). See also J. Steinberger, Phys. Rev. 76, 1180(1949) and J. Schwinger, Phys. Rev. 82, 664 (1951).

16. The equal time commutator of $\hat{\phi}$ and $d\hat{\phi}/dt$ has the "wrong" sign.

17. The operator s(x) can create an initial state of a quark and an anti-quark on opposite branches of the light cone. Since there are no transverse photons in two dimensions, j^{μ} cannot do this.

18. As calculated here the matrix elements of s(x) do not have good cluster properties. Good cluster properties can be obtained by a more suitable choice of the vacuum, as discussed by J. Lowenstein and J. Swieca, Ann. Phys. (NY) 68, 172 (1971). These authors also realized that there are no asymptotic fermions in Schwinger's model. Regretfully their work was not known to us when reference 1 was prepared. One of us (L.S.) thanks Sidney Coleman for a conversation on these points.

19. This theory offers an explicit example of light cone dominance in $e^+e^- \rightarrow$ hadron + anything and growing, $\bar{n}(q^2) \sim \ln q^2$, multiplicities. There has been much confusion concerning this in the literature. For general clarifications see J. Ellis and Y. Frishman, Phys. Rev. Lett. 31, 135 (1973).

20. S.M. Berman, J.D. Bjorken, and J. Kogut Phys. Rev. D4, 3388 (1971), R.P. Feynman, Photon-Hadron Interactions (Benjamin, New York 1972).

21. P.W. Higgs, Phys. Lett. 12, 132 (1964), Phys. Rev. Lett. 13, 508 (1964), and Phys. Rev. 145, 1156 (1966); F. Englert and R. Brout, Phys. Rev. Lett. 13, 321 (1964); G.S. Guralnik, C.R. Hagen and T.W.B. Kibble, Phys. Rev. Lett. 13, 585 (1964); T.W.B. Kibble Phys. Rev. 155, 1554 (1967).

22. J. Goldstone, Nuovo Cimento 19, 154 (1961); J. Goldstone, A. Salam and S. Weinberg, Phys. Rev. 127, 965 (1962).

23. For a recent discussion of color quark models see H. Fritzsch and M. Gell-Mann, in Proceedings of the Sixteenth International Conference on High Energy Physics, The University of Chicago and National Accelerator Laboratory, 1972, edited by J.D. Jackson and A. Roberts (National Accelerator Laboratory, Batavia, IL., 1973), Vol. 2, p. 135.

24. K.G. Wilson, Phys. Rev. D3, 1818 (1971), and references cited therein.

25. This form of the renormalization group is appropriate for a theory with one dimensionless coupling constant. For more general cases see reference 24.

26. This supposes that $g(\lambda \approx 0)$ lies in the free field domain. See reference 24. This assumption is a working hypothesis in the investigations done to date on non-abelian gauge theories.

27. For a recent review of such theories see K.G. Wilson and J. Kogut, "The Renormalization Group and the ϵ Expansion", Institute for Advanced Study preprint COO-2220-2 (to appear in Physics Reports).

28. This is just the gauge invariant $g_{\mu\nu}$ piece of the propagator. See R.J. Crewther, S.-S. Shei and T.-M. Yan, CLNS-214, (March, 1973) for a thorough discussion.

29. K.G. Wilson, Phys. Rev. 179, 1499 (1969).

30. G. Mack, Nucl. Phys. B35, 592 (1971).

31. A clear exposition and application of this idea appears in N. Christ, B. Hasslacher and A. Mueller, Phys. Rev. D6, 3543 (1972).

32. D.J. Gross and F. Wilczek, NAL-PUB-73/79 (July, 1973) H. Georgi and H.D. Politzer, Harvard preprint (revised version, August 1973).

33. The physical picture briefly described here can be developed in considerable detail to treat field theories whose short distance interactions are characterized by a single dimensionless coupling constant $g* \neq 0$. The results of formal field theory studies (and some additional ones) have been obtained thereby in a physical, transparent fashion. See J. Kogut and Leonard Susskind, "A Scale Invariant Parton Model" (to appear in Phys. Rev.) and A. Casher, J. Kogut and Leonard Susskind, "Consequences of the Scale Invariant Parton Model for Deep Inelastic Neutrino Scattering" (to appear in Phys. Rev.).

34. This argument presupposes that the reader is familiar with the modern formulation of the renormalization group, K. Wilson's momentum-space slicing technique and references 33.

35. A. Litke et.al., Phys. Rev. Lett. 30, 1189 (1973).

36. A popular speculation is that charmed hadrons and/ or Han-Nambu quarks (M.Y. Han and Y. Nambu, Phys. Rev. 139, B1006 (1965)) are being produced. The possibility of new structure appearing in strong interactions at distances of the order 10^{-15} has been discussed by M.S. Chanowitz and S.D. Drell, Phys. Rev. Lett. 30, 807 (1973).

UNIFIED GAUGE THEORIES OF SPIN $J \leq 1$[*]

M. B. Halpern

Department of Physics and Lawrence Berkeley Laboratory
University of California, Berkeley, California 94720

ABSTRACT

In this talk, I want to give an overview of structure and development within the unified gauge theory of
strong, weak, and electromagnetic interactions. This type
of model gives an explicit renormalizable description of
all known particles with spin $J \leq 1$, plus a few conjectured ones like W-mesons etc. By "all", I mean all,
including such diverse particles as ρ-mesons, quarks,
pion, kaons, Buddha (1235) meson, ρ' (1600), leptons,
etc. In these models, all spectra and forces between
particles derive from spontaneously broken gauge invariance and incorporate the ideas of Yang and Mills,[1]
Weinberg,[2] Salam,[3] 'tHooft,[4] and others.

I will begin by briefly reviewing the structure of
these models, go on to describe some of the more striking
results therein, and finally end by comparing these
models with the "underlying-field" or quark models
advocated by other workers. Although there are some
important differences, it appears that, in general, our
models here (M-models) are closely connected to the quark
models--the former providing a lower energy explicit
realization of the latter. The M-models also provide
us with a surprising number of high-energy bonuses.

GAUGE THEORY OF HADRONS

As a matter of history, the hadronic sector[5] of the M-models
was written first. With K. Bardakci, we constructed models of the
type

$$q_L \qquad V_L \qquad M_L$$
$$\Sigma$$
$$q_R \qquad V_R \qquad M_R$$

The theories can be written for $SU(n) \otimes SU(n)$, but I will talk generally in terms of $SU(3) \otimes SU(3)$. Here $(V_L \pm V_R)$ represent octets
of vector and axial-vector mesons. q is (say) a triplet of quarks
(or baryons). Σ is a $(3,\bar{3})$ pion-sigma field of the type you are
familiar with. The "magic" of the model is in the spin-zero fields
$M_{L,R}$, assumed to transform under the strong gauge group as

[*] Work supported in part by the U.S. Atomic Energy Commission.

$$M_{L,R} \;\to\; S_{L,R}\,M_{L,R}$$

where S is a local unitary transformation. Thus the M's transform as aggregates of zero-spin-triplets. They may be thought of as $3 \times N$ matrices with $N \geq 3$.

The point is that under spontaneous breakdown $\langle M_{L,R} \rangle \equiv \kappa$, all the vector mesons acquire mass. With $\langle \Sigma \rangle \equiv v$, the mass spectrum agrees with nature. In fact the model provides a renormalizable analogue of the "effective Lagrangians"[6] of some years back, and naturally incorporates essentially all of these older results.

Before passing onto nonstrong interactions, a number of remarks are worth making here.

(a) Mixing nature of the pion. Before spontaneous breakdown, there are two "pions" in the model: A $(3,\bar{3})$ pion in Σ, and an $(8,1)$ pion in M_L-M_R. A particular combination of these two is "eaten" as the A_1 acquires mass, leaving the one physical pion with mixed $SU(3) \otimes SU(3)$ classification. The mixing angle between $(3,\bar{3})$ and $(8,1)$ is $45°$, and we shall mention this later in connection with the pion's form factor. In spite of this large mixing, the symmetry breaking in the theory is predominantly $(3,\bar{3})$ via an induced linear term in Σ.

(b) P-particles. There are also some new pseudo-scalar particles left in the theory from the M's. Exemplary is the one we call P, with quantum numbers $I^G(J^P)C = 0^-(0^-)-$. This particle is not in the quark model and its observation would be very exciting. I shall say more about this later.

(c) Reggeization. At least the spin-one particles of these theories lie on Regge trajectories.[4] The Higgs' scalars M play the crucial role in these calculations. Presumably, this high energy "bonus" is related to the fact that the models are the flat slope limit of dual models.[8] Indeed, we like to think of our models as the "bottom" of the dual model, and expect that many lessons learned here may be of use in dual theory.

(d) Uniqueness. These explicit hadron models are more than a year old now, and we are not aware of any alternate models. It is likely they are unique.

INCLUSION OF NONSTRONG INTERACTIONS

Although the M's were introduced to give mass to vector mesons, as soon as we make them large enough to give hadronic vector meson masses $(N = 3$ above), we see that, inescapably, an extra gauge symmetry is allowed. With Bars and Yoshimura,[9] we identified this with the nonstrong gauge group

$$M \;\to\; M(S')^{-1}$$

With $N = 4$ (to suppress neutral $\Delta S = 1$ currents), the extension to leptons is extremely natural. Graphically, we write these theories

$$
\begin{array}{ccccc}
q_L & V_L & M_L & W_L & L \\
 & \Sigma & & \emptyset & \\
q_R & V_R & M_R & W_R & R
\end{array}
$$

where W_L, B are (say) Weinberg's gauge mesons, $\emptyset$ is his scalar, and L,R are leptons. Now the same spontaneous breakdown $\langle M \rangle = \kappa$ that gives strong vector masses also induces strong-not-strong mixing. The upshot is universal vector-meson dominance (in lowest order).

In these models, the relations among strong, weak, and electromagnetic interactions are quite intimate--and intriguing. For example, (a) the known hadrons "prefer" certain weak interaction theories: Weinberg's theory works with the minimum number of M-columns; other theories need many more scalars. Further, (b) the weak interactions feed back again on the strong, determining the direction $(3,\bar{3})$ and sometimes the magnitude of hadron symmetry breaking.[10] We shall return to this below.

$\rho'(1600)$ AND PION MASS MODELS

Bars and Lane[11] have studied an extended model of this type including the $\rho'(1600)$. It has the form

$$
\left.
\begin{array}{cc}
V_L & M_L \\
\Sigma & \\
V_R & M_R
\end{array}
\right\rangle \quad \rho'M' \quad .
$$

In this model, the (small) ratio $\Gamma(\rho' \to 2\pi)/\Gamma(\rho' \to 4\pi)$ is explained on the basis of $\rho\rho'$ mixing (and the pion "mixing" above). Actually, they attempted also to calculate the pion mass in this model. The pion can be taken as a pseudo-Goldstone meson, and the ρ' loop does give a mass. Unfortunately, the known ρ' total width demands a much too large pion mass. This is certainly not surprising, but is important to note that their result for the pion mass is an extremely slowly varying function of m_ρ^2 (slope $\sim 10^{-2}$). The model is also not easily extended to the weak interactions.

To rectify all these difficulties simultaneously, Bars, Lane, and I proposed another model,[12] completing the chiral symmetry, and predicting an A_1' particle. We wrote

$$q_L \quad V_L \quad M_L \;\vdots\; V'_L \quad M'_L \;\vdots\; W_L \quad L$$

$$\Sigma \qquad\qquad\vdots\;\; \Sigma' \qquad\quad\vdots\;\; \emptyset$$

$$q_R \quad V_R \quad M_R \;\vdots\; V'_R \quad M'_R \;\vdots\; B \quad R$$

which is the natural extension of the original unified model.[5,9] In fact, one can add more and more hadronic "blocks" (set off by dashed lines) if desired to include ρ'', etc. The model enjoys an exciting number of predictions

(a) The ρ' branching ratio is retained.

(b) The magnitude of the ρ' decay is in agreement with the pion mass! To within experimental errors, we calculate from ρ' data that $m_\pi^2 \sim 0.02$ (GeV)^2. Again, the result is extremely insensitive to precise masses of either ρ' or A'_1. (Intuitively, we expect $m_{A_1}^2 \sim 3$ GeV^2, where it would be in a dual model.) This small number out of hadronic parameters is nearly miraculous. It is easily traced to the small slope mentioned above for ρ' alone, and the fact that A'_1 contributes with the opposite sign.

In a current-algebraic treatment of the model, we can trace things even further: The smallness is due to the interplay of the two chiral symmetries (ρA_1 and $\rho' A'_1$)--and can be phrased in terms of asymptotic chiral symmetry and Weinberg's second spectral function sum rule. With these two ingredients, one can make a nonperturbative estimate of m_π^2, agreeing with our one-loop calculation.

(c) Form factors. In this model, baryon form factors are dipole because the photon must mix sequentially with just ρ' and then ρ. For the pion, the situation is different. The $(3,\overline{3})$ pion (in Σ) is dipole, but the $(8,1)$ pion (in M) is monopole. The physical pion is half-monopole-half-dipole! Quantitatively, for $|q^2| < 4$ (GeV)^2, we obtain

$$F_\pi(q^2) = \frac{m_\rho^2\, m_\rho'^2}{(q^2 - m_\rho^2)(q^2 - m_{\rho'}^2)}\left[1 - \frac{q^2}{4m_\rho^2}\right]$$

This form is a perfect fit to the data.[13] We are seeing then in the form factor data, direct evidence for the mixing structure of our pion.

INCLUSION OF THE BUDDHA

Recently, we[14] have also shown how to extend the basic models to include vector mesons with $CP = -1$, such as the $B(1235)$. The essential idea is that various vector mesons are included in a (large) "pseudospin" gauge multiplet generated by

$$F^{a\alpha} = t^a \lambda^\alpha \qquad (a = 0,1,2,3; \; \alpha = 0,1,\cdots,8) \; .$$

Here λ^α are the usual $SU(3)$ matrices, while t^a is a set of Pauli matrices (pseudospin). CP may be defined by spontaneous breakdown (or quarks), such that the particle content of the multiplet is

$$t_0 \sim \rho, \quad t_3 \sim A_1, \quad t_2 \sim B, \quad t_1 \sim \rho' \; .$$

With the inclusion of such particles in our models, we complete our description of all particle-types with $J \leq 1$.

The pseudospin symmetry evidently relates among "daughters" (relative to a Chew-Frautschi plot), and may be a quite useful tool for the future. For now, I will only mention some striking mass relations obtainable in such models: For example,

$$m_\rho^2 + m_{\rho'}^2 = 2m_B^2 = 2m_D^2 \; .$$

The first equality describes nature excellently, while the second predicts an isoscalar A_1 near the B. The particle $D(1285)$ is certainly a candidate for this. In another model, we find

$$m_\rho^2 + m_{\rho'}^2 = 2m_{A_1}^2 = 2m_h^2$$

where h is a (predicted) isoscalar B. This model is more like a dual model in that the ρ' here must have $m_{\rho'}^2 \sim 3/2$. This is the "first" ρ' of dual models, not the "second" (which has been observed).

These B-models also ameliorate the old problem $G_A = \frac{1}{2}$ of the original models. In the present models, as a reult of ρ,ρ' mixing, G_A comes out approximately correct.

CONNECTIONS WITH "QUARK" MODELS

In the models discussed above, all particles with spin $J \leq 1$ are represented by fields. Another type of model works in terms of quarks (and gluons) for the hadrons. I want to discuss the correspondences between these two classes of models. First, however, it is worth mentioning that these two approaches (explicit hadrons versus underlying field) are much older than gauge theories. The philosophical position that "explicit" theories (S-matrix, bootstrap, dual models, M-models, etc.) are complementary with the underlying field (quark, etc.) approach, the two being a fundamental "duality" of nature, is rather old and consistently attractive. I believe that, in many respects, we are seeing just this duality here.

Let me first explain that there is a one-to-one correspondence between our hadron models and quark models. We have been calling this a "correspondence" principle[9] for some time now: Suppose one has chosen, say in a quark model, a particular weak interaction characterized by some (local) transformations S' on the quarks

$$q^T \rightarrow q^T (S')^{-1} .$$

Here "T" means transpose. In particular, suppose N quarks are needed. Then to make the transition to an M-model, one throws away the quarks and uses instead the $3 \times N$ fields M

$$M \rightarrow M(S')^{-1} .$$

Thus, the quark theory gives rise "dynamically" to an explicit hadron model. The group theory of the two models is essentially the same. When a hadronic symmetry breaking is calculable in one it is calculable in the other.

There are some differences with regard to parity and hypercharge violation in the strong interactions. For example, in the quark model, parity violation of order α (from a weak loop) can always be rotated away by a redefinition of the quark field.[15] In the M-models, Bars[16] has shown that order α parity-violation occurs only where there are counterterms. Thus in the M-model parity violation can and must be set to order G_F by hand. I want to emphasize then that, contrary to certain claims, no order α parity violation appears in the M-models. The mechanism for this must, however, be viewed as "phenomenological"--presumably related to the fact that, after all, we do not have all hadrons.

There may be another way out. If "parity-conserving groups" are used for (say) the weak interactions, the order α parity violation may not occur. By "parity-conserving" I mean groups where parity is broken spontaneously, rather than by representation content. For example, in a weak interaction based on the "pseudospin" group above (with greatly suppressed but not zero second-class currents), "right" and "left" gauge groups are dynamically locked and no strong parity violating counterterms are available. In this sense, the parity problem may be telling us more about the weak than the strong interactions.

SCALING AND ASYMPTOTIC FREEDOM

Some months before the interesting ideas of asymptotic freedom,
Bars, Levy, and I[17] noticed that the M-models scale in perturbation
theory no worse than the gluon model. The point is that our models
show modified field current identities, again due to the Higgs'
scalars M,

$$J^\mu \sim (M + \kappa)^2 \rho^\mu .$$

Thus the currents have asymptotic dimension 3, as they should. In
parton language, we know that (current constituents) = (partons) and
so we get the dominant scaling mechanism as a "di-parton"

Explicit calculation verifies that this diparton state indeed gives
a nonvanishing and scaling W_1, as well as a νW_2. In the absence
of a Drell-Levy-Yan cutoff (i.e., the actual perturbation theory),
one also finds a logarithmic nonscaling contribution to νW_2.

Continuing without cutoff in the actual perturbation theory,
one would expect a resultant anomalous dimension, as in the
(Abelian) gluon model--i.e., it is doubtful that the M models are
asymptotically free.[18] The reason appears to be the Higgs' scalars.
In any case, one learns that vectors and Higgs scalars can give
nonvanishing contributions to W_1; this casts doubt on the standard
conclusion that known scaling implies only fermionic constituents.

This may be then another indication of the phenomenological
character of the M-realizations. The improvement over "old" Yang-
Mills, bringing things up to the level of Abelian gluon models, is
in my opinion another high energy "bonus". It would be interesting
to see if the situation improved as we added ρ', ρ'' $\cdots$ contributions, i.e., as we approached a more realistic description of the
hadrons.

P-PARTICLE

To conclude, I want to say some more about the characteristic
P-particle (C = -1) of the M-models. Except for P, the spectrum
of the model is perfect, predicting ρ, A_1, π, $\epsilon(700)$, $S^*(997)$. P
is a "second-class exotic" which inescapably appears in the models
as A_1 acquires mass. The mass of P itself is undetermined.
Bars and I have studied its role in the theory from other viewpoints.

In various scattering processes, we find that in general P "smooths" A_1 exchange, allowing unitarity bounds for the tree graphs. In particular $\underline{P}$ is essential in the Reggeization of A_1. Trajectories involving P give simple solutions to exchange degeneracy requirements. Indeed it appears that the M-models provide in general simple solutions to requirements of exchange degeneracy.

These studies have suggested some natural masses for P, being near 0 or 1 $(GeV)^2$. Surprisingly enough, Bars and I[19] have not been able to rule out P at either of these masses, though a $\underline{P}$ under the A_1 is more favorable. The discovery of this particular exotic would be very exciting for hadron spectroscopy.

REFERENCES

1. C. N. Yang and R. L. Mills, Phys. Rev. 96, 191 (1954).
2. S. Weinberg, Phys. Rev. Letters 19, 1264 (1967).
3. A. Salam, Elementary Particle Physics, edited by N. Svartholm (Almquist and Wiksells, Stockholm, 1968), p. 367.
4. G. 'tHooft, Phys. Letters 39B, 195 (1971); Nucl. Phys. B35, 167 (1971).
5. K. Bardakci and M. B. Halpern, Phys. Rev. D6, 696 (1972).
6. S. Gasiorowicz and D. A. Geffen, Rev. Mod. Phys. 41, 531 (1969), and references therein.
7. M. T. Grisaru, H. J. Schnitzer, and H. S. Tsao, Phys. Rev. Letters 30, 811 (1973).
8. J. L. Gervais and A. Neveu, Nucl. Phys. B46, 381 (1972).
9. I. Bars, M. B. Halpern, and M. Yoshimura, Phys. Rev. Letters 29, 969 (1972); Phys. Rev. D7, 1233 (1973). I. Bars and M. B. Halpern, Phys. Rev. D7, 3043 (1973).
10. K. Bardakci, Nucl. Phys. B51, 174 (1973).
11. I. Bars and K. Lane, Berkeley preprints. A similar model has been recently constructed by Fujikawa.
12. I. Bars, M. B. Halpern, and K. Lane, Hadronic Origin of the Pion Mass, to be published.
13. C. N. Brown et al., Phys. Rev. Letters 26, 991 (1971).
14. M. B. Halpern, Gauge Theories Including the Buddha, Lawrence Berkeley Laboratory Report LBL-2071, July 1973, to be published.
15. S. Weinberg, Current Algebra and Gauge Theories I, Phys. Rev. D8, 605 (1973).
16. I. Bars, Parity Violation and Comparisons Between Quark Schemes and M-Schemes···, to be published.
17. I. Bars, M. B. Halpern, and D. Levy, Scaling in Unified Gauge Theories, to be published in Phys. Rev.
18. D. J. Gross and F. Wilczek, Phys. Rev. Letters 30, 1343 (1973); H. D. Politzer, ibid., 1346 (1973). Also see G. 'tHooft, to be published.
19. I. Bars and M. B. Halpern, work in progress.

Chapter II
Hadron Spectroscopy and
Production Mechanisms

K^* R $\int$ $_T$ ^B_U ρ^-

Melosh

Constituent

Current

Exotics

$SU(6)_W$

SU(3) Quark Models

Amplitude Analysis

Regge Trajectories

Factorization

Exchange Degeneracy

HADRON SPECTROSCOPY*

J. L. Rosner†
Stanford Linear Accelerator Center
Stanford University, Stanford, Calif. 94305

ABSTRACT

Recent experimental and theoretical developments in the
field of hadronic resonances are reviewed.

INTRODUCTION

This review will deal with new developments in the mesons (Section II),
the baryons (Section III), and in resonance theory (Section IV). In past years,
these subjects were generally covered by three different rapporteurs. Consequently, I must apologize for being brief on some subjects, referring the
readers to some excellent "mini-reports" that cover certain topics in more
detail.

The field of hadron spectroscopy no longer consists of "bump-hunting".
The pattern of resonances is largely filled in and hasn't changed much recently. The emphasis has shifted instead to more detailed questions regarding the structure of pionic decays and electromagnetic transitions. These
problems are of considerable interest, just as atomic spectral line intensities and selection rules played a role in the development of quantum mechanics.

Experimental and theoretical developments in this new area of resonance physics have kept pace with one another. The study of the decays of
the B meson, and of the reactions $\pi N \to \pi \Delta$ and $\gamma N \to \pi N$ in the resonance
region, have been matched by renewed interest in symmetries beyond SU(3)
which can explain the new data.

Older questions of resonance physics continue to receive attention.
The successful classification of states according to the quark model is by
now a compelling regularity of the lowest-lying mesons (below ~ 1.7 GeV)
and baryons (below ~ 2 GeV). The gaps in this scheme are continuing to be
filled, while studies of "exotic" states — ones that do not fit the scheme —
are proceeding, and within the next year perhaps one will finally have evidence for one or two exotic baryon isomultiplets. In contrast, nearly thirty
meson isomultiplets and fifty baryon isomultiplets have been conclusively
observed which can be regarded as levels of a quark and an antiquark ($q\bar{q}$)
or three quarks (qqq), respectively.[1,2]

MESONS

Some new developments in meson resonances are shown in Table I.

* Work supported in part by U. S. Atomic Energy Commission under Contract No. AT-(11-1)-1764.
† Alfred P. Sloan Foundation Fellow. Permanent address: School of
Physics and Astronomy, University of Minnesota, Minneapolis, Minn.
55455.

Table I New meson data

L(q$\bar{q}$)	J^{PC} values	Remarks
1	1^{+-}	New B $\to \omega\pi$ analyses; predictions
	1^{++}	Predictions for A_1 decay
	0^{++}	$\pi\pi$, Kπ scattering $\delta \to \eta\pi$ observed again
2	3^{--}	Firmer evidence for g, K_N
	2^{-+}	Question of resonant nature of A_3
	1^{--}	ρ'? [Could also be kinematic effect or q$\bar{q}$ (L=0) state.]
Other effects, J^{PC} uncertain		Narrow bump in $\sigma_T(\bar{p}p)$, m $\sim$ 1930 GeV
		New $\bar{p}p \to \pi^+\pi^-$, K^+K^- differential cross sections, 0.8 to 2.4 GeV/c
		Possible J $\geq$ 4 K_N(2100)

1. Analyses of B decays

The B(1235) is a resonance whose J^P is almost certainly 1^+, and which decays to $\omega\pi$.[3,4] The helicity structure of the ω's is of interest in many models and higher symmetries.

We may define normalized helicity amplitudes F_λ such that

$$|F_0|^2 + 2|F_1|^2 = 1 .$$ (1)

A purely S-wave decay corresponds to $|F_0|^2 = |F_1|^2 = 1/3$. SU(6)$_W$, by virtue of its selection rule demanding that the third component of quark spin be conserved [$\Delta S_Z = 0$], implies $|F_0|^2 = 1$. In various new theories, $|F_0|^2$ need not be 1 but is constrained by other data. If we call the orbital angular momentum of quarks in a hadron L, $|F_0|^2$ turns out to be sensitive to $\Delta L_Z = 0$ and $|F_1|^2$ to $\Delta L_Z = \pm 1$ transitions. The latter are forbidden in SU(6)$_W$, but are certainly important, as we can gauge from B $\to \omega\pi$ data.

As of last year,[3] most analyses agreed that $|F_0|^2$ was less than 1/3, implying a detectable amount of D wave in B decay. One analysis (of 7 GeV/c π^+p data) seemed to imply no D wave at all.

Recently the 7 GeV/c π^+p data have been re-analyzed, leading to two values of $|F_0|^2$ in substantial accord with one another: depending on the method of analysis,[4,5]

$$|F_0|^2 = 0.16 \pm 0.04$$ (2)

or

$$|F_0|^2 = 0.12 \pm 0.04 \tag{3}$$

The former result allows for coherently produced 1^- and 0^- $\omega\pi$ background, while the latter allows for all J^P in the background but without interference. We have used the result (2) below for the sake of definiteness.

A new contribution from the Weizmann Institute[6] has studied $\pi^+ p \to B^+ p$ at 5 GeV/c and finds

$$|F_0|^2 = 0.01 \pm 0.07 \tag{4}$$

The two values, Eqs. (2) and (4), are shown in Fig. 1.

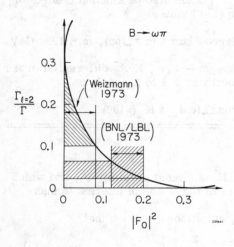

FIG. 1-- Values of $|F_0|^2$ obtained in analyses of $B \to \omega\pi$. LBL: Ref. 5; Weizmann: Ref. 6. The curve shows the fraction of D-wave ($\ell=2$) in the decay for each value of $|F_0|^2$.

Previous world data are compared with the new results in Table II (compiled from Ref. 3). The B decay involves roughly 6% D-wave $\omega\pi$, with $|F_0|^2 = 0.13 \pm 0.05$. (The errors are scaled because of the discrepancy between Ref. (5) and (6). The width is slightly above that of Ref. (7).

A recent study of $\pi^- n \to B^- p\pi^-$ is consistent with $|F_0|^2 = 0$, but no detailed analysis has been performed.[8]

Figure 1 and Table II show that the transversely polarized ω's certainly dominate in $B \to \omega\pi$. The world average for $|F_0|^2$ is now four standard deviations away from pure S wave; moreover, the Weizmann Institute group has yet to analyze all of their data. There has also been a high-statistics study of $\pi^+ p$ interactions at 13 GeV/c presented to this conference,[9] whose B signal is appreciable. We may expect some additions to Table II in the next year or two.

2. Predictions for A_1 and B decays

The ingredients for these predictions (whose theoretical basis will be discussed in Section IV) are: (i) $SU(6)_W \times 0(3)$ for the initial and final states, and (ii) single-quark selection rules for pion emission. The second is weaker than the assumption of an $SU(6)_W$-invariant decay. In addition we must fix parameters of the theory via one D-wave decay (e.g., $f_0 \to \pi\pi$ or $A_2 \to \rho\pi$) and one S-wave decay. The best source of the latter is the

Table II World B decay data

Reference[3]	Events	Γ_B	$|F_0|^2$	$\Gamma_{\ell=2}^{(\omega\pi)}/\Gamma^{(\omega\pi)}$
Illinois, 1970	686 ±35	144 ±21	.184 ±.051	3%
BDNPT 1970	226 ±20	120 ±20	.06 ±.10	13%
DGHMS 1972	130 ±14	125 ±30	.09 ±.07	9%
BNL/LBL 1973[5]	~1200	150 ±20	.16 (or .12) ±.04	4%
Weizmann, 1973[6]	≥ 500	156 ±22	.01 ±.07	25%
Total or average	~2750	141[a] ±14	.13 ±.05	6%

[a] Reference (7) quotes an average of 118 ± 8 MeV.

estimate

$$\Gamma_{\ell=0} (B \rightarrow \omega\pi) \simeq 130 \text{ MeV}, \tag{5}$$

based on Table II.

The output involves all partial widths for the decays

$$2^{++} \rightarrow 1^-0^-, \ 0^-0^-$$
$$1^{+\pm} \rightarrow 1^-0^- \tag{6}$$
$$0^{++} \rightarrow 0^-0^-$$

as well as the helicity structure for $1^{+\pm} \rightarrow 1^-0^-$.

There are different theories giving such predictions. They have the same algebraic structure but different kinematic factors. In the covariant approach of Ref. (10), based on a quark-pair-creation model suggested earlier,[11] the partial widths Γ_ℓ for decays into final states with orbital angular momentum ℓ behave as

$$\Gamma_\ell \sim p^{2\ell+1}/m_A^2 \quad \text{(Ref. 10)}, \tag{7}$$

where p is the magnitude of the CM 3-momentum and A is the decaying resonance. In the more recent approach[12-14] based on the work of Melosh[15] and PCAC, these partial widths all behave as[16]

$$\Gamma_\ell \sim p(m_A^2 - m_B^2)^2/m_A^2 \tag{8}$$

for any decay $A \to B\pi$, no matter what the ℓ of the $B\pi$ system.

Both theories have in common the addition of a new term describing pion emission:

$$\Delta L_z = \pm 1 \tag{9}$$

which allows for the transverse motion of quarks in an L-excited hadron. The old, $SU(6)_W$-invariant term with

$$\Delta L_z = 0 \tag{10}$$

is also retained.

The resulting predictions are shown in Table III.

Table III Predictions for A_1 and B decays[2]

		$A_1(1100) \to \rho\pi$	$B(1235) \to \omega\pi$	
$\Gamma_\ell = 0$	$p^{2\ell+1}$	460 ± 70		
	PCAC	175 ± 25	$130 \pm (\sim 20)$	
	Expt.	?	input	
$\Gamma_{\ell=2}$	$p^{2\ell+1}$	≈ 2	14	from $A_2 \to \rho\pi$, or
	PCAC	≈ 8	24	$f_0 \to \pi\pi$
	Expt.	?	$\simeq 8$	
$|F_0|^2$	$p^{2\ell+1}$	.40	.08	
	PCAC	.54	.04	
	Expt.	?	$.13 \pm .05$	

Phase constraint (Ref. 10):

$$2\left(\frac{F_1}{F_0}\right)_{A_1 \to \rho\pi} = \left(\frac{F_0}{F_1}\right)_{B \to \omega\pi} + 1 .$$

(Exact in PCAC approach;[12-14] approximate in $p^{2\ell+1}$ approach.[10])

Table III indicates a rather prominent and well-defined A_1, especially in the PCAC approach (which has some other advantages). The D-wave admixture in $A_1 \to \rho\pi$ should be clearly visible. The input (5) may have been an overestimate, as it would seem difficult to hide so broad an A_1 under diffractive background. (Such background is almost certainly present in $\pi^- p \to \rho^0 \pi^- p$.[17]) The "resonant" A_1 still has not shown up, and if it goes undetected a while longer we should begin to worry.

One further test of these predictions involves decays of 0^+ mesons, to which we now turn.

3. Predictions for $\delta(970) \to \eta\pi$ and $K_N(0^+) \to K\pi$

Table IV shows the status of some predictions similar to those of Table III but for 0^+ decays.

Table IV

	$\Gamma(\delta(970) \to \eta\pi)$ (MeV)	$\Gamma(K_N(1100) \to K\pi)$ (MeV)
$p^{2\ell+1}$	185 ± 30	450 ± 70
PCAC	90 ± 15	485 ± 75
Expt.	$60 ^{+50}_{-30}$ [a]	?

[a] Ref. 18.

The experimental width for δ (assuming 100% $\eta\pi$ decay), is based on a new experiment[18] which studies

$$\pi^- p \to \delta^- p$$
$$\quad\quad\quad\; \hookrightarrow \eta\pi^-$$
$$\quad\quad\quad\quad\;\; \hookrightarrow \gamma\gamma \tag{11}$$

at 4.5 GeV/c, resulting in a cross section of only about $2\mu b$ for δ^- production. Reference 7 quotes $\Gamma_\delta = 50 \pm 30$ MeV.

It thus appears that unless the B is <u>much</u> narrower than in Eq. (5), the $p^{2\ell+1}$ factor is unreliable for S-wave decays, and should be replaced by the PCAC factor of Eq. (8).

The prediction of a relatively wide $K_N \to K\pi$ is common to both approaches, and should be testable in the near future when precise studies of $K\pi$ scattering become available. At present, all we know of the 0^+ $K\pi$ system is that it has no resonances hiding under the $K^*(890)$,[19] and the $K\pi$ phase shift stays around 70^0 from 1100 to 1300 MeV.[7] This behavior is reminiscent of that of the 0^+ I=0 $\pi\pi$ phase shift around and above the $\epsilon(700)$.

4. $\pi\pi$ scattering

Recent high-statistics samples of data have been analyzed in[20]

$$\pi^+ p \rightarrow \pi^+\pi^-\Delta^{++} \qquad (12)$$

and[2]

$$\pi^- p \rightarrow \pi^+\pi^- n \qquad (13)$$

These give rise to <u>three</u> I=Y=0 candidates for 0^{++} mesons, as shown in Table V.

Table V 0^{++} I=Y=0 candidates

Name (mass)	Width (MeV)	Decay mode(s)
ϵ (700)	≥ 350	$\pi\pi$
S*(997)	10 to 50	$K\bar{K}$ ($\pi\pi$ weak)
ϵ '(1240)	~ 200	$\pi\pi$ ($K\bar{K}$ weak)

The Argand circle for the I=Y=0 S-wave amplitude is shown near the mass of the ϵ '(1240) in Fig. 2 (from Ref. 21).

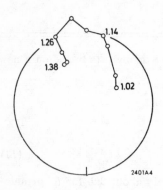

FIG. 2--Argand circle for I=Y=0 S-wave $\pi\pi$ amplitude near the mass of ϵ '(1240).[21]

The existence of the S-wave state under the f_0 has been noted[22] and discussed theoretically[23] before. <u>Three</u> I=Y=0 0^{++} states are an embarrassment to the quark model, which predicts only two. The additional state can be a "dilaton", i.e., a Goldstone boson of spontaneously broken scale invariance.[24]

A hypothetical 0^{++} "decimet" (nonet plus singlet) is shown in Fig. 3. It is interesting that the masses of the nine states at the top of the figure are consistent with those of an "ideal" nonet. On the other hand, as Table V shows, their couplings are quite substantially different from what we would expect from such a nonet. This can be ascribed to mixing with the additional "dilaton". Quantitatively, the coupling of the dilaton to pairs of pseudoscalar mesons must be quite strong in order for this scheme to work, leading to an $\epsilon(700)$ which is more broad than it is massive! (See Ref. 2.)

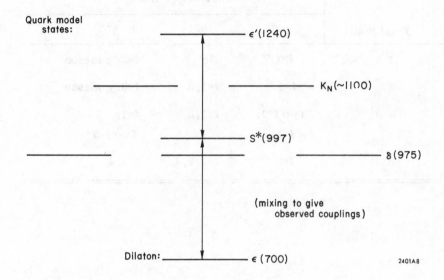

FIG. 3--Hypothetical 0^{++} nonet plus singlet.

5. Even-G I=1 mesons, 1.6-1.8 GeV

The Purdue group has presented a study of mesonic states in the "R" mass region, based on a 750,000-picture 13 GeV/c π^+p bubble chamber exposure.[9] The final states they discuss are shown in Table IV.

The masses and widths of the three latter final states are compatible with one another (m $\simeq$ 1680 MeV, $\Gamma \simeq$ 100 MeV), but the $\pi\pi$ effect seems somewhat lighter (m $\simeq$ 1630 MeV) and narrower ($\Gamma \simeq$ 40 MeV) than the others. In Table IV we have indicated the possible orbital angular momenta between the two final particles for various states expected in the quark model. Quite a few questions are left unanswered by the Purdue data.

(a). $\pi\pi$ final state. Partial-wave analyses favor a 3^- state, confirmed here. The CERN-Munich experiment, reaction (13), also may see some evidence for a 1^- state near this mass.[25,26] What are the bounds on the existence of such a state here?

(b). $\omega\pi$ final state. The angular distributions are compatible with being due entirely to 3^-, but bounds on 1^- and 2^- states are needed.

Table VI Study of the R region, $I^G = 1^+$ (Ref. 9)

Final State	Possible $q\bar{q}$, L=2 J^{PC}		
	1^{--}	2^{--}	3^{--}
$\pi^0 \pi^+$	$\ell=1$	No	$\ell=3$: g meson
$\omega \pi^+$	$\ell=1$	$\ell=1, 3$	$\ell=3$: g meson
$\rho^0 \rho^+$	Two $\ell=1$; $\ell=3$	$\ell=1, 3$	$\ell=1$; Two $\ell=3$
$(A_2 \pi)^+$	$\ell=2$	$\ell=0, 2, 4$	$\ell=2, 4$

(c). $\underline{\rho^0 \rho^+ \text{ final state.}}$ This is a difficult state to study, involving two broad resonances. The Purdue group sees only a 1σ signal.

(d). $\underline{(A_2\pi)^+ \text{ final state.}}$ It is difficult to distinguish $(A_2 \to 3\pi)$a from $\rho\rho$. Purdue sees a 1 1/2 σ signal.

These results fall short of sorting out the R region, but they give us an idea of the scale of effort that will be needed to study this region in counter experiments, as has been proposed.

6. Study of the A_3

A new analysis has been performed of the reaction

$$\pi^+ p \to \pi^+ \pi^- \pi^+ p \tag{14}$$

at 13 GeV/c.[27] It is concluded that the $A_3(1640)$ may be a resonant (rather than a Deck-type) effect, and that it may have a $\rho\pi$ mode. Both these conclusions are in disagreement with those of the Illinois group based on $\pi^- p$ data.[28]

The cuts against Δ^{++} in reaction (14) have more of an effect than in the corresponding $\pi^- p$ reaction. We suspect these may be the reason for the discrepancy.

7. Heavy K*'s

A study of 9 GeV/c K^+d interactions[29] confirms the existence of a $J^P=3^-$ $K_N(1760)$ decaying to $K\pi$ and possibly other final states, and a possible $K_N(2100)$ with $J^P \geq 4$. This last state is in the right place to be the Regge recurrence of the $K^{**}(1420)$, and bears watching.

8. The ρ' (~ 1500)

There are no new data here; only a polemic.[29'] The point is well taken: one must be on guard against kinematic enhancements, which are hard to eliminate in multi-body final states. The present status of various ρ' experiments has been reviewed in Ref. 26; we would prefer to wait for more colliding e^+e^- data.

9. Low-energy $\bar{p}p$ interactions

The recent measurement of low-energy total cross sections at Brookhaven[30] has turned up a number of interesting effects. One of them is a bump whose width is comparable to experimental resolution in $\sigma_T(\bar{p}p)$ and $\sigma_T(\bar{p}d)$ at the mass of the "S(1929)" meson first reported in missing-mass studies.[31] This comes at a time when missing-mass experiments seem to have abandoned the very narrow S.[32]

At higher masses, there have been new measurements of differential cross sections for $\bar{p}p \rightarrow \pi^+\pi^-$,[33] and $\bar{p}p \rightarrow K^+K^-$ [34] between 0.8 and 2.4 GeV/c. Structure is seen in $d\sigma/d\Omega$, but it does not change rapidly with increasing laboratory momentum. Partial-wave analyses await polarized target asymmetry data, forthcoming in the next year or two. Meanwhile one can make no statements about resonances in these channels.

Some other aspects of heavy mesons have been reviewed here, notably in the "T" (~ 2200 MeV) and "U" (~ 2385 MeV) regions.[35]

BARYONS

Table VII shows some new aspects of baryon resonance physics.

1. Δ residue calculation

The phases of residues will be of some interest when we come to discuss inelastic processes like $\pi N \rightarrow \pi \Delta$, where these phases are sometimes extracted from K-matrix fits. An example based on the first resonant particle ever discovered, the $\Delta(1236)$, shows that phases of pole residues can be misleading unless interpreted properly.[36]

One can use accurate π^+p scattering data to find the pole of the Δ, obtaining[37]

$$M = 1211 - 50\,i \tag{15}$$

$$R = 53\,e^{-0.81\,i} \tag{16}$$

Table VII New baryon data

L(qqq)	J^P values	Remarks
0	$3/2^+$	Δ residue calculation
	$1/2^+$	Eventual $g_{\Sigma\Lambda\pi}$ value
1	All (also L=2)	Magnitudes and phases in $\pi N \to \pi\Delta$, $\gamma N \to \pi N$; SU(6) fits to decays
	$5/2^-$, others	$N\eta$ studies
	$1/2^-$	$\Sigma\eta$ near threshold
2	All (also L=1)	πN charge exchange: new forward dispersion relation calculation; new polarization
	All (also L=1)	New $\overline{K}N$ phase shift analysis
Other effects, J^P uncertain		No diffractive $\Sigma^- \to \Lambda\pi^-$ resonances
		σ_T (K^-n): bump at 1580
		σ_T (KN): Z_0^* (~ 1800)?
		K^+P: Z_1^* (~ 1900) uncertain

One's initial expectation might be that the residue R should be real. This is not the case. When one includes the effects of unitarity, analyticity, the p^3 (p-wave) threshold factor, the correct kinematics at zero total energy, and some other reasonable dynamical assumptions, one obtains a residue which is almost exactly Eq. (16).

The threshold factor itself provides <u>more</u> than enough deviation from a real residue. This factor would be present if we interpreted the Δ as an "elementary" spin-3/2 particle (with complex mass) coupled to the πN system. In such a case the coupling constant of this particle would be considerably more real than one would suppose from Eq. (16).

2. Resonant $\pi N \to \pi\Delta$ amplitudes

A massive analysis of $\pi N \to \pi\Delta$ in the range 1.3 GeV $\le E_{CM} \le 2$ GeV is now nearing completion.[38,39] Many resonances are seen quite clearly decaying into $\pi\Delta$. The magnitudes and phases of resonant amplitudes can be compared with predictions of the single-quark selection rule models mentioned above.[10-14,40-42] Basically, this works because the N and Δ are in the same SU(6)$_W$ multiplet. Hence, the phases of resonant amplitudes in

$\pi N \rightarrow \pi\Delta$ are related in a known way to those in elastic πN scattering whose imaginary parts must be positive, by the optical theorem. The process $\pi N \rightarrow \pi\Delta$ is an example of an "SU(3)-inelastic" reaction,[43] since it is not related to elastic scattering via SU(3).

Some resulting Argand circles are shown in Fig. 4, along with magnitudes of resonant amplitudes. In a combination like "PP11", the first letter refers to the incident (πN) orbital angular momentum, the second to the $\pi\Delta$ orbital angular momentum, the first number to 2I, and the second to 2J.

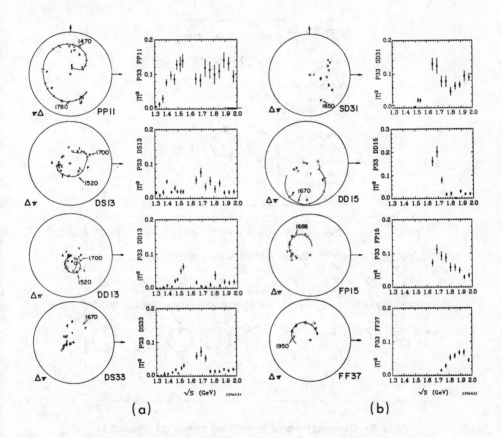

(a)   (b)

FIG. 4--(a,b) $\pi N \rightarrow \pi\Delta$ amplitudes, Ref. 38.

One notices that the imaginary parts of resonant amplitudes seem to have well-defined phases: positive or negative. One also notes (on the right-hand side of the figures) rather well-defined bumps, <u>except in the region of a gap between 1540 and 1650 MeV</u>.

The authors of Ref. 38 bridge the gap by demanding continuity of the PP11 wave (the first in Fig. 4). Two resonances appear in this wave: one above and one below the gap. The relative phase of amplitudes below and above the gap thus hangs on this rather slender thread.

It would of course be better to use <u>data</u> in the gap. These data exist, but are the subject of private smaller-scale analyses whose results should be available within the next year.

Figure 5 shows the phases of the 1972 solution[38] along with symmetry predictions. The arrows denote predicted phases in the Argand diagram, referred to a <u>baryon-first</u> isospin convention. [The phases in Fig. 4 refer to the isospin convention $\pi N \to \Delta\pi$, and thus have reversed relative $I = 1/2$ $-I=3/2$ phase.] The crosses are the experimental phases in the baryon-first convention.

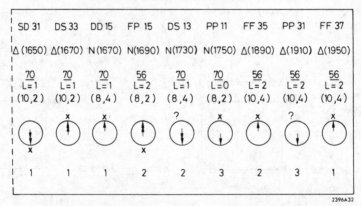

FIG. 5--Comparison of predicted resonant phases in $\pi N \to \pi\Delta$ (arrows, from Ref. 42) with experiment (crosses, from Ref. 30). Baryon-first isospin convention used here.

A double-headed arrow in Fig. 5 indicates a phase which is sensitive to which value of ΔL_z dominates: $\Delta L_z = 0$ (the "$SU(6)_W$" solution), or $\Delta L_z = \pm 1$ (the "anti-$SU(6)_W$" solution). For definiteness, we have shown the "anti-$SU(6)_W$" solution. The names stem from the relative phases of D/S and F/P waves: those of $SU(6)_W$ when $\Delta L_z = 0$ dominates, and opposite to those of $SU(6)_W$ when $\Delta L_z = \pm 1$ dominates.[40,41]

The figure is cut in two at the gap.

The phases are defined with respect to the prominent FF37 resonance.[38,44] One then sees that, above the gap, all of the "first-class predictions" hold that would be expected if $\Delta L_z = \pm 1$ dominated for 70, L=1 decays. (A "first-class prediction" is one that cannot be affected by mixing. A second-class prediction is one for which mixing can occur but is thought to be understood and does not change the predictions for unmixed states.[45,46] A third-class prediction is one where the assignment is based on an educated guess.)

In fact, $\Delta L_z = \pm 1$ is expected to dominate in certain "realistic-quark" models based on harmonic oscillator wavefunctions,[47,48] both for 70, L=1 and for 56, L=2 decays. In the case of the latter, however, we see that $\Delta L_z = 0$ seems to dominate.[49]

The disagreements above the gap in PP11 and PP31 are both for states to whose assignments we are not committed firmly at present. Apparently our estimate of the experimental DS13 situation[42] was incorrect, and the data actually agree with our prediction.[39] (This is one case in which the phase is not too well defined, since there are two overlapping DS13 resonances.) Hence one can be rather pleased with the overall pattern above the gap.

Below the gap, however, the disagreement is complete, leading one to suspect the continuation. At the urging of D. Faiman after the Purdue Conference in May, a new continuation was sought, and seems to have been obtained, in which the relative phase across the gap has changed and is now in accord with theory.[50] The situation has changed often enough that a little patience is probably in order untill things settle down. (At one point, Faiman and I had our isospin conventions wrong!) Nonetheless, the situation looks very encouraging at present.

Analyses of $\pi N \rightarrow \rho N$ and $\pi N \rightarrow \epsilon N$ are also contained in Ref. 38. There may be some disagreement with the quark model in $\pi N \rightarrow \rho N$;[48] this should also apply, in principle, to the approach of Refs. 42 and 51, through the predictions still have not been worked out in full. The Melosh approach[12-15] makes no predictions for this reaction without additional assumptions. A different analysis of $\pi^+ p \rightarrow \pi\pi N$,[44] sees very little evidence for resonant ρ production, in contrast to Ref. 38, and ascribes the large ρ signal to one-pion exchange. Hence results of this channel should be treated with some caution.

3. Resonances in $\gamma N \rightarrow \pi N$

A large-scale analysis of single-pion photoproduction in the resonance region has recently been carried out.[52] This analysis leads to resonant phases (and approximate magnitudes) which agree with quark model predictions.[47,53]

A less predictive (and more general) discussion of resonant phases in $\gamma N \rightarrow \pi N$ may be founded on the Melosh transformation.[54,55] Here one needs the transformation properties of the dipole operator D_+ which induces electromagnetic transitions.

The analysis of Gilman and Karliner[54] assumes the dipole operator to transform as a sum of

$$\underline{35}, (8, 3)_{W_z = \pm 1}, \quad \Delta L_z = 0$$

$$+ \underline{35}, (8, 1)_{W_z = 0}, \quad \Delta L_z = \pm 1 \tag{17}$$

$$+ \underline{35}, (8, 3)_{W_z = \mp 1}, \quad \Delta L_z = \pm 2$$

A term also seems to be present which transforms as[55]

$$\underline{35}, (8, 3)_{W_z = 0}, \quad \Delta L_z = \pm 1 . \tag{18}$$

This term is required in the model of Ref. 51 as well.

By neglecting the term (18) and the last term in (17), one obtains vertices for electromagnetic transitions which have the same algebraic structure as the quark model.[47,53] There seems to be no compelling phenomenological need for the other terms at present. Based on the first two terms in Eq. (17), one can predict the signs of the resonant amplitudes in $\gamma N \to \pi N$. The results are shown in Fig. 6.

From Fig. 6 one sees that all the significant signs are in agreement with the theoretical expectations of Ref. 54. Moreover, the sign of the contribution of the S-wave πN resonance $\Delta(1610, 1/2^-)$ is that expected if $\Delta L_z = \pm 1$ dominates in $\underline{70}$, L=1 pionic decays, as suggested by the $\pi N \to \pi \Delta$ case. Occasional discrepancies can almost certainly be traced to oversimplified (unmixed) assignments. Now, one will have to await quantitative comparisons, which are forthcoming. Since the algebraic structure is the same as the quark model, which does not fare too badly, one can expect reasonable agreement; the question is whether the agreement will be significantly better.

4. SU(6) fits to decays

In the past couple of years there have been several fits to baryonic decays,[13,14,40,41,45,56] based on the algebraic structure suggested by the Melosh transformation.[15] (Some of these fits guessed the structure ahead of time.) The most recent of these[56] attempts to fit the decays of $\underline{70}$, L=1 members whose intramultiplet mixing is specified by diagonalizing mass matrices.

The agreement is not spectacular, indicating that the process of decay or mixing (or both) is not understood. We would tend to suspect the mixing assumptions. Quark model states with the same J^P are likely to mix via shared physical intermediate states. These have different effects in every case (since even their masses break SU(3)), and it may be risky to expect a few well-chosen mass operators (essentially quark spin-spin and spin-orbit terms, quark masses, etc.) to describe the mixing fully.

One point on which all the analyses agree is the likely existence of low-spin hyperon resonances coupling weakly to $\overline{K}N$ and much more strongly to $\Sigma\pi$ and $\Lambda\pi$. Perhaps studies of $\Sigma\pi$ scattering in hyperon beams will help.

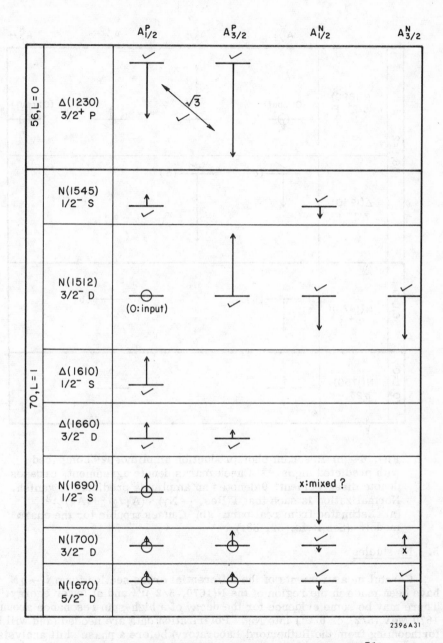

FIG. 6--(a) Resonant photoproduction amplitudes[51]
compared with predicted signs. [53]

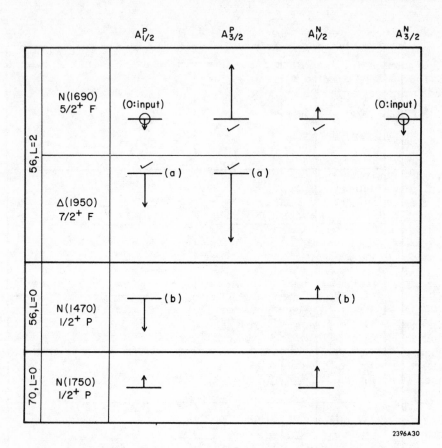

FIG. 6--(b) Resonant photoproduction amplitudes[52] compared with predicted signs.[54] Check marks denote agreement, crosses denote disagreement, 0 denotes an amplitude predicted to vanish. Normalization is such that $\Gamma(\text{Res.} \rightarrow N\gamma) \sim (A_{1/2})^2 + (A_{3/2})^2$. (a) Estimated from real part. (b) Causes trouble for the quark model. (See Refs. 52, 53.)

5. Nη studies

Careful measurements of the differential cross section for $\pi N \rightarrow \eta N$ have been made in the region of the N(1670, 5/2$^-$)[57] and at lower energy.[58] There may be some evidence for the decay of a high-spin resonance around 1670 MeV (5/2$^-$ or 5/2$^+$) into Nη. Polarization data are needed (and will be forthcoming from the Rutherford Laboratory) before a phase shift analysis can be undertaken.

6. $\Sigma\eta$ near threshold

In a study of the reaction $K^-p \rightarrow \Sigma\eta$ near threshold,[59] based on a Chicago-Berkeley bubble chamber exposure, it was found that the $\Sigma(1750, 1/2^-)$

had an appreciable $\Sigma\eta$ branching ratio:

$$\sqrt{x_{NK}x_{\Sigma\eta}} = \pm(0.23 \pm 0.01) \qquad (19)$$

This number will be an important constraint on models for mixing the three $\Sigma(1/2^-)$ states expected in the quark model. However, partly as a result of indeterminacy in the $\overline{K}N$ channel, the $\Sigma(1/2^-)$ states remain somewhat of a mystery.[45]

7. πN charge exchange

(a). Forward dispersion relations. At Batavia it was mentioned[60] that a new measurement of the differential cross section for $\pi^- p \to \pi^0 n$ disagreed with forward dispersion relations.[61,62]
Recently a new calculation of the real part of forward πN amplitudes has appeared.[63] The real part is substantially lower, improving the agreement with the new measurements. The calculation is performed using two subtractions, which emphasizes the contribution of the low-energy regime in contrast to the approach of Ref. 62.

(b). Polarization measurements. A Berkeley group[64] has measured πN polarization at 1030, 1245, 1440, 1590 and 1790 MeV/c. Preliminary values agree well with phase shift solutions of both CERN[65] and Saclay[66] at the lowest three energies. This is reassuring since the polarization predictions of the two solutions agree well with each other in this range. At higher energies some deviation sets in, especially from the CERN solution at 1790 MeV where the disagreement is quite severe. (Problems with the CERN analysis at this energy were already shown by the new differential cross section data.)[60,61]
On the basis of the new charge-exchange measurements, we can certainly expect some refinement of nonstrange baryon resonance parameters around $m = 2$ GeV in the next year or two.

8. New $\overline{K}N$ phase shift analysis

Preliminary results of an analysis by the UC-LBL group of $\overline{K}N \to (\overline{K}N, \pi\Sigma, \pi\Lambda)$ were quoted at Batavia.[60] At this conference more recent results were presented in the range 1.7 GeV $\le E_{CM} \le 1.9$ GeV.[67] The standard resonances[7] were well-fit, as well as some less well-established effects which have appeared before from time to time.[7] These are shown in Table VIII. The $\Lambda(1890, 3/2^+)$ could conceivably be an SU(3) partner of the $N(1890, 3/2^+)$, though the quark model suggests other $\Lambda(3/2^+)$ states as well in this mass range. There is some question whether one or two $\Sigma(1/2^-)$ states exist around 1720 MeV. The parameters of the $\Lambda(1750, 1/2^+)$ vary considerably among different analyses.[7]

9. $\Sigma^- \to \Lambda\pi^-$ dissociation

A group working with a 20 GeV/c Σ^- beam at BNL[68] has studied

$$\Sigma^- + (\text{nucleus}) \to \Lambda\pi^- + (\text{nucleus}) \qquad (20)$$

Table VIII "New" hyperon resonances (Ref. 67)

$\Lambda(1890, 3/2^+)$	$x_{N\bar{K}}$	$= .23 \pm .05$	$\Gamma = 80 \pm 10$ MeV
	$\sqrt{x_{N\bar{K}}x_{\pi\Sigma}}$	$\leq .04$	
$\Sigma(1720, 1750, 1/2^-)$	$x_{N\bar{K}}$	$\lesssim .1$	$\Gamma \simeq 65$ MeV
$\Lambda(1750, 1/2^+)$	$\sqrt{x_{N\bar{K}}x_{\Sigma\pi}}$	$\simeq -.11;$	$\Gamma \simeq 50$ MeV
	$x_{N\bar{K}}$ small		

and finds no evidence for diffractively produced resonances up to 1.6 GeV in mass.

On the other hand, if the process (20) is described by a Deck-type mechanism, in which the Σ first dissociates into $\Lambda\pi$ and the pion then scatters the nucleus, one has a source of the $\Sigma\Lambda\pi$ coupling constant, to compare with the $NN\pi$, $N\Lambda K$, and $N\Sigma K$ constants via SU(3). Analyses are in progress to determine the $\Sigma\Lambda\pi$ coupling.

10. $\bar{K}N$ and KN total cross sections; K^+p analysis

The BNL group[30] finds evidence for a bump in $\sigma_T(K^-n)$, $m \simeq 1580$ MeV, $x \simeq .1$, width narrower than experimental resolution (30 MeV). Phase shift analyses in this region are very spotty,[69] so the effect could indeed be a new resonance. Its narrowness is puzzling. However, if it were the SU(3) partner of the Roper resonance $N(1470, 1/2^+)$, belonging to a $\underline{56}$, L=0 multiplet (so that f/d = 2/3), one predicts its dominant decay modes to be $\Sigma\pi$ and $\Lambda\pi$ (not $\bar{K}N$), and its total width to be only about 25 MeV.

The KN total cross sections also have been remeasured.[30] In the interesting[60] I=0 channel, they display a broad, elastic bump around 1800 MeV, with $\Gamma \simeq 600$ MeV, probably corresponding to a $P_{1/2}$ or $S_{1/2}$ resonance. Final interpretation of this effect as a genuine Z_0^* resonance will have to await KN charge-exchange polarization measurements at the energy in question.[60]

In the I=1 KN channel, a new measurement has been made[70] of backward K^+p scattering between 1 and 1.5 GeV/c, and a new partial-wave analysis performed.[71] No partial wave need be resonant in this new analysis; the behavior of the $P_{3/2}$ partial wave is explicable purely in terms of the opening of the (nonresonant) $K\Delta$ channel.

11. Resonances that need attention

We conclude this section in a theoretical vein by noting those resonances not discussed here which might have been, since they are important.

(a). $N(1730, 3/2^-)$. This state is the last (of 7) nonstrange baryons to be discovered in the $\underline{70}$, L=1 multiplet. It was seen weakly in elastic πN

scattering,[66] strongly in $\pi N \to \pi \Delta$,[38] and also in one of two $\pi N \to K\Sigma$ solutions.[72] Its substantial inelasticity was expected on the basis of SU(6);[41,45] this was what made it so hard to find.

(b). $\underline{N(\sim 2000, 7/2^+)}$. This state has been on the verge of being established for several years. Both recent πN phase shift analyses see it,[65,66] but we have seen that some adjustments around 2 GeV are necessary. The resonance would belong to a $\underline{70}$, L=2 multiplet, whose existence is important for the quark model[73] and duality.[46,74,75]

(c). $\underline{\Delta(\sim 2200, 9/2^-)}$. This is a resonance important for the quark model and duality (a $\underline{56}$, L=3 candidate).[46,73-75] We should start seeing it soon.

THEORY

The selection rules and intensities characterizing hadronic transitions are being mapped out in an encouraging way. We have various languages in which to interpret these rules. The most recent is that suggested by the work of Melosh,[15] but other approaches — notably the quark model[47,48] and the so-called $^3P_0$ quark-pair-creation picture[10,11,40] — serve as useful complements and guides to the intuition. The theories are different, and it is useful to see how.[76]

The "relativistic" quark model[47,48] describes pion or photon emission in terms of a transition operator evaluated between specific wavefunctions, which are usually taken to be those of a harmonic oscillator.[73] These wavefunctions specify the problem completely: one thus obtains relations among decays involving different SU(6) multiplets, and relations between $\Delta L_Z = 0$ and $\Delta L_Z = \pm 1$ pionic transitions.

The quark-pair-creation picture bears some relation to duality graphs.[77,78] The apparent connectedness of quark graphs in SU(3)[1,79] encourages us to draw similar graphs in which the quarks carry spin. When a hadron decays, some of its quarks end up in one hadron and some in the other. To conserve triality, an additional $q\bar{q}$ pair must be produced, each member of which ends up in one of the final hadrons.[11] One can imagine such a picture following from certain dual models, in which the "string" of which hadrons are assumed to be made is really an infinite number of virtual $q\bar{q}$ pairs. The "breaking" of the string between one such pair would then correspond to this model for decays.

The $^3P_0$ picture has sometimes been referred to as "ℓ-broken SU(6)$_W$", though it is now clear that it is somewhat more general.[80] In this picture, the amplitudes corresponding to $L_Z = \pm 1$ and $L_Z = 0$ of the $q\bar{q}$ pair are left free with respect to one another, so that the term "$^3P_0$" is somewhat of a misnomer. A covariant formulation of the picture exists.[10] The relative freedom of $L_Z = \pm 1$ and $L_Z = 0$ amplitudes is the source of "ℓ-breaking."[40]

The "current-quark" approach is based on the observation[81] that the quarks by which one realizes current algebra[82] and those composing a hadron ($q\bar{q}$ for a meson, qqq for a baryon) are not necessarily the same.[83] The two types of quarks lead to inequivalent algebra of SU(6)$_W$.[84] In one algebra, that of "current" quarks, the currents and charges have simple transformation properties, and the states are complicated mixtures of representations.[85] In the other, it is the states which are pure representations.

A transformation V connects the two languages; it is the study of the properties and effects of V in the free quark model[15] that has led to numerous successful applications.[12-14,54,55,80]

As an example, let us consider the evaluation of a pionic decay. The decay amplitude for $A \rightarrow B\pi$ is related via PCAC[86] to the matrix element of the axial charge Q_5:

$$M(A \rightarrow B\pi) \sim (m_A^2 - m_B^2) <B|Q_5|A> . \tag{21}$$

The evaluation of $<B|Q_5|A>$ was difficult until recently. In the "current-quark" representation, Q_5 transforms simply, i.e.,

$$Q_5 \sim \underline{35}, \ (8,3)_{W_Z=0} , \quad L_Z = 0 , \tag{22}$$

in $SU(6)_W$. (Here and in Eqs. (17) and (18), the numbers in parentheses refer to SU(3) and $SU(2)_W$ dimensions, respectively.) On the other hand, as mentioned, A and B are mixed states. It was fashionable at one time to construct models for the mixing.[85] Now, however, by assuming that there is a transformation V converting the states A and B to pure current-quark representations:

$$|\widetilde{A}>_{(pure)} = V|A>_{(mixed)} , \tag{23}$$

one can cast the complexity onto the operators:

$$<B|Q_5|A> = <\widetilde{B}|V Q_5 V^{-1}|\widetilde{A}>$$

$$\equiv <\widetilde{B}|\widetilde{Q}_5|\widetilde{A}> \tag{24}$$

where it remains to find the properties of the transformed operator

$$\widetilde{Q}_5 = V Q_5 V^{-1} \tag{25}$$

In the free quark model, the properties of $\widetilde{Q}_5$ are remarkably simple:[15]

$$\widetilde{Q}_5 \sim \underline{35}, \ (8,3)_{W_Z = 0}, \quad L_Z = 0$$

$$+ \underline{35}, \ (8,3)_{W_Z = \mp 1}, \quad L_Z = \pm 1 \tag{26}$$

One sees in Eq. (26) the $\Delta L_Z = 0$ and $\Delta L_Z = \pm 1$ pieces to which we have referred earlier. Their matrix elements between any pair of multiplets are free parameters. The second piece may be thought of as an effect of transverse motion of quarks.

It has been shown[80] that the $^3P_0$ picture leads to precisely the same rules as Eq. (26) for pionic transitions. An important difference is that, while the kinematic factor in the $^3P_0$ picture is indeterminate, and is thus usually taken to be Eq. (7), the PCAC hypothesis (21) leads to the <u>unique</u> factor in Eq. (8). (Equation (21) arises when Q_5 is evaluated between infinite-momentum states, so one's intuition regarding the need for conventional centrifugal barriers such as (7) may fail.)

Numerically, there is not much basis for distinction between Eqs. (7) and (8) as yet: We have mentioned that S-wave meson decays fare better with Eq. (8), as does the relation between $f_0 \rightarrow \pi\pi$ and $A_2 \rightarrow \rho\pi$.[13] On the other hand, certain baryon decays become better with Eq. (7).[13,40,41]

Some further comparisons among the various models are discussed by Kugler.[76] Whatever the language, it is clear that we now have a whole new set of symmetry predictions for hadronic three-point functions which are worthy of experimental tests. This is because recent efforts have striven toward symmetries <u>lower</u> than $SU(6)_W$ (which would, for example, keep only the first term in Eq. (26)). As we have seen from the $B \rightarrow \omega\pi$ example, $SU(6)_W$ does not work.

If the symmetries discussed here are ever ruled out by the data, there is a "rear-guard" set of $SU(3) \times SU(3)$ symmetries to which one can retreat[12,87] before being beaten back to $SU(3)$. At the moment, such a retreat seems unnecessary, but we invite our colleagues to try to force us back!

ACKNOWLEDGMENTS

I am particularly grateful to Fred Gilman, Moshe Kugler, and Gordon Moorhouse for discussions regarding relations among various theories. Roger Cashmore, Lina Galtieri, Bob Kelly, Gerry Lynch, Moishe Pripstein, Gerry Smith, Bob Tripp, and many others have been patient in explaining the experimental situation, for which I thank them. It is a pleasure to acknowledge the hospitality extended by SLAC during the preparation and writing of this report.

REFERENCES

1. M. Gell-Mann, Phys. Letters $\underline{8}$, 214 (1964); G. Zweig, CERN reports TH-401 and TH-412, 1964 (unpublished). See also "Quarks for Pedestrians," by H. J. Lipkin, submitted to Physics Reports.

2. Details of classification according to the quark model are contained in the review "The Classification and Decays of Resonant Particles," by J. L. Rosner, submitted to Physics Reports. This article also treats some of the theoretical topics contained in the present report in more detail, and makes suggestions for future experiments on resonances.

3. S. U. Chung, in Proceedings of the XVI International Conference on High Energy Physics, Batavia, Illinois, 1972, edited by J. D. Jackson, A. Roberts, and R. Donaldson, National Accelerator Laboratory, Batavia, Ill., 1973, Vol. I, p. 96.

4. G. R. Lynch, mini-rapporteur's talk, this conference.

5. S. U. Chung, et al., "Spin-parity analysis of the B meson," to be published.

6. Y. Eisenberg, et al., paper no. 141, this conference.

7. T. Lasinski, et al., Rev. Mod. Phys. $\underline{45}$, S 1 (1973).

8. T. Ferbel, et al., paper no. 119, this conference.

9. R. McIlwain, et al., paper no. 105, this conference.

10. E. W. Colglazier and J. L. Rosner, Nucl. Phys. B $\underline{27}$, 349 (1971); E. W. Colglazier, Thesis, Calif. Inst. of Technology (1971).

11. L. Micu, Nucl. Phys. B $\underline{10}$, 521 (1969). (The first use of a $q\bar{q}$ "spurion" in describing hadron decays was by J. C. Carter and M. E. M. Head, Phys. Rev. $\underline{176}$, 1808 (1968). See also D. Horn and Y. Ne'eman, Phys. Rev. D $\underline{1}$, 2710 (1970); R. Carlitz and M. Kislin Phys. Rev. D $\underline{2}$, 336 (1970). Only the last article makes reference to connected quark graphs, however.)

12. F. Gilman and M. Kugler, Phys. Rev. Letters $\underline{30}$, 518 (1973); A.J.G. Hey and J. Weyers, Phys. Letters $\underline{44}$ B, 263 (1973).

13. F. Gilman, M. Kugler and S. Meshkov, SLAC report SLAC-PUB-1235 (1973) to be published in Phys. Letters B, and SLAC report SLAC-PUB-1286, to be published in Phys. Rev.

14. F. Gilman, SLAC report SLAC-PUB-1256, to be published in Proceedings of the Purdue Conference on Baryon Resonances, West Lafayette, Indiana, April 20-21, 1973.

15. H. J. Melosh, Thesis, California Institute of Technology, 1973 (unpublished), and this conference.

16. For a discussion of the PCAC "Barrier factor", see, e.g., D. Horn, Phys. Rev. Letters $\underline{17}$, 778 (1966).

17. See, e.g., Y. Antipov, et al., in Experimental Meson Spectroscopy-1972 (Third Philadelphia Meson Conference), edited by A. Rosenfeld and K.-W. Lai, New York, American Institute of Physics, 1972, p. 164; G. Ascoli, 1972 Batavia Conference, op cit., Vol. I, p. 3.

18. G. Conforto, et al., submitted to the 1973 International Conference on Elementary Particles, Aix-en-Provence, France.

19. A. Barbaro-Galtieri, et al., Lawrence Berkeley Laboratory report LBL-1772, 1973, to be published in Proceedings of the International Conference on $\pi\pi$ Scattering and Associated Topics, Tallahassee, Fla., March 28-30, 1973.

20. S. D. Protopopescu, et al., Phys. Rev. D 7, 1279 (1973).
21. P. Estabrooks, et al., CERN report TH-1661, 1973, to be published in Proceedings of the 1973 Tallahassee Conference, op cit.
22. J. T. Carroll, et al., Phys. Rev. Letters 28, 318 (1972).
23. H. J. Lipkin, Phys. Rev. D 7, 1561 (1973).
24. For a review, see P. Carruthers, Physics Reports 1 C, 1 (1971).
25. W. Blum, Seminar at CERN, February, 1973.
26. K. Moffeit, this conference.
27. R. L. McIlwain, et al., paper no. 106, this conference.
28. G. Ascoli, et al., Phys. Rev. D 7, 669 (1973).
29. D. D. Carmony, et al., paper no. 32, this conference.
29'. T. Ferbel and P. Slattery, paper no. 120, this conference.
30. A. S. Carroll, mini-rapporteur's talk, this conference.
31. M. N. Focacci, et al., Phys. Rev. Letters 17, 890 (1966).
32. D. Bowen, et al., Phys. Rev. Letters 30, 333 (1973).
33. A. S. L. Parsons, et al., paper no. 10, this conference.
34. C. Hovjat, et al., paper no. 9, this conference.
35. G. A. Smith, this conference.
36. F. Henyey and G. Kane, this conference.
37. J. S. Ball, P. S. Lee, and G. L. Shaw, Phys. Rev. D 7, 2789 (1973).
38. D. J. Herndon, et al., SLAC report SLAC-PUB-1108 (1972), presented to 1972 Batavia Conference, op. cit.
39. R. Cashmore, SLAC report SLAC-PUB-1257, June, 1973, to be published in Proceedings of the 1973 Purdue Conference, op. cit.
40. W. P. Petersen and J. L. Rosner, Phys. Rev. D 6, 820 (1972).
41. J. L. Rosner, in Proceedings of the 1972 Batavia Conference, op. cit., Vol. 3, p. 149.
42. D. Faiman and J. L. Rosner, CERN report TH-1636, 1973, to be published in Phys. Letters B.
43. I gather this name is due to R. G. Moorhouse.
44. A. Kernan, et al., Lawrence Berkeley Laboratory report LBL 2017 (1973), presented at 1973 Purdue Conference, op. cit.; see also U. Mehtani, et al., Phys. Rev. Letters 29, 1634 (1972).
45. D. Faiman and D. Plane, Nucl. Phys. B 50, 379 (1972).
46. D. Faiman, J. L. Rosner and J. Weyers, Nucl. Phys. B 57, 45 (1973).
47. R. Feynman, M. Kislinger and F. Ravndal, Phys. Rev. D 3, 2706 (1971).
48. R. G. Moorhouse and N. Parsons, paper no. 159, this conference.
49. A model has indeed been constructed in which this is the case. See F. Buccella, F. Nicolo, A. Pugliese, and E. Sorace, Nuovo Cimento, 9 A, 120 (1972).
50. R. Longacre, mini-rapporteur's talk, this conference; R. Cashmore, "Amplitude Analyses in Three-Body Final States," SLAC report, presented at the 14th Scottish Universities' Summer School on Physics, July 29-August 18, 1973.
51. W. P. Petersen and J. L. Rosner, Phys. Rev. D 7, 747 (1973).
52. R. G. Moorhouse, H. Oberlack and A. Rosenfeld, to be published, and H. Oberlack, mini-rapporteur's talk, this conference.
53. R. G. Moorhouse, mini-rapporteur's talk, this conference; see also R. G. Moorhouse, in Proceedings of the 1972 Batavia Conference, op. cit., Vol. 1, p. 182.

154

54. F. Gilman and I. Karliner, SLAC report SLAC-PUB-1271 (1973) to be published.

55. A.J.G. Hey and J. Weyers, CERN report TH-1718 (1973) to be published.

56. M. Jones, R. Levi-Setti and T. Lasinski, Enrico Fermi Institute report no. EFI 73-21, June, 1973, to be published in Nuovo Cimento.

57. M. Pripstein, mini-rapporteur's talk, this conference; R. B. Chaffee, et al., paper no. 78, this conference.

58. Y. Lemoigne, et al., Saclay preprint, 1973, presented to 1973 Purdue Conference, op.cit.

59. M. Jones, paper no. 60, this conference.

60. C. Lovelace, Rapporteur's talk, 1972 Batavia Conference, op.cit., Vol. 3, p. 73.

61. M. Pripstein, mini-rapporteur's talk, this conference; J. E. Nelson, et al., Lawrence Berkeley Laboratory report LBL-2002, May, 1973, to be published.

62. G. Höhler and R. Strauss, "Tables of Pion-Nucleon Forward Amplitudes," Karlsruhe preprint, 1971; see also G. Höhler and H. P. Jacob, Z. Phys. $\underline{240}$, 377 (1970).

63. A. A. Carter and J. R. Carter, Queen Mary College and Cavendish Laboratory, report RL-73-024, May 1973 (unpublished).

64. S. Shannon, et al., submitted to 1973 Aix Conference, op.cit.; M. Pripstein, this conference.

65. S. Almehed and C. Lovelace, Nucl. Phys. B $\underline{40}$, 157 (1972).

66. R. Ayed, P. Bareyre and Y. Lemoigne, Saclay report, 1972, submitted to 1972 Batavia Conference, op.cit., paper no. 990.

67. D. Merrill, paper no. 18, this conference.

68. V. Hungerbuehler, et al., paper no. 72, this conference.

69. R. Tripp, mini-rapporteur's talk, this conference.

70. U. Adams, et al., paper no. 52, this conference.

71. R. E. Cutkosky, et al., paper no. 167, this conference.

72. W. Langbein and F. Wagner, Nucl. Phys. B $\underline{53}$, 251 (1973).

73. D. Faiman and A. Hendry, Phys. Rev. $\underline{173}$, 1720 (1968).

74. S. Mandelstam, Phys. Rev. D $\underline{1}$, 1734 (1969).

75. J. L. Rosner, Phys. Rev. D $\underline{7}$, 172 (1973).

76. M. Kugler, mini-rapporteur's talk, this conference.

77. H. Harari, Phys. Rev. Letters $\underline{22}$, 562 (1969).

78. J. L. Rosner, Phys. Rev. Letters $\underline{22}$, 689 (1969).

79. S. Okubo, Phys. Letters $\underline{5}$, 165 (1963).

80. A.J.G.Hey, J. L. Rosner and J. Weyers, CERN report TH-1659 (1973) to be published in Nuclear Physics B.

81. R. F. Dashen and M. Gell-Mann, Phys. Rev. Letters $\underline{17}$, 340 (1966); M. Gell-Mann, CERN report TH 1543 (1972), unpublished (Schladming lectures).

82. M. Gell-Mann, Phys. Rev. $\underline{125}$, 1067 (1962); Physics $\underline{1}$, 63 (1964).

83. Y. Ohnuki and A. Toyoda, Nuovo Cimento $\underline{36}$, 1405 (1965), have suggested that quarks realizing various SU(6) algebra may not be the same, and may be related by a transformation.

84. H. Lipkin and S. Meshkov, Phys. Rev. Letters $\underline{14}$, 670 (1965) and Phys. Rev. $\underline{143}$, 1269 (1966); K. J. Barnes, P. Carruthers and F. von Hippel, Phys. Rev. Letters $\underline{14}$, 82 (1965); R. F. Dashen and M. Gell-Mann, Phys. Letters $\underline{17}$, 142, 145 (1965), and others.

85. See, e.g., H. Harari, Phys. Rev. Letters <u>16</u>, 964 (1966); <u>ibid.</u>, <u>17</u>, 56 (1966); G. Altarelli, R. Gatto, L. Maiani and G. Preparata, Phys. Rev. Letters <u>16</u>, 918 (1966); I. S. Gerstein and B. W. Lee, Phys. Rev. Letters <u>16</u>, 1060 (1966); D. Horn, Phys. Rev. Letters <u>17</u>, 778 (1966); F. Gilman and H. Harari, Phys. Rev. <u>165</u>, 1803 (1968); F. Buccella, <u>et al.</u>, Nuovo Cimento <u>69</u> A, 133 (1970) and Ref. 49.

86. A good discussion is given by Horn, Ref. 85. The matrix element is evaluated in the infinite-momentum frame.

87. J. L. Rosner, Phys. Rev. D <u>6</u>, 1781 (1972).

REVIEW OF EVIDENCE FOR HIGH MASS K* STATES[†]

D. Duane Carmony

Purdue University, W. Lafayette, Indiana 47907

ABSTRACT

Evidence for strange mesons above the K*(1420) is reviewed. The $K_N(1760)$ now appears to be well confirmed with a 9 GeV/c K+n experiment reporting a mass of 1769±12 MeV and a width of 130±50 MeV and a 7.2 GeV/c K−p experiment finding a mass of about 1760 MeV and a width of less than 80 MeV. Decays into Kπ, Kρ, K*(890)π and K*(890)ρ are seen. The K+n experiment also reports a state of mass 2115±45 MeV and width 300±100 MeV which is identified with a previously reported antilambda-nucleon state. Decays into Kπ, K*(890)π, Kρ, K*(890)ρ, K*(1420)π and Kf are also found. A 12 GeV/c K+n experiment finds a single broad enhancement in the high Kπ mass region.

INTRODUCTION

I would like to review the evidence for high mass K* states as presented in our contribution to this conference (K+n at 9 GeV/c, about 10 events per microbarn)[1] as well as discuss the other evidence for or against these states which comes primarily from a K−p experiment[2] at 7.2 GeV/c and from a K+n experiment[3] at 12 GeV/c.

THE Kπ FINAL STATE

The dominant features of the reaction

$$K^+n \rightarrow pK^+\pi^- \text{ or } K^-p \rightarrow nK^-\pi^+ \tag{1}$$

are a low mass enhancement in the nucleon-pion system (M < 1.7 GeV) and a number of resonances in the Kπ system. Fig. 1 shows the Kπ mass spectrum for 4581 events of the 9 GeV/c K+ experiment with the events with $M(p\pi^-) > 1.7$ GeV shown shaded. The solid curve is a fit to the data from 1.0 to 3.0 GeV (a small K*(890) tail is removed) assuming quadratic background and three simple Breit-Wigner resonances. The X^2 probability of the fit is 37%. The probability of a fit is 1% with one broad resonance (dashed curve) or one narrow resonance (dotted curve) above the K*(1420). Additional evidence for two states above the K*(1420) is the observation that the lower enhancement is also present when we require that $M(p\pi^-) > 1.7$ GeV whereas the upper state is made primarily in association with this low mass enhancement. Furthermore, we present in Fig. 2 the unnormalized moments $\langle Y_6^o \rangle$, $\langle Y_8^o \rangle$, and $\langle Y_{10}^o \rangle$. The Kπ scattering moments are determined in the Jackson frame and

[†]Work supported in part by the U. S. Atomic Energy Commission

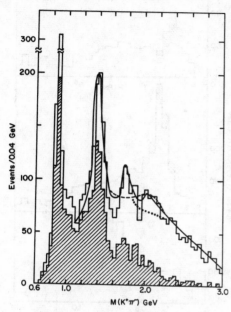

Fig. 1:
Kπ effective mass at 9 GeV/c
from reaction (1)

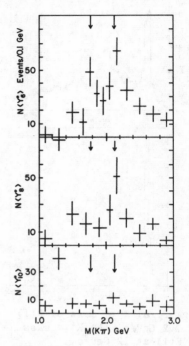

Fig. 2:
Y_6^o, Y_8^o, and Y_{10}^o moments
of the Kπ system for
$t' < 0.2$ GeV^2/c^2
(Jackson system)

we require that the four-momentum
transfer $t'(K,K\pi)$ be less than
0.2 GeV^2/c^2. The Y_8^o moment is
large only in the $K_N(2100)$ region
whereas the Y_6^o moment is large both in the $K_N(1760)$ and $K_N(2100)$
region. In Fig. 3a the $K^-\pi^+$ mass spectrum of 5330 events of
reaction (1) is shown from an experiment at 7.2 GeV/c. A bump
at 1.76 GeV with a width of less than 80 MeV is seen. In Fig. 3b
the $K^+\pi^-$ mass spectrum from 6400 events of reaction (1) at 12 GeV/c
is shown. Although the resolution is comparable (about 15 MeV),
the two states are not resolved. The broad enhancement seen could
well contain these structures which would be less important at this
energy if pion exchange is the primary production mechanism.

THE Kπππ FINAL STATE

We turn now to a study of 1540 events of the final state

$$K^+n \rightarrow pK^o\pi^+\pi^- \tag{2}$$

In Fig. 4 the $p\pi^-$, $K^o\pi^+$ and $\pi^+\pi^-$ effective mass distributions are
shown. Shown shaded are the $\Delta^o(1236)K^*(890)$ events which have been
removed from the analysis. The $K^o\pi^+\pi^-$ effective mass spectrum is
shown in Fig. 5a. The $K_N(1760)$ is clearly seen and there is also
an excess of events at a mass of 2.1 GeV. The histogram has been

158

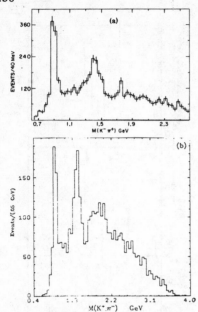

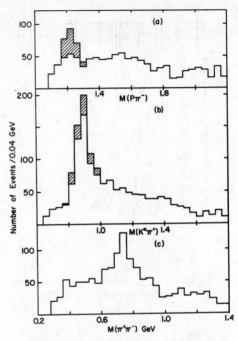

Fig. 3: a) K⁻π⁺ mass of R(1)
at 7.2 GeV/c. b) K⁺π⁻ mass
of R(1) at 12 GeV/c.

Fig. 4: a) M(pπ⁻). b) M(K⁰π⁺)
c) M(π⁺π⁻) from R(2) at 9 GeV/c.
Δ(1236)K events are shaded.

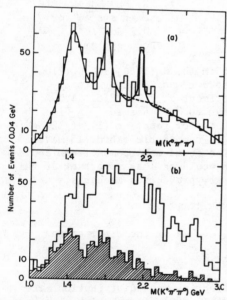

Fig. 5: a) M(K⁰π⁺π⁻) of R(2)
b) M(K⁺π⁻π⁰) from final state
pK⁺π⁻π⁰ with K*⁰π⁰ shaded.

fitted with a quadratic background plus two (dotted curve)
or three (solid curve) Breit-
Wigner resonances. An acceptable fit (11%) can be obtained
without the third resonance but
then the 2100 MeV region shows a
4 standard deviation excess. The
probability of the fit rises to
67% with the inclusion of the
third state. In Fig. 5b we show
the K⁺π⁻π⁰ effective mass distribution of 1984 events of the
final state pK⁰π⁺π⁰. This reaction contains considerable
contamination and is of poor resolution but if a K*(890)⁰ is
required (shaded histogram) a
significant $K_N(1760)$ signal is
seen.

If the Kπ and K⁰π⁺π⁻ en-
hancements are assumed to be
different decay modes of the

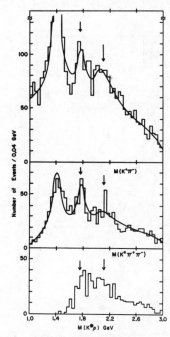

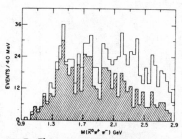

FIG. 7. $\bar{K}^0\pi^+\pi^-$ mass spectrum from the final state $\bar{K}^0\pi^+\pi^- n$. The shaded histogram results from selecting either $K^*(890)$ or ρ intermediate states in the $\bar{K}^0\pi^+\pi^-$ system.

Fig. 6: a) $K^+\pi^-$ mass. b) $K^0\pi^+\pi^-$ mass. c) $K^*\rho$ mass. Curve is fit to a and b.

same states and if only one resonance is assumed in addition to the $K^*(1420)$ the mass spectra are incompatible since the probability of a simultaneous fit is 0.05%. If, however, we assume separate quadratic backgrounds and resonant amounts for the above two reactions but require the same masses and widths for the three resonances we obtain the solid curve in Fig. 6a,b which is a good fit to the data (10% prob.).

In the 7.2 GeV/c K^-p experiment 920 events of the final state $n\bar{K}^0\pi^+\pi^-$ also show evidence of a three meson decay at 1.76 GeV especially if a $K^*(890)$ or ρ is required (Fig. 7). The $K^0\pi^+\pi^-$ effective mass distribution at 12 GeV/c is given in Phys. Rev. Letters $\underline{26}$,1460 (1971) and may also show a slight excess at 1.76 GeV.

ADDITIONAL EVIDENCE FOR HIGH MASS STATES

We have considered the two reactions at 9 GeV/c:

$$K^+n \rightarrow pK^+\pi^+\pi^-\pi^- \quad \text{(1310 events)} \qquad (3)$$

and

$$K^+n \rightarrow pK^0\pi^+\pi^-\pi^0 \quad \text{(710 events)} \qquad (4)$$

In reaction (3) the K^+/π^+ ambiguity is resolved by kinematics if the spectator proton is seen and even if the spectator isn't seen, those events which are p $K^*(890)\rho$ have a unique track assignment. The $K^+\pi^-$ and $\pi^+\pi^-$ effective mass distributions for reaction (3) with two combinations per event are shown in Fig. 8 and the dominance of the $K^*(890)$ is clearly seen. Rho production is also important especially in association with a K^* in the other meson pair (shaded histogram of Fig. 8b). The two body masses for the other reaction (4) are not shown but are similar. The $K^*(890)\rho$

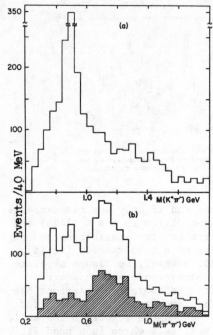

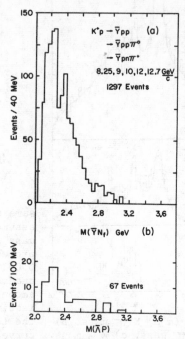

Fig. 8: a) $K^+\pi^-$. b) $\pi^+\pi^-$ mass (two comb./event. The $\pi\pi\pi$ with associated K^* is shaded.

Fig. 9: $\bar{\Lambda}N$ mass. a) from several K^+p experiments. b) this experiment.

mass spectrum from reactions (3) and (4) combined is shown in Fig. 6c. The arrows indicate the masses found in the simultaneous fit to the $K\pi$ and $K\pi\pi\pi$ channels. The dominant feature of the $K^*(890)\rho$ effective mass distribution is an enhancement(s) from 1.68-2.2 GeV. Although there is a three standard deviation dip at 1.85 GeV, we cannot rule out a single broad enhancement (about 500 MeV) but the most reasonable interpretation is that both the $K_N(1760)$ and $K_N(2100)$ decay into two vector mesons. In reaction (4) we find ~10 $K\omega$ decays of the $K_N(1760)$ but there is insufficient data to determine much more than an upper limit to this decay (not shown).

We have also examined the antilambda-nucleon effective mass distribution choosing that nucleon in the final state $\bar{\Lambda}ppn$ which gives the lowest momentum transfer between the incident K^+ and the outgoing $\bar{\Lambda}N$. In Fig. 9 we show the lambdabar-nucleon mass spectrum for a number of K^+p experiments in the energy range 8-13 GeV[4] and in Fig. 9b for our experiment. We conclude the $K_N(2100)$ also has an antilambda-nucleon decay mode.

Finally, we have also examined the $K\pi\pi$ mass spectrum in the non charge exchange reaction $K^+N \rightarrow NK^0\pi^+$. We see a small $K_N(1760)$ signal (Fig. 10) which because of the known $K\pi/K\pi\pi\pi$ branching implies $K_N(1760)$ production in the reaction $KN \rightarrow N(K\pi\pi\pi)$. Since the $K_N(1760)$ has nearly the same mass as the L-meson, this presumably explains why some authors[5], particularly at lower energies have

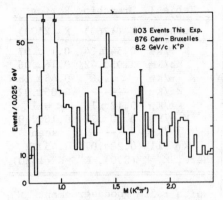

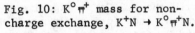

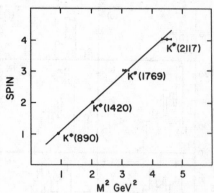

Fig. 10: $K^0 \pi^+$ mass for non-charge exchange, $K^+ N \rightarrow K^0 \pi^+ N$.

Fig. 11: Spin of the strange mesons as function of mass^2.

reported $K^* \pi$ and $K\rho$ decay modes for the L-meson whereas the highest energy experiments are consistent with the L-meson being purely $K^*(1420)\pi$.

SPIN AND PARITY

The $K_N(1760)$ and $K_N(2100)$ are both isospin 1/2 states and the existence of two and three body decay modes restricts the spin and parity J^P to the values 1^-, 2^+, 3^-, 4^+... As can be seen in Fig. 2 the Y_6^0 moment is large in the 1760 MeV region (and all higher moments are zero) and the Y_8^0 moment is large in the 2100 MeV region (and higher moments are zero). An analysis of the events which are produced backward in the Gottfried-Jackson system and thus do not overlap with the low mass proton-pion enhancement finds three standard deviation evidence for $J^P = 3^-$ for the $K_N(1760)$ (see Phys. Rev. Letters 27 1160 1971). If this J^P is assumed then the ρ_{00} density matrix element for events with $t' < 0.2$ GeV^2/c^2 is 0.75 ± 0.12 indicating that pion exchange plays a dominant role in the production process. If we were to speculate that the meager evidence provided by the Y_8^0 moment implies spin = 4 for the $K_N(2100)$, we can produce a Chew-Frautschi plot (Fig. 11) and we see that the hypothesis of linear degenerate Regge-trajectories would be well satisfied.

BRANCHING RATIOS

The fraction of $K^*(890)\pi$ and $K\rho$ as well as uncorrelated three body decays of the two high mass states was found using a maximum likelihood fit to the Dalitz plot. Only for the 1760 region is a background subtraction meaningful. In the $K_N(1760)$ region we now find $33\pm12\%$ $K^*(890)\pi$ and $48\pm14\%$ $K\rho$ whereas we earlier reported 40% and 60% respectively. In addition, the amount of $K_N(1760) \rightarrow K\pi\pi$ increased somewhat when we allowed for an additional higher mass state and thus we now find the ratio $(K^*\pi + K\rho)/K\pi\pi = 1.60\pm0.44$

162

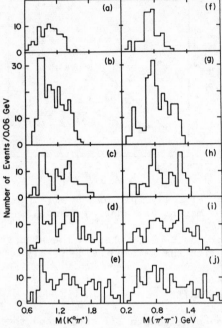

Fig. 12: $K^0\pi^+$ and $\pi^+\pi^-$ mass for various $K^0\pi^+\pi^-$ masses, from top 1.57-1.67, 1.67-1.87, 1.87-2.05, 2.05-2.25, and 2.25-2.65 GeV.

Table I Branching Ratios

Quant.	$K_N(1760)$	$K_N(2100)$
$K^*\pi/K\pi$	$0.54\pm.24$	$0.17\pm.07$
$K\rho/K\pi$	$1.05\pm.42$	$0.16\pm.06$
$K^{**}\pi/K\pi$	<0.06	$0.45\pm.18$
$Kf/K\pi$	------	$0.05\pm.02$
$K\omega/K\pi$	$0.12\pm.10$	<0.1
$K^*\rho/K\pi$	$0.60\pm.22$	$0.18\pm.10$
$\overline{\Lambda}N/K\pi$	------	seen
$K\pi/all$	$0.28\pm.07$	$0.45\pm.2$

Here, $K^*=K^*(890)$, $K^{**}=K^*(1420)$

which is in good agreement with the 7.2 GeV/c experiment which finds (using our new $K^*\pi$ and $K\rho$ fractions) 1.35 ± 0.8.

In Fig. 12 we present the $K^0\pi^+$ and $\pi^+\pi^-$ effective mass distributions for various slices of $K^0\pi^+\pi^-$ mass: a) 1.57-1.67, b) 1.67-1.87 i.e. the $K_N(1760)$ region, c) 1.87-2.05, d) 2.05-2.25 i.e. the $K_N(2100)$ region and e) 2.25-2.65 GeV. In contrast to the background slices, which unfortunately have considerable resonance tail effects, the $K_N(2100)$ appears to have $K^*(1420)\pi$ and Kf decay modes. The various branching ratios corrected for unseen decays are given in Table I.

CONCLUSIONS

Evidence for two high mass K^* states is found. The $K_N(1760)$ with mass 1769±12 MeV and width 130±50 MeV decays into $K\pi$, $K^*\pi$, $K\rho$, and $K^*\rho$ and appears to be the companion to the g meson in the 3^- nonet. The $K_N(2100)$ with mass 2115±45 MeV and width 300±100 MeV decays into $K\pi$, $K^*\pi$, $K\rho$, $K^*(1420)\pi$, Kf, $K^*\rho$, and $\overline{\Lambda}N$.

REFERENCES

1. D. Carmony et al., High Mass K^* Production in K^+d at 9 GeV/c.
2. M. Aguilar-Benitez et al., Phys. Rev. Letters 30 672 1973.
3. A. Firestone et al., Physics Letters 36B 513 1971.
4. P. Slattery, U. Rochester report UR 875-332.
5. See Review of Particle Properties, Rev. Mod. Physics 45 S104 1973. Except for the 4.6 GeV/c experiment which finds 0.2±0.2 for the ratio $K^*(1420)\pi/all$, the experiments listed are all 10-13 GeV experiments and are consistent with nearly 100% $K^*(1420)\pi$.

THE R-S-T-U MASS REGION*

Gerald A. Smith
Physics Department
Michigan State University
East Lansing, Michigan 48823

ABSTRACT

Contributed papers to the session on hadronic spectroscopy are reviewed. The relationship of these contributions to existing knowledge on the R-S-T-U meson states is discussed.

I. INTRODUCTION

My purpose in this talk is to review papers contributed to this Conference dealing with the R-S-T-U mass region for non-strange mesons (~1600-2500 MeV). To place things in their proper context, I shall initially review the overall situation. In this endeavor, I have borrowed heavily from other recent conference proceedings, particularly those of the 1972 Chexbres Symposium On Nucleon-Antinucleon Annihilations[1], the 1972 Philadelphia Experimental Meson Spectroscopy Conference[2], the 1972 XVI International Conference on High Energy Physics (Chicago-Batavia)[3], and various publications and preprints available at the time of this talk.

II. REVIEW OF THE R-S-T-U REGION

In 1965 first reports[4] from the CERN Missing Mass Spectrometer Group (CMMS) revealed considerable narrow structure for X^- in the reaction

$$\pi^- p \to X^- p \tag{1}$$

at incident momenta of 12 GeV/c and momentum transfers squared $0.2 \lesssim t \lesssim 0.4$ GeV^2 in the mass region above the A_2. The principal and statistically significant structures evident above the A_2 were the $R_{\bar{1}}$, $R_{\bar{2}}$, $R_{\bar{3}}$ (1632, 1700, 1748 MeV respectively), the S^-(1929 MeV), the T^-(2195 MeV) and the U^-(2382 MeV). More recently, however, the Northeastern-Stony Brook group has redone these measurements under similar kinematic conditions.[5,6] With higher statistics and

---

*Review talk given at the meeting of the Division of Particles and Fields, American Physical Society, Berkeley, California, 13-17 August, 1973.

comparable mass resolution they confirmed the R enhancement, but without any evidence for internal R_1, R_2, R_3 structures, and found no significant evidence for the S, T and U. Comparisons with expectations of S, T and U production based on the CMMS results clearly demonstrated that the Northeastern-Stony Brook data and the CMMS were incompatible. However, a few points should be made. First, W. Kienzle of the CERN group has published recently new information on the size of the S, T and U peaks from the original CMMS data. He reports that the original cross sections were too large by a factor of 4[']. He notes: "While this does not affect the statistical significance of the peaks, it is important for any comparison with other experiments." Second, the broad R meson is apparently real. It has been observed by CMMS, Northeastern-Stony Brook, CERN-IHEP[8], and the Brookhaven 180° missing mass experimenters[9]. In addition, various other broad structures (g(1680), ρ'(1700) and A_3(1640)) have been reported from bubble chamber studies[10].

Turning now to antiproton-nucleon formation experiments, the precision total cross section measurements of Abrams et al.[11] at Brookhaven revealed three broad structures, called $\pi_1^+(2190)$, $\pi_1^*(2350)$ and $\pi_0^*(2375)$. After unfolding the separate isospin contributions to the scatterings on hydrogen and deuterium, the resulting cross sections showed three structures. These enhancements, and particularly their proximity to the earlier reported T and U states from the CMMS group, have lead in a great deal of experimental activity. Counter-spark chamber experiments pursued, in general, two-particle final states, such as

$$\bar{p}p \rightarrow p\bar{p} \quad , \qquad (2)$$
$$\rightarrow \pi^-\pi^+ \quad , \qquad (3)$$
$$\rightarrow K\bar{K} \quad , \qquad (4)$$

whereas bubble chamber experiments concentrated on multiparticle and strange particle final states.

The more recent work of the Rutgers group[12] has provided a confirmation of the BNL work and has added new information on particle multiplicities associated with the two enhancements seen in $\bar{p}p$ interactions. This was a pure counter experiment which counted charged tracks and differentiated forward tracks to permit later cuts to eliminate peripheral, or non-annihilation, types of events. The T and U meson structures were clearly evident. Other checks on the data indicated satisfactory agreement with the results of Abrams et al.[11] The T data showed a dependence at both low multiplicity (1) and high multiplicity (~4). The high multiplicity region was interpreted to be associated with multi-particle annihilations, perhaps from the intermediate state $\rho\rho\pi$. The low multiplicity region may be associated with elastic scattering in the forward direction or one-pion production ($N\bar{N}\pi$). The U meson data were much less dramatic, with the low multiplicity points (0,2) substantially larger than those in the T region.

In an effort to isolate resonant effects from diffractive effects, several measurements of backward $\bar{p}p$ elastic scattering have been made. Yoh et al.[13] have reported considerable structure near 180° as a function of energy for incident $\bar{p}$'s from 0.7 to 2.16 GeV/c. These data span the T and U regions. However, there has been considerable difficulty in separating true resonant effects from diffractive effects. Although the diffraction calculations usually ignore spin and are somewhat simplified, they are rather easily capable of producing energy dependent structure at these relatively low energies. Extensive studies of backward elastic scattering in the S region by the Wisconsin group and the College de France, Paris (CDF) group have been carried out in the last few years.[14] The Wisconsin data show a clear indication of an enhancement near 1930 MeV (500 MeV/c) for $-0.9 < \cos \theta *\bar{p}p < -1.0$. The CDF data show a similar enhancement also. However, again we are aware of two rather simple diffraction calculations which reproduce the general features of these data, namely those of Bizzarri[14] and Pumplin[15]. Comments of a similar nature have been made by R. R. Burns et al.[16] in their study of backward $\bar{p}p$ elastic scattering from 700-1100 MeV/c.

Another interesting development in the S region was the observation of an enhancement in the cross section for $\bar{p}p \rightarrow K_S^\circ K_L^\circ$.[14] However, the Massachusetts-Tokyo collaboration does not see the same effect, as reported to the Batavia Conference.[17]

Turning to the T region, several bubble chamber studies have concentrated on multiparticle final states. One of these[18] reported on an enhancement in the cross section for $\bar{p}p \rightarrow \rho^\circ \rho^\circ \pi^\circ$ at 1.33 GeV/c, or the position of the T. The width was reported as $20 < \Gamma(MeV) < 80$. One may interpret data from an Argonne experiment to be consistent with this effect[19], although an earlier interpretation by the Argonne group was much less conclusive[20]. As mentioned earlier, the Rutgers annihilation data, particularly their multiplicity distribution in the T region, are consistent with a five-pion final state. Another Rutgers group has reported on an excess of double ρ° events near the momentum of the enhancement reported in reference 17[21]. However, the authors are still studying systematics and adding to their statistics. A Liverpool-Paris group, to the contrary, reported no evidence for this effect at the 1972 Batavia meeting[22].

Reactions (3) and (4) have been studied, principally in the Cal Tech-Rochester-BNL experiment[23] of a few years past. The data, from 0.7 to 2.4 GeV/c, were combined with earlier Cal Tech-BNL data to obtain angular distributions folded about 90° in the C.M. Results of a resonance model fit for $\pi^-\pi^+$ required a J=3 resonance with M=2.13 GeV and a J=5 resonance with M=2.28 GeV. Both states are quite broad (several hundred MeV) and have I=1, P=-1, G=+1 and do not coincide in mass with the enhancements reported by Abrams et al. The K^-K^+ data were consistent with simple exchange processes. However, a Yale group has made a measurement of the asymmetry for the production of $\pi^-\pi^+$ off polarized protons at 1.64 GeV/c[24]. There is poor agreement between the data and the model of Nicholson et al.[23]

Finally, we note that there has been considerable work on multiparticle final states above the T region, specifically near the U. Oh et al.[25] and Chapman et al.[26] have reported $K^*\overline{K}_{\pi\pi}$ and $K^+K^-\omega$ enhancements at the U respectively. However, to date no convincing confirmations of these effects have come forth.

III. REVIEW OF PAPERS SUBMITTED TO THIS CONFERENCE

(1) "Study of the R Region Produced by 13 GeV/cπ^+ Mesons", G. Thompson et al. (Purdue).

This paper reports on the missing mass spectrum opposite the proton (X^- in reaction (1)) in a 750,000 picture bubble chamber exposure of 13 GeV/cπ^+. The spectrum is investigated in terms of two and four pion channels. In Figure 1 a compilation for all two and four prong events of high missing mass observed opposite the proton is shown. A cut P_{LAB}(proton) < 1.2 GeV/c has been imposed and the average resolution is ~40 MeV in the 2 GeV region. Statistics are only slightly less than present counter experiments. The shaded events are a subset with $0.1 < t < 0.3$ GeV^2. Structures in the A_2 and R regions are apparent.

Concentrating on even G-parity states, the Purdue group has studied the reaction

$$\pi^+ p \to p\pi^+\pi^+\pi^-\pi^\circ \qquad (5)$$

with Δ^{++} events ($1.12 \leq M(p\pi_S^+) \leq 1.32$ GeV) removed. The four pion mass spectrum is shown in Figure 2. A large enhancement appears in the 1.6-1.8 GeV region. A single Breit-Wigner plus peripheral phase space background fit gives M=1670 ± 10 MeV and Γ=106 ± 25 MeV. The insert in Figure 2 shows the result of adding three components of the R with maximum widths permitted by CMMS and the same mass spacing. Cross-sections are based on CMMS, with a factor of 4 reduction[7]. The quality of fits may be improved by moving all components down by 35 MeV, consistent with other Northeastern-Stony Brook observations on masses quoted by CMMS. In the R region the $(4_\pi)^+$ differential cross section has an $e^{At'}$ dependence, with A=7.3 ± 0.3 (GeV/c)^2 for $0 < |t'| < 0.5$ GeV^2. It is clear that the observed R signal is associated with low t'. A cut $|t'| < 0.08$ GeV^2 (shaded histogram of Figure 2) sharpens the leading edge of the R with possible internal components which associate very well with the CMMS $R_1-R_2-R_3$ spacing.

Probing for quasi-two-body decay modes of the R^+, the Purdue group has studied the $\omega^\circ\pi^+$ mass spectrum, shown in Figure 3, where the ω° is defined as $0.74 \leq M(\pi^+\pi^-\pi^\circ) \leq 0.86$ GeV. There is clear B^+ signal as well as an R^+ signal, thus fixing $I^G=1^+$ for this state. The measured branching fraction is

$$\frac{\sigma(R^+ \to \omega^\circ \pi^+)}{\sigma(R^+ \to \pi^+\pi^+\pi^-\pi^\circ)} = 32.6 \pm 6.4\% \tag{6}$$

Because of the large signal/noise ratio observed in the R^+, decay angles have been studied. Fits to a $J^P=3^-$ state produced by one-pion exchange are preferred over $J^P=1^-$, but indistinguishable from $J^P=5^-$.

We now turn to $\rho\rho$, $A_2\pi$ decay modes of the R. Defining $0.6 \leq M(2\pi) \leq 0.85$ GeV and $1.24 \leq M(3\pi) \leq 1.36$ GeV as cuts for the ρ and A_2 respectively, the resultant mass plots are shown in Figures 4 and 5. There is a strong kinematical overlap of the $\rho\rho$ and A_2 channels. In Figure 5 the shaded histogram shows events which cannot be simultaneously $\rho^+\rho^\circ$. It is clear that a large protion of the R signal occurs in events which are simultaneous candidates for these channels. A careful and lengthy subsequent analysis results in

$$\frac{\sigma(R^+ \to \rho^+\rho^\circ)}{\sigma(R^+ \to \pi^+\pi^+\pi^-\pi^\circ)} = 8.1 \pm 8.7\% \tag{7}$$

and

$$\frac{\sigma(R^+ \to A_2^{\pm}\pi^{\mp})}{\sigma(R^+ \to \pi^+\pi^+\pi^-\pi^\circ)} = 21.0 \pm 13.4\% \tag{8}$$

A possible $S^+ \to \rho^+\rho^\circ$ signal is also observed in Figure 4. Studies of possible decays $R^+ \to (\rho\pi\pi)^+$, $\eta^\circ\pi^+$ and $\phi^\circ\pi^+$ give no indication of structure at the R.

Turning now to the two-prong events of the type

$$\pi^+p \to p\pi^+(MM) \quad (MM > M(2\pi^\circ)) \tag{9}$$

and

$$\pi^+p \to p\pi^+\pi^\circ, \tag{10}$$

the π^+MM spectrum from (9), with a cut $P_L(\pi^+) < 2$ GeV/c to remove f°'s from the reaction

$$\begin{array}{l} \pi^+p \to pA_3^+ \\ \qquad \lower2pt\hbox{$\mathrel{\rule{0pt}{6pt}}\!\!\!\to$} f^\circ\pi^+ \\ \qquad\qquad \lower2pt\hbox{$\mathrel{\rule{0pt}{6pt}}\!\!\!\to$} \pi^\circ\pi^\circ \end{array} \tag{11}$$

and hence remove reaction (11) as a source of background and a cut to remove Δ^{++} events, shows a small enhancement near the R. The $\pi^+\pi^\circ$ spectrum from (10) also shows a small spike at the R. The fitted branching ratio is

$$\frac{\sigma(R^+ \to \pi^+\pi^\circ)}{\sigma(4\pi^+) + \sigma(2\pi^+)} = 0.08 \pm 0.05 \tag{12}$$
$$= \eta(\text{elasticity})$$

Finally, the reaction

$$\pi^+p \to \Delta^{++} \pi^+\pi^- \tag{13}$$

has been studied for neutral decay of the R. A small R signal is observed.

In conclusion, new and significant data on the R meson have been presented. The results of this effort in terms of observed final states, fitted masses and widths are shown in Figure 6.

(2) "Structure In the $\omega\pi\pi$ Mass Spectrum", W. Fickinger et al (Case Western Reserve-Carnegie-Mellon).

This group has studied the reaction

$$\pi^+ d \rightarrow p_s p \pi^+ \pi^+ \pi^- \pi^- \pi^\circ \tag{14}$$

in a high statistics bubble chamber experiment at 6 GeV/c. In Figure 7 is shown the $\pi^+ \pi^- \pi^\circ$ mass spectrum for five and six-prong events and just six-prong events. A clear ω° signal is observed. Applying an ω° cut (750 < M(3π) < 825 MeV), the $\omega^\circ \pi^+ \pi^-$ spectrum is studied in Figure 8. A clear signal at 1320 MeV is seen, and a hint of a broad shoulder near 1660 MeV is also apparent. These data include all five and six-prong events.

Turning to the reaction

$$\pi^+ d \rightarrow p_s p \pi^+ \pi^- \pi^\circ \tag{15}$$

the $\pi^+ \pi^- \pi^\circ$ spectrum is indicated in Figure 9, showing ω°, 1320 and 1660 MeV signals. The same data, with $\rho^{\pm}$ cuts, are shown in Figure 10. The 1660 MeV object is very clear, with a decay mode $\rho^\circ \pi^\circ$, thus indicating I=0. The authors have measured the branching ratio

$$\frac{\omega(1660) \rightarrow \omega\pi\pi}{\omega(1660) \rightarrow \rho\pi} = 0.60 \pm 0.20 \tag{16}$$

(3) "Precision Measurements of $K^{\pm}$ & $\bar{p}$ Total Cross Section on Hydrogen and Deuterium Below 1.1 GeV/c", D. N. Michael et al (Brookhaven).

Total cross section measurements of $\bar{p}$'s on hydrogen and deuterium have been extended down to 350 MeV/c by a Brookhaven group. An enhancement near 1930 MeV is observed in both hydrogen and deuterium. The height of the bump is ~10mb and the width is consistent with their experimental resolution, or $\Gamma \approx 30$ MeV. The authors have deferred the question of the isotopic spin of the enhancement until further study of the data has been completed. The total cross sections are shown in Figure 11.

(4) "The Differential Cross-Section For $\bar{p}p \rightarrow K^- K^+$ Between 0.8 and 2.4 GeV/c", C. Hojvat et al (Queen Mary College, Liverpool, Daresbury, RHEL).

This counter-spark chamber experiment has measured reaction (4) at CERN at 20 momenta from 0.8-2.4 GeV/c spanning the T and U regions for -0.95 < cos θc.m. < 0.95 with ~300 events per momentum. In order to cover the C.M. angular range, the spectrometer magnet, spark chambers and recoil chambers could be rotated from 15° to 55° about the target. A check of the apparatus and analysis was made by measuring $\pi^- p$ elastic scattering, which has kinematics similar to those of reactions (3) and (4).

The observed total cross sections are shown in Figure 12. We note that this experiment measures the odd and even Legendre moments, in contrast to Nicholson et al.[23] who measured only even moments. No attempt has been made to interpret the data in terms of s-channel effects until some meaningful understanding of reaction (3) has been achieved.

(5) "The Differential Cross-Section For $\bar{p}p \rightarrow \pi^-\pi^+$ Between 0.8 and 2.4 GeV/c", A. S. L. Parsons et al (RHEL, Queen Mary College, Liverpool, Daresbury).

The data result from the same experiment described in paper 4. In this case (reaction (3)) there are about 2000 events per momentum. Legendre moments are shown in Figure 13. The agreement with the even moments of Nicholson et al.[23] (open points) is only moderate, with a 30% normalization discrepancy, well outside of errors. The authors state that the resonance results of Nicholson et al.[23] do not agree with their odd Legendre coefficients. Although their analysis is preliminary, the authors find no clear support for the resonant states of Nicholson et al.[23] and, in addition, agree with the Yale polarization data[24].

(6) "An Isospin Analysis for the Reaction $\bar{p}N \rightarrow \overline{N}N\pi$ Between 1.09 and 2.90 GeV/c", Z. Ming Ma et al (Michigan State).

In this paper the authors have analyzed the reactions

$$\bar{p}p \rightarrow \bar{p}p\pi^\circ , \tag{17}$$

$$\bar{n}p\pi^- , \tag{18}$$

and $$\bar{p}n \rightarrow \bar{p}p\pi^- \tag{19}$$

from threshold to 2.90 GeV/c in an attempt to isolate the isospin zero and one cross-section dependence with energy. The motivation for this stems from the observation by Abrams et al.[11] of two isospin one and one isospin zero enhancements in $\bar{p}p$ and $\bar{p}d$ total cross sections. A complete isospin analysis has been carried out. Specifically, there are two s-channel diagrams corresponding to the formation of $N\pi$ and $\overline{N}\pi$ resonances and two t-channel diagrams also corresponding to the production of $N\pi$, and $\overline{N}\pi$ resonances. Assuming that isospin zero exchange in the t-channel is negligible, reactions (17-19) can be used to solve a closed set of equations for σ_0 and σ_1. The results of this calculation are shown in Figure 14. The shaded bands correspond to ± one standard deviation errors. It is obvious that the ~5 mb $\pi^*(2190)$ bump of Abrams et al.[11] near 1.3 GeV/c cannot be explained in terms of the $N\overline{N}\pi$ I=1 final state. Because of the nature of the turnover in σ_1, near 1.8 GeV/c, it is not so apparent that $N\overline{N}\pi$ effects do not play a role in enhancement formation near the U-meson region, specifically the ~2 mb $\pi_1^*(2350)$ enhancement. On the other hand, it is obvious the $N\overline{N}\pi$ I=0 final state does not contribute to the $\pi_0^*(2375)$. To test the $\pi_1^*(2350)$ case, the σ_1 data were fit to a sum of polynomial background plus Breit-Wigner resonance, where the resonance parameters used were those of Abrams et al.[11] The results indicate that the $N\bar{N}\pi$ final state may be as much as 25 ± 8% of the $\pi_1^*(2350)$ effect.

(7) "A Search for $\rho^\circ\rho^\circ\pi^-$ Enhancement in Antiproton-Neutron Annihilation Between 1.09 and 1.43 GeV/c", Z. Ming Ma et al (Michigan State).

The work of Kalbfleisch et al.[18] on the reaction $\bar{p}p \to \rho^\circ\rho^\circ\pi^\circ$ in the T meson region has been discussed previously. They reported a 0.5 ± 0.1 mb enhancement at 1.33 GeV/c (average of 1.31, 1.33 and 1.35 GeV/c data) for this state relative to zero cross section at neighboring momenta of 1.11 and 1.52 GeV/c. This effect was attributed to the formation of an $I^G=1^-$ state, the $\pi_1^*(2190)$. Ma et al. have studied the reaction

$$\bar{p}d \to p_s\rho^\circ\rho^\circ\pi^- \to p_s 2\pi^+ 3\pi^-, \qquad (20)$$

where p_s is a spectator proton, at incident momenta of 1.06, 1.16, 1.27, 1.40. 1.60. 1.75. 1.85. 2.00. 2.15, 2.30. 2.45. 2.60 and 2.90 GeV/c. The events are highly constrained (4C or 4C with weak constraints on the spectator proton) bubble chamber events. The half width at half maximum spread due to beam optics and energy loss in the deuterium in the region near 1.3 GeV/c is typically ±25 MeV/c, or ±9 MeV C.M. energy. To this one must fold in the Fermi motion of the neutron target, estimated to be ±20 MeV C.M. energy. Hence, the final C.M. energy resolution is ~ ±22 MeV. The Kalbfleisch et al.[18] effect is observed equally at three momenta (1.31, 1.33 and 1.35 GeV/c) and not at 1.11 and 1.52 GeV/c, implying a width of 20 $\leq$ Γ $\leq$ 80 MeV. Hence, if the width of the effect were 20 MeV, Ma et al., would probably not be very sensitive to the effect at their closest point, 1.27 GeV/c. On the other hand, if the width were 50 MeV, for example, Ma et al., would be quite sensitive to the effect, both at 1.27 and 1.40 GeV/c.

The cross section data of Ma et al., are shown in Figure 15. No enhancement is observed in the cross sections for $\bar{p}n \to 2\pi^+ 3\pi^-$, or the subset of cross sections for $\rho^\circ\pi^+ 2\pi^-$ and $\rho^\circ\rho^\circ\pi^-$. In the latter case, a direct comparison is made with the Kalbfleisch et al., data, multiplied by two to account for incident isospin in a direct channel I=1 resonant model. The authors note that rather strong correlations were observed in fitting the single and double ρ final states. However, the determination of the average number of ρ's, also shown in the Figure, does not have this ambiguity and is clearly without structure. They note that any substantial peaking in $\rho^\circ\rho^\circ\pi^-$ would be accompanied by a dip in $\rho^\circ\pi^+ 2\pi^-$. Neither effect is seen.

REFERENCES

1. Proceedings of the Symposium of Nucleon-Antinucleon Annihilations, Chexbres, Switzerland, 27-29 March, 1972 and published as CERN report 72-10, 15 June, 1972.

2. Proceedings of the Experimental Meson Spectroscopy Conference-1972, Philadelphia, Pennsylvania, 28-29 April, 1972 and published as AIP Conference Proceedings #8, Particles and Fields Subseries #3, edited by A. N. Rosenfeld and K. W. Lai, 1972.

3. Proceedings of the XVI International Conference on High Energy Physics, Chicago-Batavia, Illinois, 6-13 September, 1972.

4. M. Focacci et al., Phys. Rev. Letters 17, 890 (1966).

5. "Measurements of Missing Mass (MM) Spectra from $\pi^-p \rightarrow (MM)^-p$ at 8, 11, 13.5 and 16 GeV", D. Bowen et al., reference 2, page 215.

6. D. Bowen et al., Phys. Rev. Letters 30, 332 (1973).

7. W. Kienzle, Physical Review D, 7, 3520 (1973).

8. Y. M. Antipov et al., Physics Letters 40B, 147 (1972).

9. E. W. Anderson et al., Phys. Rev. Letters 22, 1390 (1969).

10. "Review of Particle Properties", T. A. Lasinski et al., Rev. Mod. Phys. 45, 51 (1973).

11. R. J. Abrams et al., Phys. Rev. D, 1, 1917 (1970).

12. J. Alspector et al., Phys. Rev. Letters 30, 511 (1973) and K. J. Cohen, reference 2, page 242.

13. J. K. Yoh et al., Phys. Rev. Letters 23, 506 (1969).

14. For an excellent review of these experiments, see M. Laloum, reference 1, page 1 and references cited therein.

15. "Antiproton-Proton Elastic Scattering", J. Pumplin, preprint, Michigan State University, 1973.

16. "pp Elastic Scattering In the Backward Hemisphere From 686 to 1098 MeV/c", R. R. Burns et al., University of California (Irvine) Technical Report #73-39.

17. R. Diebold, reference 3, page 61.

18. G. Kalbfleisch, R. Strand and V. Vanderburg, Physics Letters 29B, 259 (1969).

19. K. J. Cohen, reference 2, page 247.

20. M. Derrick, Proceedings of the Boulder Conference on High Energy Physics, 18-22 August, 1969, p. 314.

21. P. Yamin et al., Bull. Am. Phys. Soc. 18, 125 (1973).

22. R. Diebold, reference 3, page 60.

23. H. Nicholson et al., Phys. Rev. D, 7, 2572 (1973).

24. R. D. Ehrlich et al., Phys. Rev. Letters 28, 1147 (1972). See also A. Astbury, reference 1, page 80.

25. B. Y. Oh, et al., Phys. Rev. Letters 24, 1257 (1970). See also P. S. Eastman et al., Nuclear Physics B51, 29(1973); B. Y. Oh et al., Nuclear Physics B51, 57 (1973) and Z. Ming Ma et al., Nuclear Physics B51, 77(1973) for detailed comments on searches for multiparticle structure near the U-meson.

26. J. W. Chapman et al., Phys. Rev. D4, 1275 (1971).

172

<u>FIGURE CAPTIONS</u>

Figs. 1- 6 - Purdue data on $\pi^+p \rightarrow pX^+$ at 13 GeV/c. See text for details.

Figs. 7-10 - Case Western Reserve-Carnegie Mellon data for π^+d $p_s p 2\pi^+ 2\pi^- \pi^\circ$ and $p_s p \pi^+ \pi^- \pi^\circ$ at 6 GeV/c. See text for details.

Fig. 11 - Brookhaven $\bar{p}p$ and $\bar{p}d$ total cross section data below 1.1 GeV/c.

Figs. 12-13 - Queen Mary College, Liverpool, Daresbury, Rutherford data on $pp \rightarrow \pi^+\pi^-$, K+K-. See text for details.

Fig. 14 - Michigan State data on $\bar{p}N \rightarrow N\bar{N}\pi$. See text for details.

Fig. 15 - Michigan State data on $\bar{p}d \rightarrow p_s\rho^\circ\rho^\circ\pi^- \rightarrow p_s 3\pi^- 2\pi^+$. See text for details.

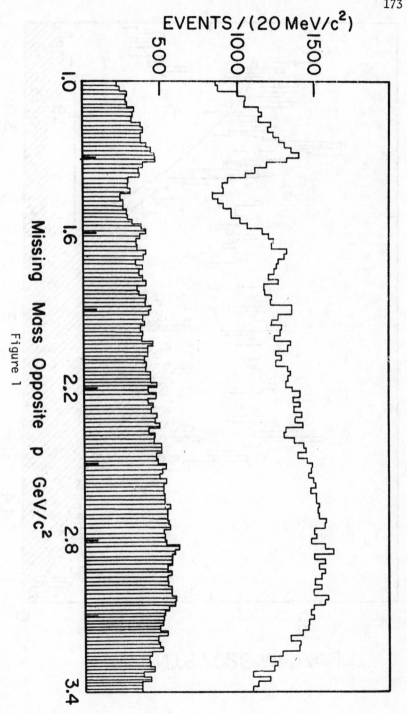

Figure 1

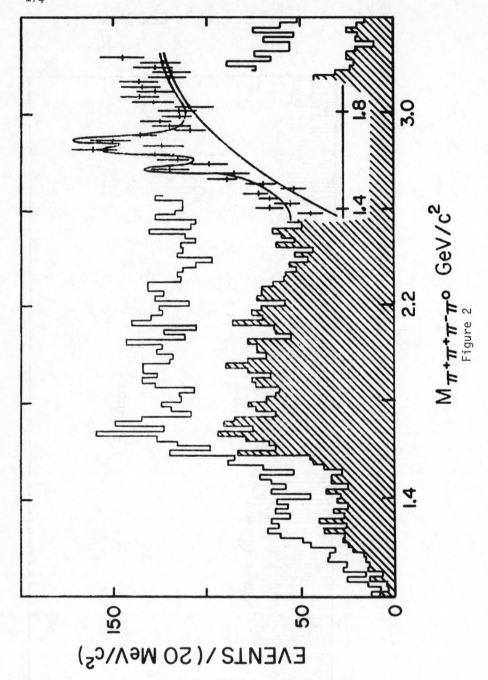

EVENTS/(20 MeV/c^2)

M$_{\pi^+\pi^+\pi^-\pi^o}$ GeV/c^2

Figure 2

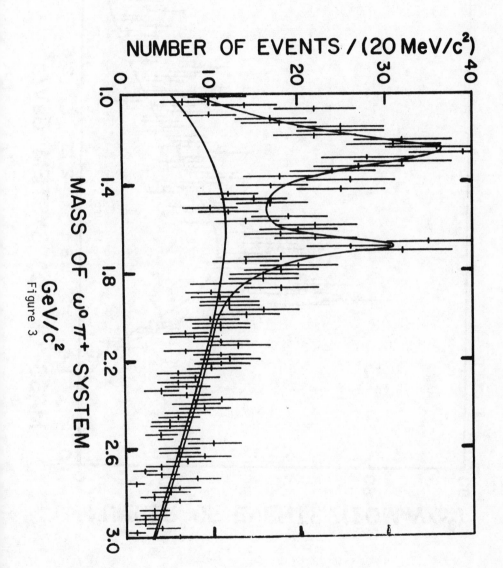

Figure 3

176

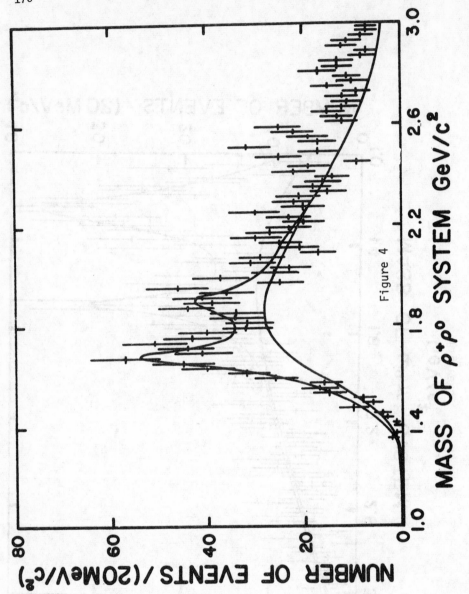

NUMBER OF EVENTS/(20MeV/c²)

MASS OF $\rho^+\rho^0$ SYSTEM GeV/c²

Figure 4

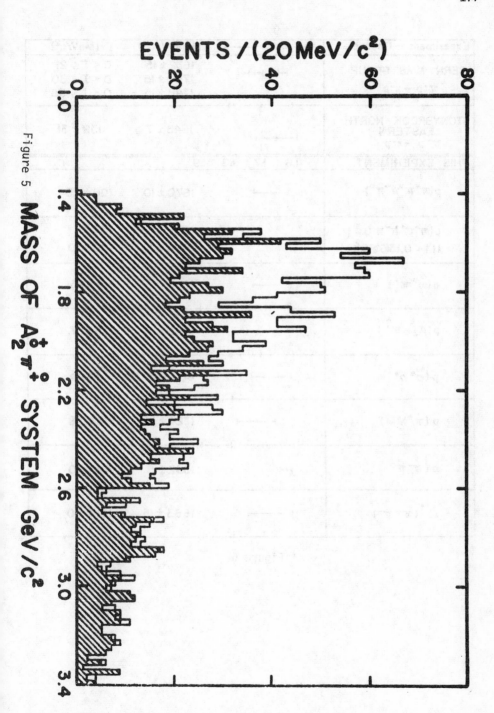

Figure 5

EVENTS /(20MeV/c²)

MASS OF A₂$^{\pm}$ π$^{\pm}$ SYSTEM GeV/c²

Experiment — Channel	— — Mass ⟶	M(MeV/c²)	Γ (MeV/c²)
CERN MMS GROUP $\pi^- p \rightarrow x^- p$	⊢⊣ ⊢⊣⊢⊣	1632 ± 15 1700 ± 15 1748 ± 15	0 < Γ ≤ 21 0 < Γ ≤ 30 0 < Γ ≤ 38
STONYBROOK—NORTH- EASTERN $\pi^- p \rightarrow x^- p$	⊢—•—⊣	1648 ± 7	139 ± 31
THIS EXPERIMENT	1.6 1.7 1.8 1.9		
$p(\pi^+\pi^+\pi^-\pi^\circ)$	⊢—•—⊣	1670 ± 10	106 ± 25
$p(\pi^+\pi^+\pi^-\pi^\circ)$ $|t'| < 0.15 (GeV)^2$	⊢⊣ ⊢—•—⊣	1593 ± 10 1684 ± 10	10 ± 10 109 ± 30
$p(\omega^\circ \pi^+)$	⊢—•—⊣	1686 ± 9	89 ± 25
$p(A_2^\delta \pi^2)$	⊢—•—⊣	1682 ± 11	128 ± 27
$p(\rho^\circ \rho^+)$	⊢—•—⊣	1671 ± 9	127 ± 35
$p(\pi^+ MM)$	⊢—•—⊣	1724 ± 14	86 ± 38
$p(\pi^+ \pi^\circ)$	⊢•⊣	1632 ± 5	42 ± 20
$\Delta^{++}(\pi^+ \pi^-)$	⊢—•—⊣	1683 ± 15	151 ± 50

Figure 6

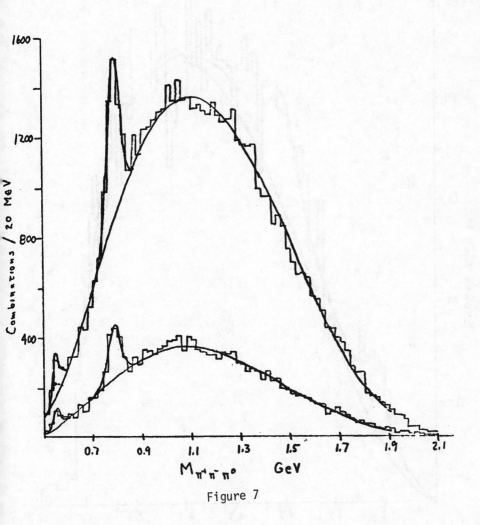

Figure 7

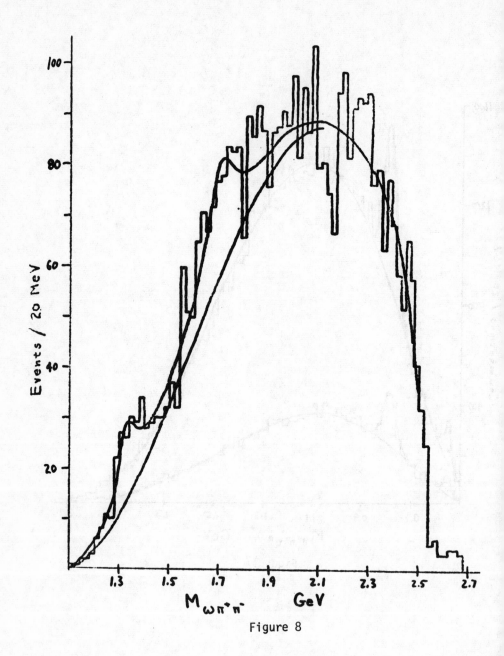

Figure 8

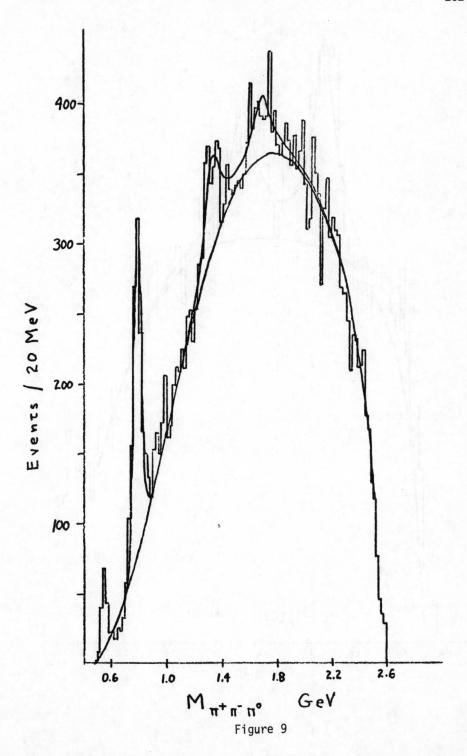

Figure 9

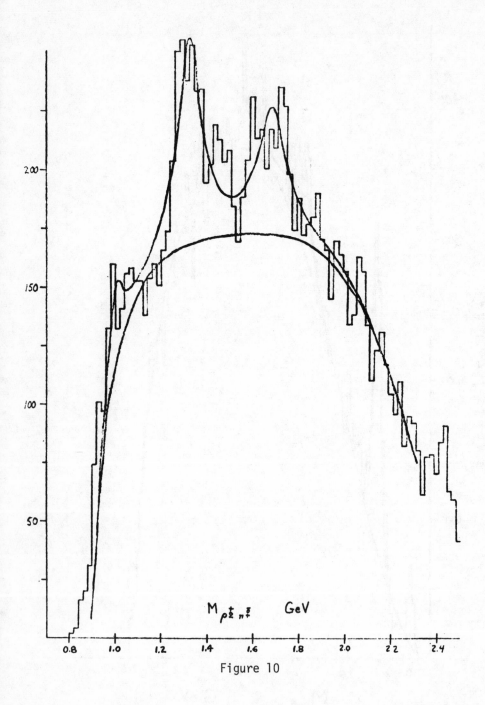

$M_{\rho^{\pm}\eta^{\mp}}$ GeV

Figure 10

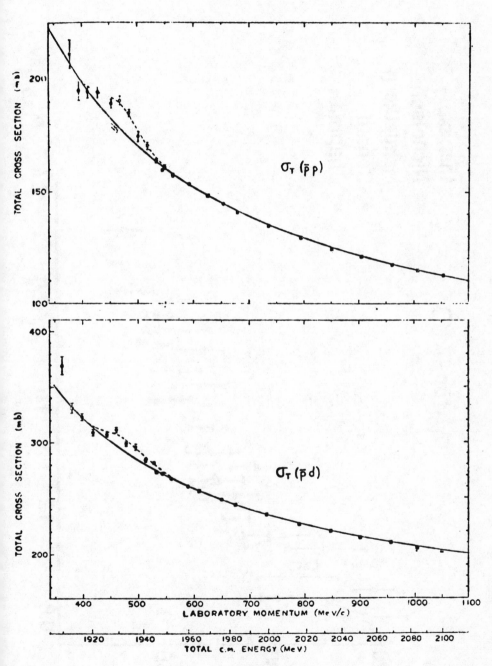

Figure 11

184

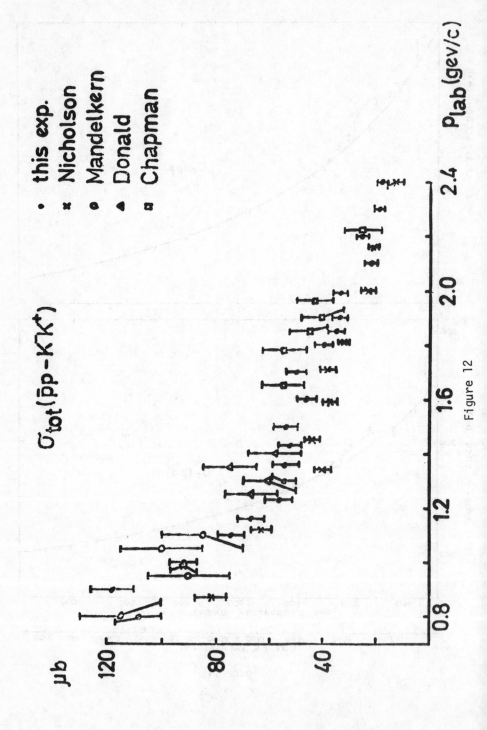

Figure 12

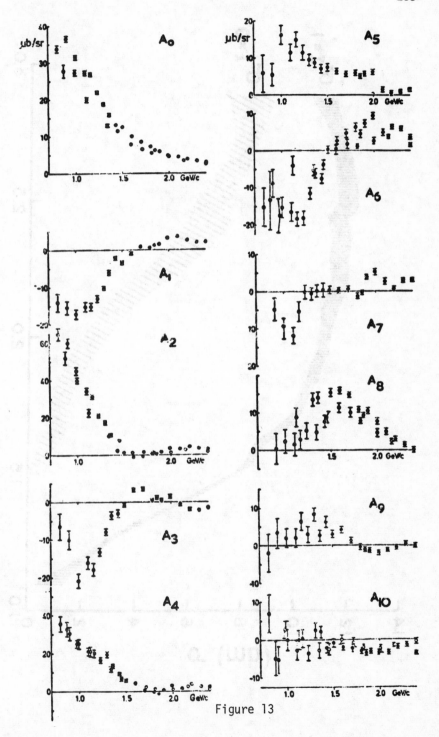

Figure 13

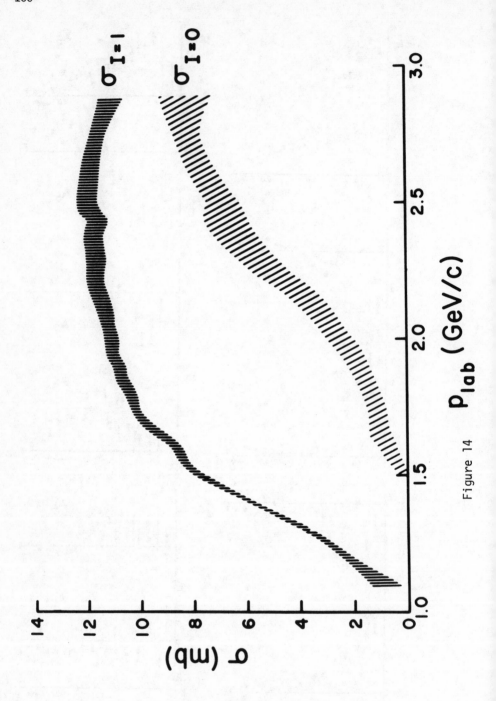

Figure 14

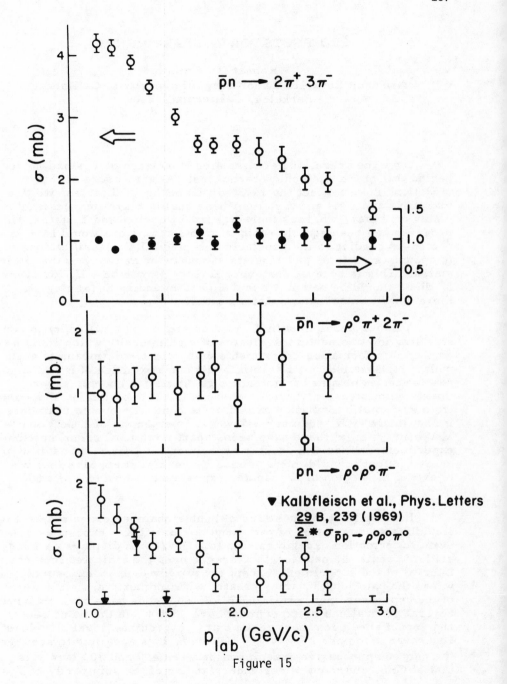

Figure 15

PROSPECTS FOR Y^* EXPERIMENTS[†]

Robert D. Tripp
Lawrence Berkeley Laboratory, University of California
Berkeley, California 94720

Over the years, the accumulated knowledge of Y^*s has lagged behind that of the nucleonic resonances. As a measure of this retardation, if we inspect the 1973 edition of the PDG tables[1] we find that there are 22 N and Δ states whose quality classification is either 3 star or 4 star, whereas there are but 21 such Λ and Σ states. If progress had been equally rapid in both domains one would have expected—according to the popularly accepted SU(3) classifications into decuplets, octets, and singlets—about twice as many of the latter states. This is because for every Δ there should be a Σ, for every N there should be both a Λ and a Σ, and including SU(3) singlets there should be solitary Λ states as well.

A major problem with Y^* studies stems from difficulty in constructing low-momentum K^- beams of high intensity which could be employed in formation experiments using electronic means to accumulate high statistics. Essentially all our knowledge of N and Δ resonances is obtained from such high-statistics counter experiments with intense $\pi^\pm$ beams, whereas the bulk of data on Y^*s come from systematic formation experiments done with bubble chambers in low-intensity K^- beams. Below a K^- momentum of 1 GeV/c (1790 MeV c.m. energy) there have been, apart from total cross-section experiments, no fruitful counter experiments. Now as a result of a greater effort to build more intense K^- beams, it appears feasible to extend the region of K^- counter experiments down to about 500 MeV/c.

Looking first at the status of bubble chamber experiments, Fig. 1 exhibits a compilation of path lengths[2] for all K^-p exposures relevant to formation experiments up to 2 GeV/c. It displays on a logarithmic scale the path length averaged over the indicated momentum interval of the experiment (except for two low-energy exposures where the path length varies greatly with momentum). In many of the exposures only certain reaction topologies have been analyzed. Several generations of experiments are shown. In the more recent and unpublished ones most regions are covered at a level of at least 1000 events/mb per 25 MeV/c. However, it is appalling to see that the only comprehensive experiment between 450 and 800 MeV/c is that of CHS, and most of our understanding of the spin parity of Y^*s

---

[†]Work done under the auspices of the U. S. Atomic Energy Commission.

in this region is based upon this relatively-low-statistics experiment. Forthcoming Tennessee-Massachusetts data will improve
the upper momentum region, as will a higher statistics CERN-
Heidelberg-Munich experiment whose analysis is just beginning. As
indicated by the dashed line, a track-sensitive target (a hydrogen
target surrounded by a hydrogen-neon mixture) is now running at the
Rutherford laboratory and plans call[2a] for extending this exposure into
the critically deficient region below 600 MeV/c. The chamber has
an average gamma-ray detection efficiency of about 20% so that separa-
tion of $\Lambda \pi^0$, $\Sigma^0 \pi^0$, and $\Lambda \pi^0 \pi^0$ will also be more reliable than in a conventional bubble chamber experiment. It is interesting to note that the
most recent experiments are all being done in European laboratories
—the U.S. has essentially abandoned and is dismantling its capacity
to do systematic high-statistics studies, despite the obvious deficiency of currently published experiments to do any more than ex-
pose the dominant resonant structures.

Figures 2 and 3 display corresponding path-length plots for K^--
deuterium[3] and K^0_L-p[4] bubble chamber experiments. The deuterium
exposures are in reasonable balance with respect to the hydrogen
experiments, and the K^0_L bubble chamber activity—long in coming—
appears now at a level where it may contribute substantially to the
knowledge of the pure I = 1 state of $\overline{K}N$. In particular the recent
RGEPB exposure in the CERN 2-meter chamber uses an essentially
monoenergetic K^0_L beam of $\Delta P/P = \pm 2.5\%$. This additional constraint permits the study of more reactions types.

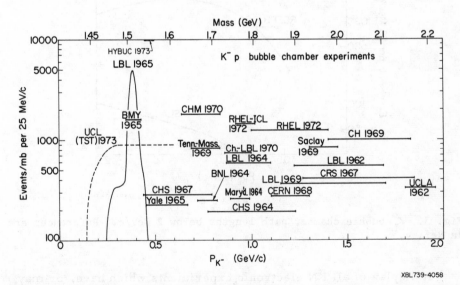

XBL739-4058

Fig. 1. K^-p bubble chamber path lengths below 2 GeV/c. Numbers
refer to the approximate date of the exposure. Horizontal lines show
the momentum interval and the average level of the exposure over that
interval. Abbreviations and references are in Ref. 2.

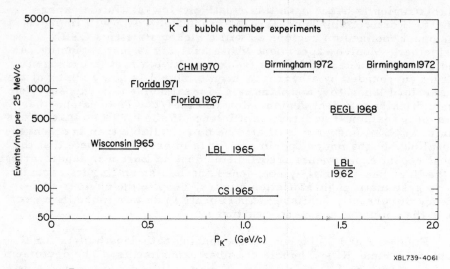

Fig. 2. K⁻ deuterium bubble chamber path lengths below 2 GeV/c. Numbers refer to the approximate date of the exposure. Abbreviations and references are in Ref. 3.

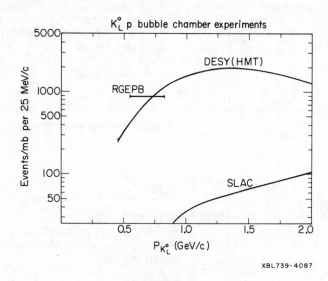

Fig. 3. K_L^0 bubble chamber path lengths below 2 GeV/c. References are in Ref. 4.

A display of all $\overline{K}N$ electronic experiments which have, or may in the near future, contribute to Y^* studies is shown in Fig. 4.[5] Of recent interest is the BNL total cross-section experiment,[5d] as yet unpublished, which has revealed new structure at a momentum of 540 MeV/c. Two RHEL experiments, still being analyzed, promise to improve the statistics on K⁻p elastic scattering; despite several

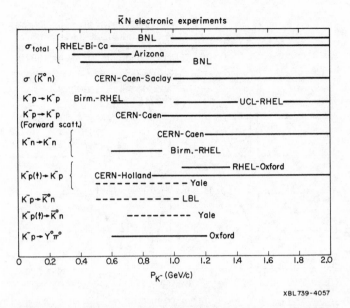

Fig. 4. $\overline{K}N$ electronic experiments relevant to Y^* studies. Horizontal lines indicate the momentum interval covered. Dashed lines are proposed experiments. References are in Ref. 5.

previous efforts of electronic experiments to overwhelm bubble chamber data with this simplest of reactions, the latter still dominate Y^* analysis. In 1972 CERN-Caen did a wire chamber experiment in the Coulomb-nuclear interference region to obtain the real part of the K^-p forward scattering amplitude. This will be a useful constraint in future Y^* partial wave analyses. Two K^-n elastic scattering experiments are also in the analysis stages and should improve considerably the knowledge of the $I = 1$ elastic scattering amplitude, both in statistics and in the purity of the data compared with the same bubble chamber reaction in deuterium.

An obvious way in which electronic experiments can contribute to the study of Y^*s is through experiments with polarized targets. In the past this has been extended down to a momentum of 865 MeV/c, below which beam fluxes became prohibitively low. Although no new resonances or spin-parity assignments were revealed by the two experiments, they did serve to instill greater confidence in the energy-dependent elastic partial wave analyses since they had correctly predicted the subsequently measured polarizations. (These analyses had to that time been based only upon elastic and charge exchange angular distributions.) In contrast, energy-independent pion-nucleon analyses in recent years have been notoriously deficient in their predictive powers with respect to new experiments.[6] That such success will not be the case at lower K^- momenta and for other K^- reactions is apparent in Fig. 5, where polarization predictions for three elastic partial wave analyses are shown[7, 9e, 2m] for K^-p

192

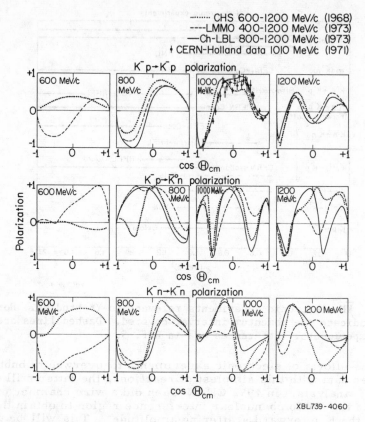

Fig. 5. Polarization predictions from three $\overline{K}N$ partial wave analyses at 600, 800, 1000, and 1200 MeV/c. Only K^-p polarization has been measured and only from a momentum of 865 MeV/c upward.

elastic and charge exchange scattering and for K^-n elastic scattering. In particular the K^-p polarization predictions for two analyses at 600 MeV/c are vastly different. An experiment has been proposed by the Yale group to extend the K^-p polarization measurements down to 500 MeV/c, using the BNL high-intensity K^- beam.[8] Figure 6 shows the fluxes of K^+, K^-, and $\bar{p}$ available from this beam per 10^{12} protons; several times this number can currently be delivered to the target by the AGS per pulse. The Yale group is also considering an experiment to measure charge exchange polarization down to comparable momenta. We (LBL) are proposing to measure the charge exchange angular distribution from 500 to 1000 MeV/c at a series of momenta with a statistical precision of a bubble chamber exposure of 10 000 events per mb per 25 MeV/c; i.e., corresponding to an experiment at the top of Fig. 1. This would also utilize the BNL K^- beam. A K beam of comparable intensity is coming into operation at ANL, so that we may anticipate an enhanced experimental effort on Y^* formation experiments.

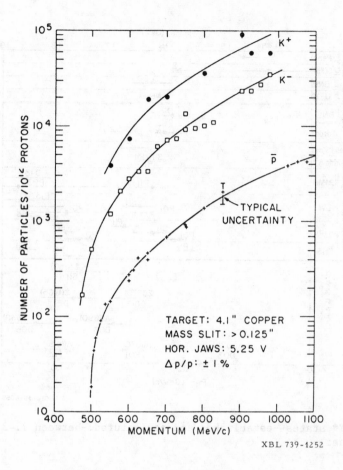

Fig. 6. Particle fluxes from the BNL partially separated low-energy beam.

The present situation concerning hyperon resonances accessible to formation experiments up to a mass of 1.9 GeV is summarized in Fig. 7.[9] The well-established 3-star and 4-star resonances are shown at the bottom. Above those appears a chaos of possible resonant states suggested with varying degrees of conviction by a number of partial wave analyses of bubble chamber data augmented by total cross-section and K⁻p polarization data. About the only persistent suggestion in these analyses is that there appears to be, in addition to $\Sigma(1670)$, another Σ resonance in the vicinity of 1620 MeV either in the S-wave or P wave. As indicated farther up in the figure, such a state has been reported in the recent BNL total cross-section experiment but, alas, at a significantly different mass and width. (There was also a suggestion for such a state in the earlier Arizona total cross-section measurements.)

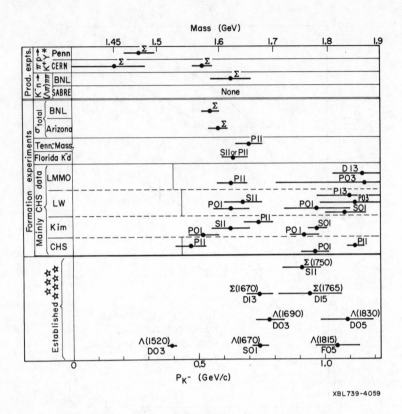

Fig. 7. Y* states--established and conjectured--between 1.43 and 1.9 GeV mass.

The first evidence for a Σ resonance in the vicinity of 1600 MeV appeared many years ago in production experiments; this is shown at the top of Fig. 7. The BNL-CCNY bubble chamber experiment[9k] found indications in the reaction $K^- n \rightarrow (\Lambda \pi)^- \pi^+ \pi^-$ at a $\Lambda \pi$ mass of 1620 MeV, whereas a European collaboration (SABRE)[9j] doing a similar experiment at a slightly lower bombarding energy did not confirm such a state.

Much earlier than these experiments, in the all-but-forgotten past, there were two $\pi^- p \rightarrow Y^{*-}_9\ell K^+$ missing-mass type experiments done with counters at CERN,[9ℓ] where only the K^+ was detected as the bombarding energy was varied. One of these observed the K^+ at 0° in the cm while the other covered the K^+ c.m. angular region $0.8 > \cos \theta > -0.5$. The former is shown in Fig. 8a, where in addition to enhancements at the Σ and $Y^*(1385)$ masses, structure is suggested at 1570 MeV, similar in mass and width to the BNL total cross-section bump. At the time, the evidence was understandably found to be unconvincing both statistically and because a plausible alternative explanation could be invoked to explain the structure,

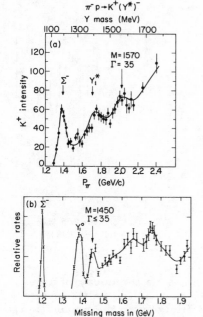

$\pi^- p \to K^+ (Y^*)^-$

Fig. 8. Evidence for Σ resonant states from CERN missing-mass experiments (Ref. 91). In (a) the K^+ is produced at 0° in the c.m. and in (b) it is produced at larger angles. Masses and widths are estimated.

XBL739-4080

namely a changing amplitude in the s-channel of the pion-nucleon system as the incident pion momentum was changed to sweep through the mass region of the Y^* sampled by the apparatus. Likewise Fig. 8b shows the result of the latter experiment, where evidence for another Σ resonance at a mass of 1450 MeV was presented. Such a state has also been claimed in the same reaction at approximately the same incident pion momentum (1.7 GeV/c) in a high-statistics bubble chamber production experiment.[9m] The evidence from that experiment is shown in Fig. 9, where a suggestion of structure is seen at 1475 MeV. Occasional evidence for such a state has also been rumored in K^-N formation experiments,[2b,10] but the indications are weak. If the state exists at all its branching fraction into the $\overline{K}N$ channel is very low so that it is formed with only a small amplitude. The additional path length of the new track-sensitive target exposure shown in Fig. 1 may be sufficient to clarify this mass region.

I have touched on some production experiment evidence for Y^*s, although I do not think that this type of experiment will be of great value in the future compared with high-statistics formation experiments which determine at the same time the spin and parity of the resonance. The reason for discussion production experiments at all is that if the coupling of the Y^* to the $\overline{K}N$ channel is very small, then they may be the only way in which the Y^*s existence can be revealed. Indeed, in some SU(3) octets the D and F couplings can be such that the Λ or Σ resonance has an exceedingly small branching fraction into the incident $\overline{K}N$ channel. Then a production experiment

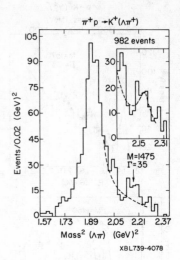

Fig. 9. Distribution of the $\Lambda\pi^+$ effective mass squared for the reaction $\pi^- p \to K^+\Lambda\pi^+$. Dashed line shows the tail of $Y^*(1385)$ plus background. In the insert another resonance is added in order to fit the observed enhancement.

proceeding either by K^* exchange or perhaps via the decay of an s-channel nucleon resonance into Y^* and K may be the only feasible way of detecting the hyperon resonance. Hints from the production experiments just described suggest that these Y^*s are produced most copiously slightly above threshold. A more elaborate version of a missing-mass experiment using a streamer chamber or a hybrid bubble chamber to selectively trigger on the K^+ and at the same time permitting analysis of the missing-mass disintegration products would appear to be the most favorable means of exposing such elusive states.

REFERENCES

1. Rev. Mod. Phys. 45, S1 (1973).

2. Reading from left to right, the abbreviations and references are:
   (a) UCL(TST)[University College London (Track Sensitive Target)]: D. J. Miller - RHEL/R 245 and private communication. Path length distribution is roughly estimated. The precise momentum range and distribution are still to be determined.
   (b) LBL 1965: R. Tripp, UCRL-20655 (1971).
   (c) HYBUC 1973 (Hyperon Bubble Chamber): R. Settles, private communication. The exposure was made for measurement of Σ^+ magnetic moment. If other topologies are measured, they may be useful for Y^* studies.
   (d) BMY 1965 (Brookhaven, Massachusetts, Yale): D. Berley et al., Phys. Rev. D 1, 1996 (1970).
   (e) Yale 1965: N. S. Wong, Nuovo Cimento 2A, 353 (1971).
   (f) CHS 1967 (CERN, Heidelberg, Saclay): R. Armenteros et al., Nucl. Phys. B21, 15 (1970).
   (g) CHM 1970 (CERN, Heidelberg, Munich): H. Oberlack, private communication.
   (h) Tenn.-Mass. 1969 (Tennessee - Massachusetts): E. Hart, private communication.
   (i) BNL 1964: D. Berley et al., Phys. Rev. Lett. 15, 641 (1965).
   (j) CHS 1964: R. Armenteros et al., Nucl. Phys. B8, 233 (1968).
   (k) Maryland. 1964: R. P. Uhlig et al., Phys. Rev. 155, 1448 (1967).
   (ℓ) LBL 1964: D. F. Kane, Phys. Rev. D 5, 1583 (1972).
   (m) Ch.-LBL 1970 (Chicago - LBL): D. Merrill et al., Berkeley APS Meeting 1973.
   (n) RHEL - ICL 1972 (Rutherford-Imperial College London): G. Kalmus, private communication.
   (o) CERN 1968: M. Ferro-Luzzi, CERN/D. Ph. 11/Phys. 71-9.
   (p) Saclay 1969: M. Ferro-Luzzi, ibid.
   (q) LBL 1962: D. O. Huwe, Phys. Rev. 181, 1824 (1969).
   (r) CRS 1967 (College de France, Rutherford, Saclay): P. J. Litchfield et al., Nucl. Phys. B30, 125 (1971).
   (s) CH 1969 (CERN-Heidelberg): M. Ferro-Luzzi, ibid.
   (t) UCLA 1962: P. M. Dauber, UCLA report 90024 (Thesis) (1966).

3. Reading from left to right, the abbreviations and references are:
   (a) Wisconsin 1965: D. Cline et al., Phys. Rev. Lett. 21, 1372 (1968).
   (b) Florida 1967, 1971: J. Albright, private communication.

(c)   CHM 1970 (CERN, Heidelberg, Munich): H. Oberlack, private communication.

(d)   LBL 1965: N. Jew and G. Kalmus, Nucl. Phys. B22, 205 (1970).

(e)   CS 1965 (CERN-Saclay): R, Armenteros et al., Nucl. Phys. B18, 425 (1970).

(f)   Birmingham 1972: R. Armenteros, private communication.

(g)   BEGL 1968 (Birmingham, Edinburgh, Glasgow, Imperial College London): G. F. Cox et al., Nucl. Phys. B19, 61 (1970).

(h)   LBL 1962: A. Barbaro-Galtieri et al., Phys. Lett. 6. 296 (1963).

4.   (a)   RGEPB (Rutherford, Glasgow, Edinburgh, Pisa, Bologna): G. Kalmus, private communication.

        (b)   DESY(HMTA) (Heidelberg, Minnesota, Tel-Aviv): E. Coleman, private communication.

        (c)   SLAC: D. Leith, private communication.

5.   Reading from the top down, the references are:

        (a)   BNL: R. L. Cool et al., Phys. Rev. D 1, 1887 (1970).

        (b)   RHEL-Bi-Ca: Bugg et al., Phys. Rev. 168, 1466(1968).

        (c)   Arizona: T. Bowen et al., Phys. Rev. D 2, 2599 (1970).

        (d)   BNL: A Carroll et al., Paper presented at Berkeley APS Meeting, August 1973.

        (e)   CERN-Caen-Saclay: C. Bricman et al., Phys. Lett. 31B, 148 (1970).

        (f)   Birm.-RHEL, UCL-RHEL: from G. Manning, UCRL-20655 (1971).

        (g)   CERN-Caen: T. Ypsilantis, Purdue conference on Baryon Resonances, 1973.

        (h)   CERN-Caen: M. Ferro-Luzzi, private communication.

        (i)   Birm.- RHEL: from G. Manning, UCRL-20655 (1971).

        (j)   RHEL-Oxford: C. R. Cox et al., Phys. Rev. 184, 1443 (1969).

        (k)   CERN-Holland: C. Daum et al., Nucl. Phys. B6, 273 (1968); and S. Anderson-Almehed et al., Nucl. Phys. B21, 515 (1970).

        (ℓ)   Yale: BNL Proposal (1973).

        (m)   LBL: BNL Proposal (1973).

        (n)   Yale: Possible BNL Proposal, M. Zeller, private communication.

        (o)   Oxford: from G. Manning, UCRL-20655 (1971).

6.   M. Ferro-Luzzi, CERN/D. Ph. II Internal Note 71-2. J. Nelson et al., LBL-2002 (1973).

7.   R. Armenteros et al., Nucl. Phys. B8, 195 (1968).

8.   BNL report of D. N. Michael (1973).

9.   Reading from the bottom up, the abbreviations and references are:

        (a)   Established 3- and 4-star resonances refer to the Particle Data Group classification, Rev. Mod. Phys. 45, S1 (1973).

        (b)   CHS (CERN-Heidelberg-Saclay): R. Armenteros et al., in Proceedings of the Duke Conference on Hyperon Resonances (1970), edited by E. Fowler.

(c)   Kim: Phys. Rev. Lett. 27, 356 (1971).

(d)   LW (Langbein and Wagner): Nucl. Phys. B47, 477 (1972).

(e)   LMMO (Lea, Martin, Moorhouse, and Oades): Nucl. Phys. B56, 77 (1973).

(f)   Florida: W. A. Morris (thesis), Florida State University, 1973.

(g)   Tenn. - Mass.: Tennessee - Massachusetts Collaboration paper presented by E. L. Hart at Purdue Conference on baryon resonances, 1973.

(h)   Arizona: Bowen et al., Phys. Rev. D 2, 2599 (1970).

(i)   BNL: Preliminary data presented by A. Carroll at Berkeley APS Meeting, August 1973.

(j)   SABRE: (Saclay, Amsterdam, Bologna Rehovoth, Ecole Polytechnique Collaboration) Nucl. Phys. B16, 201 (1970).

(k)   BNL: Crennell et al., Phys. Rev. Lett. 21, 648 (1968) and Lund Proceedings (1969).

(ℓ)   CERN: Dowell et al., Phys. Lett. 1, 53 (1962) and Blackall et al., Phys. Lett. 16, 336 (1965).

(m)   Penn.: Pan and Forman, Phys. Rev. Lett. 23, 806 (1969).

10.   D. Cline et al., Lett. Nuovo Cimento 6, 205 (1973).

HYBUC AND PRELIMINARY REPORT ON THE Σ^+ MAGNETIC MOMENT EXPERIMENT.[†]

N. Doble, K. Gottstein, G. Hansl, I. Herynek,[*] A. Manz,
J. Marrafino, W. Matt, R. Settles, G. Wolf,
Max-Planck-Institut fur Physik und Astrophysik, MÜNCHEN

E. Dahl-Jensen
Niels Bohr Institute, COPENHAGEN

S. Reucroft, C. Roos, M. Webster
Vanderbilt University, NASHVILLE, TN 37235

The HYperon BUbble Chamber, HYBUC, is a 32 cm hydrogen bubble chamber which is situated in a 110 kilogauss magnetic field produced by a superconducting magnet.

The first experiment involves a precision measurement of the Σ^+ magnetic moment μ_{Σ^+}, the goal of the experiment being an accuracy of $\delta\mu_{\Sigma^+} \sim 0.15$ nuclear magnetons.[1] A summary of the published Σ^+ data is given in Figure 1. along with an overview of various theoretical predictions. The seven experiments published to date have all estimated an absolute error of ~ 1 n.m.,[2] the combined value for μ_{Σ^+} being 2.59 ± 0.46 n.m.[3].

The principle of the experiment is similar to that of previous ones.[2] Polarized Σ^+ hyperons are produced in the reaction $k^-p \to \Sigma^+\pi^-$; the polarization vector $\vec{P}$ is precessed in the magnetic field $\vec{B}$. The direction of polarization at decay is detected in the $\Sigma^+ \to p\pi^\circ$ parity violating decay distribution, $\frac{dN}{d\phi} \sim [1 + \frac{\pi}{4} \alpha P \sin (\phi-\phi_0)]$, where ϕ is the angle between the decay product and the normal magnetic moment polarization vector projected onto the plane of precession in the Σ rest frame, ϕ_0 is the angle of precession and α is the decay asymmetry parameter. The statistical error of the magnetic moment measurement goes as $(B\alpha P\sqrt{N})^{-1}$, so Σ^+'s of maximum polarization are required. Exposures were made at several values of beam momentum in the 450-500 MeV/c region, where the Σ^+ polarization is high.[4] With $\sim 2 \times 10^7$ k^- incident on the chamber in $\sim 2 \times 10^6$ pictures, the design accuracy should be achieved in the final analysis.

[*] On leave of absence from the Institute of Physics, CSAV, PRAGUE.
[†] Supported in part (Vanderbilt U.) by the U. S. National Science Foundation.

A diagram of the apparatus is given in Figure 2(a). The fiducial volume has a length of 32 cm and a diameter of about 11 cm. The expansion of the chamber is by a piston which is moved by a hydraulically driven actuator. The expansion is completely forced (non-resonant), and the system is capable of rapid-cycling having been tested to a repetition rate of 50 Hz.[5] Rapid cycling is not used in the Σ^+ experiment, but will be necessary for the Ξ^- magnetic moment measurement and subsequent experiments.

The magnet is a compound solenoid with outer coils of stabilized, twisted, NbTi superconductor and an inner coil made of Nb_3Sn tape. The peak field of 117 kilogauss was within 1% of the short sample limits of the superconductors.[6] The magnet has operated reliably at fields above 110 kilogauss for the past two years. The liquid helium for the magnet is supplied from a dewar, and the bubble chamber is cooled by a refrigerator. The bubble chamber and magnet are mounted separately on the upper plate of the vacuum tank.

The flashlamps and film transport sit $\sim$1 meter behind the chamber in a region of low field. There are five objectives arranged at stereoangles ranging from 17° to 30°, four viewing from off the chamber axis and one on the axis. The objectives have two sets of lenses plus a field lens to give intermediate imaging and transport of the image out of the high field region. The f/D ratio is 34 with a 1 mm aperture stop situated in front of the first lens. This permits close proximity of the flash image to the optical axis as required by the use of Scotchlite. The illumination is bright-field for the off-axis views and dark-field for the central view on the chamber axis. All views are brought via mirrors to the same film as seen in Figure 2(b).

The k^- beam enters the chamber along the magnetic and optical axes so that the Σ polarization at production, which is perpendicular to the plane of production, is perpendicular to the field direction.

Approximately 1.7 of the 2 million pictures have already been taken with the rest scheduled this fall. The analysis is proceeding well. Scanning along the beam poses no problems and a scanning speed of $\sim$50 pictures per hour per scanning machine has been reached.

About 15,000 $\Sigma^{\pm}$ events have been passed through the reconstruction programs; there is no evidence for systematic biasses in these events which would affect the magnetic moment calculation. The sample will be used for an intermediate publication on μ_{Σ^+} around the end of the year after further checking all the known sources of systematic errors. The final analysis should be completed in about two years.

The resolution of the apparatus can be characterized by an $\epsilon \sim 50-80\mu$ (where ϵ is the average deviation of measured points from the tracks as reconstructed by the CERN geometry program LBCG). The optical constants are being improved, after which it is expected to reduce ϵ substantially.

Figure 3 shows various distributions made up from a subsample of the raw data: 3(a),(b),(c) show the missing mass distributions for the $\Sigma^+ \to p\pi^\circ$, $\Sigma^+ \to \pi^+ n$ and $\Sigma^- \to \pi^- n$ decays; 3(d),(e),(f) show the ϕ distributions for the $\Sigma^+ \to p\pi^\circ$, $\Sigma^+ \to \pi^+ n$ and $\Sigma^- \to \pi^- n$ decays, the lower curve in Figure 3(d) shows only those $\Sigma^+ \to p\pi^\circ$ decays where the Σ^+ is produced in the backward hemisphere; 3(g),(h) show the Σ^+ and Σ^- production angular distributions, where θ^* is the C.M. angle between the π^+ and incident k^-. The crosses represent the data of reference 4. (455 and 475 MeV/c).

The final $\sim$150000 Σ sample will give much higher statistics for partial wave analysis than presently exists (e.g. Ref. 4), in the momentum range 450-500 MeV/c; in addition good information will be available on the Σ^+ and Σ^- lifetimes and rare decay modes. Also, if Σ^- are polarized in this momentum region, a first measurement of μ_{Σ^-} could be obtained, even though the decay parameter α is small (~-0.07).[3]

Finally, the rapid-cycling feature of HYBUC is indicated in Figure 4[5] where the stroke and dynamic pressure curves for the expansion system operating at 50 Hz for 20 expansions are shown. This type of operation would distribute the 20 expansions over the 400 msec slow spill of the CERN PS. An experiment to measure the Ξ^- magnetic moment using HYBUC as a rapid-cycling device is at present in planning; various possibilities are being studied for enrichment of the desired events in the pictures (e.g. flash trigger, vidicon scan, etc.).

References

1. N. Doble, K. Gottstein, G. Hahn, I. Herynek, A. Manz, V. Scheuing, R. Settles, M. Watschoder and E. Dahl-Jensen, "Proposal for a Precision Measurement of the Σ^+ Magnetic Moment," CERN/TCC 69-26 (unpublished report, 1969).

2. A. D. McInturff and C. E. Roos; Phys. Rev. Lett. 13, 266 (1964). C. R. Sullivan, A. D. McInturff, D. Kotelchuck and C. E. Roos, Phys. Rev. Lett. 18, 1163 (1967).

    V. Cook, T. Ewart, G. Masek, R. Orr and E. Plattner; Phys. Rev. Lett. 17, 223 (1966).

    D. Kotelchuck, E. R. Goza, C. R. Sullivan and C. E. Roos; Phys. Rev. Lett. 18, 1166 (1967).

    Terry S. Mast, Lawrence K. Gershwin, Margaret Alston-Garnjost, Roger O. Bangerter, Angela Barbaro-Galtieri, Joseph J. Murray, Frank T. Solmitz and Robert D. Tripp; Phys. Rev. Lett. 20, 1312 (1968).

    J. Combe, E. Dahl-Jensen, N. Doble, E. Evans, L. Hoffman, Ph. Rosselet, W. Toner, W. N. Gibson, K. Green, P. Tolun, N. A. Whyte, G. Charriere, M. Gaillond, B. Wanders, R. Weill, C. Carathanassis, W. Puschel, V. Scheuing, R. Settles, G. Baroni, A. Manfredini, G. Romano and V. Rossi; Nuovo Cimento 57A, 54 (1968).

    P. W. Alley, J. R. Benbrook, V. Cook, G. Glass, K. Green, J. F. Hague and R. W. Williams; Phys. Rev. D3, 75 (1971).

    M. Saha, J. G. Fetkovich, W. Heintzelman, C. Meltzer, and C. T. Murphy; Phys. Rev. D7, 3295 (1973).

3. "Review of Particle Properties," Rev. Mod. Phys. 45, 2 (1973).

4. R. Armenteros, P. Baillon, C. Bricman, M. Ferro-Luzzi, E. Pagiola, J. O. Petersen, D. E. Plane, N. Schmitz, E. Burkhardt, E. Filthuth, E. Kluge, H. Oberlack, R. R. Ross, R. Barloutaud, P. Granet, J. Meyer, J. P. Porte, and J. Prevost; Nucl. Phys. B21, 15 (1970).

5. A. Manz, S. Reucroft and R. Settles; "Proceedings of a Seminar on Track Analysis for Rapid Cycling Bubble Chambers," Rutherford Laboratory Report RHEL/R271, p. 48 (1971).

6. CERN Courier 11, 64 (1971).

204

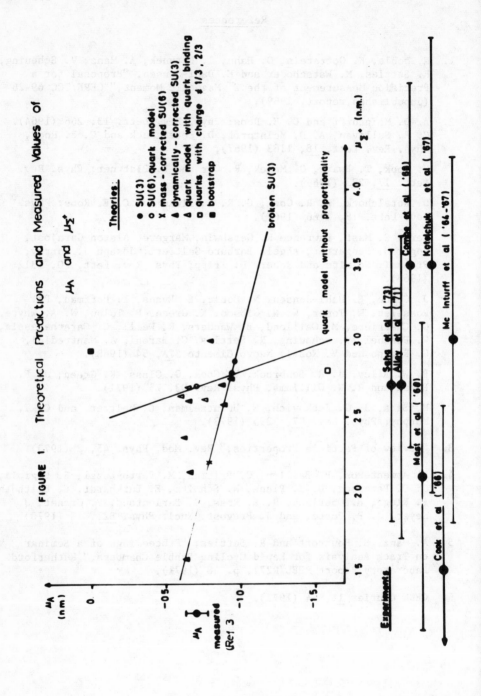

FIGURE 1: Theoretical Predictions and Measured Values of μ_Λ and μ_{Σ^+}

a) HYBUC Cross-Section Sketch.

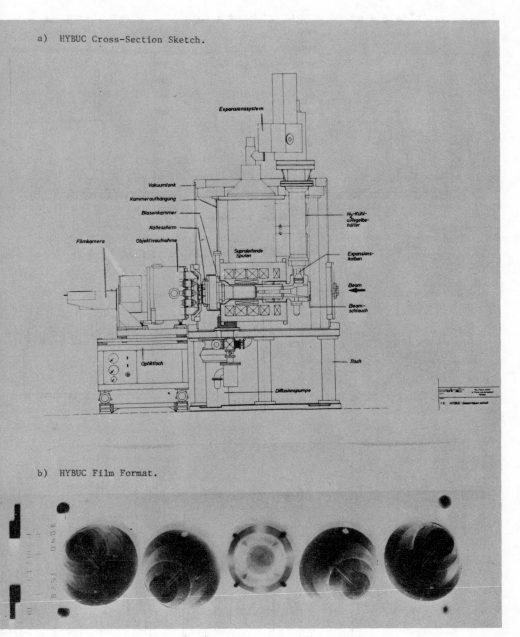

b) HYBUC Film Format.

Figure 2.

206

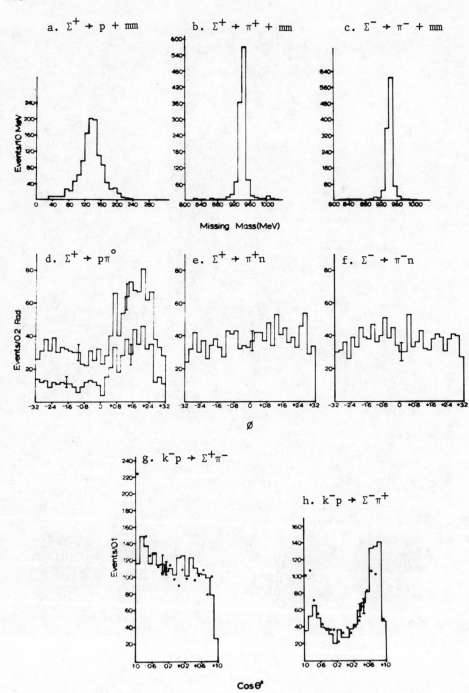

Figure 3.

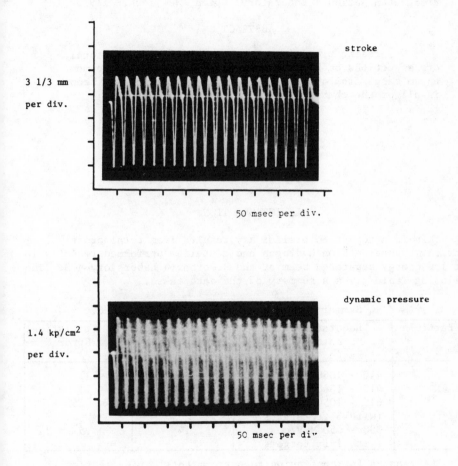

stroke

3 1/3 mm
per div.

50 msec per div.

dynamic pressure

1.4 kp/cm^2
per div.

50 msec per div.

Figure 4

Stroke and dynamic pressure with expansion system operating at 50 Hz

for 20 expansions.

PRECISION MEASUREMENTS OF K± and P̄ TOTAL CROSS SECTIONS*
ON HYDROGEN AND DEUTERIUM BELOW 1.1 GEV/C

A.S. Carroll, I-H. Chiang, T.F. Kycia, K.K. Li,
P.O. Mazur, D.N. Michael‡, P.M. Mockett+,
D.C. Rahm and R. Rubinstein
Brookhaven National Laboratory, Upton, New York,   11973

ABSTRACT

We present precision measurements of K± and p̄ total
cross sections on both hydrogen and deuterium in the momentum range from 400 to 1100 MeV/c. Structures are seen
in all of the channels.

I. INTRODUCTION

This is a report on preliminary results from total cross
section measurements on hydrogen and deuterium performed recently in
the low energy separated beam at the Brookhaven Laboratory AGS. The
following Table gives a summary of the data taken.

Summary of total cross sections measured.

Particle	Laboratory Momentum Range	Number of Data Points	Statistical Error
K⁺	410 - 1060 MeV/c	19	< 1%
K⁻	410 - 1060 MeV/c	37	< 1%
p̄	615 - 1050 MeV/c (with 3 ft. targets)	11	< .25%
	380 - 650 MeV/c (with 1 ft. targets)	14	.5 to 3%

The reasons for continuing to perform total cross section
experiments are that they are simple, straight-forward experiments
which are capable of very high statistical precision and reasonably
well understood systematic effects. The past history of these
measurements is that the "structures" seen in total cross section
experiments have often been shown to be resonances in subsequent

*Work performed under the auspices of the U.S.Atomic Energy Comm.
‡Present Address:Schocken Books, 200 Madison Ave., New York, 10016
+Present Address:University of Washington,Seattle,Washington 98105

experiments and the agreement between different total cross section experiments on the existence of structure is good. A new low energy separated beam at the AGS made this particular set of measurements possible.[1,2]

II. APPARATUS AND TECHNIQUES

The measurements were performed by the usual transmission method with improvements for better stability and smaller systematic error. A plan view of the apparatus is shown in Fig. 1. B_1, B_2 and B_3 were scintillation counters defining the incident beam. Kaons were selected by time of flight from B_1 to B_2 and by a liquid differential Cerenkov counter, C. Antiprotons were selected by time of flight and fast particles were rejected by using $\overline{C}$ in anti-coincidence. These methods of selection were sufficient to reduce the contamination from unwanted particles to less than 10^{-3} for all measurements. G was a counter which vetoed particles out of the beam line. Each of three identical targets could be moved automatically into the beam: one containing liquid hydrogen, one containing liquid deuterium, and one which was evacuated. The counter $\overline{T}$ vetoed interaction products which scattered through the end flanges or the side walls of the targets. Nine circular counters, T_1 - T_9, ranging in diameter from 6 to 18 inches, were used to measure the amount of beam transmitted through the targets, and the counter E was used to measure the efficiencies of the transmission counters, T_1 - T_9. For each incident momentum, the transmission counters were moved along the beam line so that they would subtend the same range of four momentum transfer (t) for elastic scattering, and the beam was focussed to a small spot at the transmission counters. Cross sections were computed for each transmission counter from the ratio of full to empty target transmitted beam. For each momentum, typically four cycles of measurements were made for each of the three targets.

The apparatus and techniques described so far are similar to those of most previous total cross section experiments.[3] In the present experiment, however, three new features were added which significantly reduced systematic effects. The first was the elimination of tails from the beam spot at the final focus, and the second was the elimination of absorption losses in the transmission counters. Both of these effects can introduce systematic errors into the extrapolation to zero detector size. The third was the on-line monitoring of the apparatus and the on-line computation of the total cross section. This reduced the effect of any instabilities and enabled us to check inconsistencies immediately.

Tails from the beam spot were eliminated by using two multi-wire proportional chambers, MWPC1 and MWPC2, which were placed in the incident beam as shown in Fig. 1. A matrix of coincidences was formed between appropriate wires from the two chambers, to insure that each incident particle trajectory would pass through a 2.8x2.8 inch square at the final focus. The effect of the matrix coincidence on the projected beam distributions at the final focus is shown in Fig. 2 for the case of 700 MeV/c antiprotons. The unshaded histograms show the horizontal and vertical distribution of all incident particles at the final focus, computed from the coordinates observed in MWPC1 and MWPC2. The shaded portion of the histogram shows the distribution of those incident particles accepted by the matrix coincidence. It is seen that this method has eliminated tails from the beam distribution and minimized effects due to beam steering.

The second important low-energy systematic effect, that of absorption losses in the transmission counters, was eliminated by combining, by electronic OR, the signal from each transmission counter, T_i, with the signals from all transmission counters which were upstream of T_i. In Fig. 3, the extrapolation to zero detector size is shown with (solid line) and without (dashed line) the electronic OR, for K^+ 500 MeV/c. It can be seen from the figure that there was a significant difference between the extrapolated cross sections obtained from the two methods, and that this difference tended to be larger for deuterium. The discrepancy decreased as the momentum increased, and became negligible for the highest momenta in the experiment.

Third, throughout the experiment, the transmission data, the efficiencies of the transmission counters, important voltages, and magnet currents were monitored during the data taking with a PDP-15 computer. At the end of each momentum, the data were transferred to a PDP-6 computer which calculated cross sections and made extrapolations. Measurements were repeated at different times for many different momenta and were found always to be consistent within statistical errors. This on-line monitoring enabled a continuous check of the consistency of the results and the stability of the apparatus.

The vapor pressure of the outer container of the jacketed targets was regulated to 18.00 ± 0.01 psia, which maintained a constant density in the inner transmission targets to better than $\pm 0.05\%$. The inner targets as shown were 6 inches in diameter by 3 feet in length. The targets were shortened to 1 ft. during part of the running by moving the upstream window downstream. This enabled the measurements for antiprotons to be extended below 600 MeV/c incident laboratory momentum.

By taking the ratio of transmitted beam from full to empty targets, most of the effect of the target vessel was eliminated from the measurements. For kaons, however, an important correction must be made for the different decay loss of the beam after the full compared with the empty target as a result of the momentum loss in the hydrogen or deuterium in the full target. These decay corrections were large and required precise knowledge of the incident momentum and the momentum loss in the full targets. The absolute momentum of the beam was known to within $\pm 0.5\%$ from magnet calibrations[4] and this was verified below 900 MeV/c to the same level of accuracy by time-of-flight measurements on protons at each momentum. A precise calculation for momentum loss was used.[5] The decay corrections were checked at an incident momentum of 550 MeV/c to a statistical precision of ± 0.4 mb, and at 700 MeV/c to ± 0.2 mb, by

changing the distance between the transmission counters and the
targets at each momentum.

Other corrections have been made to the kaon data for single
Coulomb scattering, Coulomb-nuclear interference, and for HD contamination in the deuterium.[3] The real parts of the K-nuclear scattering
amplitudes used in the interference corrections were taken from the
dispersion relation calculations of Carter.[6] The Coulomb and Coulomb-
nuclear interference corrections were always less than 1.5 mb for the
kaon data. The HD contamination was measured in gas samples taken
from the deuterium target at the end of each running period; corrections to the data of less than 1% were required.

For the kaon data, the overall systematic error on the absolute
values of the measured cross sections is estimated to be less than
± 1%; the point to point variation from systematic effects is estimated to be less than the statistical error. The momentum resolution
of the measurements, caused by the momentum spread in the incident
beam (± 1%) and the momentum loss in the targets from ionization, is
± 40 MeV/c at 450 MeV/c, and less than ± 30 MeV/c above 700 MeV/c.
All data are, of course, plotted as a function of the average laboratory momentum of the beam in the full target. The isospin decomposition of the kaon cross sections is the same as in previous experiments.[12]

For the antiproton data, no corrections have yet been made to
the data, so the absolute values are not yet known to within a few
percent; however, the point to point variation from systematic effects is again expected to be less than the statistical error. The
momentum resolution of the measurements with the 3 ft. targets is
less than ± 35 MeV/c above 700 MeV/c, but rapidly increases below
this momentum. The momentum resolution with the 1 ft. targets varies
from ± 60 MeV/c at 30 MeV/c to ± 15 MeV/c at 650 MeV/c.

III. K^+ - NUCLEON TOTAL CROSS SECTIONS

The K^+ - nucleon total cross sections have already been published.[10] Fig. 4 shows the I = 0 cross section which shows a broad
structure below the inelastic rise centered at about 700 MeV/c and
the sharper structure at 1100 MeV/c along with previous data.[11-15]
The reader should see Ref. 10 for further details on the analysis
and interpretation.

IV. K^- - NUCLEON TOTAL CROSS SECTIONS

The K^- - nucleon total cross sections for the pure I = 0 and
I = 1 states, obtained from the Brookhaven K^-p and K^-d data using the
previously mentioned technique,[3] are shown in Fig. 5 in the same
extended region of laboratory momentum.[16] Except for the highest
mass ones, most of the structures indicated in the figure have been
confirmed to be resonances in other experiments.[17]

The K^-p and K^-d total cross sections measured in the present
experiment are shown in Fig. 6, and the K^- - nucleon total cross
sections for the pure I = 0 and I = 1 states are shown in Fig. 7. In

both figures, statistical errors only are shown where they are larger than the plotted point.

The I = 1 total cross sections are dominated by structure from the formation of two known resonances in this region; the $\Sigma(1765)$ and the $\Sigma(1670)$. A new structure, with a mass of 1580, is seen for the first time in this data. If this is a resonance it would be the formation of the $\Sigma(1580)$. There is also a possibility of a new structure near 1610 MeV, but more data would be required to be certain.

The I = 0 total cross sections in this region are dominated by large structure from the formation of three known resonances: the $\Lambda(1520)$ (only the upper half appears in the present data), the $\Lambda(1690)$, and the $\Lambda(1815)$. An interesting question raised by the new data is whether or not there is a new structure near 1530 MeV. There are also indications of possible new structure near 1600 MeV and 1750 MeV, but again more data would be required to be certain about this. We have not yet performed quantitative fits to the data to determine precise values of the masses and widths of the structures or to determine the statistical significance of the smaller structures.

V. $\overline{P}$ - NUCLEON TOTAL CROSS SECTION

In this experiment the precision measurements of $\overline{p}p$ and $\overline{p}d$ above 1.0 GeV/c[16] were extended down to 360 MeV/c. In the previous experiment broad structures were seen at the masses of the T and U mesons of the CERN missing mass experiment.[18]

Preliminary data from the present experiment are shown in Fig.8. The closed squares are the data taken with 3 ft. targets, and the closed circles are the data taken with 1 ft. targets. The statistical errors are shown wherever they are larger than the plotted point. Above about 600 GeV/c, both the $\overline{p}p$ and the $\overline{p}d$ data follow closely the smooth curves, which are of the functional form a + b/p, where p is the laboratory momentum. Below 600 GeV/c, there is a striking peak in both the $\overline{p}p$ and $\overline{p}d$ cross sections. The center of this peak is at about 1930 MeV, the mass of the S meson. The width of the structure is comparable to the experimental resolution (15 MeV).

Since the cross sections are so large, the usual approximations used in the Glauber-Wilkin method of computing the screening correction in the deuteron are no longer valid.[12] For this reason, it is not yet possible to say which isospin states contribute to the new structure.

VI. CONCLUSIONS

We have found, as in previous total cross section measurements at higher momenta, that the kaon and antiproton cross sections below 1.1 GeV/c are very rich in structure which could be due to resonance formation. The discovery of new structure in this experiment indicates that the measurement of total cross sections continues to be a powerful tool in hadron spectroscopy.

REFERENCES

1. J.D. Fox, EPS Division Technical Notes No. 7 and No. 20 (Brook-haven National Laboratory, 1967 and 1968, unpublished); also M. Zeller, L. Rosenson, and R.E. Lanou, BNL AGS Summer Study, BNL 16000, p. 193 (Brookhaven National Laboratory, 1970, unpublished).

2. A.S. Carroll, I-H. Chiang, T.F. Kycia, K.K. Li, D.N. Michael, P.O. Mazur, P.M. Mockett, D.C. Rahm, and R. Rubinstein, EPS Division Technical Notes No. 54 and No. 64 (Brookhaven National Laboratory, 1972 and 1973, unpublished).

3. See reference 12 for further details.

4. G.T. Danby, Accelerator Department Internal Report, GTD-2 (Brookhaven National Laboratory, 1961, unpublished).

5. F.R. Huson, BNL 11386 (Brookhaven National Laboratory, 1967, unpublished).

6. A.A. Carter, HEP 68-10 (Cavendish Laboratory, 1968, unpublished), and Phys. Rev. Letters $\underline{18}$, 801 (1967).

7. Hyperon Resonances - 70, ed. by E.C. Fowler, pp. 9-57 (Durham, 1970).

8. C.J. Adams, J.D. Davies, J.D. Dowell, G.H. Grayer, P.M. Hatter-sley, R.J. Howells, C. McLeod, T.J. McMahon, H.B. van der Raay, L. Rob, C.J.S. Damerell, R.J. Homer, M.J. Hotchkiss, Phys. Rev. $\underline{4D}$, 2637 (1971); see also J.D. Dowell, XVI International Confer-ence on High Energy Physics, Vol. 1, p. 40 (Chicago-Batavia,1972).

9. R.J. Abrams, R.L. Cool, G. Giacomelli, T.F. Kycia, K.K. Li and D.N. Michael, Physics Letters $\underline{30B}$, 564 (1969); also see reference 7.

10. A.S. Carroll, T.F. Kycia, K.K. Li, D.N. Michael, P.M. Mockett, D.C. Rahm and R. Rubinstein, Physics Letters 45B, 513 (1973).

11. D.V. Bugg, R.S. Gilmore, K.M. Knight, D.C. Salter, G.H. Stafford, E.J.N. Wilson, J.D. Davies, J.D. Dowell, P.M. Hattersley, R.J. Homer, A.W. O'Dell, A.A. Carter, R.J. Tapper, and K.F. Riley, Phys. Rev. $\underline{168}$, 1466 (1968).

12. R.L. Cool, G. Giacomelli, T.F. Kycia, B.A. Leontic, K.K. Li, A. Lundby, J. Teiger, and C. Wilkin, Phys. Rev.$\underline{D}$ 1, 1887 (1970).

13. T. Bowen, P.K. Caldwell, F.N. Dikmen, E.W. Jenkins, R.M. Kalbach, D.V. Petersen and A.E. Pifer, Phys. Rev. D $\underline{2}$, 2599 (1970).

14. T. Bowen, E.W. Jenkins, R.M. Kalbach, V.D. Petersen, A.E. Pifer and P.K. Caldwell, Phys. Rev. D $\underline{7}$, 22 (1973).

15. G. Giacomelli, P. Lugaresi-Serra, F. Mercatali, A. Minguzzi-Ranzi, A.M. Rossi, F. Griffiths, A.A. Hirata, I.S. Hughes, R. Jennings, B.C. Wilson, G. Ciapetti, P. Guidoni, G. Martellotti, A. Nappi, D. Zanello, E. Castelli, P. Poropat, and M. Sessa, Nuclear Physics $\underline{B37}$, 577 (1972).

16. R.J. Abrams, R.L. Cool, G. Giacomelli, T.F. Kycia, B.A. Leontic, K.K. Li, and D.N. Michael, Phys. Rev. D $\underline{1}$, 1917 (1970).

17. T.A. Lasinski, A. Barbaro-Galtieri, R.L. Kelly, A. Rittenberg, A.H. Rosenfeld, T.G. Trippe, N. Barash-Schmidt, C. Bricman, V. Chaloupka, P. Söding, M. Roos, Rev. Mod. Phys. $\underline{45}$, No. 2, Part II, 1973.

18. M.N. Focacci, W. Kienzle, B. Levrat, B.C. Maglic, and M. Martin Phys. Rev. Letters $\underline{17}$, 890 (1966).

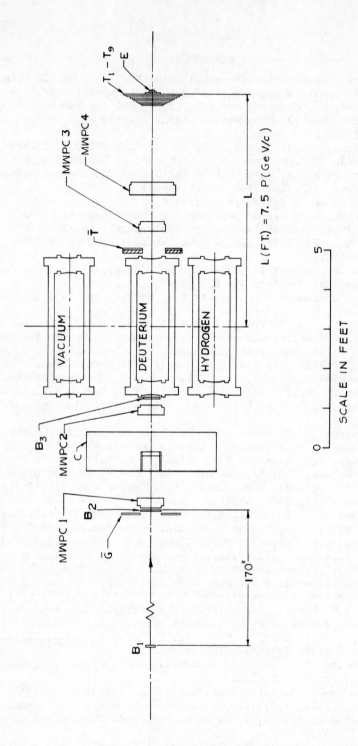

Figure 1
Plan view of experimental apparatus

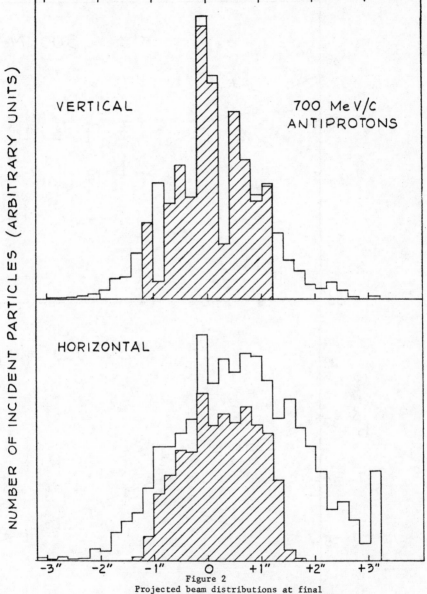

VERTICAL

700 MeV/C
ANTIPROTONS

HORIZONTAL

-3"   -2"   -1"   O   +1"   +2"   +3"

NUMBER OF INCIDENT PARTICLES (ARBITRARY UNITS)

Figure 2
Projected beam distributions at final
focus. The apparent gaps in distributions
are an artifact of the logic which
handled the triggering of adjacent wires.

216

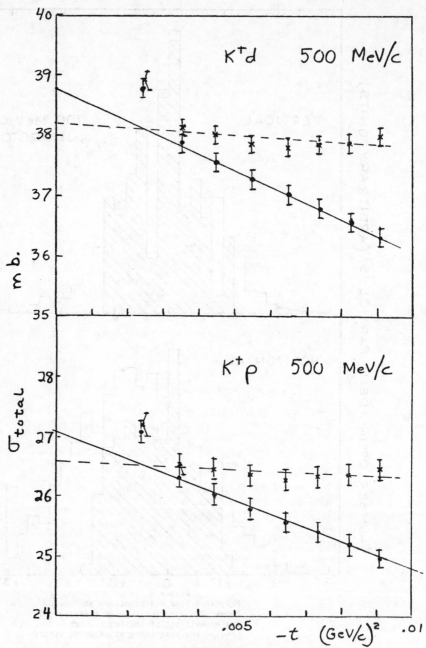

Figure 3
K⁺ cross sections obtained in transmission
counters, with (solid line) and without
(dotted line) electronic OR.

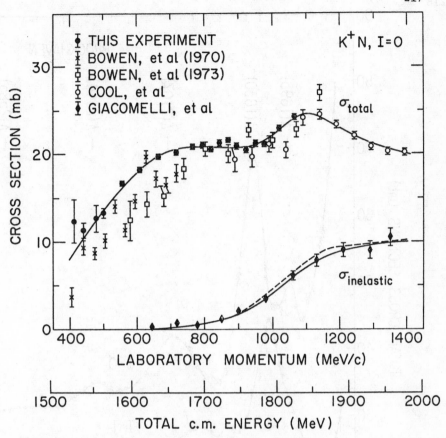

Figure 4
K+-nucleon total cross sections for I=0

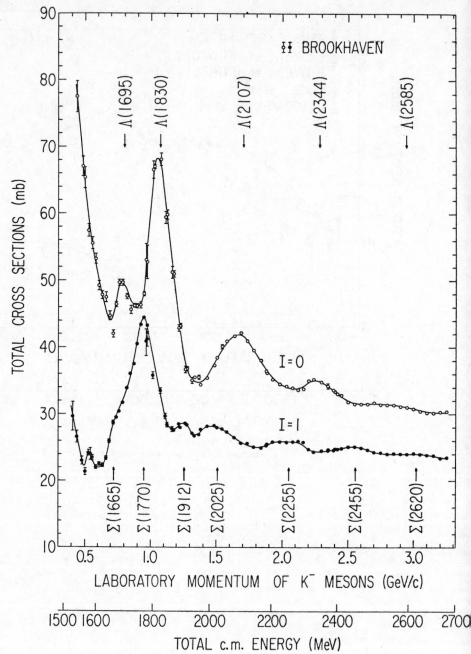

Figure 5
K⁻-nucleon total cross sections for I=0 and
I=1 below 3.3 GeV/c

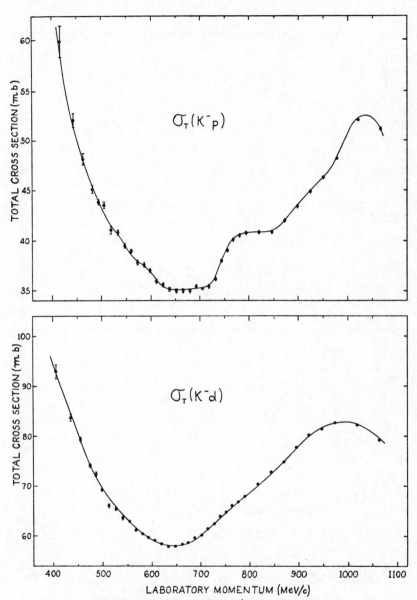

Figure 6
Preliminary K⁻p and K⁻d total cross
sections from present experiment.

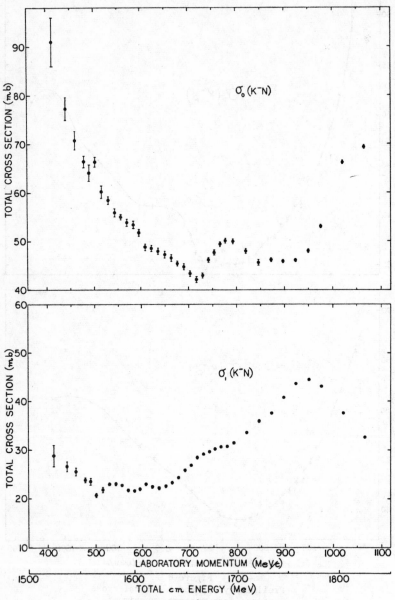

Figure 7
Preliminary K⁻-nucleon total cross sections
for I=0 and I=1 from present experiment.

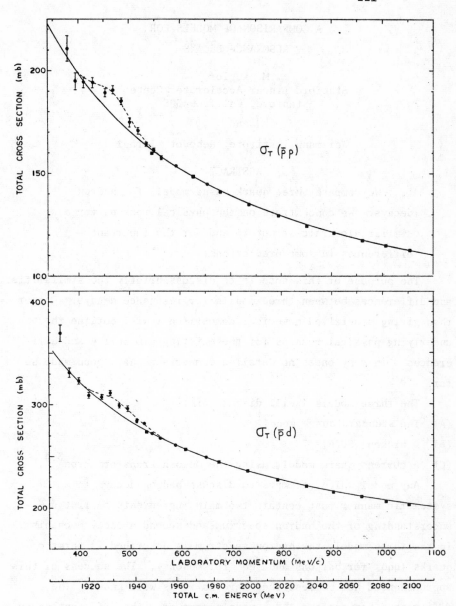

Figure 8
Preliminary $\bar{p}p$ and $\bar{p}d$ total cross sections
from present experiment

A COMPARISON OF MODELS FOR

RESONANCE DECAYS

M. Kugler
Stanford Linear Accelerator Center
Stanford, Calif. 94305

and

Weizmann Institute, Rehovot, Israel

ABSTRACT

We compare three quark based models for hadron
decays. We concentrate on the physical reasons for a
similar algebraic structure and for the important
differences in some predictions.

The purpose of this note is to discuss briefly the similarities
and differences between three models for resonance decays. Rather
than giving a detailed numerical comparison I will outline the
underlying physical reasons for the existing similarity and differences. In many cases no detailed comparisons have been made so
far.

The three models I will discuss are:

(A) The standard quark model[1]

(B) ℓ-broken $SU(6)_W$ [2]

(C) A current quark model, using the Melosh transformation[3,4].

Any model which attempts to discuss hadron decays in a
systematic manner must contain two main ingredients. First an
understanding of the hadron spectrum and second a decay mechanism.
In the three models the hadron spectrum is described in terms of
quarks (qqq for baryons and $q\bar{q}$ for mesons). The success of this
approach need not be described here as it is well known. The
differences between the three models stem from the different decay
mechanisms that are used.

(A) In the quark model, quarks move in a potential well, and
their wave functions are determined by the interaction. Thus, given
the wave function, we can calculate transitions due to quarks

emitting pions, vector mesons, or photons. Graphically this may be described as in figure 1.

Figure 1. Particle emission in the quark model

The quark model is thus an attempt to construct a complete theory, where everything can be calculated from a basic input.

(B) The ℓ-broken $SU(6)_W$ scheme is not a complete theory, it is an attempt to guess how a hadron symmetry is broken in decay processes. A decay is described by the creation of a $q\bar{q}$ pair in a ^3P_o state graphically represented by figure 2.

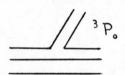

Figure 2. The decay mechanism in ℓ-broken $SU(6)_W$

Only algebraic properties are abstracted from this scheme. The decays of several resonances can be related to a small number of reduced matrix elements but one does not attempt to calculate these.

(C) In the current quark model the decay mechanism is due to the algebra of charges Q^α and Q_5^α. The matrix elements of Q_5^α are related to pionic transitions by means of PCAC. As this model is less widely known than the previous ones, I must discuss it here in more detail.

The algebra of currents and charges as proposed by Gell-Mann is abstracted from a free quark model. Shortly after the algebra was proposed it became apparent that three "constituent quarks" as used in describing the nucleon wave function in the quark model cannot be identified with the quark fields underlying the algebra[5]. The latter quarks are therefore different and have been named "current quarks" by Gell-Mann. The nucleon wave function in terms of current quarks, has to be evaluated at infinite momentum. This "current quark" wave function of the nucleon is more complicated than the symmetric qqq wave function used in the quark model[6]. One may then hope that the exact current quark wave function is given by applying an operator V to the irreducible representation wave function used in the non relativistic quark model

$$|N> = V|I.R.> \tag{1}$$

where I.R. stands for irreducible representation. Graphically this is described in figure 3.

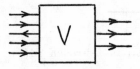

Figure 3. V operating on the qqq wave function gives the physical state in terms of current quarks

One would then like to evaluate the matrix element of Q_5^α between physical states. (This matrix is connected to the pionic decay width by PCAC and its square measures a contribution to the Adler Weisberger sum rule.)

$$<N'|Q_5^\alpha|N> = <IR'|V^{-1} Q_5^\alpha V|IR> \tag{2}$$

So, rather than evaluating the physical operator between the physical states we can evaluate the matrix element of an effective operator $V^{-1} Q_5^\alpha V$ between states which transform in a simple way under current algebra, this is described in figure 4.

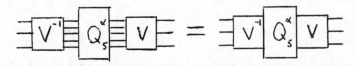

Figure 4. Evaluation of matrix elements in a current quark scheme

The algebraic properties of the effective operator $V^{-1} Q_5^\alpha V$ and of V are abstracted from the free quark study of Melosh[3] which has recently reopened this field of study. One thus assumes following Melosh, that $V^{-1} Q_5^\alpha V$ and similar operators behave under the algebra of charges like the most general single quark operators consistent with SU_3 and Lorentz invariance. This assumption alone is sufficient to give many results[4].

The similarity in algebraic structure is now apparent. In all the models discussed, the decay is described by a single quark operator as seen in figure 5.

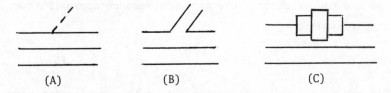

(A)   (B)   (C)

Figure 5. The single quark nature underlying the decay mechanism in the three models

The algebraic structure is therefore dictated by this common assumption of the theories. This is why some predictions are similar in the three models. The major prediction concerns signs of amplitudes in $\pi N \to \pi \Delta$ and $\gamma N \to \pi N$ [7].

Connection between matrix elements and partial widths. This is a major difference between models.

(A) The connection can be calculated from the non relativistic wave function it behaves roughly as

$$\Gamma \propto p^{2\ell+1} |M|^2 \qquad (3)$$

is the decay where M is the matrix element and ℓ orbital angular momentum.

(B) The kinematic factors describing the connection between width and matrix element stem from mass breaking within an $SU(6)_W$ multiplet. These kinematic factors are not given by the model and an extra assumption has to be made, usually one assumes

$$\Gamma \propto p^{2\ell+1} |M|^2 \qquad (4)$$

(C) In this approach $|\langle N^* | Q_5^\alpha | N \rangle|^2$ is the contribution of the N^* to the Adler Weisberger sum rule. Thus the theory has an unambiguous way of connecting matrix elements to widths. In principle one could do this by directly integrating over the data without having to resort to approximations. This is not yet practical and one often uses the narrow resonance approximation. In this approximation

$$\Gamma \sim p^3 |M|^2 \qquad (5)$$

Note that the factor p^3 is independent of the angular momentum. The source of this factor is in the use of PCAC and of the infinite momentum frame.

The three approaches may give strikingly different predictions for widths in spite of the fact that the matrix elements appear identical. Differences of factors of two or three are not uncommon.

In comparing $A_2 \to \pi\rho$ and $f \to \pi\pi$ for instance the use of p^3 or $p^{2\ell+1}$ differs in a factor of two. In this case the p^3 factor seems favoured. In general we cannot yet decide which factor is favoured by the data.

Relations between multiplets. Only the quark model (A) can give connections between different multiplets. Such connections are given by the wave functions which are assumed to be known in this model. The other models cannot predict intermultiplet connections. The sensitivity of these intermultiplet relations to the exact form of the wave function has not been investigated yet. A preliminary point of contradiction seems to emerge. The quark model predicts identical signs for $\pi N \to N^*(1688) \to \pi\Delta$ with incoming F wave and outgoing P wave and $\pi N \to \Delta(1880) \to \pi\Delta$ with F waves in both channels, whereas the data[9] seem to point in the opposite direction. The other two models can accommodate either sign.

Electromagnetic transitions, are predicted in all models but the predictions differ significantly.

(A) Electromagnetic transitions in this model are described by a mechanism similar to that of π emission, some connections between the two exist because of the wave functions.

(B) The ℓ-broken SU(6) scheme does not make any direct predictions about γ emission. The predictions made so far are indirect; they involve calculating vector meson emission and the use of vector dominance. (Inherent in the latter is a very large error.) The existing connection between pseudoscalar and vector meson transitions impose connections between γ and pseudoscalar transitions.

(C) In a current quark scheme, γ emission is described in different terms than π emission. Whereas the latter is connected by PCAC to the matrix element of Q_5^α new operators are defined for γ transitions. These, so called dipole operators, are given by

$$D_{\pm} = \int d^3x \; (x \pm iy) \; J_o(x) \tag{6}$$

where J_o is the time component of the electromagnetic current.
The new operators D and their matrix elements are not connected
to Q_5^α and thus there are no connection between electromagnetic
transitions and π transitions.

The extension of the current quark scheme to $q^2 \neq 0$ has not
been investigated yet; indeed the extension may prove very difficult
theoretically as it may involve the solution of a major part of the
"Gell-Mann program".[5] If such an investigation bears fruit some
results must hold. The most obvious of these is that there will be
no relation in this scheme between longitudinal and transverse γ's
in contrast with vector dominance based schemes.

Vector meson emission is predicted in A and B in the same
way as π emission. The matrix elements for ρ emission can be
calculated once the π matrix elements are known. Model C cannot
give any direct predictions about decays into vector meson since
these are not connected to matrix elements of charges. Only if
vector meson dominance is assumed can we relate these decays to
matrix elements of $D_\pm$. If however predictions will be made within model C for matrix elements of the vector current at $q^2 \neq 0$
then an extension to $q^2 = m^2$ may be possible. In any case there
will be no simple connection between $N^* \rightarrow N\pi$ and $N^* \rightarrow N\rho$.

In principle, any of the differences mentioned here could
serve as a way to distinguish which of the three models agrees
best with nature. One could at this point invent a scenario for
possible developments, but I think that we will not be able to
pronounce a verdict for a while. We should also keep in mind that
possibly all three models may fail simultaneously because of their
similarities if, for instance, the phases in $\pi N \rightarrow \pi\Delta$ will
contradict the theory.

If any of the models turns out to work well we still must try
hard to understand why the model works. All three models contain
some ad-hoc assumptions whose validity in a realistic theory must
still be justified. We thus face a need for what may be called
a house-broken theory; that is a theory where nothing need be
swept under the rug.

Many of the points mentioned in this paper arose during the past year in discussions with F.J. Gilman and S. Meshkov. Many of the points were part of a panel discussion at this conference. I have thus benefitted from discussions with A. Barbaro-Galtieri, J.H. Melosh, G. Moorhouse and J.L. Rosner.

REFERENCES

1. See for example R.P. Feynman, M. Kislinger and F. Ravndal, Phys. Rev. D3, 2706 (1971) and references quoted there.

2. L. Micu, Nucl. Phys. B10, 521 (1969),
   E.W. Colglarier and J.L. Rosner, Nucl. Phys. B27, 349 (1971),
   W.P. Petersen and J.L. Rosner, Phys. Rev. D6, 820 (1972).

3. H.J. Melosh IV, Caltech thesis (1973) (unpublished).

4. F.J. Gilman and M. Kugler, Phys. Rev. Letters 30, 518 (1973),
   F.J. Gilman, M. Kugler and S. Meshkov, Phys. Letters in press,
   For a detailed discussion, see F.J. Gilman, M. Kugler and
   S. Meshkov, SLAC Pub. 1286 (1973),
   A.J. G Hey and J. Weyers, CERN preprint TH.1614 (1973),
   A.J. G Hey, J.L. Rosner and J. Weyers, CERN preprint TH.1659 (1973).

5. M. Gell Mann, Schladming Lectures 1972, CERN preprint TH.1543 (1972) unpublished.

6. For a review, particularly of baryons, see H. Harari in Spectroscopic and Group Theoretical Methods in Physics North-Holland, Amsterdam, 1968), p. 363.

7. See F.J. Gilman et al. ref. 4, and references quoted there
   D. Faiman and J.L. Rosner, CERN preprint TH.1036 (1973) and
   R.G. Moorhouse and N.H. Parsons, Glasgow preprint (1973).

8. R.G. Moorhouse, private communication.

9. D. Herndon et al., LBL preprint LBL-1605 (1972) (unpublished)
   and R. Cashmore, private communication.
   See also, U. Mehtani et al., Phys. Rev. Letters 29, 1634 (1973),
   R. Cashmore, invited talk presented at the Purdue Conference
   on Baryon Resonances, Report No. SLAC-PUB-1257, Stanford
   Linear Accelerator Center (1973) (unpublished).

PHENOMENOLOGY OF HIGH ENERGY EXCHANGE PROCESSES[*†]

G.L. Kane
University of Michigan, Ann Arbor, Mi. 48104

INTRODUCTION

In this review I will first try to give the interested reader a feeling for the kinds of work going on in this field, the kinds of models people are considering and why. The level will be qualitative and vague, meant to give a framework to classify present and future efforts.

In addition to a general survey a number of current subjects with interesting possibilities or implications will be discussed. These are:
- --remarks on amplitude analysis
- --zeros of s-channel helicity amplitudes; fixed t or fixed u?
- --np→pn, p̄p→n̄n, dσ/dt and polarizations; important test for models
- --energy dependence; comparison of different reactions with the same exchange and different observables in the same reaction
- --production of higher spin resonances; especially the B and external Regge recurrences
- --expectations for higher energy data soon to come; especially concerning relative energy dependence of different Reggeons, shrinkage, and line reversed reactions.

In preparing this review I looked back at several recent reviews[1] and rapporteur's talks about high energy particle exchange phenomena and two body reactions. They are noteworthy for extensive treatment of the details of experimental data and the description of data in lots of models, for diligently searching out possible puzzles and contradictions, and for a lack of optimism about our hopes for progress in this field.

Hadron exclusive reactions is not a field where questions have simple yes/no answers any more. Rather we have to look for insights to the pattern of much data. The situation appears to be complicated. Even so, I think that there has been slow but steady increase in insight, and that it is appropriate here to try to give a broad overview of the general ideas at hand. In the general survey, rather than present details of many

*Research supported in part by the U.S.A.E.C.
†Invited talk at the 1973 APS Division of Particles and Fields meeting, Berkeley, August 1973

models I will simply try to discriminate among the basic approaches people use. At the present time only one model, essentially a classical absorption approach, has succeeded in describing a large body of data and has presented a large number of predictions for higher energy data; so its results are used in several sections.

HISTORICAL AND GENERAL SURVEY

To understand the present situation concerning models relevant to two body hadron reactions it is useful to briefly recall some history.

For a long time it has been apparent that it is useful to imagine that the reactions proceed via exchange of a system carrying appropriate quantum numbers. This is clear from a study of energy dependence, phase, and quantum numbers (SU(3), etc.). It was also realized early that for theoretical reasons the exchange of many partial waves must be correlated in a t-dependent way, giving Regge energy dependence $s^{\alpha(t)}$ and the associated phase from analyticity $e^{-i\alpha(t)/2}$.

On the other hand, the behavior of the Regge residues, essentially interpretable as form factors, has remained unknown. This has allowed an unhappy amount of freedom in describing data and has led to ambiguities and misunderstandings concerning Regge ideas. The Regge energy dependence and phase are unambiguous; the determination of the residue remains one of the major theoretical or phenomenological problems in hadron physics.

Still ten years ago it was realized that the external particles, being strongly interacting, must undergo important final state and initial state interactions, called absorption corrections. Much of the work in this field in the past ten years can be understood as the attempt to take account of the hadronic nature of the external particles--how should one perform absorption corrections? It has not been emphasized enough that the question should not be whether to take account of absorption but how, because it would be extraordinary if absorption did not occur when hadrons interact. To neglect absorption may turn out to be correct in some situation or amplitude, but it will require extensive theoretical justification.

Next it was realized that the absorption question had still another complication, the sum over intermediate states. This is one of the most interesting theoretical questions in the whole area. Basically the situation can be pictured as in Fig. 1. The full amplitude is given by a Reggeon exchange (wavy line) plus the elastic absorption correction plus a sum over non-elastic intermediate states c* and d* (plus appropriate contributions with intermediate

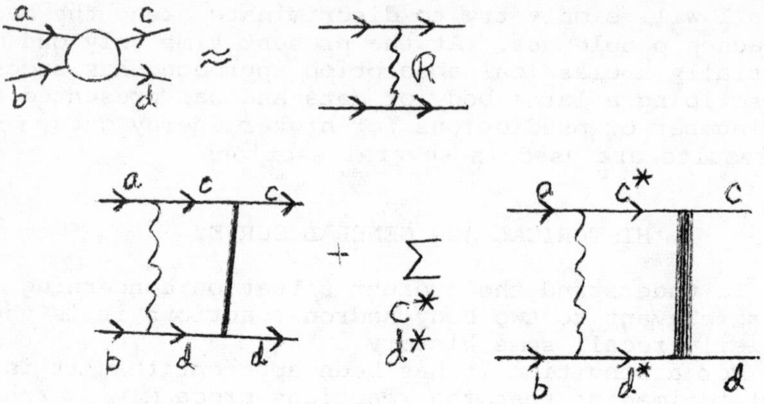

Fig. 1

states a and b, etc.). How does one calculate the sum over intermediate states?

Until recently two methods have been used to represent its value; neither can be considered a calculation. One common procedure, often used for helicity flip amplitudes, was to set sum = 0. So far this has no significant theoretical justification, and it is probably inadequate phenomenologically. It is somewhat like the situation used to be with phase shift analyses, where all phase shifts beyond a certain partial wave were set to zero; now we know that it is better to use a reasonable model for the high partial waves. On the other hand, if the Mystical Models described below turned out to be on the right track it would not be surprising if sometimes one should have sum = 0.

The second method was to assume that the sum had the same dependence on its variables as the elastic intermediate state contribution, so that elastic + sum = λ(elastic) where λ ≥ 1. This method, a useful approximation in the earliest models (e.g., "SCRAM"), is known to be inadequate in that the sum should have a different shape in impact parameter than the elastic term (peripheral vs. central) and since absorption has to do with affecting the partial wave structure that is an important thing to get right. A recent attempt along these lines is described in the Classical Absorption Model mentioned in the text.

Fortunately there will be experimental hints about how to calculate intermediate state sums; it is not merely a question of theorist's games. In addition to the absorption phenomenology itself, which provides one check, three other possible experimental tools are described in Appendix 1.

On the whole one can put the huge proliferation of
models for hadron two body reactions into one of three
classes; Romantic, Mystical, or Classical. The first two
of these have as a basic, underlying (sometimes not explicit) assumption that the ideas and tools we currently
have at hand are not adequate to arrive at a description
of the data. Some new concept, possibly a dramatic one,
is needed; at the minimum, it is felt that the results
might come from an existing theory if we could calculate
with it, but since we cannot the best we can do is look
for regularities in the data. The Romantic Models, while
requiring behavior we are not able to understand (such as
Regge pole phases for amplitudes with strong Regge cuts)
attempt to give theoretical arguments which might lead to
the behavior. The Mystical models go even further, postu-
lating models where accepted physical principles are violated (such as analyticity) to obtain agreement with data,
or where the modifications are entirely ad hoc. This
characterization should not be interpreted as critical; if
in fact the intuition that new ideas are needed is correct
it may be the right approach to search them out. The
Mystical Models have as an additional implicit assumption
that exchange degenerate poles must be the starting point.
It is well known that this leads to considerable phenomenological difficulty, and has led to some of the clever
modifications which have been introduced to allow one to
fit data.

In theClassical Models, on the other hand, the basic
point of view is that no fundamental physics is lacking
to understand the behavior of hadron experimental data.
Although the very simple models formulated in the past
have not described the data well, the difficulty, it is
argued, has mainly been in subtleties concerning phases,
and can be dealt with by a slight increase in realism
such as properly interpreting the initial or final state
rescattering phase in terms of real elastic scattering at
the same energy.

At the present time most models are capable of des-
cribing $0^{-}\frac{1}{2}^{+}\to 0^{-}\frac{1}{2}^{+}$ reactions, so one cannot conclude much
from such applications. In addition to these, one Class-
ical absorption model[2] (referred to as CAM in the following)
has been able to describe in considerable detail a number
of $0^{-}\frac{1}{2}^{+}\to 1^{-}\frac{1}{2}^{+}$[3] and $\frac{1}{2}^{+}\frac{1}{2}^{+}\to\frac{1}{2}^{+}\frac{1}{2}^{+}$[4] reactions. These involve
subtle and relevant tests of the details of amplitudes,
so to the extent that describing data can lead us to
physical insight the CAM must currently be considered
acceptable and the leading contender for a good model.
From describing a finite amount of data alone one can
never, of course, confirm a given model or theory; the
reader must decide for himself whether he is prepared to
accept the underlying physics.

TABLE 1

Model	Philosophy	Applicability Exchanges	Reactions	Validity
Dual Absorption Model (Harari)	"Romantic" ImM "absorbed" because of duality but ReM unknown or given by Regge phase. Believe we still lack important concepts	Not applicable to cross sections but only to some parts of some amplitudes. Vector,tensor mesons;baryon Not π	$0^{-}\tfrac{1}{2}^{+}\to0^{-}\tfrac{1}{2}^{+}$ (some qualitative features of $1^{-}\tfrac{1}{2}^{+}$ production)	Dubious though not proved wrong (certainly inapplicable for π exchange;tensor exchange imaginary parts probably not peripheral; energy dependence)
Modified Exchange Degenerate Pole Models (Rutherford/ Orsay;Saclay; etc.) Not Absorption Models	"Mystical" Begin with Ex. Deg. poles and introduce various ad hoc modifications to get agreement with data. Sometimes appear to violate accepted physics such as analyticity. Current ideas considered fundamentally inadequate to understand data.	Vector,tensor mesons Others?	$0^{-}\tfrac{1}{2}^{+}\to0^{-}\tfrac{1}{2}^{+}$	Consistent with data for all or some of these reactions (depending on model). Not known how to apply elsewhere, or unsuccessful.
Classical Absorption Model (Hartley, Kane,Vaughn)	"Classical" Absorb simple Regge pole in standard way, locally in b, with elastic re-scattering amplitude which must have structure of data,e.g., shrinkage, small t break, phase, correct shape in b, even signature, etc. Include sum over intermediate states peripheral in impact parameter. Believe no basic obstacle to understanding data.	Vector,tensor π mesons Can be applied to any exchange	$0^{-}\tfrac{1}{2}^{+}\to0^{-}\tfrac{1}{2}^{+}$ $\tfrac{1}{2}^{+}\tfrac{1}{2}^{+}\to\tfrac{1}{2}^{+}\tfrac{1}{2}^{+}$ $0^{-}\tfrac{1}{2}^{+}\to1^{-}\tfrac{1}{2}^{+}$ (Field and Sidhu)	So far consistent with all data above few GeV/c. Amplitudes are very Ex. Deg. at high energies but the low energy continuation is not dual

[for vector meson exchange CAM and DAM have the same t dependence and phase;elsewhere they differ]

The situation is summarized in capsule form in Table 1. Several of the detailed subjects mentioned below give further particulars of model behavior. A numer of references are given to specific models which have been applied in a limited set of reactions so the interested reader can look them up.

This short survey should leave the non-expert reader in a position to find the sort of model which he finds attractive and examine it further, or give him a framework to evaluate future work. The expert reader will not have learned much but may have been stimulated to some useful controversy.

Now we turn to specialized subjects. These have been selected because I feel that in the next year or two they are likely to be the main areas which lead us to new insights or change our present attitudes.

REMARKS ON AMPLITUDE ANALYSIS

For about two years, following the work of Halzen and Michael, who noticed that sufficient data existed for πN scattering at 6 GeV/c to extract the actual scattering amplitudes at a few angles, considerable enthusiasm has been expressed for "amplitude analysis". This in turn has stimulated extensive efforts to do "model independent" work. Laudable though these tendencies may be, there is now some evidence that a certain amount of caution is necessary. It will be very nice to know actual scattering amplitudes when it is possible to measure them. But as soon as assumptions are needed, possibly even normalization or continuity assumptions about data, the amplitude analyses become "amplitude models" and should be studied as such.

The main point can be stated as a "theorem" (it deserves that title about as much as most amplitude analyses are really amplitude analyses):

> One can rarely learn enough from model
> independent work involving data.

Two examples will illustrate the point.

(1) In the standard πN case one can, given certain continuity assumptions about the data and a knowledge of the $\pi^- p \to \pi^\circ n$ polarization, extract the amplitudes up to the well known overall phase. To compare with predictions of models, however, one needs the absolute phase. For example, the Dual Absorptive Model makes a precise statement only about the imaginary parts of the amplitudes. Thus in most cases of interest, the actual use of the amplitude knowledge requires assumptions about the (t-dependent) overall phase and is highly model dependent.

(2) A number of authors have extracted amplitudes from incomplete sets of data on hypercharge exchange (and backward reactions). It is instructive to compare the

results of different analyses. (For the backward case
the amplitudes are surprisingly not explicitly published
and obtaining them is sometimes difficult.) For the
hypercharge exchange case Fig. 2 shows a compilation from
the recent review of Fox and Quigg. If the results were
not sensitive to the assumptions all of the dashed lines
would lie on top of one another, and all of the solid
lines on top of one another. It is hard to imagine
bigger disagreements. Further, SU(3) plus the constancy
of $\sigma_T(K^+p)$ imply near equality of the imaginary parts of
the vector and tensor exchanges in the nonflip amplitude
at t = 0, a condition satisfied by none of the analyses
shown.

(3) Another way to get at the amplitudes is to
calculate them directly from the phase shifts at lower
energies and then use Regge <u>pole</u> FESR relations to get
at the high energy amplitudes, or simply invoke duality
to argue that the high and low energy s-channel helicity
amplitudes will have the same t-dependence. However,
Fukugita and Inami[6]have remarked that when full account
is taken of the zero structure of amplitudes, including
forward fixed t and backward fixed u zeros, it may happen
for some ranges of FESR cutoffs that the backward zeros
cause the amplitude to behave as if it had additional
forward zeros. They explicitly suggest that some second
zeros found in previous FESR calculations may be reinter-
preted this way.

All this is not to imply that the attempts to get
at amplitudes are not valuable, or that they are not
correct. Indeed it would be very useful if analyses such
as that of Elvekjaer, Inami, and Ringland[7] which show
interesting zero structure out to -t ~ 3 GeV^2 from phase
shift and FESR analyses,prove to be correct because such
regularities will be useful in searching for underlying
dynamics. However, as might be expected the initial rash
of enthusiasm for getting amplitudes at any cost must
now be tempered with some critical evaluation, and the
full model dependence of much of the work should be recog-
nized. That is all right; model dependence is fine when
the model is a good one.

FIXED t (t') ZEROS

In the past few years it has been increasingly
realized how important the zero structure of amplitudes
can be for understanding the basic physics. Odorico,
basing his ideas on the Veneziano Model zero structure,
has shown that a great deal of data has structure suggesting zeros often reminescent of the double pole killing
zeros, and has suggested ways to understand much of this
structure in the real world.

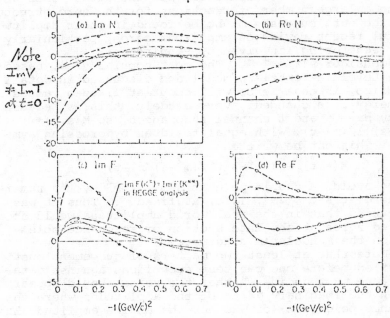

RESULTS OF AMPLITUDE
ANALYSES OF $\pi N \rightarrow K\Lambda$, $\bar{K}N \rightarrow \pi\Lambda$ AT 4 GeV/c

——— Tensor (K^{**}) Exchange
– – – Vector (K^{*}) Exchange
Methods: $\circ$ = DAM, $\times$ = REGGE, $\diamond$ = FESR
Units are $[\mu b/(GeV/c)^2]^{1/2}$

Note $Im V \neq Im T$ at $t=0$

(a) Im N

(b) Re N

(c) Im F

Im F(K^{*}) = Im F(K^{**}) in REGGE analysis

(d) Re F

$-t (GeV/c)^2$

$-t (GeV/c)^2$

Fig. 17 FOX & QUIGG

Figure 2. From the review of Ref. 1 . This shows results for hypercharge exchange amplitudes obtained by using different sorts of assumptions to compensate for the absence of a complete set of data. The reader need only note that if the results were not model dependent all of the dashed lines would give identical results for the vector exchange and all of the solid lines would give identical results for the tensor exchange. One of the methods used may be valid, although the fact that none would give a constant $\sigma_T(K^+p)$ using SU(3) for the t=0 Im(nonflip) since vector $\neq$ tensor, tends to cast doubt on all of them.

For the past year or so data and theoretical information have been accumulating which suggest that the situation may be different; in addition there is data for π exchange reactions which has never been brought to bear on this question. It is not clear what the answer is at present, but it now seems possible to state the problem rather clearly and suggest directions of attack to fully understand the zero structure of hadron amplitudes.

First we remind the reader of the simplest situation and expectations, presenting two contrasting views to provide a frame of reference to view the data. Then we examine a large number of reactions for the zero structure which the data suggests might be found in their amplitudes. A useful recent review on amplitude zeros, particularly for $\pi\pi$ scattering, is given by Pennington.

Consider $\pi^+\pi^- \to \pi^+\pi^-$. The most popular view, based on the Lovelace-Veneziano model and discussed in detail by Odorico,[9] is that zeros will occur at fixed u values as the energy s is changed. Very crudely, this is because one can have s and t channel resonances, so $M(s,t) \sim 1/(m^2-s)+1/(m^2-t)$, with equal residues by crossing symmetry. This can be written

$$M(s,t) \sim (2m^2-s-t)/(m^2-s)(m^2-t)$$

and one avoids a double pole at $s=m^2$, $t=m^2$ by the numerator zero at $s+t = 2m^2$, i.e., at fixed u. Thus it was conjectured that in the real world amplitudes would show isolated zeros at the intersection of resonance pole lines on the Mandelstam diagram.

Note that at least two matters of judgement must be settled before one can test such ideas against data. First, one must decide whether the zeros should appear only in the imaginary parts of the amplitudes where the resonance poles are; or whether the entire amplitude has a zero nearby in which case it should be observable in cross sections. Second, one must decide what paths the zeros follow between resonance lines intersections. For example, everyone agrees, as first noted by Dolen, Horn, Schmid, that the first zeros of the imaginary parts of the πN amplitudes are at $-t \approx 0.3$ at the positions of the dominant s-channel N*'s. Are these successive fixed u zeros each moving on to become a higher Legendre zero at the next resonance as the energy increases, or a single fixed t zero?[10]

A different point of view, with different answers to the above questions, suggests itself if one begins from the regularities in the high energy data rather than the resonances. Then (consider πN nonflip scattering or (presumably) $\pi\pi$ scattering) the dominant feature is the crossover zero near $-t = 0.25$ GeV^2. The crossover zero stays at the same t value (not u) over a large range of energies. In addition we know that there is a zero at a similar t value at the dominant resonances. Thus one is

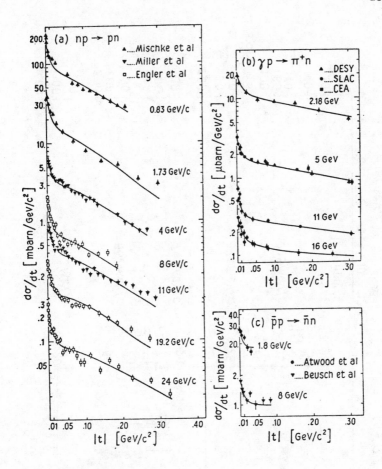

Fig. 3. Differential cross sections are shown for several
cross sections with important π exchange contributions.
The sharp peak for $-t \lesssim m_\pi^2$ corresponds to a zero at
$-t \approx m_\pi^2$ in the amplitude with net helicity flip zero
and s-channel helicity flip at the nucleon vertex. The
position of the zero is apparently approximately fixed
in t over a large range of energies. Further, the zero
occurs whether the s-channel is exotic or not (i.e.,
whether there are s-channel resonances). Any interpretation of amplitude zeros should account for the existence of this zero, in the dominantly real π exchange
contribution, at approximately fixed t, present whether
there are s-channel resonances or not, and a zero of
the full amplitude giving structure in $d\sigma/dt$. The
interpretation of Ref.10 extrapolated to this situation
attributes the zero to unitarity effects (absorption at
higher energies).

240

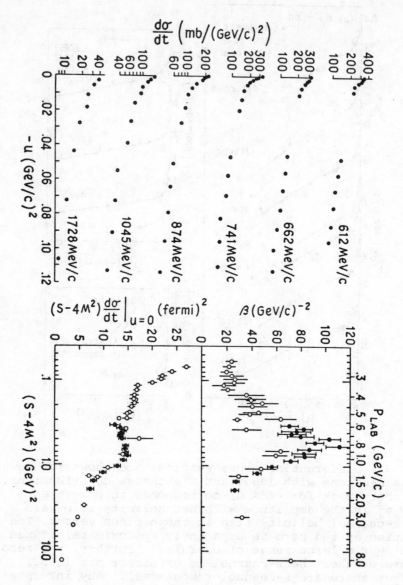

Fig. 4. For np→pn this shows more precisely the extent
to which the zero can be considered fixed in t[11].From
its high energy value of about 50 GeV^{-2} the slope β (upper
right hand corner) varies up or down by about a factor of
2 as one passes pion production thresholds. From the
cross section alone one cannot tell if the shift is due
to changes in the other incoherent amplitudes or to shifts
of order 50% in the zero position. Data from Devlin et al.
Ref. 12 .

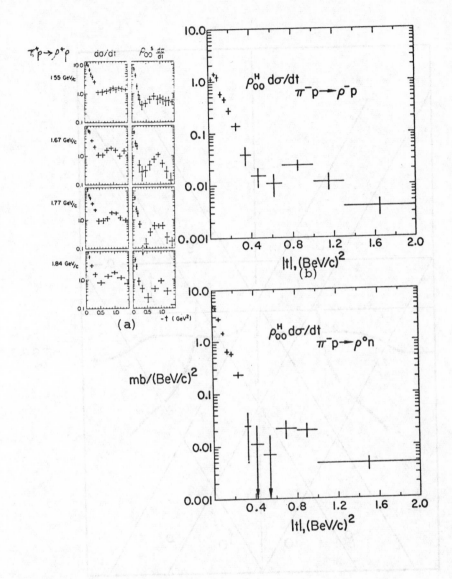

Fig. 5. Shows another fixed t zero, in ρ_{oo}^{H} dσ/dt for $\pi N \to \rho N$. This quantity isolates unnatural parity exchange, presumably π exchange. The zero, at $-t \sim 0.5$ GeV^2, persists over a large range of energies. Data for (a) are from Ref. 13, for (b) from Ref. 14, at 4.5 GeV/c.

242

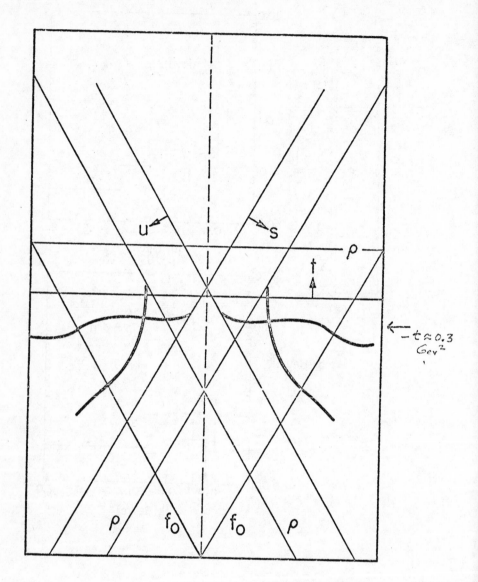

XBL733-2499

Fig. 6. The zero contours for $\pi\pi$ scattering with <u>t-channel</u> <u>isospin one only</u> can be interpreted as fixed t zeros at about the position of the crossover zero. Such a result would only be expected in the picture of Ref. 10 for the amplitudes corresponding to exchange of a definite Reggeon (not the Pomeron). Figure from Eguchi et al., Ref. 15 and 18

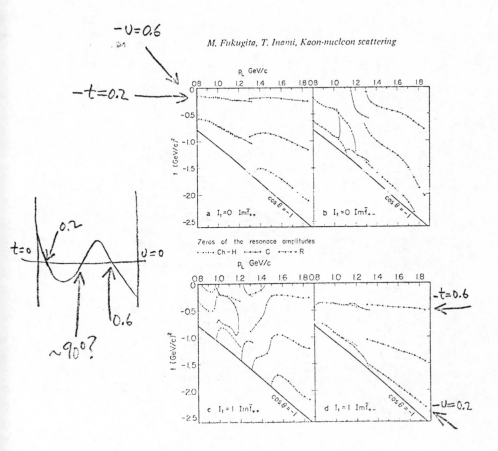

−U=0.6

M. Fukugita, T. Inami, Kaon-nucleon scattering

−t=0.2 ⟶

Zeros of the resonace amplitudes
····· Ch−H   C   R

t=0   0.2   U=0

0.6

~90°?

−t=0.6

−U=0.2

Fig. 7.   Plots for KN scattering of the zeros of amplitudes with definite t-channel quantum numbers, from Ref.
6 . A background or Pomeron contribution is subtracted
from I_t = 0. Again, the results can be interpreted as
fixed t zeros (as noted by the authors). As shown in the
insert on the left the third zero may be "trivial" in
origin to allow the amplitude to have the dynamical zeros
at 0.2 and 0.6 while having the sign of the pole residue
at the forward and backward directions. However, there
may be some inconsistency between the results of this
analysis and that of Fig. 8.

244

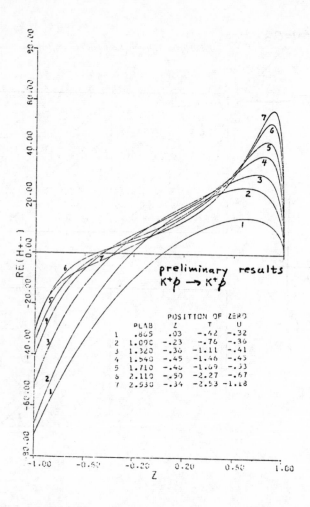

Fig. 8. Shows zero structure of the s-channel helicity
flip amplitude for $K^+p \rightarrow K^+p$; there should be no Pomeron
background present so the amplitude could have forward V
and T exchanges of both isospins and backward baryon and
decuplet exchanges. The interpretation of the results
with only one zero is not clear, and it is not clear how
to relate these results to those of Fig. 7. The situation
is complicated by the dominance of the real amplitude
(for K^+p) where zero structure is often more complicated.
Results presented at this conference by R. Kelly.[16]

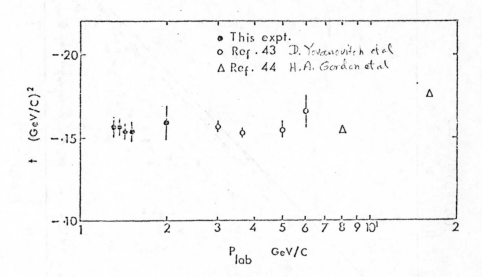

Fig. 9. Shows the t value of the p⁺⁻p crossover zero
(presumably due[19] to a zero in the imaginary part of the ω
nonflip amplitude) essentially fixed in t over a large
range of energies. The connection of the fixed t zero with
s-channel resonances is obscure here; the interpretation
in terms of absorption ideas may make sense here. Low
energy data from the QMC, Liverpool, DNPL, RHEL CERN P.S.
Experiment 599, C. Hojvat private communication.

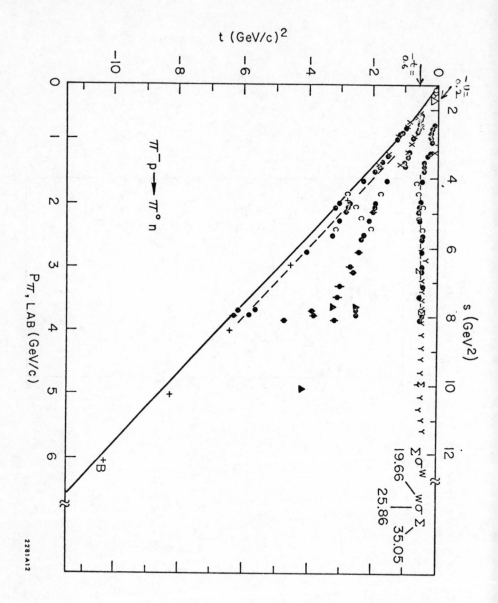

Fig. 10. Position of dips in $d\sigma(\pi^-p\to\pi^\circ n)/dt$. The dips appear in the cross section so they are not obscured by the real parts, and they are approximately fixed regardless of the presence of strong s-channel resonances at a given energy. Data from the review of Ref. 17 .

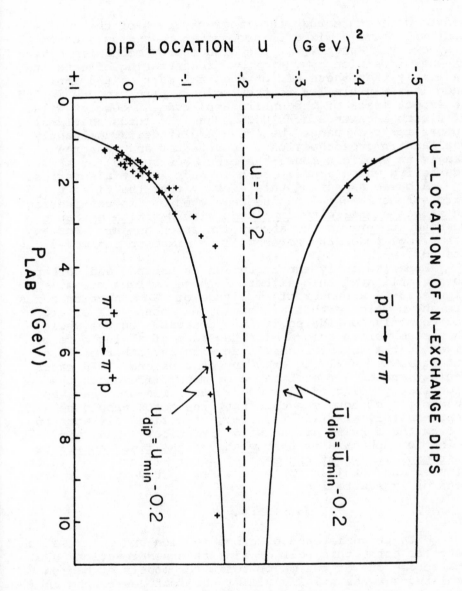

Fig. 11. Dip locations in $\pi^+ p \to p \pi^+$ and $\bar{p}p \to \pi^- \pi^+$ from the compilation of Barger, Halzen, and Phillips.[18] Results suggest dips approximately at fixed $t' \approx 0.2$ GeV^2 as in the absorptive mechanism conjecture of Ref.19 . Deviations from this simple conjecture as one passes resonances or production thresholds should be comparable to those suggested by Fig. 4.

led to conjecture[10] that the imaginary part of the amplitude will have a fixed t zero, given by a single zero trajectory. Further, if the high energy mechanism giving the zero position is absorptive rescattering effects it is likely that these affect the real part of the amplitude in a way similar to the imaginary part, so one is led to expect zeros of the entire amplitude at complex values of t with magnitude near 0.2. Thus the zeros should also appear for π exchange where the amplitude is dominantly real, and in cross sections. For vector and tensor exchanges an explicit model has been constructed[10] for ππ scattering which appears to have such zero trajectories.

A basic aspect of this view is that the fixed t zero structure should arise <u>only</u> when one is considering an <u>s-channel</u> <u>helicity</u> <u>amplitude</u> with <u>definite</u> <u>exchange</u> <u>quantum</u> <u>numbers</u> so the absorption zeros appear. For any other amplitudes the zeros will be mixed up and moved around.

Experimentally the situation is unclear and perhaps more complicated than either of these extreme views. In Figures 3-11 a number of amplitude or cross section zeros are shown which either are based on recent work or are not commonly considered in this context. On the whole they seem more in accord with the idea of a single zero, fixed in t as s increases, than with any other picture, but it is too early to draw any conclusions. (In cases where t and t' differ because of mass differences the high energy point of view where the zeros originate as absorption effects suggests[9] that the zeros should be approximately at fixed t', i.e., at a fixed distance in t from the forward or backward direction). The main point to emphasize is that <u>whatever</u> <u>the</u> <u>final</u> <u>answer</u> <u>it</u> <u>must</u> <u>explain</u> <u>all</u> <u>of</u> <u>the</u> <u>zero</u> <u>structure</u> illustrated in the figures and not just apply to a few spin 0-spin $\frac{1}{2}$ reactions or ππ scattering.

$$NP \rightarrow PN, \ \overline{PP} \rightarrow \overline{NN}$$

With the existence of cross section and polarization data[2] for both, this pair of line reversed reactions has now become one of the major tests for models of hadron amplitudes. Essentially all of the features of the amplitudes which are tested in the $0^{-}\frac{1}{2}^{+} \rightarrow 0^{-}\frac{1}{2}^{+}$ reactions are tested here too, sometimes more sensitively, and new features are present as well.

First, of course, these reactions show the absorbed π exchange forward peak. However, even inside the peak the behavior is different for the two reactions. To get the difference correct and the actual magnitude at t = 0 correct one must get a correct description of the exchanges interfering with the π.

The other exchanges should be dominated by the ρ and A_2. Even at $t = 0$ one finds important π-A_2 interference, with the forward A_2 amplitude about 40% that of the π. At larger t the $\overline{p}p \to \overline{n}n$ cross section is 1.5-2 times the $np \to pn$ cross section; this must be due to interference with the ρ which changes sign between the two reactions. Thus a knowledge of the normalized cross sections puts stringent restrictions on all the contributions since they all interfere strongly.

In pole models with ρ and A_2 about 90° out of phase none of the three exchanges would interfere. Thus the large interferences observed are sensitive probes of how one departs from pole models.

The cross sections are shown in Fig. 12.

The polarization is also very useful because it is large for $np \to pn$ and very different for the two reactions. (Polarizations, which depend sensitively on phases, are sometimes such sensitive tests that they only teach one about unimportant details.) In addition, apart from quantitative details the polarizations are determined by the ρ and A_2 alone, so they test the same amplitude structure as the more conventional $0^{-\frac{1}{2}^{+}}$ reactions.

There are five helicity amplitudes for these reactions, conventionally named φ_1-φ_5. No s-channel helicity flip occurs at either vertex in φ_1 and φ_3; one vertex flips in φ_5 and not the other, so it has net flip of one unit; and flips occur at both vertices in φ_2 and φ_4 giving one with no net flip and one with two units of flip. Since π exchange always flips the s-channel nucleon helicity, it can only contribute to φ_2 and φ_4, and it contributes a pole term which is the same for both.

The polarization is proportional to

$$\mathrm{Im}\,(\varphi_1 + \varphi_3 + \varphi_2 - \varphi_4)\,\varphi_5^*$$

so the pion pole drops out, not contributing to φ_1 or φ_3 or φ_5 and cancelling in $\varphi_2 - \varphi_4$. Thus the polarization is largely determined by the ρ and A_2 contributions (quantitatively the pion absorption correction is important at small t but qualitatively it is unimportant); polarizations test ρ-A_2 exchange degeneracy ideas here as well as in $0^{-\frac{1}{2}^{+}}$ reactions. It is amusing that the polarization is large in the exotic channel here, small in the non-exotic one. Some polarization data is shown in Fig. 13.

As with the cross sections, the CAM provides an explanation for the polarizations, starting with ρ and A_2 amplitudes which are approximately degenerate at $t = 0$ (as required by the approximate constancy of σ_T, plus SU(3)). For $np \to pn$ the explanation only depends on the properties of the dominant real amplitudes and general properties of the model, and is given in Appendix 2. For $\overline{p}p \to \overline{n}n$ the smaller imaginary parts are important so the explanation is detailed and the reader is referred to Ref. 4 ; although detailed the result is well determined

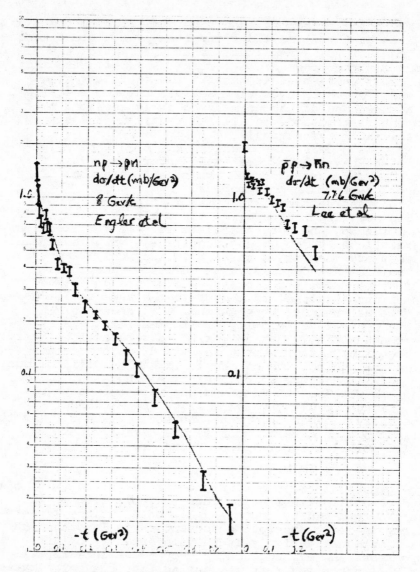

Fig. 12. These show dσ/dt for the line reversed pair
np→pn and pp→nn. Note the latter (non-exotic) channel is
larger at -t ≥ 0.02 GeV², just the opposite of the situation for line reversed pairs in $0^-\frac{1}{2}^+$ reactions; an explanation for this is given in the analysis of line
reversed reactions in the section on high energy expectations. These reactions, with polarizations also available
(See Fig. 13), provide an excellent testing ground for
models, containing most of the physics of the $0^-\frac{1}{2}^+$ reactions and much more. The theory lines show results of
the CAM, from Ref. 4.

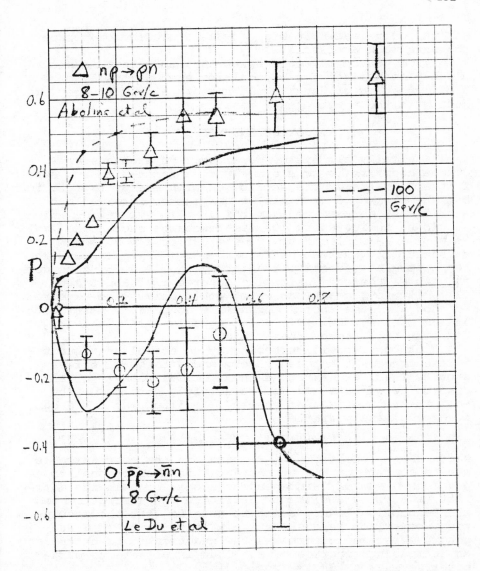

Fig. 13. Polarizations for the line reversed reactions np→pn, pp→nn. Note that the exotic channel has the larger polarization. The signs are Basel convention. The theory curves for the CAM show that the data can be understood; the pp→nn result was a prediction. In Appendix 2 a mechanism which gives the large essentially constant np→ pn polarization is given. Note, as described in the text, that the polarizations are essentially determined by ±ρ+A$_2$ exchange and so they test largely the same ideas as the $0^- \frac{1}{2}^+$ reactions.

and the curve shown in Fig. 13 was a prediction before
the data were available.

From now on it would seem reasonable that models
which base a claim for recognition even partially on
their relation to data should have to show that they can
deal with the np→pn, $\bar{p}p$→$\bar{n}n$ data.

ENERGY DEPENDENCE

Basically the energy dependence of exchange processes seems to be consistent with a Regge-like s^α (see
further remarks on the section on high energy expectations).
But the present data hints at some rather detailed but
significant departures from this, (1) Quantities which
should be dominated by the same exchange such as $\Delta\sigma_T(\pi N)$ =
$\sigma_T(\pi^-p) - \sigma_T(\pi^+p)$ and $d\sigma(\pi^-p$→$\pi^\circ n)/dt$ at t = 0, both ρ
exchange, show rather different energy dependence, with
$\Delta\sigma_T$ giving an effective trajectory $\alpha_{eff} \approx 0.65$, considerably above the conventional ρ intercept of about $\frac{1}{2}$.
(2) Different reactions which would naively be expected
to show the same energy dependence do not; in particular,
$\Delta\sigma_T(KN)$ and $\Delta\sigma_T(NN)$ fall about equally fast with energy
and both fall faster than $\Delta\sigma_T(\pi N)$.

Although it will not be easy to establish a quantitative agreement between theory and data here, effects
such as these are expected in any model with important
absorptive effects and can be simply understood. The
basic situation is that the full amplitude at t = 0 can
be approximately written

$$M(s,t) \sim s^{\alpha_o}(1-C/(B+\alpha'\ell n s))$$ (1)

where the s^{α_o} is from the Reggeon and the correction is
due to absorption. The constant C is proportional to σ_T
and B is a sum of t-independent slopes of both the diffractive elastic amplitude describing the absorption and
the Reggeon. The key point to note is that the absorption correction is destructively interfering (C,B are
positive) so as s increases the quantity in brackets is
an increasing function of s. Thus if we were to para-
meterize M as $s^{\alpha_{eff}}$, we would find

$$M(s,t) \sim s^{\alpha_{eff}}$$ (2)

$$\alpha_{eff} > \alpha_o$$ (3)

Note that the larger C is (i.e., σ_T) the greater the
difference between α_{eff} and α_o, while the larger B is
the less the difference.

From this we can make several observations. First
we consider a single exchange, relevant to (1) above.
Then note:

(a) For small t, amplitudes with net helicity flip
n = 0 feel absorption much more than those with n > 0

since the latter have their small b components (where absorption is strongest) kinematically suppressed. Thus

$$\alpha_{eff}(\text{nonflip}) > \alpha_{eff}(\text{flip})$$

(b) For vector exchanges (e.g., ρ,ω) it is observed that the imaginary parts of the amplitudes are more strongly absorbed than the real parts, so

$$\alpha_{eff}(\text{ImM},\text{vector exchange}) > \alpha_{eff}(\text{ReM},\text{vector exchange})$$

Combining these we can relate several energy dependences; e.g., <u>for</u> πN

$$\alpha_{eff}(\Delta\sigma_T) > \alpha_{eff}(d\sigma(\pi^-p\to\pi^\circ n)/dt, t=0) > \alpha_{eff}(\sigma(\pi^-p\to\pi^\circ n)).$$

Next consider Point (2). What is observed is that

$$\alpha_{eff}(\Delta\sigma_T(\pi N)) > \alpha_{eff}(\Delta\sigma_T(KN)) \approx \alpha_{eff}(\Delta\sigma_T(NN)).$$

Can we understand this? If it was only a matter of the first relation we could claim that πN feels absorption more than KN since $\sigma_T(\pi N) > \sigma_T(KN)$. But $\sigma_T(NN)$ is still larger and it behaves as KN. Since πN is dominated by ρ exchange while KN and NN are dominated by ω exchange one could claim that ω simply lies lower than ρ; while that might be true, it is no explanation and in addition the fact that crossover positions appear to show the same qualitative effect, with the πN crossover closer to t = 0 than KN or NN, strongly suggests that the explanation is a dynamical one.

It does in fact appear that the absorption dynamics gives the right effect, but to be sure we must have confidence in our knowledge of Regge residues, which is hardly justified. Thus here we can indicate how the effect probably arises, and we can await a more certain knowledge of the Regge residues to be confident. In any case, to my knowledge this is the only explanation of the data so far. The argument is simple; we assume the ρ and ω have the same trajectory intercept, by SU(3) (any difference in intercept would just add to this effect), and use Eqns. 1 and 2. Then using the numbers in the first two rows of Table 2 we get the results in the third row for the amount α_{eff} exceeds α_0. As desired, πN lies above KN and NN by a significant amount, and the latter two are about equal. With an input $\alpha_0 = 0.43$, for example, the results are consistent with the Serpukhov data. Whether the numbers used for C,B are realistic is not something we can be confident of at the present time, but they are reasonable and might be sufficiently correct.

TABLE 2

	KN	πN	NN
C	3	4.5	7
B	3.15	4	8.5
$\alpha_{eff} - \alpha_o$	0.10	0.18	0.11

Physically what is happening is clear. The effect of absorption depends not only on the strength of the inter-action (σ_{π}), but on the partial wave structure. An ampli-tude which is sharper in t is more spread out in b and feels the removal of its lowest partial waves relatively less. Thus the net effect depends on some function of $\smile$/B.

At the present time, then, the pattern of energy dependences exhibited by the data can be accommodated by models with strong absorptive effects so that the effective energy dependence of the nonflip amplitude is considerably different from that of the input tra-jectory. The effect depends on the amount of net hel-icity flip and on the reaction considered. Similar effects will appear in the phases of the amplitudes and the crossover behavior and can be correlated with the energy dependence. It will be important to find out whether other models, particularly those which insist on maintaining a phase as close to the Regge phase as possible, can accomm-odate the present data, and of course to confirm the data and observe the energy dependence over even a wider range.

HIGH ENERGY EXPECTATIONS

What can we learn from higher energy data? What behavior should surprise us? What general behavior should make us feel that we understand what is happening?

Two body hadron reactions have been around for some time, and we have become somewhat numbed to the broad implications of the data. In fact, there are important general features to be studied as well as a lot of detailed results. We are indeed at a stage of describing a very large amount of data in real detail, without averaging over lots of variables. We are really looking at the energy and angular dependence including phase of lots of individual spin amplitudes for lots of related reactions. On the other hand, the general features will be tested much better with higher energy data than ever before.

There are at least three important questions which will be resolved by the data soon to come. The first two are of extremely general significance; the third is important because we understand two body data well enough to study interference effects and it may be able to distinguish between existing points of view.

(1) It is generally thought that hadron states are composite systems and that the hadrons will lie on Regge trajectories just as bound states always do in quantum mechanics. This implies that the contribution of a given exchange will be proportional to s^{α}, where α is a power related to the particle's spin and mass, $J = \alpha(m^2)$. For example, if $\alpha \approx a+bt$ at small t, then $\alpha_{\pi}, \alpha_{B} \approx 0$ and $\alpha_{\rho}, \alpha_{\omega}, \alpha_{f}, \alpha_{A_2} \approx 1/2$.

Since $d\sigma/dt \sim s^{2\alpha}$ one expects approximately a $1/s$ suppression of π, B exchanges relative to ρ, ω, f, A_2 ($s \approx 2p_L$). Similarly, for backward reactions one expects N exchange to decrease relative to Δ by about $1/s$. Many processes which have important π or B or N contributions will change their character considerably as the energy increases.

Note that this is a deeper question than a power law falloff for general exchange processes. That could arise, for example, form the presence of large numbers of competing channels via unitarity and have nothing to do with compositeness and Regge trajectories. But then one would expect all the exchanges in a given reaction to show the same falloff and the shape or spin dependence should not change with energy. Several examples are:

(a) π exchange peaks. In $np \to pn, \gamma N \to \pi N, \pi N \to \rho N$, the π exchange contribution will go away relative to the other isovector exchanges ρ and A_2. A reasonable behavior is shown for $np \to pn$ in Fig. 14.

(b) Currently in ω production reactions, $\pi N \to \omega N$ and $\pi N \to \omega \Delta$, there are a large number of ω's produced with s-channel helicity zero, especially at small t. The (natural parity)

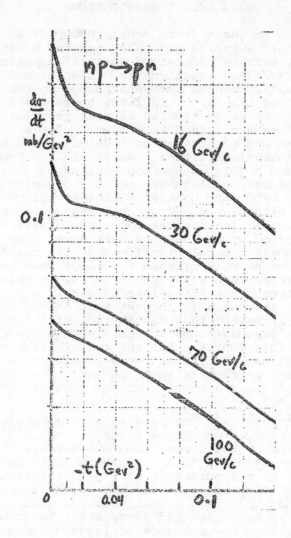

Fig. 14 . Shows predictions for high energy dσ/dt for
np→pn from Ref. 4 . The π exchange peak is expected to
disappear with energy relative to the other isovector
exchanges ρ and A₂ if hadrons lie on simple Regge trajectories. The effect should be clearly observable at
NAL energies, and possibly at Serpukhov. Other reactions
where similar effects will occur are mentioned in the
text.

ρ exchange cannot produce such helicity states, and they are presumably due to B exchange at larger t, π exchange via ρ-ω mixing at small t. Therefore as the energy increases they should go away relative to helicity 1 ω's. To see that one could, for example, plot $\rho_{00}^{s} d\sigma/dt$ (which isolates the unnatural parity exchange) vs. s at fixed t. (c) Since photon exchange has a constant cross section in energy while hadron exchanges presumably fall as a power of s, at some energy (about 1500 GeV/c) one will find $\sigma_\gamma \sim \sigma$(hadron). But at much lower energies one should see effects of the γ exchange, such as isospin violations.[23] For example, by comparing $K^+p \to K^{*+}\Delta^+$ and $K^+p \to K^{*o}\Delta^{++}$ or similar K^- reactions one can see isospin violations. In addition,[24] since the γ exchange is mainly real, the interference effects should be larger and appear at a lower energy in the K^+ reactions than in the K^- if exchange degeneracy ideas hold[24] for K^* reactions as well as for $0^- \frac{1}{2}^+$ processes.

If the higher lying exchanges do not dominate as the energy increases our ideas about composite states will need fundamental revision. If, on the other hand, things go about as expected, then we can use the detailed information to confirm or improve our present detailed ideas.

(2) <u>Shrinkage</u> must occur; i.e., if there is a dominant exchange and the amplitude goes as s^α where α is a function of t, then the t dependence will change with energy. If α is linear in t at small t, then

$$s^{a+bt} \sim e^{(b\ell n s)t}$$

and the slope will increase approximately as ℓn s. Absorptive effects and lower lying exchanges which go away will modify the simple behavior in detail, but over a large energy range the qualitative features should appear in all particle exchange processes.

However, unless some care is taken one can hide the effects in processes where structure is present. For example, Fig.15 shows the $\pi^-p \to \pi^o n$ cross section from Ref.2,26 as a function of energy. The dip moves with energy. Depending on the t region chosen one would predict shrinkage or not. For example, Fig. 16 shows the ratio of cross sections at two t values vs. energy. In part a the shrinkage is apparent, when the t range is .15 to .4; in part b the shrinkage is obscured by choosing a range including -t = .5 which senses the dip motion.

In general it is more precise and interpretable to plot cross section ratios such as in Fig. 16 rather than fitted slopes. It would be helpful if data was presented this way.

(3) <u>Line reversal at high energies</u>. In general one cannot find definitive tests of models or ways to decide between models with one experiment. However, as far as I

258

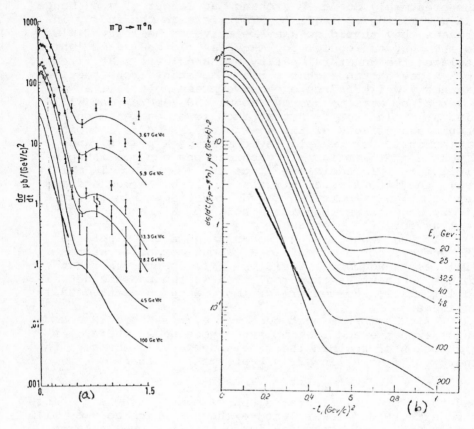

Fig. 15. Shrinkage predictions for $\pi^- p \to \pi^0 n$ from (a)
Ref. 2 , (b) Ref.26. The lines drawn in on the high
energy curves are the slope the low energy region shows
and illustrate the amount of shrinkage expected in the
t-region (0.15-0.4) shown by the vertical lines. If
the t region were to include 0.5 the shrinkage would
essentially disappear as shown on the next figure.

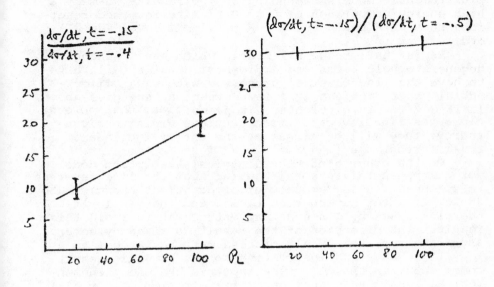

Fig.16 . Illustrates how one's perception of shrinkage
depends on the t region when structure is present.
Plotting cross section ratios as shown is a good way
to present the data. Numbers read off from Fig.15 a.

can see at the moment there is one type of experiment which can rule out either the Classical or the Mystical plus Romantic models depending on the results, namely a high energy comparison of $0^{-\frac{1}{2}^+} \to 0^{-\frac{1}{2}^+}$ line reversed reactions such as $K^- p \to K^o n$ vs. $K^+ n \to K^o p$, $\pi^+ p \to K^+ \Sigma^+$ vs. $K^- p \to \pi^- \Sigma^+$ etc.

As far as I know, all models which have exchange degenerate pole terms, regardless of details, will have to have the line reversed processes with equal differential cross sections to a few percent at energies above 10-15 GeV/c. In particular, it seems clear that however close the line reversed cross sections are at a given energy, they will be closer as the energy increases, never farther apart.

On the other hand, the Classical Absorption Model for quite general reasons requires that the line reversed reactions differ by amounts of order 50% at energies above 25 GeV/c, after having been closer together at lower energies. Again, I see at present no way to avoid this result. The direction of the result is fixed by general arguments too; the "real" process must be larger.

It is easy and instructive to see how this result comes about in the CAM. The input is the one phenomenlogical result[2] that the tensor trajectories (A_2 or K^{**}) lie lower in the J plane near t = 0 than the vector trajectories (ρ or K^*) by an amount $\Delta\alpha \approx 0.15$. (the precise value is not important to establish the effect but affects the size of the result). Next, observe that tensor exchanges are more central in impact parameter than vector ones, so tensor exchanges will feel absorption more than vector exchanges (since absorption modifies central partial waves most). As an aside, note that this raises α_{eff} above α_o more for tensor than vector exchange, so the final α_{eff}'s are closer together than the input α's.

Now follow the details of Fig. 17. Part a shows qualitatively how some (appropriately defined) strength of absorption will behave with energy. At low energies where there are few open channels there will not be much effect from absorption. At high energies where shrinkage has made the elastic rescattering peak very sharp the amount of absorption will have decreased again. At some energy, perhaps around 5-10 GeV/c, where a large number of inelastic channels are open and high energy shrinkage is beginning to set in, the strength of the absorption will be at a maximum.

Parts b-d show at a given energy how the "real" pole term will be larger in magnitude than the "rotating" one, how the "real" amplitude will be absorbed more than the "rotating" one because its cut will be closer to 180° out of phase, and how the final "real amplitude" will still be larger than the final "rotating" one, but with

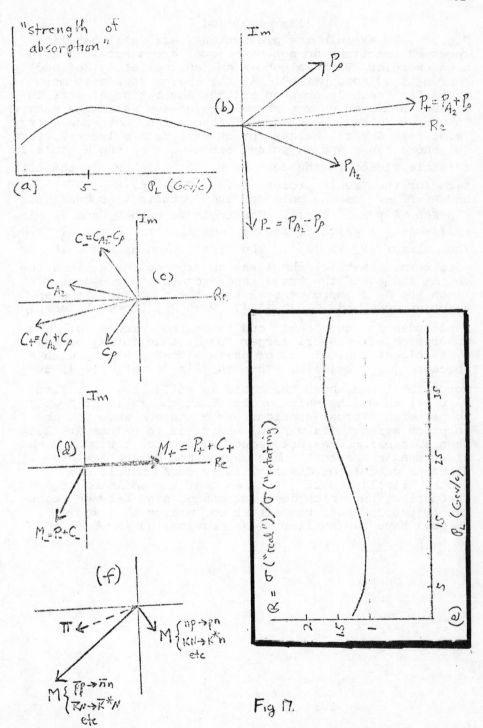

"strength of absorption"

(a) 5 $P_L \; (Gev/c)$

(b)

Im

P_ρ

$P_+ = P_{A_2} + P_\rho$

Re

P_{A_2}

$P_- = P_{A_2} - P_\rho$

$C_- = C_{A_2} - C_\rho$

Im

C_{A_2}

(c)

Re

$C_+ = C_{A_2} + C_\rho$

C_ρ

Im

(d) $M_+ = P_+ + C_+$

Re

$M_- = P_- + C_-$

(f)

π

$M \begin{cases} \pi^- p \to \rho^- n \\ KN \to K^* n \\ etc \end{cases}$

$M \begin{cases} \overline{p} p \to \overline{n} n \\ \overline{K} N \to \overline{K}^* N \\ etc \end{cases}$

$R = \sigma("real")/\sigma("rotating")$

2

1.5

1

5 15 25 35

$P_L \; (Gev/c)$

(e)

Fig 17.

(Figure caption)

Fig.17 . To explain the prediction (part (e)) that line reversed reactions do <u>not</u> have equal cross sections at high energies. Part (a) shows an (appropriately defined) "strength of absorption". As the energy increases more inelastic channels open up and the absorption effects increase, until an energy where high energy shrinkage sets in and decreases the effect of absorption. At some energy (e.g.,5-10 GeV/c) the absorption effects are largest. Part (b) shows the ρ and A_2 poles; since $\alpha_{A_2} < \alpha_\rho$ the A_2 pole is a little closer to the real axis. $P_+ \cong P_{A_2} + P_\rho$ is the pole term for the "real" process (e.g., $K^+n \to K^\circ p$, $K^-p \to \pi^- \Sigma^+$, etc.) and $P_- = P_{A_2} - P_\rho$ is the pole for the "rotating" process (e.g., $K^-p \to \overline{K^\circ}n$, $\pi^+ p \to K^+ \Sigma^+$, etc.). The angle between P_ρ and P_{A_2} is $\pi/2(1-\alpha_\rho+\alpha_{A_2})$ which is always less than $\pi/2$ since $\alpha_{A_2} < \alpha_\rho$. Thus always $|P_+| > |P_-|$. The "real" process has a larger pole term. Part (c) shows the absorption corrections for the A_2 and ρ and the "real" and "rotating" processes. Since the A_2 is more central than the ρ it feels the absorption more and $|C_{A_2}| > |C_\rho|$. Part (d) shows the complete amplitudes for the "real" and "rotating" processes. The absorption effects are larger for M_+ than for M_- because C_+ is closer to 180° out of phase with P_+ than C_- with P_- (because $|C_{A_2}| > |C_\rho|$). Thus $|M_+|/|M_-| \lesssim |P_+|/|P_-|$, but for realistic numbers the ratio is still above 1 a little. Part (e) shows the main result, that the ratio of "real" to "rotating" cross sections has a minimum when the absorption strength is maximal and rises to values $R \sim 1.5$ when absorption does not reduce P_+ so much toward P_-. As discussed in the text, this may be one of the few predictions capable of distinguishing among models and ideas. Finally, part (f) shows that the addition of a π contribution (which does not change sign between reactions) just reverses the situation, making the exotic channel have the smaller cross section, as is observed.

$$|P_+|/|P_-| > |M_+|/|M_-| > 1$$

where + stands for "real" and − for "rotating".

At the energy where the absorption is the strongest the ratio is as small as it will get, and the cross section ratio R of part e is down near unity. As s increases the absorption effect decreases and the ratio increases, reaching values such as 1.5 at energies $P_L \sim$ 30 GeV/c. The precise values are model dependent, but the effect must be large.

(Finally, having so many details present it is worth noting that by adding a π exchange contribution to part d one converts to the case of np→pn vs. $\overline{p}p$→$\overline{n}$n line reversed pairs or vector meson line reversed pairs. The π contribution does not change sign between reactions. As the figure clearly shows, this just reverses the size of the cross sections, making the "rotating" reaction larger than the "real" one. Adding a π interchanges exotic and non-exotic reactions. This is precisely what is observed in the data.)

It will be interesting to see the experimental results on high energy line reversed reactions and to see if in fact it is possible to draw clear conclusions about current models. At the present time the only relevant measurement is the Serpukhov K⁻p→K°n data at 25 and 35 GeV/c, which go in the direction of the CAM prediction, with the observed cross section smaller than expected from an exchange degenerate extrapolation of the low energy data.   K⁺n→K°p may also be measured at Serpukhov, making a comparison possible. The Σ reactions may be measurable at NAL within the next year.

(4) Many polarizations will be large at high energies. Predictions for several are shown in Fig. 18 .
As lower lying exchanges are less important the polarizations will become more useful tests of models and ideas.

264

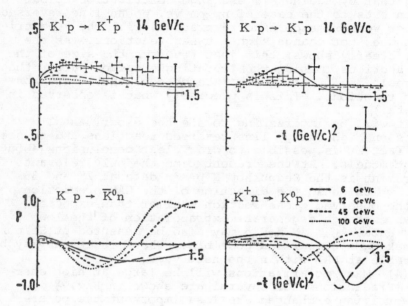

Fig. 18. Typical high energy polarization predictions for elastic and exchange reactions. Similar results hold for πN processes, hypercharge exchange, etc. Theory curves from Ref. 2 . A prediction for P(np→pn) at 100 GeV/c is shown in Fig. 13 .

PRODUCTION OF RESONANCES AND REGGE RECURRENCES

An increasingly important aspect of two body reactions is the production of higher mass and spin resonances. If the production mechanism is understood we can learn about the resonance properties and its role in other areas of hadron physics; equally well, it is a place to further test and improve our understanding of production mechanisms and models. Two kinds of questions are of particular interest.

(a) Are there any data on <u>resonance production mechanisms</u> which indicate that we do not understand what is happening, or do we seem to have a good grasp of all the production data? There is of course a lot of data where the answer is legitimately a matter of opinion at the present time, and these cases must be watched. But I am only aware of one case where a serious claim has been made that the situation is drastic; that is B meson production in $\pi N \rightarrow BN$.

Since $B \rightarrow \omega \pi$ one expects to produce a lot of B's by ω exchange. That can be done with no need to flip helicity at either vertex. The large nonflip coupling of the nucleon to the ω should allow this amplitude to be important. It should lead to a lot of zero helicity B's.

Fox and Hey[28] have calculated B production and they claim the result is very much too large. To reproduce the data they are then led to some rather surprising assumptions. However, they do not absorb the large nonflip amplitude. They do not give any arguments for this, although one of the few things all workers seemed to agree on in other reactions was that nonflip amplitudes were strongly absorbed; witness, for example, the crossover zero generally agreed to be present in ω exchange in KN and NN reactions because of absorption.

In a typical situation absorption will reduce a nonflip amplitude by about a factor of two in magnitude at $t = 0$, and sharpen the peak. The cross section integrated out to -t about .2 GeV^2 is suppressed about a factor of 7. This would appear to account for most of the missing order of magnitude of Fox and Hey. Using this and assuming that the $B\omega\pi$ coupling is mainly s wave so about equal mixtures of helicity zero and helicity one B's are produced I find cross sections within a factor of two or better agreement with the data. In addition, the absorbed nonflip amplitude has a steep slope at small t because it has a dip near $-t = 0.2$, and then a break due to the secondary maximum of the nonflip amplitude and to the rise of the flip amplitudes. The data is certainly consistent with such a shape, with a small t slope of 10 GeV^2 or more. This

266

approach requires that $\rho_{oo}^{s}(B) \gtrsim 1/2$ which does not seem inconsistent with recent data.[29] Basically the situation is as shown in Fig. 19.

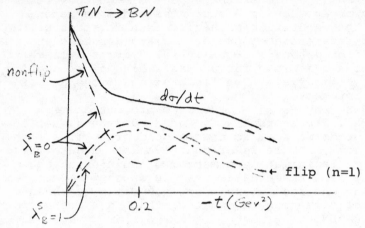

Fig. 19

Thus the rather standard absorption picture of the small t amplitudes appears to give a picture of B production which is not inconsistent with the data. More careful calculations have to be done, of course, to verify that the entire B-ω system, in exchange and production, behaves reasonably. For the present, however, it seems reasonable to believe that there is no worrisome puzzle. It is important to verify for many reactions that the size, s, t, and spin dependence are reasonably understood in terms of our present ideas.

(B) <u>Production of Regge Recurrences</u>. Another way to study the composite nature of hadrons and whether they lie on Regge trajectories is to consider external Reggeon production. In particular, one can produce a particle and its Regge recurrence and compare the behavior, perhaps learning something important in the process. There is quite a lot of data around on Regge recurrence production which is not in very public view because the statistics are not high and one is not sure what to do with it or how to analyze it.

A few reactions which can be studied are:

$\pi N \to \rho N$
$\quad \to fN$ (?)
$\quad \to gN$
$\pi N \to \pi N$
$\quad \to \pi N(1690)$
$\pi N \to \pi \Delta$
$\quad \to \pi \Delta(1920)$

and one can substitute K, K*, Λ, Σ, etc. to generate more.

A full understanding of external Reggeons would allow us to predict the s,t, dependence, which helicity states are populated, and cross section sizes. If one looks, for example, in the s-channel one finds that the ratio of total cross sections in πN scattering at the Δ mass to that at the Δ recurrence mass ($\Delta(1920)$) is a factor of 5. From a different point of view, Veneziano model calculations of Chan and Tsao[30] give a factor of 2 decrease in cross section as one goes from producing a state to producing its recurrence.

The recurrence will have higher spin. Are its higher helicity states populated?

What about energy dependence? In pure pole models the energy dependence does not depend on which amplitudes are populated, while in models with absorption it does.

The t-dependence may change with forward turnovers introduced if higher helicity states are populated.

One can also study symmetry questions; e.g., are SU(3) d/f ratios unchanged? Are K^+ reactions still mainly real at small t?

The situation theoretically has been largely ignored. The most interesting work[31,32] has been done by Hoyer, Roberts, and Roy in a paper based on finite mass sum rules. They argue that

$$X = \left(d\sigma\left(\underset{b}{\overset{a}{\longrightarrow}}\boxed{\alpha_i}\underset{R}{\overset{c}{\longrightarrow}}\right)/dt\right)\bigg/\left(d\sigma\left(\underset{b}{\overset{a}{\longrightarrow}}\boxed{}\underset{R}{\overset{c}{\longrightarrow}}\right)/dt\right) \sim \left(M_R^2\right)^{2\alpha_j(t)-2\alpha_i(t)}$$

and they give two sorts of predictions. First, if $j = \pi$ and $i = \rho, \omega, f, A_2$ they expect $X \sim (M_R^2)^{-1}$ so π exchanges are predicted to dominate increasingly over natural parity exchanges as the resonance mass increases. There seems to be some evidence that this is occurring. Second,

$$d\sigma\left(\boxed{\alpha_i}_R\right)/dt (M_R^2)^{-2\alpha_i(t)} \sim e^{-2\alpha_i(t)\ell n M_R^2}$$

so they expect less falloff in t as M_R^2 increases, an <u>anti-shrinkage</u>. It is not so clear that this is observed.

In fact, consider the following naive kinematical duality argument to compare with their second prediction. Suppose we sit at a fixed s and the cross section is dominated by a peripheral high mass resonance, so we have a Legendre function zero at an angle θ_0, and $s >> M_R^2 >> m_a^2, m_b^2$. Then

$$\Delta^2 = -t = \Delta_{min}^2 + 2qq'(1-\cos\theta_0)$$

$$\Delta_{min}^2 \approx M_R^4 m_a^2/s^2$$

$$q' \approx (s-M_R^2)/2W$$

Now increase M_R^2. Then $d\Delta^2/dM_R^2 = 2m_a^2M_R^2/s^2 - q(1-\cos\theta_0)/W$ is negative for large s, so the zero is closer to $\Delta^2=0$ and we expect <u>shrinkage</u> as M_R^2 increases. Asymptotically the Δ^2 dependence is independent of M_R^2.

The contradiction presumably has to do with the role of daughter states and lower lying contributions implicit in the two arguments. It will be instructive to see what finally happens in the data, and to try to understand the situation if the first Hoyer, Roberts, Roy prediction is more valid than the second.

(C) <u>Vector meson production</u>. There is a good deal of data submitted to this meeting on vector meson production, and an extensive phenomenologicalanalysis of the data by Field and Sidhu. On the whole their analysis indicates that the properties of the data are well understood. For example, they were able to take the model of Ref. 2 for $0^-\frac{1}{2}^+ \to 0^-\frac{1}{2}^+$ reactions and with essentially no changes produce a good description of ρ and ω and K^* data. The one place to watch is the detailed phase question of the $\rho-\omega$ interference phase for the helicity one natural parity amplitudes, where the model may be in disagreement with the data of the Argnne grap at 4-6 GeV/c. However, the higher energy SLAC data suggests that there may not be such a disagreement, and in addition (as Field and Sidhu emphasize), the phase being tested is the same as that giving the line reversal properties for K^* reactions which come out all right in the model. Thus it appears likely that the $\rho-\omega$ phase at 6 GeV/c is due to a low energy effect such as a lower lying contribution; it should be watched, however, to see that the data changes as the energy is increased. If the higher energy data is the same as the 4-6 GeV/c data then either the phase properties of the models are wrong or unexpected contributions are important or the expected contributions have unexpected energy dependence.

(D) <u>S-Channel helicity Amplitudes</u>. For some time it has been clear that the s-channel helicity amplitudes were likely to be the simplest to interpret and understand. If the Classical absorption approach is basically right this is certainly true. If the Mystical kind of models turn out to be correct, on the other hand, it is not nearly so likely and for some amplitudes a t-channel (or some other) point of view would be more useful. The Romantic models are somewhere inbetween, with s-channel structure at least for the imaginary parts.

The reason s-channel amplitudes are best if absorption is important is that one must rotate the initial Reggeon scattering amplitude to the appropriate z axis to apply the absorption, and that rotation does not mix up amplitudes for s-channel helicity amplitudes, so proper-

ties characteristic of an amplitude are not obscured by
the absorption. In addition, the absorption is largely
helicity independent so the final observable amplitudes
preserve many properties of the pole terms. For example,
if the pole terms are zero the full amplitudes are zero
only for the s-channel helicity amplitudes; one can give
many more detailed examples.

Thus however else the data is presented, experimenters should always present s-channel information whenever
possible (e.g., density matrices). For resonance production that simply corresponds to choosing a coordinate
system in the resonance rest frame with z-axis along the
recoil particle direction (rather than along the beam
direction, which gives the t-channel information).

APPENDIX 1

Here we just briefly note a few ways to get at the
sum over intermediate states experimentally. These are
not exactly the same thing needed in the absorption calculation, but they involve such a sum and it is likely
that if we can calculate it in one place we will understand it well enough.

(a)   In two body double charge exchange reactions
all calculations so far which give numerical results use
the technique of approximating the sum by one or two
lowest states. If we knew from data that that approximation was either adequate, or very bad, it would
suggest a similar conclusion for all such sums. In
particular, one could compare pairs of reactions such as
$\pi^- p \to K^+ \Sigma^-$ or $K^- p \to \pi^+ \Sigma^-$, and $K^- p \to K^+ \Xi^-$. Keeping the spin $\frac{1}{2}$
baryon intermediate states will produce a much larger
cross section for $\pi^- p \to K^+ \Sigma^-$ than for $K^- p \to K^+ \Xi^-$ just
because there are more intermediate states for the former
and they are all coherent. It would be hard to avoid an
order of magnitude ratio. Preliminary data[33] indicates
that the two cross sections are about equal, which would
suggest that the lowest intermediate states are a very
bad approximation to the sum. This is a much stronger
test than the absolute values of cross sections since the
values are sensitive to the coupling constants used.
One can find a number of other such comparisons to make
when data is available.

(b)   As originally suggested by Pumplin and Ross,[34] and
Gribov[35] there should be a contribution to the Glauber
correction on deuterium from nonelastic intermediate
states. This has recently been looked at in detail[36];
there appears to be rather good
evidence for the presence of such a contribution, and good
data on deuterons will allow one to test our ability to
calculate it and its energy dependence.

(c)   Very high energy photon exchange is observable
in certain nonelastic reactions because the hadron ex-

270

changes fall off with energy and the photon does not.
In addition, in some cases the photon exchange behaves
like a short range force,[24] localized within a.fermi.
Then it feels the effect of the strong initial and final
state interactions, which will receive contributions from
inelastic intermediate states. Because the photon pole is
known, deviations from it can be studied. With some
model dependence, at least at first, the elastic intermediate state can be separated.off. In this case the sum
encountered is the same one as in the absorption case
and will be directly relevant. There will even be such
an effect in elastic reactions but it will probably be
too small to be seen. In the inelastic short range photon
exchange reactions the rescattering effects will dominate
the structure and size of the cross sections.

APPENDIX 2

As an example of the behavior of amplitudes we describe briefly here the CAM solution to the long standing
puzzle of the large, rather constant $np \to pn$ polarization.
Complete details are given in Ref. 4 .

Recall

$$P d\sigma/dt = 2 \, \mathrm{Im}\varphi_o \varphi_5^*, \qquad \varphi_o \equiv \varphi_1 + \varphi_2 + \varphi_3 - \varphi_4$$

In the simplest case we expect no π contribution and
$\rho + A_2$ real so $P = 0$, as discussed in the text. More
realistically, at $t = 0$ the situation is approximately
as in Fig. A1, with φ_o and φ_5 both approximately real as
expected.

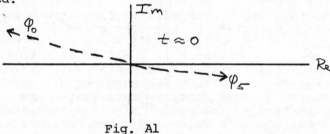

Fig. A1

As $-t$ increases, $\mathrm{Re}\varphi_1$ and $\mathrm{Re}\varphi_3$ (being n=0 amplitudes)
must have an absorption zero by $-t \sim 0.2$ GeV^2. The
natural parity poles add in $\varphi_2 - \varphi_4$, so for ρ and A_2 the
behavior is as in Fig. A2.

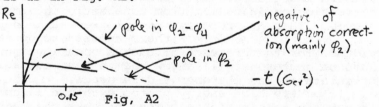

Fig, A2

So $\text{Re}(\varphi_2-\varphi_4)$ has a zero by $-t \approx 0.05$ (well before the peak of the pole). Thus all parts of φ_0 have a zero at small t, and in fact $\text{Re}\varphi_0$ has a zero by $-t \lesssim 0.1$ GeV^2. Thus Fig. A1 becomes

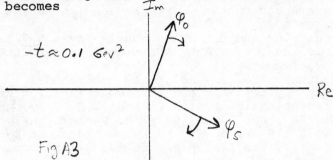

Fig A3

and the polarization is maximal since φ_0, φ_5 are $\pi/2$ out of phase. As $-t$ increases now both φ_0 and φ_5 rotate slowly around staying about 90° apart, so P stays large even though pieces of the amplitudes have zeros.

It appears difficult for other approaches to obtain such a result naturally, because they do not normally have small t zeros in the amplitudes (especially in the real parts) so φ_0 stays in the second quadrant and $P \approx 0$. The CAM zeros in the _real_ _parts_ of ρ and A_2 give both the sign and magnitude of P correctly, assuming exchange degenerate structure at $t = 0$ and no rapid variation with t except in $n = 0$ amplitudes where it is implied by the effects of absorption.

REFERENCES

1. The recent review by G.C. Fox and C.Quigg, Stony-brook preprint ITP-SB-73-22, has a very complete list of references running from reviews to recent attempts at models.
2. B.J. Hartley and G.L. Kane, Nucl. Phys. B57,157 (1973)
3. R.Field and D.P. Sidhu, BNL preprint, submitted to this conference.
4. M. Vaughn and G.L. Kane, to be published.
5. For DAM applications and references see for example the recent analysis of J.L. Loos and J.A.J. Matthews, Phys. Rev. D6, 2463 (1973); M. Davier, Phys. Lett. 40B, 369 (1972); or for backward reactions Y. Takash-ashi and Y. Kohsaka, preprint TU/73/106, Dept. of Physics, Tohoku Univ., Sindai, Japan.
   For Mystical Models see G. Girardi et al., Saclay preprint DPh-T/73/44; G. Girardi, R. Lacaze, R. Pechanski, G. Cohen-Tannoudji, F. Hayot, and H. Navelet, Nucl. Phys. B47, 445 (1972); G.A. Ringland, R.G. Roberts, D.P. Roy, and J. Tran Thanh Van, Nucl. Phys. B44, 395 (1972).
   For CAM see Ref. 2-4 and A. Martin and P.R. Stevens, Phys. Rev. D5, 147 (1972).
   Various other applications, such as Complex Pole Models (e.g., see B. Desai and P.R. Stevens, Riverside preprin UCR-73-4) are more difficult to categorize. The duality properties of these models are discussed by R. Worden, Michigan preprint
6. M. Fukugita and T. Inami, Nucl. Phys. B44, 490 (1972).
7. F. Elvekjaer, T. Inami, and G. Ringland, Rutherford preprint RPP/T/42.
8. M.R. Pennington, Zeros in $\pi\pi$ Scattering, Proceedings of the Florida State International Conference on $\pi\pi$ Scattering, March 1973.
9. See, for example, R. Odorico, Phys. Lett. 38B, 411 (1972) and references there.
10. G. Cohen-Tannoudji, R. Lacaze, F.S. Henyey, D. Richards, W.J. Zakrzewski, and G.L. Kane, Nucl. Phys. B45, 109 (1972).
11. R. Wilson, Ann. of Phys. 32, 193 (1965).
12. R.E. Mischke, P.F. Shepard, and T.J. Devlin, Phys. Rev. Lett. 23, 542 (1969).
13. Y. Williamson et al., Phys. Rev. Lett. 29, 1353 (1972).
14. S. Barish, private communication.
15. T. Eguchi, M. Fukugita, and T. Shimada, Phys. Lett. 43B, 56 (1973).
16. R. Kelly, private communication.
17. J.A.J. Matthews, Proceedings of the Florida State International Conference on $\pi\pi$ Scattering,March 1973.

18. V. Barger, F. Halzen, and R.J.N. Phillips, Wisconsin preprint.

19. M. Ross, F.S. Henyey, and G.L. Kane, Nucl. Phys. B23, 269 (1970).

20. For recent data and references to other data see
    $d\sigma(np \to pn)/dt$:
    M.B. Davies et al., Phys. Rev. Lett. 29, 39 (1972)
    E.L. Miller et al., Phys. Rev. Lett. 26, 984 (1971).
    J. Engler et al., Phys. Lett. 34B, 528 (1971).

    $d\sigma(\bar{p}p \to \bar{n}n)/dt$:
    J.G. Lee et al., Nucl. Phys. BJ2, 292 (1973)

    $P(np \to pn)$:
    M.A. Abolins et al., Phys. Rev. Lett. 30, 1183 (1973)

    $P(\bar{p}p \to \bar{n}n)$:
    P. LeDu et al., Phys. Lett. 44B, 390 (1973).

21. A similar result is found for photoproduction, R. Worden, Nucl. Phys. B37, 253 (1972).

22. Further examples are given in Ref. 17.

23. R. Nicot and Ph. Salin, Nucl. Phys. B38, 247 (1972); G. Berlad et al., Ann. of Phys. 75, 461 (1973).

24. M.M. Block, I. Drummond, and G.L. Kane, Michigan preprint

25. R. Field has emphasized the importance of verifying that exchange degeneracy ideas hold for vector meson reactions.

26. S.T. Sukhorokov and K.A. Ter-Martirosyan, Nucl. Phys. B54, 522 (1973).

27. V.I. Belovsov et al., Phys. Lett. 43B, 76 (1973).

28. G.C. Fox and A.J.G. Hey, Cal Tech preprint CALT-68-373.

29. S. Protopapescu, private communication; G. Lynch, private communication.

30. H.M. Chan and T.S. Tsao, Phys. Rev. D4, 156 (1971).

31. P. Hoyer, R.G. Roberts, and D.P. Roy, Nucl. Phys. B56, 173 (1973).

32. After this was written another related paper by C. Michael, CERN preprint TH1684, was brought to my attention.

33. C. Akerlof, D. Meyer, private communication.

34. J. Pumplin and M. Ross, Phys. Rev. Lett. 21, 1178 (1968).

35. V.N. Gribov, JETP (Sov. Phys) 56, 892 (1969).

36. See A.B. Kaidalov and L.A. Kondratyuk, Nucl. Phys. B56, 90 (1973); D.P. Sidhu and C. Quigg, Phys. Rev. D7, 755 (1973).

INELASTIC SCATTERING AMPLITUDES*

J. A. J. Matthews
Stanford Linear Accelerator Center
Stanford University, Stanford, Calif. 94305

ABSTRACT

New results from inelastic two-body scattering reactions are reviewed. Although predictions of SU(3), factorization and simple Regge theory are found to be qualitatively in agreement with the data, direct channel or absorption effects afford the simplest interpretation of the detailed features of the scattering amplitudes.

INTRODUCTION

As an introduction to the forward scattering data, consider the "parton's eye view" of two body reactions presented in Fig. 1. In this figure an assortment of reactions[1] near 4 GeV/c are shown out to scattering angles exceeding 90° in their center of mass ($|t| \geq 3$ GeV^2). Interestingly all four reactions have approximately equal cross sections for $|t| \geq 2.5$ GeV^2 (to within a factor of 5 or 10), whereas at $t \approx 0$ the cross sections differ by ~ 3 orders of magnitude! Data at 5 GeV/c reflect this same behavior.

The large $|t|$ data may therefore be intrinsically simpler (cf. parton models)[2] than data at small values of momentum transfer. Nevertheless, we now proceed to the subtleties of the "Regge" scattering region (possibly defined by $0 \leq |t| \leq 2$ GeV^2 as suggested by Fig. 1) where t channel exchanges are important.

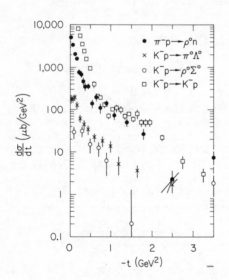

FIG. 1--Assorted large angle differential cross sections at ~4 GeV/c, Ref. 1.

FORWARD SCATTERING DATA

As a framework for discussing the data, we keep in mind the form of typical s channel Regge and absorption[3] model helicity amplitudes:

* Work supported by the U. S. Atomic Energy Commission.

$$\text{(Regge)} \quad f_{\Delta\lambda}(s,t) \propto (\sqrt{-t})^{\Delta\lambda/2} (s/s_0)^{\alpha(t)} (\pm 1 - e^{-i\pi\alpha(t)}) \qquad (1)$$

$$\left(\begin{array}{c}\text{Absorption}\\ \text{Harari}\end{array}\right) \quad f_{\Delta\lambda}(s,t) \propto J_{\Delta\lambda}(r\sqrt{-t}) (s/s_0)^{\widetilde{\alpha}(t)} (? + i) \qquad (2)$$

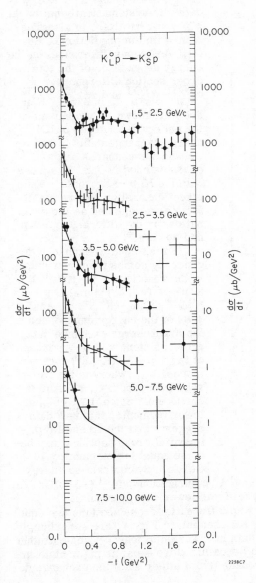

FIG. 2--Forward $K_L^0 p \to K_S^0 p$ cross sections, Ref. 5.

where $\Delta\lambda$ is the net helicity flip in the reaction. As suggested by Eq. 2, absorption models predict phases and energy dependences of scattering amplitudes that generally differ from simple Regge models. However, this is particularly true of helicity nonflip amplitudes which provide the strongest evidence for absorption in the data.[4]

1. Pseudoscalar-meson baryon scattering

A particularly straightforward study of Regge exchanges and absorption is possible with the new $K_L^0 p \to K_S^0 p$ scattering data.[5] This reaction is of interest due to its similarity with the well studied reaction $\pi^- p \to \pi^0 n$; in particular simple SU(3) relates the $K_L^0 p \to K_S^0 p$ and $\pi^- p \to \pi^0 n$ scattering amplitudes:

$$A_{K_L^0 p \to K_S^0 p} = \frac{1}{2}\left\{(4F-1)\omega^0 - \rho\right\}$$

$$\equiv (2F-1)V$$

$$A_{\pi^- p \to \pi^0 n} = \sqrt{2}\,\rho \equiv \sqrt{2}\,V$$

$$(3)$$

with the single constant F.[6]

The forward peaking of the $K_L^0 p \to K_S^0 p$ differential cross sections,[5] Fig. 2, indicates the importance of the helicity nonflip amplitude in this reaction in agreement with SU(3) predictions.[5,6] However, the absence of a dip in the $K_L^0 p \to K_S^0 p$ cross section near $|t| \sim 0.6\ \text{GeV}^2$ is in contrast to $\pi^- p \to \pi^0 n$ differential

276

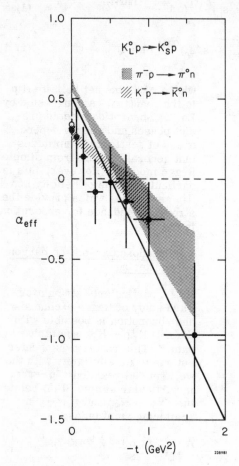

FIG. 3--Effective Regge trajectories for $K_L^0 p \to K_S^0 p$, $\pi^- p \to \pi^0 n$ and $K^- p \to \bar{K}^0 n$ reactions.

cross section data, and to the prediction of Eq. (1). A comparison of the energy dependences of these reactions, Fig. 3, reveals a further discrepancy: for $|t| \lesssim 0.4$ GeV^2 the $K_L^0 p \to K_S^0 p$ data[5] lie systematically below the $\pi^- p \to \pi^0 n$ results,[7] in disagreement with the prediction of Eq. (3). Analogous differences in the energy dependence of the total cross section differences,[8] $\sigma_{\pi^- p}^{TOT} - \sigma_{\pi^+ p}^{TOT}$ and $\sigma_{K^- n}^{TOT} - \sigma_{K^+ n}^{TOT}$ are well known. By comparison the energy dependence of KN charge exchange data[9] (ρ and A_2 t channel exchanges), shown cross hatched in Fig. 3, agrees with the $K_L^0 p \to K_S^0 p$ data! Thus direct channel or absorption effects are suggested as the explanation for the differences in Kp and πp data.[5]

Fresh input to exchange degeneracy comes from new data in the reactions $\pi^- p \to K^0 (\Lambda^0, \Sigma^0)$,[10] $\bar{K}^0 p \to \pi^+ (\Lambda^0, \Sigma^0)$[11] and $K^+ p \to K^0 \Delta^{++}$, $K^- n \to \bar{K}^0 \Delta^-$.[12] Analyses of the energy dependence of the hypercharge exchange data are consistent with no shrinkage of the $\pi^- p \to K^0 (\Lambda^0, \Sigma^0)$ forward slopes, $b_{\pi p}$, whereas the $\bar{K}p \to \pi(\Lambda, \Sigma)$ slopes, $b_{\bar{K}p}$, do exhibit shrinkage. Since $b_{\bar{K}p} < b_{\pi p}$ at lower momenta, this new data suggests that the πp and $\bar{K}$p differential cross sections may become equal for momenta $\gtrsim 10$ GeV/c. By contrast no energy dependence is observed in the $\bar{K}^0 p \to \pi^+ \Lambda^0$ polarization data[11] ($\sim$3-10 GeV/c), or in the $\pi^- p \to K^0 \Lambda^0$ data[13] (5 GeV/c) from lower energy results.

Although $K^- p \to \bar{K}^0 n$ and $K^+ n \to K^0 p$ differential cross sections are equal by $\sim$5 GeV/c,[14] the new data in the KΔ channel,[12] Fig. 4, are surprisingly unequal at 6 GeV/c. However KΔ data at lower energies[12,15] indicate that the $K^+ p$ and $K^- n$ cross sections are becoming more equal as momentum increases, the data appearing to approach (from either side) the exchange degenerate SU(3) prediction:[16]

$$\left(\frac{d\sigma}{dt}\right)_{K^+p\to K^0\Delta^{++}} = \left(\frac{d\sigma}{dt}\right)_{K^-n\to \bar{K}^0\Delta^-} = \frac{1}{2}\left(\frac{d\sigma}{dt}\right)_{\pi^+p\to \pi^0\Delta^{++}} + \frac{3}{2}\left(\frac{d\sigma}{dt}\right)_{\pi^+p\to \eta^0\Delta^{++}}$$

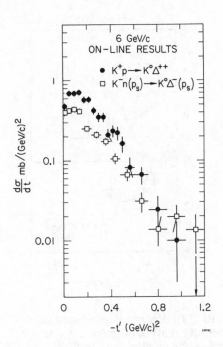

FIG. 4--Forward $K^+p\to K^0\Delta^{++}$ and $K^-n\to \bar{K}^0\Delta^-$ cross sections at 6 GeV/c, Ref. 12.

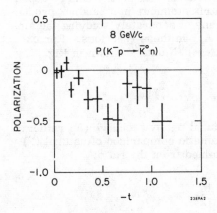

FIG. 5--Polarization in $K^-p\to \bar{K}^0n$ scattering at 8 GeV/c, Ref. 17.

We also note that the long awaited KN charge exchange polarization has been measured. Preliminary results in the reaction $K^-p\to \bar{K}^0n$ at 8 GeV/c[17] are shown in Fig. 5. The data are in agreement with most theoretical predictions: in particular the polarization in $K^-p\to \bar{K}^0n$ is,

$$\mathscr{P}(K^-p\to \bar{K}^0n) \approx \mathscr{P}(\pi^-p\to K^0\Lambda^0)$$

$$\approx -\mathscr{P}(\pi^-p\to K^0\Sigma^0)$$

in agreement with simple SU(3) models.[6] No polarization data in the potentially more interesting channel $K^+n\to K^0p$ exists however.

2. Vector-meson baryon production

Recently there has been increased interest in studying the difficult to analyze B meson data. Preliminary results at 5 GeV/c[18] in the reaction $\pi^+p\to B^+p$ find that the B is produced dominantly with s channel helicity zero, $<\frac{H}{\rho_{00}}>$ = 0.69 ± 0.18. The background subtracted differential cross section and $\frac{H}{\rho_{00}}\frac{d\sigma}{dt'}$ distribution for this data are shown in Fig. 6. Interestingly the $\frac{H}{\rho_{00}}\frac{d\sigma}{dt'}$ data are suggestive of the absorption prediction of Eq. (2) if the helicity nonflip amplitude dominates (ω^0 exchange rather than A_2 exchange). Detailed questions of the importance of isospin one exchanges,[18,19] reliability of background subtractions, and the relative couplings of ω^0 and A_2 exchanges to helicity zero B mesons are not yet answered however.

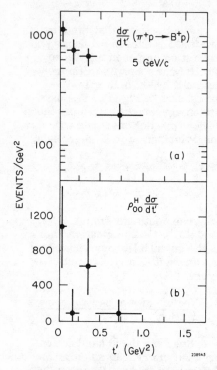

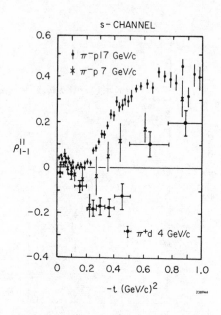

FIG. 6--Background subtracted forward cross sections for $\pi^+p \to Bp$ at 5 GeV/c, Ref. 18.

FIG. 7--Energy dependence of ρ^0 density matrix element ρ^H_{1-1} in $\pi N \to \rho^0 N$ scattering, Ref. 20.

Several recent papers have provided evidence for strong energy dependences in some vector meson density matrix elements in ρ^0 and ω^0 production reactions. These data provide a means of separately studying the amplitudes for (natural/unnatural) parity exchange, $A_\pm$, in these reactions. For example the rapid increase in ρ^H_{1-1} in the $\pi N \to \rho^0 N$ data[20] shown in Fig. 7, where

$$\rho^H_{1-1} \frac{d\sigma}{dt} = \frac{1}{2} \left(|A_+|^2 - |A_-|^2 \right) ,$$

indicates the increased importance of natural parity exchange (A_2 rather than π) as energy increases. A more dramatic comparison of natural (N) and unnatural (U) parity exchanges is obtained from the ratio:

$$\frac{\rho_+}{(1 - \rho_+)} = \frac{N}{U}$$

where $\rho_+ = (\rho^H_{1-1} + \rho^H_{1-1})$ isolates natural parity exchange. Comparison of $\pi^+p \to \omega^0\Delta^{++}$ data at 2.67 and 7.1 GeV/c,[21] Fig. 8, again indicate the

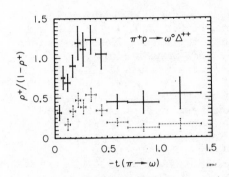

FIG. 8--Energy dependence of ω^0 density matrix elements in $\pi^+ p \to \omega^0 \Delta^{++}$ scattering, Ref. 21. Dotted (solid) data at 2.67 (7.1) GeV/c.

substantial increase in natural-parity exchange (ρ rather than B) with energy. Extraction of the effective Regge trajectories for unnatural parity exchange amplitudes from the ρ^0 and ω^0 data find approximate agreement with π-B exchange degeneracy.[21,22]

SUMMARY

The new results presented to this conference confirm the old prejudices that simple Regge theory, SU(3) and factorization provide a qualitative understanding of the data, but emphasize the need to understand direct channel or absorptive effects if real progress is to be made in two body scattering reactions.

ACKNOWLEDGMENT

I wish to thank Y. Eisenberg, D. Grether and C. Ward for assistance with their data, and D. Leith for his support.

REFERENCES

1. M. Aguilar-Benitez, et al., Phys. Rev. D 4, 2583 (1971); Phys. Rev. D 6, 29 (1972); L. Moscoso, et al., Nucl. Phys. B 36, 332 (1972); B. Haber, et al., "An Investigation of ρ Meson Production in πp Interactions at 3.9 GeV/c," MIT preprint (1973).

2. J. F. Gunion, S. J. Brodsky, R. Blankenbecler, SLAC-PUB-1183 (1973).

3. For example the dual absorptive model: H. Harari, Phys. Rev. Letters 26, 1401 (1971); Ann. of Phys. (N.Y.) 63, 432 (1971).

4. M. Davier and H. Harari, Phys. Letters 35 B, 239 (1971); A. B. Wicklund, et al., Phys. Rev. Letters 29, 1415 (1972); P. Johnson et al., Phys. Rev. Letters 30, 242 (1973); G. Cozzika et al., Phys. Letters 40 B, 281 (1972).

5. G. W. Brandenburg, et al., "K_L^0p $\rightarrow$ K_S^0p Scattering from 1 to 10 GeV/c," SLAC preprint (1973).

6. A. D. Martin, C. Michael, R.J.N. Phillips, Nucl. Phys. B 43, 13 (1972).

7. G. Höhler, et al., Phys. Letters 20, 79 (1966).

8. S. P. Denisov, et al., Phys. Letters 36 B, 415 (1971).

9. V. N. Bolotov, et al., "Investigation on K$^-$p $\rightarrow$ K^{0}n Charge Exchange at Momenta 25 and 35 GeV/c, Serpukhov preprint (1973).

10. K. J. Foley, et al., Phys. Rev. D 8, 27 (1973); C.E.W. Ward, et al., Argonne preprint ANL/HEP 7336 (1973).

11. R. J. Yamartino, et al., "A Study of the Reactions $\bar{K}^0$p $\rightarrow$ $\pi^+\Lambda^0$ and $\bar{K}^0$p $\rightarrow$ $\pi^+\Sigma^0$ from 1 to 10 GeV/c, SLAC preprint (1973).

12. W. T. Meyer, et al., "Preliminary Results from a Study of the Reactions K$^+$p $\rightarrow$ $\bar{K}^0\Delta^{++}$ and K$^-$n $\rightarrow$ K$^0\Delta^-$ at 4 and 6 GeV/c," Argonne preprint (1973).

13. C.E.W. Ward, et al., "Polarization in π^-p $\rightarrow$ K$^0 \Lambda^0$ at 5 GeV/c," Argonne preprint (1973).

14. D. Cline, J. Matos, D. D. Reeder, Phys. Rev. Letters 23, 1318 (1969).

15. D. D. Carmony, et al., Phys. Rev. D 2, 30 (1970); K. Buchner, et al., Nucl. Phys. B 45, 333 (1972).

16. R. D. Matthews, Nucl. Phys. B 11, 339 (1969).

17. W. Beusch, et al., "Measurement of the Polarization in K$^-$p $\rightarrow$ $\bar{K}^0$n Charge Exchange at 8 GeV/c," CERN preprint (1973).

18. U. Karshon, et al., "Production and Decay Mechanism of the B Meson in π^+p Interactions at 5 GeV/c," Weizmann preprint (1973).

19. D. Cohen, T. Ferbel and P. Slattery, Phys. Rev. D 8, 23 (1973).

20. J. A. Charlesworth, et al., Rutherford preprint RPP/H/116 (1973).

21. W. F. Buhl, et al., "A Determination of the Effective B and ρ Trajectories from the Reaction π^+p $\rightarrow$ $\omega^0\Delta^{++}$," LBL preprint (1973).

22. P. Estabrooks, A. D. Martin, Phys. Letters 42 B, 229 (1972).

EXPERIMENTAL RESULTS ON
PSEUDOSCALAR MESON PHOTOPRODUCTION[*]

D. J. Quinn

Tufts University, Medford, Mass. 02155

ABSTRACT

We summarize the preliminary results of an experiment
on photoproduction of the final states $\pi^{\pm}N$, $\pi^{\pm}\Delta$ (1236),
$K^{+}\Lambda$ and $K^{+}\Sigma^{\circ}$ from hydrogen and deuterium targets using
a 16 GeV linearly polarized photon beam. Momentum
transfers (t) lie between -0.002 and -1.5 GeV^2. The
photon polarization allows the separation of natural
and unnatural parity exchange contributions to these
reactions. The natural parity exchange cross sections
dominate in all reactions for $|t| \gtrsim 0.8$ GeV^2, where they
all fall off approximately as e^{3t}. Combined with lower
energy data, our results for $\gamma n \to \pi^{-}p$ are consistent with
a simple pion Regge Pole behavior for the unnatural parity
exchange cross section. Some results are compared with
the vector dominant related reactions $\pi^{-}p \to \rho n$ and
$\pi p \to \rho \Delta$.

INTRODUCTION

In this paper, an abridged version of my talk at Berkeley, I
summarize some preliminary results from a measurement of polarization
asymmetries for 16 GeV charged pion and kaon photoproduction[1], then
compare these reactions with the related reactions $\pi^{-}p \to \rho^{\circ}n$ and
$\pi^{\pm}p \to \rho^{\circ}\Delta$.

In pseudoscalar meson photoproduction, a polarized photon beam
can be used to determine the parity sequences of the exchanges in
the t channel. Photons polarized parallel (perpendicular) to the
reaction plane contribute only to interactions with unnatural
(natural) parity exchange to lowest order in t/s.

The photon carries isospin 0 or 1, with corresponding
G parities -1 and +1. (Thus, isovector incident photons correspond
to negative G parity exchange to the nucleon when a single pion is
produced.) These states are coherent, and can interfere; the
isoscalar - isovector interference term changes sign going from
proton to neutron initial states. Thus, detecting both $\pi^{\pm}$ from
hydrogen and deuterium allows one to isolate the isoscalar -
isovector photon interference term. Note that "isoscalar - isovector"
refers to the incident photon, while "natural - unnatural parity"
and "positive - negative G parity exchange" refer to the state
exchanged in the t channel.

The experiment used a crystalline graphite absorber to linearly
polarize a SLAC 16 GeV bremsstrahlung beam. A second assembly of

*Work supported by the U.S. Atomic Energy Commission

282

crystalline graphite was used in a separate experiment in conjunction with a pair spectrometer to measure the beam polarization.[2] In the region 14 - 16 GeV, the beam spectrum was similar in shape to bremsstrahlung, and had a measured polarization of 0.255 ± .020. The SLAC 20 GeV spectrometer was then used to detect single charged pions and kaons at small angles to the beam, from both hydrogen and deuterium targets. We obtained results on the final states $\pi^{\pm}N$, $\pi^{\pm}\Delta(1236)$, $K^{+}\Lambda$, and $K^{+}\Sigma^{0}$.

We measured both the polarized photon asymmetry*, $\Sigma = (\sigma_{\perp} - \sigma_{\shortparallel})/(\sigma_{\perp} + \sigma_{\shortparallel})$ and the cross section, $\sigma = (\sigma_{\perp} + \sigma_{\shortparallel})/2$, and extracted values of $\sigma_{\perp,\shortparallel}$, where $\perp$, $\shortparallel$ represent the photon polarization with respect to the reaction plane. In all figures except for Fig. 2, the error bars represent statistical and other point-to-point uncertainties only; the overall ±8% beam polarization uncertainty and the cross section normalization uncertainties have not been included. Our cross sections agree with the unpolarized measurements of Boyarski et al.[3] in t dependence and in the ratios of different reactions. The ratio of our unpolarized cross sections for $\gamma p \rightarrow \pi^{+}n$ to those of Boyarski et al. is 1.12±.07.

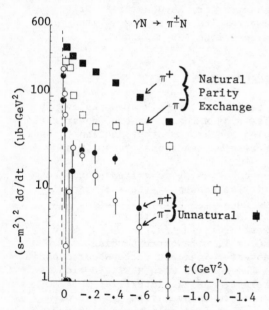

Fig. 1: Single pion photoproduction. Natural and unnatural parity exchange cross sections are shown for $\gamma p \rightarrow \pi^{+}n$ and $\gamma n \rightarrow \pi^{-}p$. The unnatural parity cross sections are both near zero at $t \simeq -m_{\pi}^{2}$. The natural and unnatural parity cross sections for any given reaction must be equal at zero degrees.

PHOTOPRODUCTION RESULTS

Fig. 1 shows the single pion data out to the largest angles we measured. Except for $|t| < m_{\pi}^{2}$, the cross sections for single pion photoproduction are dominated by natural parity exchange. The π^{-}/π^{+} ratio appears to differ from unity in both polarizations, implying interference between even and odd G-parity exchanges with unnatural parity as well as natural parity. The evidence in the unnatural parity exchanges is only at the level of a few standard deviations.

Since $\gamma p \rightarrow \pi^{+}n$ and $\gamma n \rightarrow \pi^{-}p$ are related by line reversal, their cross sections should approach each other for large energies. They are not equal at our value of $s = 31$ GeV^2.

*The symbol σ stands for $d\sigma/dt$ throughout this paper.

By combining our measurements with earlier polarized photon measurements below 3.4 GeV [4] and measurements of energy dependence from 5 to 16 GeV,[5] we extract the Regge effective α's appearing in the formula

$$\sigma_{\perp,\parallel}(s,t) = \beta_{\perp,\parallel}(t) \, s^{2\alpha_{\perp,\parallel}(t)-2} \quad (1)$$

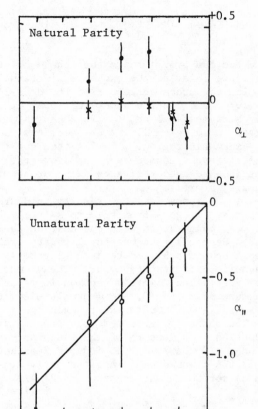

Values of α from unpolarized photoproduction of pseudoscalar mesons are near zero for all processes measured to date. It is thus no surprise that the dominant natural parity exchange amplitudes give $\alpha_\perp \simeq 0$ as shown in Fig. 2. But $\alpha_\parallel$ (unnatural parity exchange) is consistent with the contribution of a simple linear trajectory of slope 1 GeV^{-2} passing through the pion pole in both π^- and, with larger uncertainties, π^+. (Even though the energy dependence is consistent with a simple pion pole, contributions from exchanges of both G parities may be required to explain the ratio of the cross sections as explained above.)

We next turn to the reactions $\gamma N \to \pi^\pm \Delta$. We detected the four charge states of this reaction involving charged pions from proton and deuteron targets. The allowed isospins and G parities of the exchanges are 1^+, 1^-, and 2^-. The four reactions are related by

Fig. 2: Energy dependence of $\gamma N \to \pi N$. The top graph shows the Regge effective α for natural parity exchange in $\gamma p \to \pi^+ n$ (crosses) and $\gamma n \to \pi^- p$ (dots). The bottom graph is α (unnatural parity exchange) for $\gamma n \to \pi^- p$. (The corresponding quantity for $\gamma p \to \pi^+ n$ has larger uncertainties). The line corresponds to a simple pion Regge trajectory with slope 1 GeV^{-2}. The error bars include contributions from normalization and beam polarization uncertainties.

$$\sigma \begin{pmatrix} \gamma p \to \pi^- \Delta^{++} \\ \gamma n \to \pi^+ \Delta^- \end{pmatrix} = \sum_{i=1}^{8} \left| -\sqrt{3}\, A_{1-}^i \ (\pm)\sqrt{3}A_{1+}^i \ + \frac{1}{\sqrt{3}}\, A_{2-}^i \right|^2 \quad (2a)$$

$$\sigma \quad \begin{pmatrix} \gamma n \rightarrow \pi^- \Delta^+ \\ \gamma p \rightarrow \pi^+ \Delta^\circ \end{pmatrix} = \sum_{i=1}^{8} \mid A_{1-}^i \; (\mp) \; A_{1+}^i + A_{2-}^i \mid^2 \quad (2b)$$

where the sum over i represents the 8 helicity amplitudes, and the subscripts refer to the exchanged t channel isospin and G parity. Assuming the cross section from the deuteron is the simple sum of the proton and neutron cross sections, it contains no interference terms between I = 1 and I = 2 exchanges. (Deuteron effects have been shown to be small in the reactions $\gamma p \rightarrow K^+ \Lambda$ and $\gamma p \rightarrow \pi^+ n$ in this kinematic region.) I will thus use the deuterium results to elucidate the presumed dominant isovector exchanges, then use the deuterium-hydrogen ratios to find out about the isovector-isotensor exchange interference.

Fig. 3 summarizes the results on deuterium. After rising sharply as $|t|$ goes from t_{min} to m_π^2 (the natural and unnatural parity exchange cross sections must be equal at a production angle of zero degrees), the unnatural parity exchange cross sections fall steeply and smoothly. The natural parity exchange cross sections show quite different behavior. The π^- one has a dip near t = -0.15 GeV^2. The π^+ cross section is much larger, and has little structure near t = -0.15. Isoscalar-isovector photon interference terms are large in both parity exchange cross sections.

The ratio of deuterium to hydrogen target rates for $\pi\Delta$ production is a measure of the isotensor-isovector exchange interference. If there were no isospin 2 exchange, $\sigma(\gamma d \rightarrow \pi^+ \Delta N_s)/\sigma(\gamma p \rightarrow \pi^+ \Delta^\circ)$ would be 4, and the equivalent ratio for $\pi^-\Delta$ production from deuterium and hydrogen would be 4/3. We see some evidence for

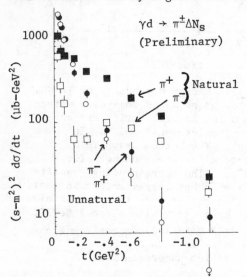

I = 2 exchange in both parity states for $\pi^-\Delta$ production (only weak evidence in the unnatural parity exchange part, which is small where the I = 2 effect is large); we do not see a definite effect in the less sensitive $\pi^-\Delta$ case.

If this effect occurs in both parity sequences, it cannot be due to the exchange of a single exotic I = 2 particle. It is possibly due to Regge-Regge cuts coming from two I = 1 particles. Goldstein[6] has pointed out, however, that the leading Regge-Regge cut, $\rho \times A_2$, is ruled out by a selection rule of Worden[7] since it is an odd signature leading cut. A $\rho \times \pi$ cut would be possible. The energy dependence of this

Fig. 3: Photoproduction of $\pi\Delta$ final states from deuterium. N_s refers to a spectator nucleon.

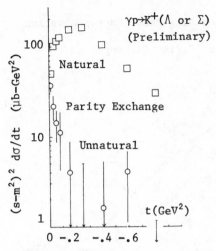

Fig. 4: Combined cross sections for $\gamma p \to K^+\Lambda$ and $\gamma p \to K^+\Sigma$.

effect will provide an interesting handle on it and should be measured.

Finally, Fig. 4 shows our results for the sum of the reactions $\gamma p \to K^+\Lambda$ and $\gamma p \to K^+\Sigma$. (Our results for either reaction separately are less accurate than for the sum, due to the difficulty of separating the reactions at 16 GeV/c.) We note that the unnatural parity cross section has a dip or zero at $t \simeq -m_K^2$ and is in fact consistent with zero (to two standard deviations) beyond that point.

Four years ago, when the reactions discussed here had been measured with unpolarized photon beams, Diebold prepared a graph[8] comparing many pseudoscalar meson photoproduction processes. The approximate $(s - m^2)^{-2}$ dependence of these cross sections allowed the plot to be relatively energy independent. Now we have measured the polarization dependence of some of these reactions, and found natural parity exchange dominance for $|t| \gtrsim 0.8$ GeV^2. Anderson et al.[9] have found the same thing in the reaction $\gamma p \to \pi^0 p$. In $\gamma N \to \pi^\pm N$ we have determined that $\alpha_\perp \sim 0$ over the whole t range. It is thus tempting to plot the natural parity exchange cross sections together, as in Fig. 5; this plot may also be relatively independent of energy. In this figure, one notices that in contrast to the varied dips and wiggles at lower t, all cross sections have relatively similar behaviors for larger t.

These regularities for $|t| \gtrsim 0.8$ GeV^2 include:
a) Natural parity exchange dominates.
b) σ falls smoothly as e^{3t}.
c) $\alpha \sim 0$.
d) All cross sections are of the same order of magnitude.
e) $\sigma_\perp(\gamma d \to \pi^-\Delta N)/\sigma_\perp(\gamma d \to \pi^+\Delta N) \simeq \sigma_\perp(\gamma n \to \pi^-p)/\sigma_\perp(\gamma p \to \pi^+n) \simeq 0.6$.

These common features are difficult to explain using current theories. Does there exist a simple explanation for all or most of these points?

VECTOR DOMINANCE COMPARISONS

The vector dominance model can be used in a simple way to relate the single pion photoproduction reactions to $\pi^- p \to n\rho^0_{transverse}$.[10] One considers the incident photon to be a coherent mixture of ρ^0, ω, and ϕ mesons. Adding the cross sections for $\gamma p \to \pi^+ n$ and $\gamma n \to \pi^- p$ eliminates the isoscalar-isovector interference term, and the ρ^0 term dominates what is left to within a few percent.

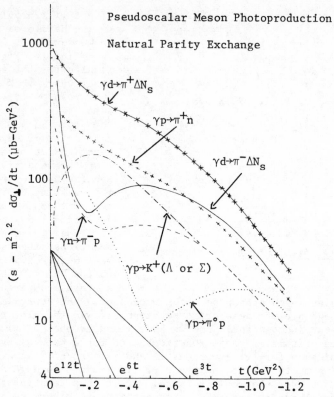

Fig. 5:
Schematic indication of natural parity cross sections for pseudoscalar meson photoproduction (photon polarized perpendicular to production plane). The π° data is from reference 9, at 6 GeV, the rest from our experiment. The quantity $(s-m^2)^2 \, d\sigma_\perp/dt$ is nearly independent of energy for these processes, in every instance where it has been measured.

Pseudoscalar Meson Photoproduction

Natural Parity Exchange

$\gamma d \to \pi^+ \Delta N_s$

$\gamma p \to \pi^+ n$

$\gamma d \to \pi^- \Delta N_s$

$\gamma n \to \pi^- p$

$\gamma p \to K^+ (\Lambda \text{ or } \Sigma)$

$\gamma p \to \pi^\circ p$

$(s - m^2)^2 \, d\sigma_\perp/dt \; (\mu b \cdot GeV^2)$

e^{12t} e^{6t} e^{3t} $t \, (GeV^2)$

The VDM prediction is:

$$\sigma_{\perp, \parallel}(\gamma p \to \pi^+ n) + \sigma_{\perp, \parallel}(\gamma n \to \pi^- p) = \frac{2\pi\alpha}{\gamma_\rho^2} \, [\rho_{11} \pm \rho_{1-1}] \sigma(\pi^- p \to \rho^\circ n) \quad (3)$$

This comparison is shown in Fig. 6, which shows reasonable agreement for the unnatural parity exchange cross section and disagreement for the natural parity part.

Estabrooks and Martin (EM) have looked at the energy dependence of $\pi^- p \to \rho^\circ n$[11]. They use data at 7, 15, and 17 GeV/c, and fix the relative normalizations by constraining α for the extrapolated $\rho_{\circ\circ} \sigma$ to go through zero at $t = +m_\pi^2$. They find the contribution of unnatural parity exchange to the longitudinal ρ ($\rho_{\circ\circ}\sigma$) and transverse ρ (($\rho_{11} - \rho_{1-1})\sigma$) cross sections gives α consistent with an elementary pion pole (Fig. 7). The latter corresponds to transverse polarization in the plane of production for $\gamma N \to \pi N$, and agrees qualitatively with our result. For the natural parity contribution $(\rho_{11} + \rho_{1-1})\sigma$, EM find an α consistent with an A_2 Regge trajectory, going to $\alpha = 0.5$ at $t = 0$, while we found α near zero for all t in the VDM time-reversed reaction (photon polarization perpendicular to the reaction plane). The disagreement is not serious if the combined uncertainties are taken into account. Thus, while the

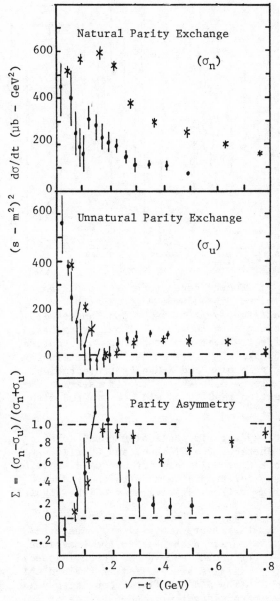

$(s - m^2)^2 \ d\sigma/dt \ (\mu b - GeV^2)$

Natural Parity Exchange (σ_n)

Unnatural Parity Exchange (σ_u)

$\Sigma = (\sigma_n - \sigma_u)/(\sigma_n + \sigma_u)$

Parity Asymmetry

$\sqrt{-t}$ (GeV)

Fig. 6: Vector dominance comparison of $\gamma N \to \pi N$ (crosses) with $\pi^- p \to \rho^o_{tr} n$ (dots) (see equation 3 in the text). We use $\gamma_\rho^2/4\pi = 0.5$ in the top two graphs; the parity asymmetries are independent of γ_ρ as well as of the experimental normalizations.

unnatural parity exchange contributions agree, the natural parity contributions to $\gamma N \to \pi N$ and $\pi p \to \rho_{tr} n$ disagree in both t and s dependence.

The reaction $\gamma N \to \pi \Delta$ is somewhat more difficult to relate to a pion-induced reaction -- it involves line reversal as well as VDM, not merely time reversal as does $\gamma N \to \pi N$. Any interference term between Regge exchanges of opposite signature will change sign under line reversal. Assuming such interference terms are small, and playing the same game as above to eliminate the $\rho-\omega$ interference term, one predicts:

$$\sigma(\gamma p \to \pi^- \Delta^{++}) + \sigma(\gamma n \to \pi^+ \Delta^-) = \frac{2\pi\alpha}{\gamma_\rho^2} \rho_{11} \ \sigma(\pi^+ p \to \rho^o \Delta^{++}) \quad (4)$$

and a similar relationship involving $\gamma p \to \pi^+ \Delta^o$, $\gamma n \to \pi^- \Delta^+$, and $\pi^- p \to \rho^o \Delta^o$. If contributions from $I = 2$ are small, then these two predictions are equivalent. Carnegie et al.[12] have compared their cross section results on $\pi^\pm p \to \rho^o \Delta$ with Boyarski et al.[13] and have found good agreement. Since the cross sections agree, Fig. 8 compares the natural versus unnatural parity exchange asymmetries. This comparison does not depend on experimental normalization or the value of γ_ρ. Agreement is surprisingly good up to $t = -0.1 \ GeV^2$. The disagreement beyond this point could be attributed to an interference term between

288

exchanges of opposite signature, or could be a symptom of the same disease that affects $\pi p \rightarrow \rho N$. It would be interesting to see the $\pi^{\pm}p$ data extended to higher values of t, to investigate this effect and the I = 2 exchange interference terms beyond t = -.25 GeV^2.

An experiment going to higher t values has been performed by Eisenberg et al.[14] Unfortunately for our comparison, it was at 5 GeV/c, and only used incident π^+. One striking result of the experiment is the dip-bump structure in the natural parity exchange contribution (Fig. 9), which is reminiscent of structure we found in $\gamma p \rightarrow \pi^- \Delta^{++}$ and not in $\gamma n \rightarrow \pi^+ \Delta^-$.

Much of the material I have presented

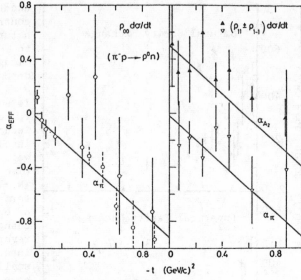

Fig. 7: Energy dependence of $\pi^- p \rightarrow \rho^0 n$ as determined by Estabrooks and Martin. Regge effective $\alpha(t)$ vs. t for longitudinal ρ production with unnatural parity exchange, and for transverse ρ production with natural and unnatural parity exchange. The lines are simple pion and A_2 Regge trajectories with slopes 0.9 GeV^{-2}. The transverse production results should be compared with Fig. 2.

is due to the work and ideas of my experimental colleagues, John Rutherfoord, Mike Shupe, Dave Sherden, Bob Siemann, and Charlie Sinclair. I would like to thank Gary Goldstein for useful discussions, and R. Carnegie and M. Eisenberg for providing me with their data. Celia Mees has typed the paper as well as drawing many of the figures.

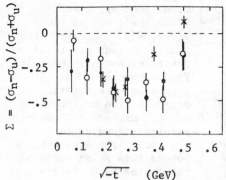

Fig. 8: Comparison of parity asymmetry (natural vs. unnatural parity exchange) in the reactions $\pi^{\pm}p \rightarrow \rho^0 \Delta^0$ and $\gamma N \rightarrow \pi \Delta$. Open (closed) circles are ρ_{1-1}/ρ_{11} for $\pi^+ p \rightarrow \rho^0 \Delta^{++}$ ($\pi^- p \rightarrow \rho^0 \Delta^0$). (Their consistency is consistent with the absence of I=2 exchange contributions in this t region). Also plotted (crosses) is the parity asymmetry for the sum of the two reactions $\gamma d \rightarrow \pi^+ \Delta N_s$ and $\gamma d \rightarrow \pi^- \Delta N_s$. The crosses should be equal to a weighted average of the open and closed circles under assumptions discussed in the text.

289

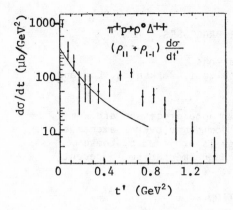

Fig. 9: Natural parity exchange contribution to transverse ρ production in $\pi^+p\to\Delta^{++}\rho^\circ$ at 5 GeV/c, as measured by Eisenberg et al.

REFERENCES

1. D.J. Sherden et al., Phys. Rev. Lett. 30, 1230 (1973) and contributions 163 - 166 to this conference.
2. R.L. Eisele et al., IEEE Trans. on Nucl. Sci. 20, 447 (1973) and Nucl. Instrum. Methods (to be published).
3. A.M. Boyarski et al., Phys. Rev. Lett. 20, 300 (1968); 21, 1767 (1968); 22, 1131(1969); 25, 695(1970).
4. C. Geweniger et al., Phys. Lett. 28B, 155(1968) and 29B, 41(1969); Z. Bar-Yam et al., Phys. Rev. Lett. 24, 1078(1970) and 25, 1053 (1970).
5. A.M. Boyarski et al., Phys. Rev. Lett. 20, 300(1968) and 21, 1767 (1968).
6. G. Goldstein, Tufts Pub. 73/15.
7. R.P. Worden, Phys. Lett. 40B, 260(1972).
8. R. Diebold, in Proceedings of the Boulder Conference on High Energy Physics, edited by K.T. Mahanthappa et al., Colorado Associated University Press, Boulder, Colorado (1970).
9. R.L. Anderson et al., Phys. Rev. D4, 1937(1971).
10. F. Bulos et al., Phys. Rev. Lett. 26, 1457(1971).
11. P. Estabrooks and A.D. Martin, Phys. Lett. 42B, 229(1972).
12. R.K. Carnegie et al., Contribution to XVI Int. Conf. on High Energy Physics, Batavia (1972) (unpublished).
13. A.M. Boyarski et al., Phys. Rev. Lett. 25, 695(1970).
14. Y. Eisenberg et al., Contribution 140 to this conference.

BARYON EXCHANGE PROCESSES

A. S. L. Parsons
Rutherford Laboratory, Chilton, Didcot, Berkshire, England

ABSTRACT
Data from recent hyperon exchange processes are summarised. Direct evidence for Λ dominance over Σ exchange above about 2.5 GeV/C c.m. energy is provided by these data. The dip structure and exchange mechanism in recent $\bar{p}p \to \pi^- \pi^+$, $K^- K^+$ data are discussed.

INTRODUCTION

I shall present results from four papers submitted to this meeting. All have some relevance to baryon exchange with emphasis on hyperon exchange; specifically the first three have something to say about the relative importance of Λ and Σ exchange.

Barger [1] showed in 1969 that backward K^+p elastic scattering data could be described by exchange degenerate Λ_α and Λ_γ trajectories and the Σ contribution could be ignored. There was at that time indirect support for this assumption. Here we have some more direct evidence. We can select processes in which hyperon exchange is believed to be dominant and then compare those channels for which $I_{exchange} = 1$ (Σ only) and those for which $I_{exchange} = 1$ or 0 (Σ or Λ); see Figure 1. To indicate the conclusions before presenting the evidence, we find, indeed that Σ exchange processes are suppressed above 2 - 2.5 GeV/C c.m. energy. Below the situation is less clear - presumably the u-channel Regge description loses its validity.

Now let us turn to the experiments.

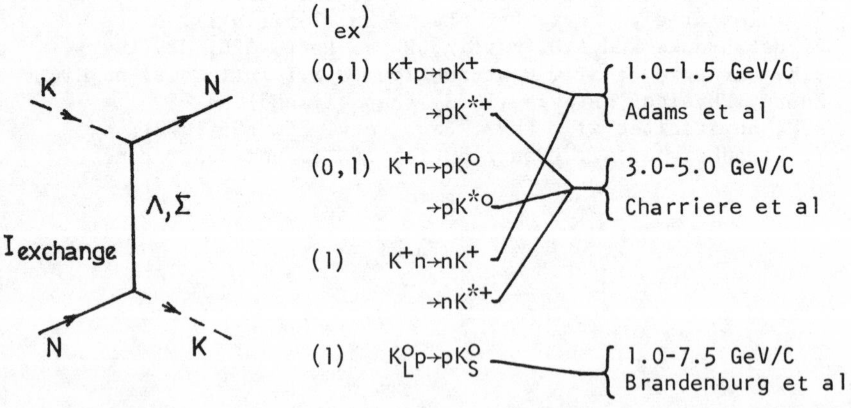

(I_{ex})

(0,1) $K^+p \to pK^+$
$\to pK^{*+}$ — 1.0-1.5 GeV/C, Adams et al

(0,1) $K^+n \to pK^0$
$\to pK^{*0}$ — 3.0-5.0 GeV/C, Charriere et al

(1) $K^+n \to nK^+$
$\to nK^{*+}$

(1) $K^0_L p \to pK^0_S$ — 1.0-7.5 GeV/C, Brandenburg et al

Fig. 1.

$$K^+p \to pK^+, \; K^+n \to nK^+$$

These cross sections have been measured by University of Washington [2] at 180° using hydrogen and deuterium targets associated with spark chambers and counters. The incident momentum range was 1.0 to 1.5 GeV/C. In order to show that the nuclear physics of deuterium does not affect the measurements one compares the cross section measured off free and bound protons. The good agreement is shown in Figure 2. Figure 3 shows the momentum dependance of the K^+p and K^+n elastic scattering cross sections at 180°. (Note the $\cos\theta*$ range is 0.01.)

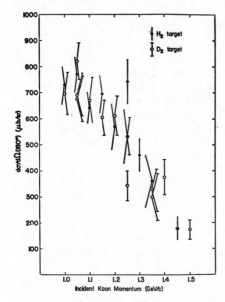

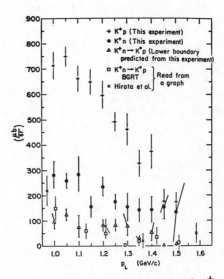

Fig. 2. K^+p backward scattering compared for free and bound protons.

Fig. 3. Energy dependance of K^+n backward elastic scattering.

K^+n is pure Σ exchange while K^+p can be Λ and Σ. We see that $\sigma(K^+n)$ is roughly equal to $\sigma(K^+p)$ at 1.5 GeV/C ($E* \simeq 2.0$ GeV) so there is clearly no question of Λ dominance at these energies.

On the same figure the lower bound of the charge-exchange cross-section, calculated from the above two measured processes is shown. The measured charge-exchange data [3] lies on this lower bound just as does π^-p charge exchange over a large momentum range.

Lastly we note that in spite of the above conclusions regarding the lack of Λ dominance in this energy range, the s-dependence of this K^+p backward data has just the behaviour one would expect from Barger's Λ dominant model [1]; that is, it is consistent with the higher energy s-dependence.

292

$$K_L^o p \to pK_S^o$$

This SLAC data has been recently published [4] and spans the momentum range 1.0 to 7.5 GeV/C. Since the backward scattering has to be mediated by Σ exchange, by comparison with $K^+p \to pK^+$, we have the opportunity to observe the onset of Λ dominance. Figure 4 shows the momentum dependance of the backward cross sections for this process, K^+p, K^-p and a single K^+n point.

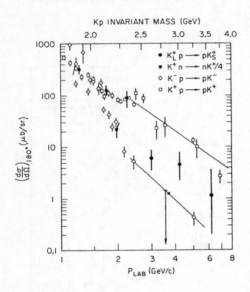

Fig. 4. Energy dependance of various KN backward elastic scattering processes.

The features we note above about 2.0 Gev/C are:

$$\sigma(K^+p \to pK^+) \sim 5 \times \sigma(K_L^o p \to pK_S^o)$$

$$\sigma(K_L^o p \to pK_S^o) \sim 5 \times \sigma(K^-p \to pK^-)$$

K^-p backward scattering requires an exotic u-channel exchange and we can infer from its behaviour that in the $K_L^o p \to pK_S^o$ amplitude $K^o p$ dominates over $\overline{K}^o p$. Then from the relative magnitude of K^+p over $K^o p$ we deduce the dominance of Λ exchange above, say, 2 GeV/C.

$K^+N \to N$ + vector meson

Charriere et al [5] have measured the backward cross sections for the above between 3.0 and 5.0 GeV/C; we wish to concentrate on the following channels:

$$K^+p \to pK*^+ (892) \qquad\qquad (1)$$

$$K^+n \to pK*^\circ (892) \qquad\qquad (2)$$

$$K^+n \to nK*^+ (892) \qquad\qquad (3)$$

(1) and (2) can be Λ or Σ exchange while (3) is pure Σ. It is noted that the $K*^+$ (892) signal in (3) is barely discernible in contrast to (1) and (2). This therefore supports Λ dominance in this energy range.

The cross sections for (1) and (2) are the same within their errors and their momentum dependance agrees well with that of K^+p backward elastic, and is consistent with a Regge exchange picture, (see Figure 5). Note however that the angular distributions for (1) and (2) are much flatter in the backward direction than for K^+p elastic, as shown in Figure 6.

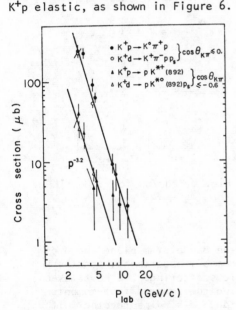

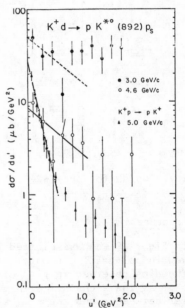

Fig. 5. Energy dependance of the backward cross-sections for reactions (1) and (2).

Fig. 6. $d\sigma/du'$ distribution for reaction (1) and for $K^+p \to pK^+$.

$$\overline{p}p \to \pi^-\pi^+, K^-K^+$$

The differential cross sections for the above processes have been measured by a British collaboration [6] between 0.8 and 2.4 GeV/C. The angular range in the centre of mass was $-0.95 < \cos\theta* < 0.95$. Here we present those aspects of the data which are relevant to baryon exchange.

In Figures 7 and 8 we show the differential cross sections at 10 of the 20 momenta at which measurements have been made. The smooth curves are fits to a sum of Legendre polynomials. Let us discuss first some features of the $\pi^-\pi^+$ data before turning to the K^-K^+.

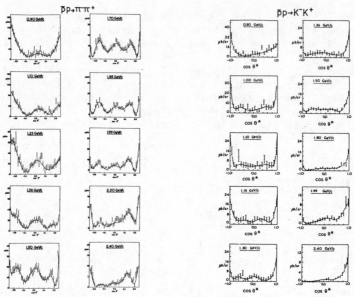

Fig. 7. $d\sigma/d\Omega$ for $\overline{p}p \to \pi^-\pi^+$. Fig. 8. $d\sigma/d\Omega$ for $\overline{p}p \to K^-K^+$.

Dip Structure

In Figure 9 we have plotted in the Mandelstam plane the dips observed in $\overline{p}p \to \pi^-\pi^+$, as obtained from our experiment, together with the dips observed in $\pi^\pm p$ elastic scattering. We have taken $\overline{p}p \to \pi^-\pi^+$ as the s-channel with t being the squared four-momentum transfer between $\overline{p}$ and the π^-. The $\overline{p}p \to \pi^-\pi^+$ dips together with their errors were obtained from a visual inspection of the Legendre fits to the data.

Odorico [7,8] has suggested that the zeros arising from the intersection of poles in the Mandelstam plane should propogate in straight lines into the physical regions, where they will manifest themselves as dips in the cross-sections. The high energy π^+p backward data have a prominent dip at t = - 0.15 which in this model could be attributed to the intersection of the $\rho(765)$ and $\Delta(1236)$ at t = -0.32. If this dip persists through the unphysical region we should observe a similar constant t dip in the $\overline{p}p \to \pi^-\pi^+$ channel. Our π^- forward dip is at roughly t = -0.4, but there is evidence that at the higher momenta it deviates from constant t.

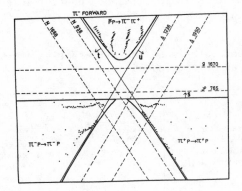

Fig. 9. Position of dips in
$\overline{pp} \rightarrow \pi^-\pi^+$ and $\pi^\pm p \rightarrow \pi^\pm p$. Poles
in the Mandelstam plane are shown
dashed.

Unfortunately the $\overline{pp} \rightarrow \pi^-\pi^+$ experiments above 2.4 GeV/C [9,10] do not
have the statistics and t-range to confirm these trends.

The explanation of the other dips in $\overline{pp} \rightarrow \pi^-\pi^+$ is less clear.
However we note:

(a) The π^+ forward dip may be correlated with the structure
in π^-p backward elastic scattering, which although less pronounced
than the π^+p backward dip, does have some constant u features.

(b) When the residues of the intersecting poles are equal but
of opposite sign, one would expect to see a line of dips at (u - t)
= constant [7]. This could explain the middle two of our four lines
of dips. One could invoke, say, the N(1470) and the Δ(1650) poles,
with residues at their intersections with the N(938) and Δ(1236)
being approximately equal but of opposite sign.

We conclude that the $\overline{pp} \rightarrow \pi^-\pi^+$ dips show some of the qualitative features of Odorico's dip predictions but their linear
propagation through the Mandelstam plane is not strictly adhered
to.

Recently Barger et al [11] have conjectured that dips associated
with particle exchanges occur at a fixed distance in momentum
transfer from the physical boundary, and hence defined a variable
$t' = t - t_{min}$. Although this would place the π^+p backward dip at
$t = -0.35$ in the $\overline{pp} \rightarrow \pi^-\pi^+$ channel, approximately the value we
observe, we conclude that constancy in t' does not appear to be
appropriate in our momentum range.

Within the framework of Odorico's model we would expect to observe no fixed t dips for $\bar{p}p \to K^-K^+$ since its u-channel, K^+p elastic scattering, is exotic. There is no reason why fixed u dips should not exist, but this feature is not apparent in our data.

s-Dependance

Figures 10(a) and 10(b) show the differential cross-sections $d\sigma/dt$ for $\bar{p}p \to \pi^-\pi^+$ as a function of s.

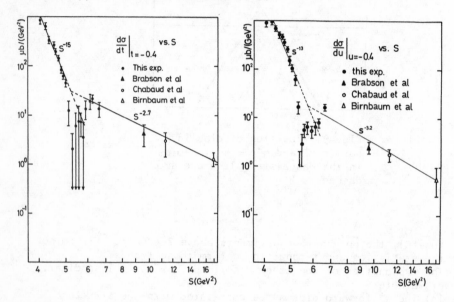

Fig. 10a. s-dependance of $d\sigma/dt$ for $\bar{p}p \to \pi^-\pi^+$ at t = -0.4 GeV². Fig. 10b. s-dependance of $d\sigma/du$ for $\bar{p}p \to \pi^-\pi^+$ at u = -0.4 GeV².

The pronounced dip at s = 5.5 corresponds to the dip structure discussed in the previous section. A feature of this $\bar{p}p \to \pi^-\pi^+$ data is the break in the slope at about the same point, suggestive of a change in the dynamics of the process. Above this energy the behaviour is characteristic of t-channel Regge exchange (n = 2.7 ± 0.7 for π^- forward and n = 3.2 ± 0.3 for π^+ forward, where $d\sigma/dt \sim s^{-n}$).

As shown in Figure 11 the s-dependence for $\bar{p}p \to K^-K^+$ (K^- forward) shares many characteristics with the $\pi^-\pi^+$ data, with a break at about s = 4.5 followed by a slope of n = 3.1 ± 0.2 consistent with Regge exchange. For the line reversed process, backward K^+p elastic scattering, n = 3.9 ± 0.2 [12]. The K^+ forward cross-section rapidly disappears through our momentum range (n = 7.7 ± 0.7; this may be compared with n = 9.0 ± 0.3 [12] for K^-p backward elastic scattering). In terms of t-channel exchanges this has a ready explanation since for K⁺ forward an exotic object has to be exchanged.

We may take the above features as evidence of Regge exchange effects becoming important in $\bar{p}p \to K^-K^+$ at about 1.50 GeV/C noting that K⁺p backward elastic scattering may also be dominated by u-channel exchanges at a fairly low energy, where one does not expect resonant contributions. We have therefore applied a simple Regge model simultaneously to both $\bar{p}p \to K^-K^+$ (K⁻ forward) data above 1.50 GeV/C (-t < 1.0) and the K⁺p backward data between 2.45 and 5.0 GeV/C (-u < 1.0) [13]. Following Barger's arguments [1] the dominant amplitudes will be associated with $\Lambda_\alpha(1115, \frac{1}{2}^+)$ and $\Lambda_\gamma(1520, \frac{3}{2}^-)$ particles lying on an exchange degenerate trajectory.

We parametrized the invariant A and B amplitudes by:

$$\beta(\sqrt{u})\,(1+\tau.e^{-i\pi(\alpha(u)-\frac{1}{2})})\,\Gamma(\tfrac{1}{2}-\alpha(u))\,\left(\frac{s-u}{2s_o}\right)^{\alpha(u)-\frac{1}{2}}$$

where the trajectory function is $\alpha(u) = -0.72 + 0.96u$, the residue function is chosen to be $\beta(\sqrt{u}) = a + bu$, and $s_o = 1$. In this way a and b for each amplitude are the only free parameters.

The fit is shown in Figure 12. A χ^2 per degree of freedom of 2.70 is obtained for 114 data points, the overall shape and energy dependence being fitted well, with the exception of the $\bar{p}p \to K^-K^+$ data at 5.0 GeV/C [12].

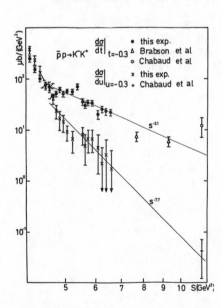

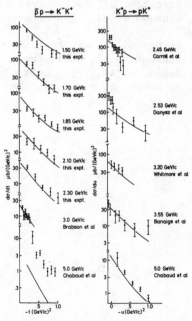

Fig. 11. s-dependance of dσ/dt for $\bar{p}p \to K^-K^+$ at t = -0.3 GeV² and u = -0.3 GeV².

Fig. 12. dσ/dt for $\bar{p}p \to K^-K^+$ and K⁺p → pK⁺. The solid line is fit of model described in the text.

REFERENCES

1. V Barger, Phys. Rev. 179, 1371 (1969).
2. V Adams et al, K$^+$ Nucleon Elastic Scattering at 180° between 1.0 and 1.5 GeV/C Incident Momentum. Paper submitted to this meeting.
3. Bologna, Glasgow, Roma and Trieste collaboration. Nucl. Phys. B42, 437 (1972).
4. G. W. Brandenburg et al, Phys. Rev. Lett 30, 145 (1973)
5. G Charriere et al, Backward production of K*(892) in the reactions K$^+$N → KπN in hydrogen and deuterium for the incident momentum range 3-5 GeV/C. Paper submitted to this meeting.
6. E. Eisenhandler, W. R. Gibson, C. Hojvat, P. I. P. Kalmus, L. C. Y. Lee Chi Kwong, T. W. Pritchard, E. C. Usher, D. T. Williams (Queen Mary College, London); M. Harrison, W. Range (University of Liverpool); M. A. R. Kemp, A. D. Rush, J. N. Woulds (Daresbury); G. T. J. Arnison, A. Astbury, D. P. Jones, A. S. L. Parsons (Rutherford).
7. R. Odorico, Nucl. Phys. B37, 541 (1972).
8. R. Odorico, Lett. Nuovo Cim.11, 655 (1969).
9. A. Brabson, et al, Phys. Lett. 42B, 287 (1972).
10. V. Chabaud et al, Phys. Lett 41B, 209 (1972).
11. V. Barger et al, Nucl. Phys. B57, 401 (1973).
12. V. Chabaud et al, CERN Preprint (1973). (To be submitted to Nucl. Phys.)
13. A. S. Carroll et al, Phys. Rev. Lett. 21, 1282 (1968).
    J. Banaigs et al, Nucl. Phys. B9, 640 (1969).
    V Chabaud et al, Phys. Lett. 38B, 445 (1972).
    J. A. Danysz et al, Nucl. Phys. B14, 161 (1969).

PREDICTING K^{*0} AND $\overline{K}^{*0}$ PRODUCTION FROM ρ^0 AND ω^0 PRODUCTION[*][/]

R. D. FIELD

Brookhaven National Laboratory, Upton, New York 11973

and

Lauritsen Laboratory of High Energy Physics
California Institute of Technology[//]
Pasadena, California 91109

I. INTRODUCTION

In recent years our knowledge of the behavior of two-body production amplitudes has increased primarily because of the measurement of additional observables (P, A, R, $\rho_{nn'}^{mm'}$, etc.) which allows for model independent amplitude analyses.[1] In cases where such an analysis is not possible because of the lack of experimentally measured observables one must resort to model fitting. The structure of the resulting amplitudes is then examined. This is somewhat inferior to a model independent analysis since the model determined amplitudes are seldom unique. Nevertheless one can, by studying a set of reactions simultaneously, place great restrictions on such high energy models. One such set of reactions is the six charge-exchange vector-meson production reactions

$$\pi^- p \rightarrow \rho^0 n \qquad\qquad (1.1)$$

$$\pi^+ n \rightarrow \rho^0 p \qquad\qquad (1.2)$$

$$\pi^- p \rightarrow \omega^0 n \qquad\qquad (1.3)$$

$$\pi^+ n \rightarrow \omega^0 p \qquad\qquad (1.4)$$

$$K^- p \rightarrow \overline{K}^{*0} n \qquad\qquad (1.5)$$

$$K^+ n \rightarrow K^{*0} p \quad . \qquad\qquad (1.6)$$

The reactions $\pi N \rightarrow \omega^0 N$ and $\pi N \rightarrow \rho^0 N$ are related to the reactions $\overline{K}N \rightarrow \overline{K}^{*0}N$ by SU(3). Given the amplitudes for ω^0 and ρ^0 production one can predict the amplitudes for $\overline{K}^{*0}$ production. In fact if one is willing to neglect absorption effects and assume EXD trajectories for the π and B, and for the ρ and A_2 (i.e., $\alpha_\pi(t) = \alpha_B(t)$, $\alpha_{A_2}(t) = \alpha_\rho(t)$), then one can use SU(3) to directly relate the observables for ω^0, ρ^0, and $\overline{K}^{*0}$ production as follows:

----

[*] Work performed under the auspices of the U.S. Atomic Energy Commission.

[/] Invited talk presented at the 1973 Meeting of the Division of Particles and Fields of the APS, Berkeley, California, August 13-17, 1973.

[//] Present address.

$$\frac{1}{2}\left\{\rho_{00}{}^{H}\frac{d\sigma}{dt}(\omega^0 n) + \rho_{00}{}^{H}\frac{d\sigma}{dt}(\rho^0 n)\right\} = \rho_{00}{}^{H}\frac{d\sigma}{dt}(\overline{K^{*0}}n), \qquad (1.7a)$$

$$\frac{1}{2}\left\{\rho_{\pm}{}^{H}\frac{d\sigma}{dt}(\omega^0 n) = \rho_{\pm}{}^{H}\frac{d\sigma}{dt}(\rho^0 n)\right\} = \rho_{\pm}{}^{H}\frac{d\sigma}{dt}(\overline{K^{*0}}n), \qquad (1.7b)$$

when $\rho_{\pm}{}^{H} = \rho_{11}{}^{H} + \rho_{1-1}{}^{H}$. Such a comparison is shown in Fig. 1. The agreement is quite good for $\rho_{00}{}^{H}\frac{d\sigma}{dt}$ and not so good for $\rho_{\pm}{}^{H}\frac{d\sigma}{dt}$.

Obviously the assumptions used to arrive at (1.7a) and (1.7b) cannot hold exactly since they predict

$$\frac{d\sigma}{dt}(\overline{K^{*0}}n) = \frac{d\sigma}{dt}(K^{*0}p) ,$$

which is not satisfied for $p_{lab} < 10$ GeV/c. The line reversal differences in the differential cross sections for $\overline{K^{*0}}$ and K^{*0} production can be predicted from ω^0 and ρ^0 production if one includes knowledge of the ρ-ω interference effects in the $\pi^+\pi^-$ mass spectra for $\pi N \to (\pi^+\pi^-)N$. SU(3) implies that the amplitudes for $\overline{K^{*0}}$ and K^{*0} production are related to those for ρ^0 and ω^0 production as follows:

$$A(K^-p \to \overline{K^{*0}}n) = \frac{1}{(2)^{\frac{1}{2}}}\left\{A(\pi^-p \to \omega^0 n)-A(\pi^-p \to \rho^0 n)\right\} , \qquad (1.8a)$$

$$A(K^-n \to K^{*0}p) = -\frac{1}{(2)^{\frac{1}{2}}}\left\{A(\pi^-p \to \omega^0 n)+A(\pi^-p \to \rho^0 n)\right\}. \qquad (1.8b)$$

The difference of the squares of the $\overline{K^{*0}}$ and K^{*0} amplitudes are related to the magntiude and relative phase of the ω^0 and ρ^0 production amplitudes (i.e., $A(\omega^0)/A(\rho^0)$) and this is precisely the quantity determined from ρ-ω interference effects.

In this talk I will outline the interesting lessons learned from detailed Regge pole plus absorption model fits to ρ^0 (Sec. II) and ω^0 (Sec. III) production. Particular emphasis is placed on the behavior of the resulting amplitudes.[2] These amplitudes are combined according to (1.8a) and (1.8b) to predict the amplitudes and hence the observables for $\overline{K^{*0}}$ and K^{*0} production (Sec. IV). In Sec. V I make some brief concluding remarks.

II. THE REACTION $\pi N \to \rho^0 N$

Figure 2 and Fig. 3 show a comparison of the experimental differential cross sections and density matrix elements for $\pi^-p \to \rho^0 n$, respectively, with two Regge pole plus absorption model fits.[3] Some of the interesting lessons learned from such detailed comparisons are as follows:

1. Behavior of the $\rho_{11}{}^{H}\frac{d\sigma}{dt}$ and helicity non-flip (n=0) absorption[6]:

The small $|t|$ behavior of the observable

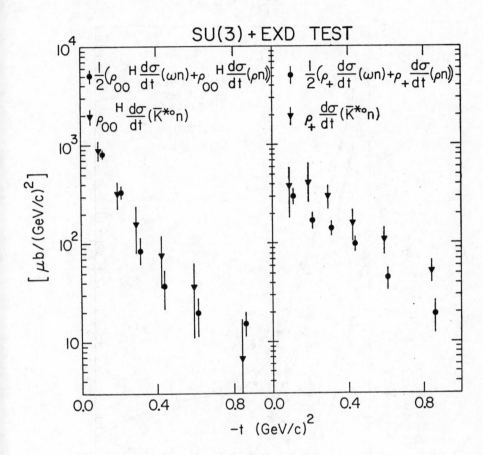

Fig. 1   SU(3) plus EXD test. Assuming no absorption and weak EXD
($\alpha_{A_2}(t) = \alpha_\rho(t)$, $\alpha_\pi(t) = \alpha_B(t)$), SU(3) implies

$$\tfrac{1}{2}(\rho_{00}^H \tfrac{d\sigma}{dt}(\pi^- p \to \omega^0 n) + \rho_{00}^H \tfrac{d\sigma}{dt}(\pi^- p \to \rho^0 n)) = \rho_{00}^H \tfrac{d\sigma}{dt}(K^- p \to \overline{K^{*0}} n)$$

and $\tfrac{1}{2}(\rho_{\pm}^H \tfrac{d\sigma}{dt}(\pi^- p \to \omega^0 n) + \rho_{\pm}^H \tfrac{d\sigma}{dt}(\pi^- p \to \rho^0 n)) = \rho_{\pm}^H \tfrac{d\sigma}{dt}(K^- p \to \overline{K^{*0}} n)$,

where $\rho_{\pm}^H = \rho_{11}^H \pm \rho_{1-1}^H$.

302

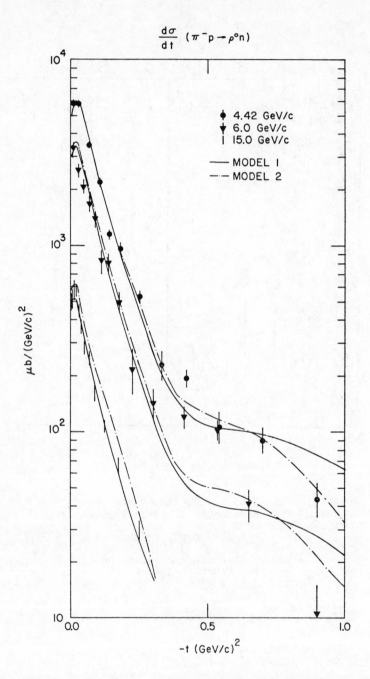

Fig. 2   Shows a comparison of model 1 ("fancy Pomeron" absorption)
and model 2 ("square-cut" absorption) with the data on the
differential cross section for $\pi^-p \to \rho^0 n$ at 4.42 (Ref. 16),
6.0 (Ref. 17), and 15.0 GeV/c (Ref. 18).

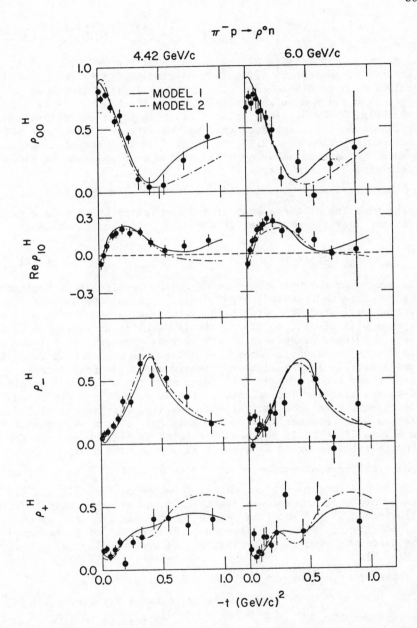

$\pi^- p \rightarrow \rho^0 n$

Fig. 3   Shows a comparison of model 1 ("fancy Pomeron" absorption)
and model 2 ("square-cut" absorption) with the data on the
vector-meson density matrix elements for $\pi^- p \rightarrow \rho^0 n$ at 4.42
(Ref. 16) and 6.0 GeV/c (Ref. 17).

$$\rho_{11}{}^H \frac{d\sigma}{dt} \propto \left\{ \left| H_{-1-;+}^{n=0} \right|^2 + \left| H_{1+;+}^{n=1} \right|^2 + \left| H_{-1+;+}^{n=1} \right|^2 + \left| H_{1-;+}^{n=2} \right|^2 \right\} \quad (2.1)$$

gives an excellent measure of the strength of the n=0 absorption. In the absence of absorption (2.1) is predicted to dip in the forward direction. Thus a dip at small $|t|$ in (2.1) implies little or no absorption, whereas a spike implies large absorption. The data displayed in Fig. 4 show a clear spike indicating large n=0 absorption. Absorption models do reproduce this spike. Figure 5 shows the pole and cut contributions to (2.1) resulting from an absorption model. In this model the A_2-cut makes up $\approx 1/3$ of the n=0 amplitude at t=0. The remaining 2/3 is π-cut.

2. Behavior of $\rho_{00}{}^H \frac{d\sigma}{dt}$ and helicity-flip (n=1) absorption:

The question of the amount of n=1 absorption has provided much controversy over the past years. Assuming no A_1 contribution the observable

$$\rho_{00}{}^H \frac{d\sigma}{dt} (\pi^- p \to \rho^0 n) \quad (2.2)$$

is the square of the n=1 amplitude $H_{0-;+}^{n=1}$ and receives contributions from π exchange and possibly a n=1 π-cut. A model with sizeable n=1 absorption will predict a dip in (2.2), whereas a model with no absorption will predict no dip. This is illustrated in Fig. 6 where (2.2) is predicted using models with varying strengths of n=1 absorption. Pure π exchange produces a structureless behavior in $|t|$. As the absorption is increased a dip appears and moves inward in $|t|$. Figure 7 shows a comparison of the data with two absorption models. The data are somewhat inconclusive. The 4.42, 6.0, and 7.0 GeV/c bubble chamber data show indications of a dip, whereas the high statistics spark chamber data at 6.0 and 17.2 GeV/c show a change in slope but no dip. It is not possible (with ro A_1 exchange) to fit the change in slope of (2.2) without also producing a dip.

3. Alternative explanation of the behavior of $\rho_{00}{}^H \frac{d\sigma}{dt}(\pi^- p \to \rho^0 n)$:

It is possible to fit the change in slope of (2.2) if one includes A_1 exchange and reduces the size of the n=1 absorption. This is illustrated in Fig. 8. The change in slope is produced by the large helicity non-flip (n=0) A_1-cut. The presence of A_1 exchange can be tested by experimental measurements with a polarized target.[2,7] (see Fig. 9).

4. Behavior of $\rho_+{}^H (\pi^- p \to \rho^0 n)$: A_2 pole versus π-cut.

The large n=0 absorption necessary to correctly predict the observed forward spike in $\rho_{11}{}^H \frac{d\sigma}{dt}(\pi^- p \to \rho^0 n)$ results in $\rho_+{}^H = \rho_{11}{}^H + \rho_{1-1}{}^H$ receiving a large π-cut contribution. Figure 10 shows $\rho_+{}^H$ before and after absorption is applied. Before absorption $\rho_+{}^H$ is given entirely by the A_2 pole, whereas with absorption present it receives an additional contribution from the π-cut (and A_2-cut).

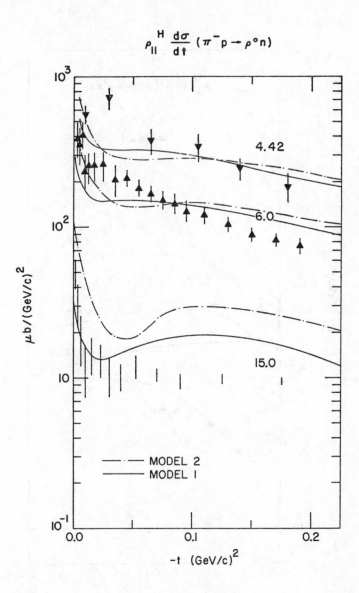

$$\rho_{\parallel}^{H} \frac{d\sigma}{dt} \ (\pi^{-}p \to \rho^{\circ}n)$$

Fig. 4   Shows a comparison of model 1 ("fancy Pomeron" absorption)
and model 2 ("square-cut" absorption) with the data on the
small $|t|$ behavior of $\rho_{11} \frac{H}{dt} \frac{d\sigma}{dt}(\pi^{-}p \to \rho^{0}n)$ at 4.42 (Ref. 16),
6.0 (Ref. 19), and 15.0 (Ref. 18).

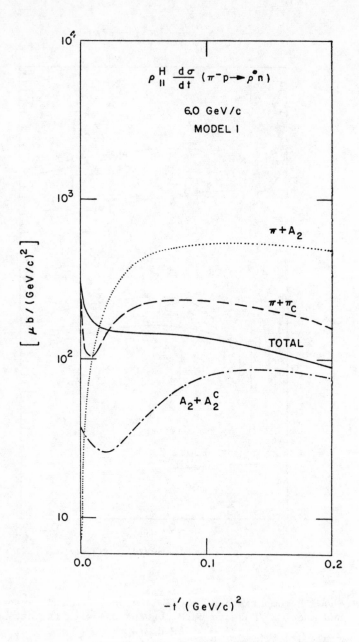

Fig. 5   Contributions to small $|t|$ behavior of $\rho_{11}^H \frac{d\sigma}{dt}(\pi^- p \to \rho^0 n)$ at 6.0 GeV/c from model 1 ("fancy Pomeron" absorption).

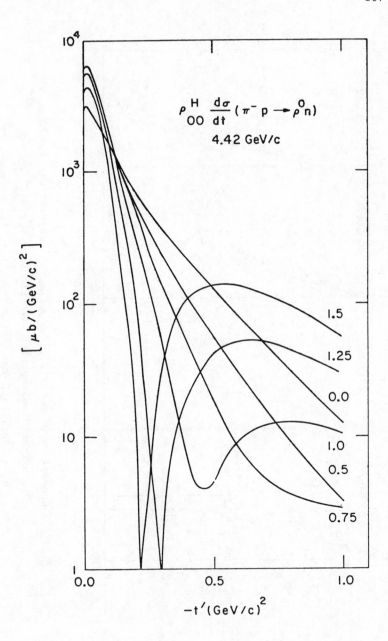

Fig. 6 Shows fits to $\rho_{00}^H \frac{d\sigma}{dt}(\pi^- p \to \rho^0 n)$ using a model with varying degrees of n=1 absorption.

308

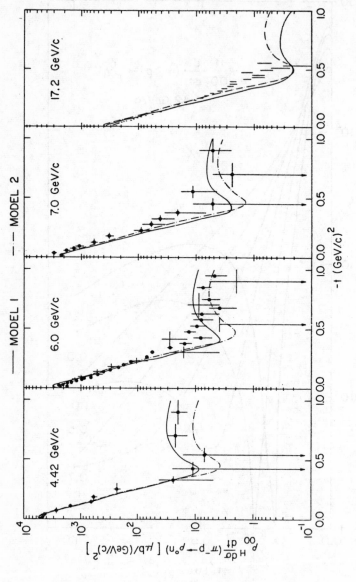

Fig. 7 Comparison of model 1 ("'fancy Pomeron" absorption) and model 2 ("square-cut" absorption) with the data for $\rho_{00}^H \frac{d\sigma}{dt}(\pi^- p \to \rho^0 n)$ at 4.42 (Ref. 16), 6.0 (solid dots, Ref. 17; crosses, Ref. 19), 7.0 (Ref. 20), and 17/2 GeV/c (Ref. 21). The normalization of the 17.2 GeV/c data shown in this figure should not be trusted (see footnote 22).

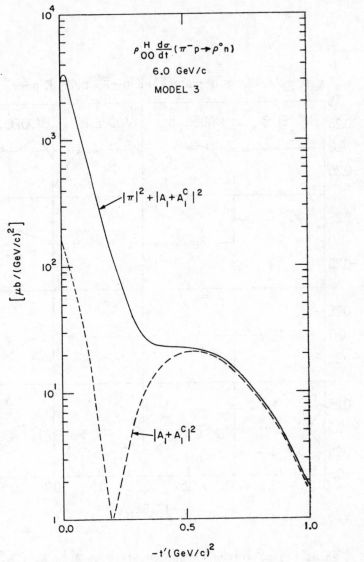

Fig. 8 Contributions to $\rho_{00}^{H} \frac{d\sigma}{dt}(\pi^- p \rightarrow \rho^0 n)$ at 6.0 GeV/c from model 3
("square-cut" absorption; only n=0 absorption, includes A_1
contribution). In this model the change in slope of this
observable is due to the A_1-cut.

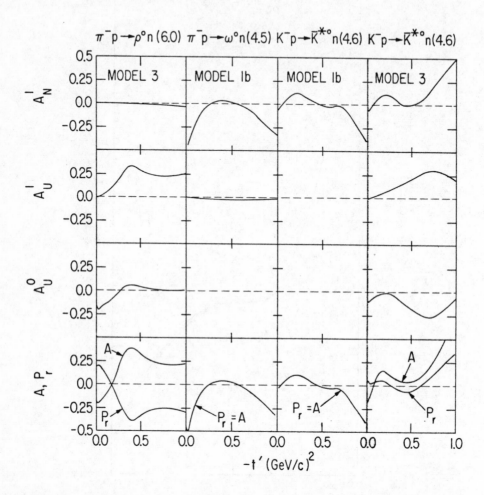

Fig. 9   Predicted polarized target observables A_N^1, A_u^1, A_u^0
($A+A_N^1+A_u^1+A_u^0$) and the recoil nucleon polarization P_r
($P_r=A_N^1-A_u^1-A_u^0$) from model 3 (includes A_1 contribution) and
model 1b (no A_1 contribution). No A_1 contribution implies
$A_u^1 = A_u^0 = 0$ and $P_r = A$.

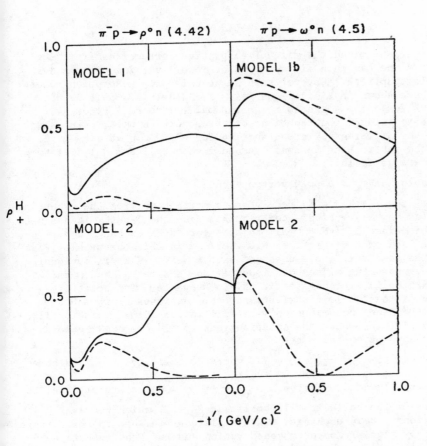

ρ_+^H

10 The observable ρ_+^H ($\rho_+^H = \rho_{11}^H + \rho_{1-1}^H$) for ρ^0 production at 4.42 GeV/c and ω^0 production at 4.5 GeV/c for model 1 ("fancy Pomeron" absorption), model 1b ("fancy Pomeron" absorption, no WSNZ for ρ trajectory), model 2 ("square-cut" absorption; includes WSNZ for ρ trajectory). The solid (dashed) curves are the values after (before) absorptive corrections are applied.

III. THE REACTION $\pi N \to \omega^0 N$

Having determined the size of absorptive corrections from fits to $\pi N \to \rho^0 N$ one can then fit $\pi N \to \omega^0 N$ by merely varying the ρ and B Regge pole couplings. Several such Regge pole plus absorption model analyses are shown in Fig. 11 and Fig. 12. Model 1a and 1b do not use a WSNZ for the ρ Regge pole whereas model 2 does.[3] Figure 13 shows the individual contributions of the ρ pole, B pole, ρ-cut and B-cut to the differential cross section for $\pi^- p \to \omega^0 n$ at 4.5 GeV/c. Some of the interesting lessons learned from detailed model fits to $\pi N \to \omega^0 N$ are as follows:

1. Behavior of ρ_+^H: ρ pole versus B-cut

Just as $\rho_+^H(\pi^- N \to \rho^0 N)$ receives a contribution from the π-cut, so does $\rho_+^H(\pi N \to \omega^0 N)$ receive a contribution from the B-cut. It has been argued that since $\rho_+^H(\pi N \to \omega^0 N)$ projects out the ρ-exchange contribution, the lack of a dip at $t = -0.6$ $(GeV/c)^2$ in this observable (Fig. 12) implies that the ρ-pole does not have a WSNZ. This is obviously fallacious reasoning since both model 1 (no WSNZ for ρ) and model 2 (with WSNZ for ρ) are able to fit this observable. The point is that even if the ρ pole contribution to ρ_+^H vanishes at $t = -0.6$ $(GeV/c)^2$ the B-cut contribution will fill in this dip. This is illustrated in Fig. 10, where the contributions to ρ_+^H are shown before and after absorption (also see Fig. 13).

2. Behavior of $\rho_{00}^H \frac{d\sigma}{dt}(\pi N \to \omega^0 N)$: where do helicity zero ω^0's come from?

The experimental observable $\rho_{00}^H \frac{d\sigma}{dt}(\pi N \to \omega^0 N)$ is proportional to the square of the helicity flip amplitude $H_{0-;+}^{n=1}$, which receives contributions from B exchange. This amplitude vanishes in the forward direction by angular momentum conservation and thus one expects very few small $|t|$ ω^0's to be produced. Figure 14 shows that the data are consistently larger for small $|t|$ than the model predictions, particularly for the reaction $\pi^+ n \to \omega^0 p$. Where do these extra helicity zero ω^0's come from? Figure 15a shows that ρ-ω mixing allows π-exchange to contribute to $\rho_{00}^H \frac{d\sigma}{dt}(\pi N \to \omega^0 N)$.[8] Since π-exchange contributions are large for $|t|$ small one expects the ρ-ω mixing effects to be largest in this region. Figure 14 shows the effect of including ρ-ω mixing using a value of $\delta = 4.0$ MeV. We see that the electromagnetically mixed reaction $\pi^+ n \to \tilde{\omega}^0 p$ is predicted to have substantially more helicity zero ω^0's than the unmixed reaction (i.e., $\delta=0$), whereas the reaction $\pi^- p \to \tilde{\omega}^0 n$ is predicted to have less helicity zero ω^0's than the unmixed case. In the absence of ρ-ω mixing isospin conservation predicts the amplitudes and hence the observables for $\pi^- p \to \omega^0 n$ to be identical to those for $\pi^+ n \to \omega^0 p$. Figure 16 shows the predicted amount of isospin violation in the observable $\rho_{00}^H \frac{d\sigma}{dt}$ due to ρ-ω mixing with $\delta = 4.0$ MeV.[9]

IV. PREDICTING K^{*0} AND $\overline{K}^{*0}$ PRODUCTION

Having determined the amplitudes for ω^0 and ρ^0 production one can

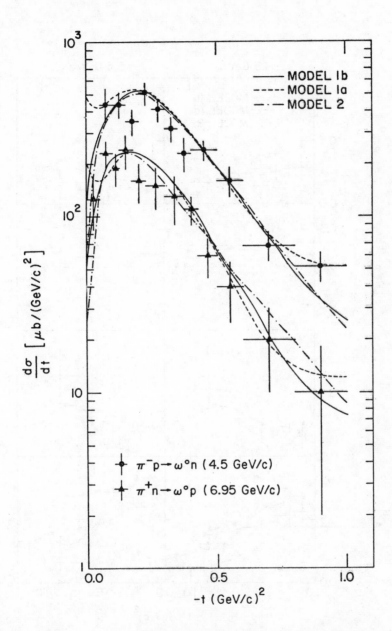

Fig. 11 Comparison of model 1a ("fancy Pomeron" absorption; uses
opposite EXD ρ-A_2 phase prediction) model 1b ("fancy Pomeron"
absorption; uses EXD predicted ρ-A_2 phase) model 2 ("square-
cut" absorption, uses EXD predicted ρ-A_2 phase) with the differential cross section for $\pi^- p \rightarrow \omega^0 n$ at 4.5 GeV/c (Ref. 23)
and $\pi^+ n \rightarrow \omega^0 p$ at 6.95 GeV/c (Ref. 24). Model 1a and 1b do
not use a WSNZ for the ρ trajectory, whereas model 2 does.

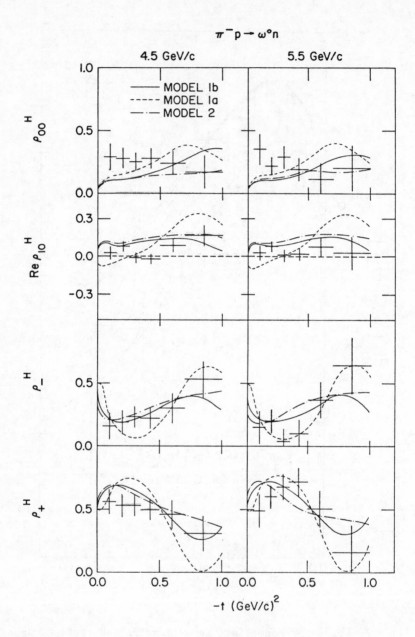

Fig. 12 Comparison of the three models in Fig. 11 with the data on the vector-meson density matrix elements ($\rho_{\pm}^{H} = \rho_{11}^{H} \pm \rho_{1-1}^{H}$) for the reaction $\pi^- p \to \omega^0 n$ at 4.5 and 5.5 GeV/c (Ref. 23).

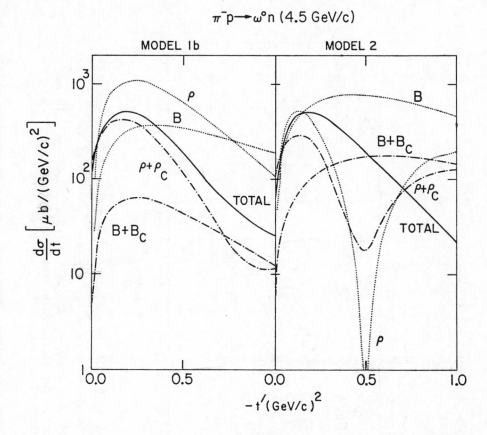

$\pi^- p \rightarrow \omega^\circ n$ (4.5 GeV/c)

Fig. 13 Contributions to the differential cross section for
$\pi^- p \rightarrow \omega^0 n$ at 4.5 GeV/c from model 1b ("fancy Pomeron" absorption; no WSNZ for ρ) and model 2 ("square-cut" absorption;
uses WSNZ for ρ)

316

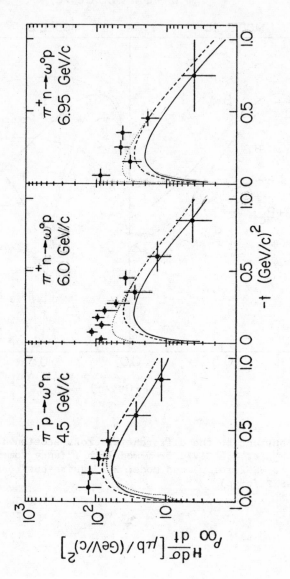

Fig. 14 Comparison of model 1b (solid curves) and model 1a (dashed curves) with the data on $\rho_{00}^H \frac{d\sigma}{dt}$ for $\pi^- p \rightarrow \omega^0 n$ at 4.5 GeV/c (Ref. 23) and for $\pi^+ n \rightarrow \omega^0 p$ at 6.0 (Ref. 25) and 6.95 GeV/c (Ref. 24). The dotted curve shows the effect on model 1a of including ρ–ω mixing with $\delta = 4.0$ MeV.

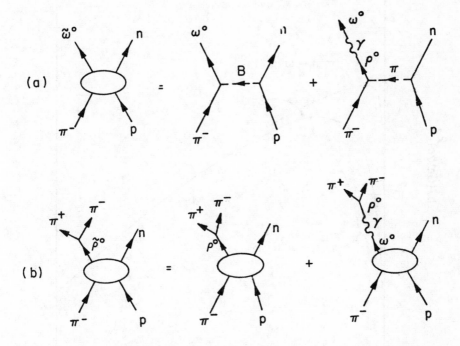

Fig. 15 Illustration of two ρ-ω mixing effects: (A) shows how ρ-ω
mixing allows π exchange to contribute to the reaction
π⁻p → ω̃⁰n; (B) shows how ρ-ω mixing effects the π⁺π⁻ mass
spectra for the reaction π⁻p → π⁺π⁻n.

$$\rho_{00}^{H} \frac{d\sigma}{dt} (\pi N \rightarrow \omega^{0}N) \ 6.0 \ \text{GeV/c}$$

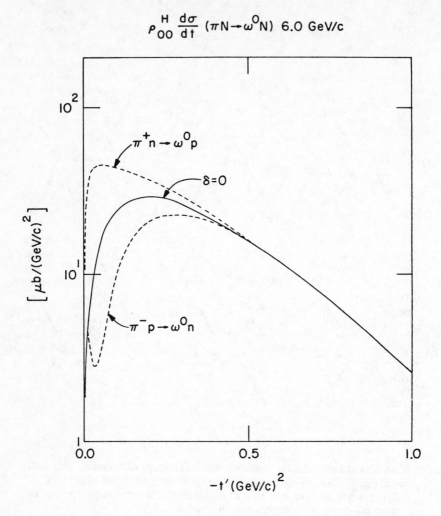

Fig. 16 Shows the predicted amount of isospin violation in the observable $\rho_{00}^{H} \frac{d\sigma}{dt}(\pi N \rightarrow \omega^{0}N)$ at 6.0 GeV/c using model 1b with $\delta = 4.0$ MeV.

then use the SU(3) relationships (1.8a) and (1.8b) to predict the amplitudes and hence the observables for the reactions $K^-p \rightarrow \overline{K^{*0}}n$ and $K^+n \rightarrow K^{*0}p$. This is shown in Figs. 17 and 18 for one of the Regge pole plus absorption models discussed above. It can be seen that this model is quite successful in describing the data including the line reversal differences between K^{*0} and $\overline{K^{*0}}$ production.[10] Figure 19 shows that the line reversal breaking is due primarily to the interference between the ρ pole and the π-cut, and to some extent to the interference between the ρ pole and the A_2-cut.[11]

V. CONCLUSIONS

We have seen that Regge-pole plus absorption models are able to fit the observables for ρ^0 production (π and A_2 exchange) and ω^0 production (B and ρ exchange), however, large absorptive corrections are necessary. This means that, in particular, a large fraction of the natural parity projection $\rho_+^H = \rho_{11} + \rho_{1-1}$ in $\pi^-p \rightarrow \rho^0 n$ at 6.0 GeV/c is π-cut and that any WSNZ dip due to ρ exchange in this observable for $\pi N \rightarrow \omega N$ is completely filled in by the B-cut. The resulting amplitudes for ρ^0 and ω^0 can then be used to successfully predict the amplitudes and observables for K^{*0} and $\overline{K^{*0}}$ production (π,B,ρ, and A_2 exchange).

Due to the lack of time I have skipped over the very interesting and worthwhile investigation into the ρ-ω interference effects on the $\pi^+\pi^-$ mass spectra for the reaction $\pi N \rightarrow (\pi^+\pi^-)N$.[12] Recent experimental results[13] place great restrictions on high energy models since they give information on the ratio of ω^0 production amplitudes to ρ^0 production amplitudes (i.e., $A(\omega^0)/A(\rho^0)$).[2,14,15]

Because of the electromagnetic mixing of the ρ^0 and ω^0 mesons, and because of the SU(3) relations (1.8a) and (1.8b), and due to the availability of vector-meson density matrix information, the six reactions (1.1)-(1.6) together with $\pi N \rightarrow (\pi^+\pi^-)N$ provide an excellent laboratory for studying production mechanisms and for investigating the nature of absorptive corrections.

ACKNOWLEDGMENTS

I gratefully acknowledge useful discussions with Drs. Deepinder Sidhu, G. Kane, C. Quigg, and G. Fox. I am very grateful to the following experimenters for interesting discussions and for allowing me access to their data: R. Diebold, D. Ayres, A. Greene, S. Kramer, A. Pawlicki and A. Wicklund at Argonne; H. Gordon, K.-W. Lai, and J.M. Scarr at BNL; S. Barish and W. Selove at Argonne. Finally, I thank Dr. R. F. Peierls for his support during the course of this work.

320

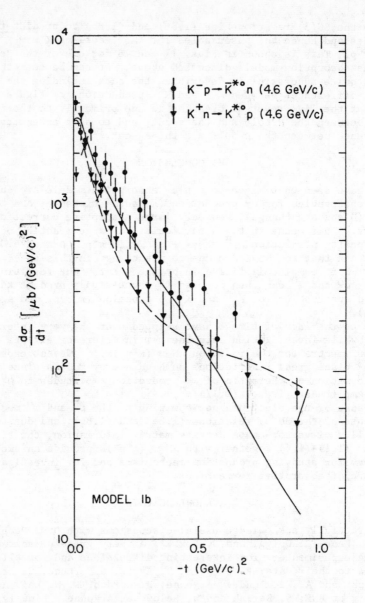

Fig. 17 Comparison of the data on the differential cross section for
$K^-p \to \bar{K}^{*0}n$ (Ref. 26) and for $K^+n \to K^{*0}p$ (Ref. 27) at 4.6
GeV/c with the predictions of model 1b. The solid (dashed)
curves are the predicted values for $\bar{K}^{*0}$ (K^{*0}) production.

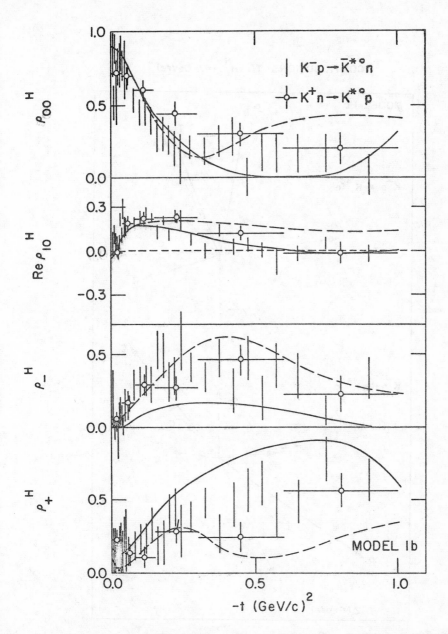

Fig. 18 Comparison of the data on the vector-meson density matrix
elements for K⁻p → K̄*⁰n (Ref. 26) and K⁺n → K*⁰p (Ref. 27)
at 4.6 GeV/c with the predictions of model 1b. The solid
(dashed) curves are the predicted values for K̄*⁰ (K*⁰)
production.

322

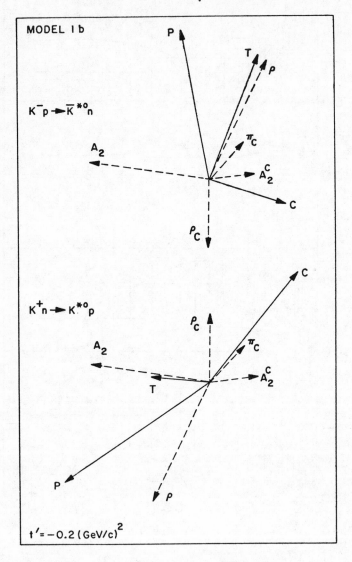

Fig. 19   Argand diagram of the contributions to the s-channel helicity
amplitude H_f^N ($H_f^N = H_{1-;+}^{n=2} + H_{-1-;+}^{n=0}$) for $\overline{K}^{*0}$ and K^{*0} production at 4.6 GeV/c and $t' \equiv t-t_0 = -0.2$ (GeV/c)^2 from model
1b.   The labels P and C correspond to the total pole ($A_2+\rho$)
and total cut ($\pi_C+A_2{}^C+\rho_C$) contributions, respectively.   The
total amplitude (pole+cut) is labelled by T.

REFERENCES

1. For a review of this subject see, for example, G.C. Fox and C. Quigg, Production Mechanisms of Two-to-Two Scattering Processes at Intermediate Energies, ITP-SB-73-22 (to be published); R.D. Field, Amplitude Analyses of Hypercharge Exchange Reactions, Proceedings of the International Conference on π-π Scattering and Associated Topics, Florida State University, March 38-40, 1973.

2. For a more complete treatment of this subject see R.D. Field and Deepinder Sidhu, Charge-Exchange Vector-Meson Production, BNL preprint (to be published in Phys. Rev. D). See also, Deepinder Sidhu (Ph.D. Thesis 1973) Institute for Theoretical Physics, Stony Brook, New York.

3. Model 1 is essentially the absorption model introduced by Hartley and Kane (Ref. 4) in their work on pseudoscalar production which uses a "fancy Pomeron" type of absorption and non-EXD type Regge signature factors (no WSNZ for the ρ trajectory). Model 2 is a generalization of the "square-cut" absorption model used by Worden in his work on photoproduction (Ref. 5).

4. B.J. Hartley and G.L. Kane, Nucl. Phys. B57, 157 (1973).

5. R. Worden, Nucl. Phys. B37, 253 (1972).

6. See also, G.L. Kane, Experimental Meson Spectroscopy, ed. C. Baltay and A.H. Rosenfeld (Columbia University Press, New York 1970).

7. See the discussions by Geoffrey Fox in the Second International Conference on Polarization and Polarized Targets, Berkeley 1971.

8. See, for example, Gerson Goldhaber, Experimental Meson Spectroscopy ed. C. Baltay and A.H. Rosenfeld (Columbia University Press, New York, 1970).

9. See, for example, N.N. Achasov and G.N. Shestakov, Nucl. Phys. B45, 93 (1972).

10. For a review of K^{*0} and $\overline{K^{*0}}$ production see R.L. Eisner in Proceedings of the International Winter Meeting on Fundamental Physics Formigal, Spain, February 1973.

11. See also the model fits and discussions of K^{*0} and $\overline{K^{*0}}$ production presented by G.C. Fox, R. Engelmann, B. Musgrave, F. Schweingruber, H. Yuta, B. Forman, N. Gelfand, and H. Schulz, Phys. Rev. D4, 2647 (1971).

12. A.S. Goldhaber, G.C. Fox and C. Quigg, Phys. Letters 30B, 249(1969).

13. D.S. Ayres, R. Diebold, A.F. Greene, S.L. Kramer, A.J. Pawlicki, and A.B. Wicklund, contributed paper presented by S.L. Kramer at the International Conference on $\pi\pi$ Scattering and Associated Topics Florida State University, March 28-30, 1973.

14. R. Diebold, Invited talk presented at the Second Aix-en-Provence Conference 1973.

15. P. Estabrooks, A.D. Martin and C. Michael, "Exchange Mechanisms for $\pi^- p \to \rho^0 n$ and ρ-ω Interference", CERN TH-1732 (1973).

16. S. Barish and W. Selove, private communication.

17. H. Gordon, K.-W. Lai and J.M. Scarr, Phys. Rev. (to be published).

18. F. Bulos, R.K. Carnegie, G.E. Fisher, E.E. Kluge, D.W.G.S. Leith, H.L. Lynch, B. Ratcliff, B. Richter, H.H. Williams, S.H. Williams and M. Beniston, Phys. Rev. Letters 26, 1453 (1971).

19. D.S. Ayres, R. Diebold, A.F. Greene, S.L. Kramer, A.J. Pawlicki, and A.B. Wicklund, Invited paper presented by R. Diebold at the International Conference on $\pi\pi$ Scattering and Associated Topics, Florida State University, March 28-30, 1973.

20. J.A.J. Matthews, J.D. Prentice, T.S. Yoon, J.T. Carroll, M.W. Firebaugh, and W.D. Walker, Nucl. Phys. B (to be published).

21. The CERN-Munich 17.2 GeV/c $\pi^-p \rightarrow \rho^0 n$ data was arrived at by calculating the observables from the amplitude analysis of P. Estabrooks and A.D. Martin, TH-1668-CERN preprint, May 4, 1973.

22. The 17.2 GeV/c CERN-Munich data was normalized such as to produce an effective α of zero at t=0 for $\rho_{00}^H \frac{d\sigma}{dt}$.

23. L.E. Holloway, B. Huld, M. Jordan, D.W. Mortara, E.I. Rosenberg, A.D. Russell, S. Bernstein, M.H. Garrell, S. Margulies and D.W. Mcleod, Phys. Rev. Letters $\underline{27}$, 1671 (1971).

24. J.A.J. Matthews, J.D. Prentice, T.S. Yoon, J.T. Carroll, M.W. Firebaugh, and W.D. Walker, Phys. Rev. Letters $\underline{26}$, 400 (1971).

25. J.C. Anderson, A. Engler, R.W. Kraemer, S. Toaff, F. Weisser, J. Diaz, F. DiBianca, W. Fickinger and D.K. Robinson, Phys. Letters (to be published).

26. M. Aguilar-Benitez, R.L. Eisner, and J.B. Kinson, Phys. Rev. $\underline{D4}$, 2583 (1971).

27. K. Buchner, G. Dehm, W. Geist, G. Gobel, W. Wittek, G. Wolf, G. Charriere, W. Dunwoodie, Y. Goldschmidt-Clermont, A. Grant, U.P. Henri, F. Muller, J. Quinguard, Z. Sekera, P. Cornet, G. de Jongh, P. Dufour, F. Grard, J. Milkin, S. Tauenier and R. Windmolders, Nucl. Phys. $\underline{B45}$, 333 (1972).

Chapter Ⅲ
<u>Experimental Hadron Physics</u>
<u>at High Energies</u>

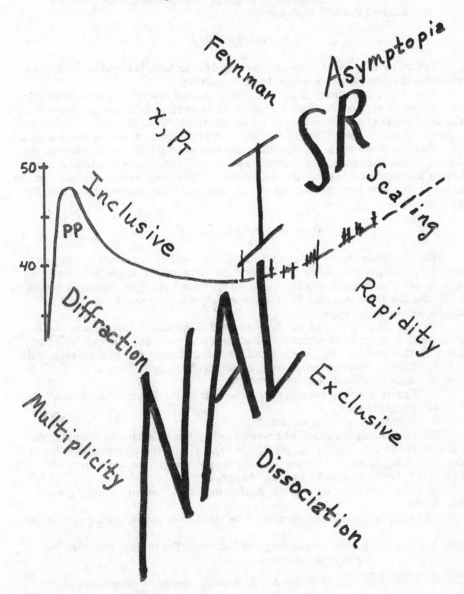

DIFFRACTIVE PROCESSES*

David W. G. S. Leith
Stanford Linear Accelerator Center
Stanford University, Stanford, Calif. 94305

ABSTRACT

New data on diffractive processes from current experiments at NAL and the ISR is reviewed.

INTRODUCTION

Let us briefly review some ideas on diffraction phenomena,[1] and then examine the new data presented to this meeting.

There are two pictures of diffraction in high energy particle scattering: an s-channel picture in which the process is seen in geometric terms, where the incident particle is scattered by an absorbing disc of a given radius and a given opacity — here the diffraction scattering is seen as the shadow of all the inelastic processes; a t-channel picture in which the scattering is mediated by the exchange of a Regge trajectory — the Pomeron, where properties are given by the energy dependence of the total cross-section and the slope of the forward differential cross-section. The trajectory is usually written

$$\alpha(t) \; = \; \alpha(0) + \alpha' \, t$$

The flat asymptotic s-dependence of the total cross-section implies $\alpha(0) = 1$, and the shrinkage of the forward differential cross-section gives $\alpha' \sim 1/3$. The Pomeron trajectory has no known particle associated with it. In all the above properties the Pomeron is quite different from the other known Regge trajectories.

Beyond these pictures we have no good theoretical description of the dynamics of diffractive processes and we rather identify diffractive reactions as those which obey some or all of the following set of empirical rules.

1. Energy independent cross sections (to factors of log s).
2. Sharp forward peak in $d\sigma/dt$.
3. Particle cross sections equal to anti-particle cross sections.
4. Factorization.
5. Mainly imaginary amplitude.
6. exchange processes characterized by the quantum numbers of the vacuum in the t-channel (i.e., I=0, C=+1). Also, the change in parity in the scattering process follows the natural spin-parity series $(-1)^J$, or $P_f = P_i \cdot (-1)^{\Delta J}$, where ΔJ is spin change.
7. The spin structure in the scattering is s-channel helicity conserving (SCHC).

The diffraction phenomenon may be studied in the following processes:

$AB \rightarrow AB$ — elastic scattering, and through the optical theorem the total cross section

---

*Work supported in part by the U. S. Atomic Energy Commission.

AB → A*B — diffraction dissociation
    AB*

AB → AX — inclusive scattering
    XB

Let us now examine the new data presented to this meeting on these various diffractive reactions.

TOTAL CROSS-SECTION AND ELASTIC SCATTERING

A. Total Cross-Section in pp Collisions

Up through 30 GeV all the measured total cross-sections appeared to have an energy dependence of the form $a + b\ s^{-1/2}$. However, measurements through the Serpukov energy range, (20-70) GeV, showed most of the cross-sections flattening out, (pp, $\pi^{\pm}p$, K^-p), and the K^+p cross-section actually rising by almost 2 mb. These data are summarized in Fig. 1.

About a year ago we had the first indications that the pp total cross-section was rising in the ISR energy region (200-3000 GeV/c equivalent lab momentum). The results are now quite firm and clearly show a 4 mb rise—see Fig. 2. The data came from two groups measuring the pp total cross-sections at the ISR by two quite different methods:

(1) CERN-Rome[2] measure the forward scattering angular distribution $d\sigma/dt$, with a scintillation counter telescope and extrapolate to find the forward cross-section, $\frac{d\sigma}{dt}\big|_{t=0}$. They also measure the real part of the forward scattering amplitude in this energy range and find it small and essentially negligible. From the optical theorem, they can then determine the total cross-section

$$\sigma_T^2 = 16\pi \left.\frac{d\sigma}{dt}\right|_{t=0}$$

This experiment normalizes their total cross-section measurement two ways — (a) internally, by observing the coulomb p-p scattering cross-section, and (b) externally, by using the Van der Meer luminosity measurement of the circulating ISR proton beams. Both methods agree well.

(2) Pisa-Stonybrook[3] measure the reaction rate in pp collisions with an almost 4π counter hodoscope. This experiment is normalized using two external methods — the Van der Meer beam displacement measurement and the actual measurement of the individual beam profiles. Again both methods agree well. Figure 2 shows the most recent measurement by this group at the highest energy of the ISR.

Both experiments agree well on the cross-section rise of ~ 4 mb through the ISR region. It is interesting to note that the two experiments depend very differently on the luminosity of the ISR

CERN-Rome $\left.\frac{d\sigma}{dt}\right|_0 \propto \sigma_T^2 \cdot L$

Pisa-Stonybrook   Rate $\propto \sigma_T \cdot L$

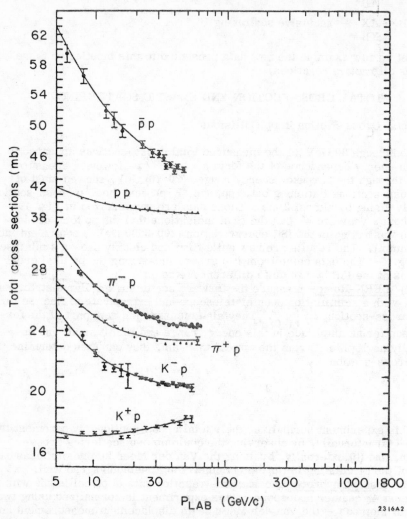

FIG. 1--Energy dependence of the p, $\bar{p}$, $K^{\pm}$, $\pi^{\pm}$ cross-sections on hydrogen.

i.e., the CERN-Rome experiment is sensitive to $\sqrt{L}$, while the Pisa-Stonybrook experiment is sensitive to L. The agreement between the resultant total cross section measurements is evidence that the ISR luminosity has been well measured.

A further interesting comment should be made on the independence of the cross section rise on the ISR luminosity measurements.[4] It is clear from the above discussion that the ratio of the measured quantity in the two ISR experiments is a measure of the total cross-section, completely

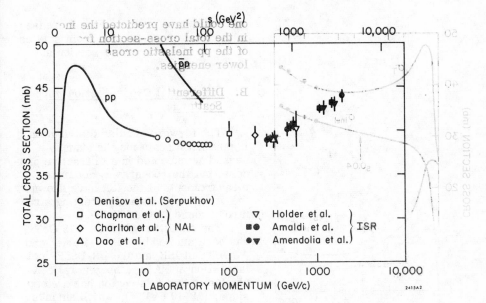

FIG. 2--Energy dependence of the total p-p cross-section.

independent of the luminosity, L.

$$\left[\frac{dt/dt\big|_{t=0}}{\text{Rate}} \quad \propto \quad \frac{\sigma_T^2 \cdot L}{\sigma_T \cdot L} = \sigma_T\right]$$

Such an experiment is planned in the near future. However, both groups ran for an appreciable time together in obtaining their respective cross-section data. If one assumes that the beam phase space and luminosity does not change round the ISR ring, then we could go through the exercise of taking the ratio of the measured quantities and derive an L-independent measurement of σ_T despite the fact that the experiments were performed in different interaction regions. The result of this interesting exercise is to confirm the detailed systematic measurements — the cross-section rises ∼ 3 mb with somewhat larger errors than in the two independent experiments.

In summary, the luminosity measurements seem to be well understood and in good agreement, and the rise in the pp total cross-section an established fact.

The CERN-Rome group[2] have also measured the elastic pp cross-section by integrating out their angular distribution data. They find the elastic cross-section rises by the same fraction as the total cross-section (i.e., ∼10%).

In Fig. 3 the total, elastic and inelastic cross-sections are plotted as function of energy.[5] It is interesting to note the inelastic cross-section rises very rapidly at first as new channels open up, and then increases smoothly above 6 GeV/c.

The cross-section data may be fit, through this energy region to $s^{0.04}$, although clearly such an overall energy dependence cannot continue. Thus

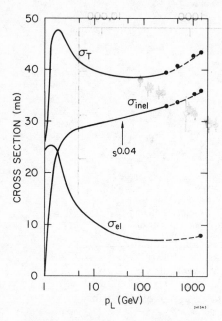

FIG. 3--Energy dependence of the total, elastic and inelastic cross-section for proton-proton collisions.

one could have predicted the increase in the total cross-section from studies of the pp inelastic cross-section at lower energies.

B. Differential Cross-Section in pp Scattering

The forward angular distribution in pp elastic scattering is sharply peaked as expected in a diffractive process, but the recent very accurate measurements at the ISR have shown the presence of some interesting structure, around $t \sim 0.15$ GeV^2.[6]

The small t region ($t < .15$ GeV^2) has been studied by CERN-Rome[7] and ACGHT[6] at ISR and the US-USSR[8] collaboration at NAL. The general conclusion is that this region has a steep slope, (12-13 GeV^{-2}), which shrinks like log s.

The large t region, $((.2 < t < .5)$ GeV^2), has been studied by the ACGHT group[6] at the ISR. This region has a somewhat flatter angular distribution, (about 2 units flatter than the small t region) and exhibits essentially no energy dependence.

Typical data is shown in Fig. 4. (a) shows data from the highest energy ISR studies of the ACGHT group[6]— the two regions of the scattering distribution are clearly visible. (b) shows data from the US-USSR collaboration[8] at one of the energies in their NAL experiment — this experiment measures entirely in the "small t region" discussed above. Notice in the very forward direction the observation of p-p coulomb scattering.

New results are available on the small t region from CERN-Rome and the NAL collaboration.

There has been much discussion as to whether there really are two distinct regions or whether the slope smoothly decreases as the scattering angle increases. New data from CERN-Rome[7] at $\sqrt{s} = 53$ GeV show that the slope is not continuously changing through the "small t region" but that one value of the slope parameter describes all of the data. If the cross-section within this small t interval is fit with $\frac{d\sigma}{dt} = \frac{d\sigma}{dt}\bigg|_0 e^{bt}$, then for

$0.01 < t < 0.06$ GeV^2, they find $\qquad b = 13.1 \pm .3$ GeV^{-2}

$0.04 < t < 0.16$ GeV^2, they find $\qquad b = 13.0 \pm .3$ GeV^{-2} .

Also the question of the variation of the parameter b as a function of energy has been studied by the US-USSR experiment[8] at NAL. This

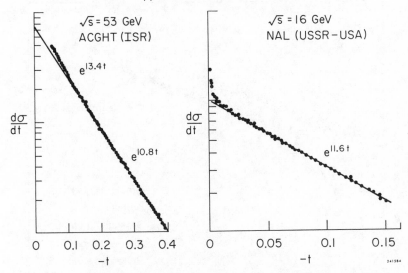

FIG. 4--Differential cross-sections, $d\sigma/dt$, taken at (a) the ISR by the ACGHT group, and (b) at NAL by the US-USSR collaboration.

experiment detects the recoil proton from beam-hydrogen gas jet collisions in an array of solid state counters. The results of this experiment are shown together with existing data for the small t region, in Fig. 5. The slope parameter b varies rapidly at small energy but for $s > 100$ GeV^2 the variation seems to settle down, and is consistent with a logarithmic growth. Fitting to data with $s > 100$ GeV^2 to the form

$$b(s) = b_0 + 2\alpha' \log s$$

the NAL group find

$$b_0 = 8.23 \pm 0.27 \text{ GeV}^2$$

$$\alpha' = 0.278 \pm 0.024 \text{ GeV}^2$$

The ACGHT group[9] have extended their studies of elastic pp scattering out to larger t by using a double arm wire chamber spectrometer with momentum analysis in both arms. This setup provides enough discrimination against the inelastic background that they can follow the cross-section down seven orders of magnitude. The scattering distributions are shown in Fig. 6. The break in the pp scattering cross-section at $t \sim 1.2$ GeV^2 observed at lower energies now becomes a sharp dip. The position of the dip and the height of the second peak are essentially independent of energy and have the properties of a diffractive dip and secondary maximum.

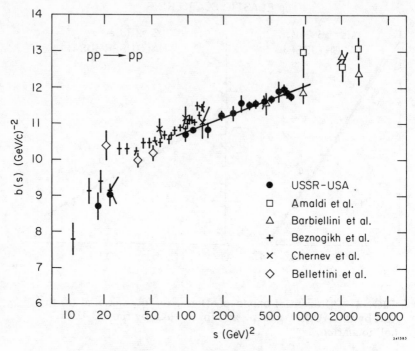

FIG. 5--The energy dependence of the slope of the differential cross-section, $d\sigma/dt$, in p-p elastic scattering.

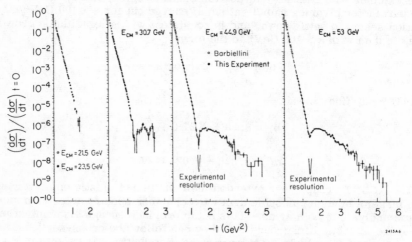

FIG. 6--The differential cross-section, $d\sigma/dt$, in pp elastic scattering out to very large t, as measured by the ACGHT group at the ISR.

These data on the total cross-section and differential cross-section provide an interesting picture of the structure of the proton: the small t data on $d\sigma/dt$ exhibiting the steep slope with fairly rapid shrinkage implies that the outer "shell" of the proton is growing as a function of energy, or more specifically that the radius is growing logarithmically; the large t data on $d\sigma/dt$ imply that the "core" of the proton is rather constant in size showing no appreciable dependence on energy; the total cross-section being very flat in the (20-200) GeV/c region implies a curious compensation between the growing size of the proton and a decreasing opacity, while the high energy rise in the cross-section indicates an end to this compensation with the opacity becoming constant or even increasing slightly with energy.

HIGH ENERGY INCLUSIVE pp SCATTERING

A. Missing Mass Distribution

It has been known for some time that inclusive pp scattering at high energy is characterized by a large quasi-elastic peak which is associated with the diffractive production of high mass states[10] (see Fig. 7). It is interesting to study the energy, mass and momentum transfer dependencies of this process to learn more of the dynamics of diffraction. A considerable amount of new data on this topic has become available recently.

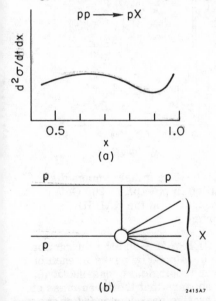

In Fig. 8 the missing mass plots from the NAL bubble chamber experiments[11] are given. The HBC pictures are scanned for slow protons which can be identified by their ionisation; for those events so identified the missing mass is then calculated. The lowest masses are seen to be produced with almost constant cross-section between 100 and 400 GeV/c.[12] For larger masses the cross-section is falling almost linearly with energy. An alternative display is in terms of the Feynman x variable, the fractional longitudinal momentum, p_L/p_{max} or $x = (1 - M^2/s)$. The 100 and 400 GeV/c data are shown, plotted as a function of x, in Fig. 9.[13] From this plot, we see the cross-section for $x \approx 1$ increasing with energy, as it must if the cross section at small masses is constant in energy. This region is presumably the classical diffraction dissociation region. For $x \sim .6$ to $.8$ region the cross-section scales in x.

FIG. 7--(a) The invariant cross-section $d^2\sigma/dtdx$, as a function of x, for the process pp$\rightarrow$pX. The cross-section exhibits a large hump for $0.2 < x < .8$ which is characteristic of the multiparticle production region, then a minimum for $0.8 < x < .9$, followed by a sharp peak for $0.9 < x < 1.0$ which is characteristic of diffractive quasi-elastic scattering shown diagrammatically in (b).

334

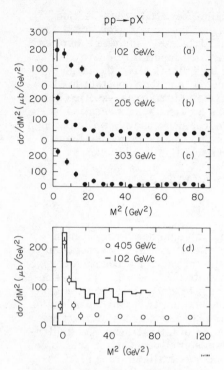

FIG. 8--The missing mass distribution in pp → pX at 100, 200, 300 and 400 GeV/c, as measured in the NAL HBC experiments.

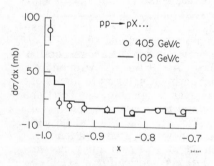

FIG. 9--The invariant cross-section for pp → pX as a function of X for the 100 and 400 GeV/c NAL HBC experiments.

The intermediate region of x ~ .95 seems to show some energy dependence indicating that the quasi-elastic peak does not quite scale in x at these energies.

The 200 GeV/c missing mass data[14] is shown again in Fig. 10 and broken down in the various topological contributions in Fig. 11. The cross-sections in the small mass region (up to masses of 4 GeV), is seen

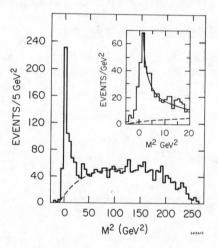

FIG. 10--The missing mass distribution in pp → pX at 200 GeV/c as measured in the NAL HBC experiment.

to fall off like M^{-2} and the diffraction peak is developed by peaks in each of the lower topological cross-sections. It also appears that the mean mass of the diffractive peak increases as the topology or multiplicity, n, increases. The total cross-section of this low mass diffraction peak is estimated at ~6 mb, independent of energy.

The same behavior is observed at ISR energies where the CHLM[10,15] and ACGHT[16] groups have demonstrated the existence of the low mass diffractive enhancement. In Fig. 12 the missing mass distribution from

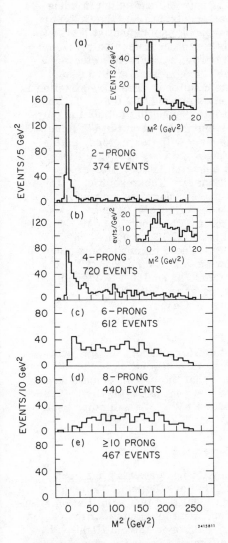

FIG. 11--The missing mass distribution in pp→pX at 200 GeV/c, for each topology, as measured in the 200 GeV/c NAL HBC experiment.

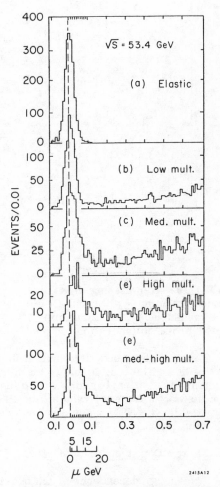

FIG. 12--The missing mass distribution in pp → pX at the ISR, as measured by the ACGHT group.

the two arm spectrometer ACGHT experiment, is shown. They are able to make a rough multiplicity assignment using a scintillation counter hodoscope round the aperture of each spectrometer. There is clear evidence for the increase of mean mass in the diffractive peak as the multiplicity increases.

It is interesting to note that the term "low mass" peak is purely relative and that these diffractive peaks include masses up to 7 GeV.

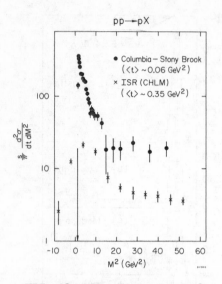

pp → pX

• Columbia – Stony Brook
($\langle t \rangle \sim 0.06$ GeV^2)
× ISR (CHLM)
($\langle t \rangle \sim 0.35$ GeV^2)

FIG. 13--The missing mass distribution in pp → pX at 300 GeV/c as measured by the Columbia-Stonybrook collaboration.

Figure 13 shows the missing mass spectrum from the Columbia-Stonybrook experiment at NAL.[17] This experiment uses polyethelene and carbon targets and detects the recoil proton in an array of solid state counters. The normalization is effected by counting the d, T, He^3 and He^4 production in both the polyethelene and carbon targets simultaneously with the protons, thus allowing for a very accurate subtraction and hence reliable proton cross-sections.[18] The resolution in missing mass squared is very good, being of order of 1 GeV^2 near x ~ 1, whereas the CHLM group has $\delta M^2 \sim 9$ GeV^2 and the ACGHT group has $\delta M^2 \sim 20$ GeV^2. Their missing mass plot shows a very sharp peak with some structure around 3-4 GeV^2 and becoming essentially flat for masses above 16 GeV^2.

This missing mass distribution is quite different from the ISR data. Part of this difference is due to the missing mass resolution of the different experiments, but part is also due to the fact that the measurements have been made at different t values; the ISR experiment has typically t ~ 0.8 GeV^2, while the NAL experiment had t ~ 0.06 GeV^2. We will come back to this point later.

B. Energy Dependence, or Scaling

The energy dependence of the quasi-elastic pp scattering has been studied at NAL from (50-400) GeV/c by the Rutgers-Imperial College group.[19] The recoil proton is detected and identified in a scintillation counter telescope with a total absorption counter. The momentum of the proton is determined from time of flight measurements over 186 cm flight path.

The invariant cross-section for four different t values is given in Fig. 14 for five energies between 50 and 400 GeV. For x values close to 0.8 there is very little energy dependence, while for x values around 0.9, close to the quasi-elastic peak, quite considerable variation is observed through this energy region. In Fig. 15 the invariant cross-section is plotted against $s^{-1/2}$ for the four t ranges measured, for x values of 0.83 and 0.91. Again substantial s-dependence is clearly visible.

They fit the data to the form

$$s \frac{d2\sigma}{dtdM^2} = A(x) \, e^{b(x)t} \, [1 + B(X) \, s^{-1/2}].$$

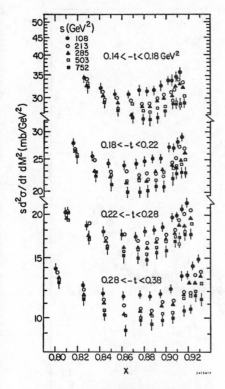

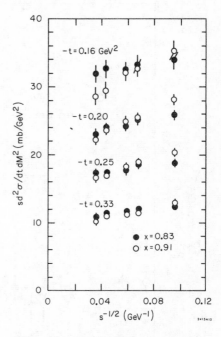

FIG. 15--The invariant cross-section for pp → pX as a function of $s^{-1/2}$ for x = 0.83 and 0.91.

FIG. 14--The invariant cross-section for pp → pX as a function of x, for $100 \leq s \leq 750$ GeV^2, as measured by the Rutgers-Imperial College group. Data is presented in four t intervals.

This form represents the data well, with b being essentially independent of x and having a value of ~6 GeV^{-2}. The best fit to the data gave

x = 0.83	A = 71 ± 7 mb/GeV^2	B = 1.9 ± .7 GeV
x = 0.91	A = 66 ± 3 mb/GeV^2	B = 4.3 ± .4 GeV

Through the NAL energy range, there is ~20% change in the cross-section for x values near unity, and the fits to the data imply that the variation remaining in the cross-section through the ISR energy range will be less than 10%.

The fall-off in the cross-section for x ~ .95 as measured in the four NAL HBC experiments and discussed above in Fig. 9 is also compatible with this s-dependence.

The experimental results from the CHLM group[15] at the ISR are given in Fig. 16, and show that in this region the cross-section is observed to

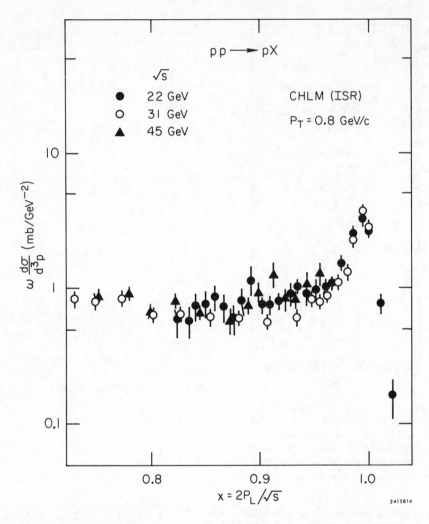

FIG. 16--The invariant cross-section for pp → pX as a function of x, for a fixed $P_T = 0.8$ GeV^2. Data comes from the CHLM group at the ISR, for $\sqrt{s}$= 22, 31 and 45 GeV.

scale to within 10%. Note that both the ISR and NAL experiments are performed at intermediate t values.

In summary then, the invariant cross-section $s(d2\sigma/dtdM^2)$ is observed to be almost energy independent for x values of order 0.8 from 50 GeV/c through 2500 GeV/c; for x $\sim$ 0.9 the cross-section is observed to have a component with $s^{-1/2}$ dependence which amounts to a 20% effect through the NAL energy region ((50-400) GeV/c), but which is <10% effect through the ISR range (200-2500 GeV/c).

C. Momentum Transfer Dependence

The momentum transfer dependence of the production of the diffraction peak has been studied at NAL by the bubble chamber experiments[11] and the Columbia-Stonybrook experiment[17] and at the ISR by the CHLM[15] and ACGHT[16] groups.

The t-dependence as a function of the missing mass squared,$(x=1-M^2/s)$, is shown in Fig. 17 from the 200 GeV/c HBC experiment.[14] For small masses, the slope of the inelastic diffractive scattering is close to, but a little less than, the elastic scattering slope. As the masses increase,

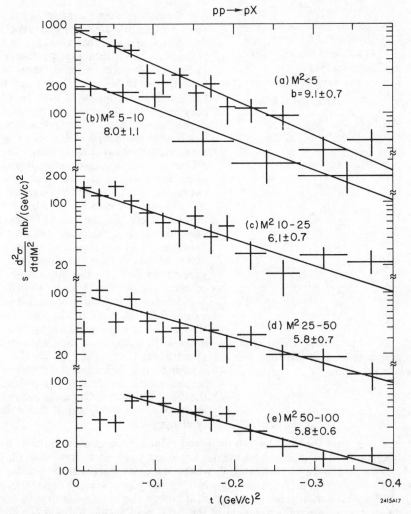

FIG. 17--The differential cross-section, $d\sigma/dt$, for pp → pX, as a function of the missing mass. Data comes from the 200 GeV/c NAL HBC experiment.

the slope decreases, until one reaches masses corresponding to an x value of ~ 0.9. For masses beyond that there seems to be only a weak M dependence left.

In Fig. 18 the t-dependence of the diffraction peak is shown, from experiments at NAL and the ISR. The cross-section is exponential but with at least two slopes. The dashed line shows a fit which behaves like e^{-7t} at small t and e^{-4t} at large t.

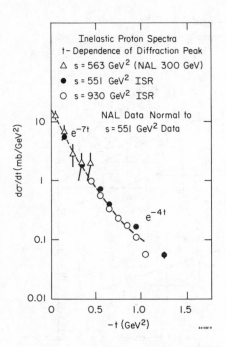

FIG. 18--The t-dependence for the production of the diffraction peak in pp → pX.

D. Aside on the Missing Mass Distribution

From the above discussion it seems plausible that the differential cross-section, $d\sigma/dt$, is mass dependent. The diffraction peak studied in Fig. 18 contains a wide range of masses (up to $M^2 \sim 50$ GeV^2) and the two exponential shape of that $d\sigma/dt$ may be just a reflection of this mass dependence. Such a dependence would imply that the shape of the missing mass distribution would change for different t values, and perhaps account for some of the difference between the ISR[15,16] and NAL (Columbia-Stonybrook)[17] mass plots (Fig. 13). Indeed, if one assigns an e^{-7t} dependence to the peak masses, and an e^{-4t} dependence to the large mass region ($M^2 \sim 20$ GeV^2) then quantitative agreement between the measured missing mass distributions results.

Further, if such a dependence exists then the peak to shoulder ratio (low mass to high mass ratio) should be seen to change for measurements at different t. In Fig. 19, 20 the missing mass squared distribution as measured by the CHLM group[15] at the ISR, for four different t ranges is shown. Clear evidence of this effect is observed.

Thus it seems that in fact the different missing mass distributions are in good agreement — there exist three separate regions in the mass plot:

1. The threshold region ($x \approx 1.0$) where the cross-section, $d^2\sigma/dtdx$, is growing linearly with s (i.e., scaling in M^2) and has a steep t dependence;

2. The diffraction peak ($1.0 > x > .9$) where the cross-section is nearly constant in s — some 20% variation in the NAL region (50-400) GeV/c and less than 10% variation at the ISR (200-2500) GeV/c, and with a $d\sigma/dt$ that depends on M^2, becoming flatter as M^2 increases.

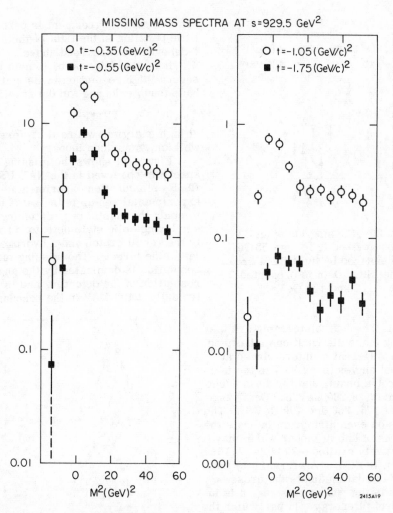

MISSING MASS SPECTRA AT s=929.5 GeV^2

FIG. 19--Missing mass spectra for pp → pX as measured by the CHLM group at the ISR, at s = 930 GeV^2 and for t = 0.35, 0.55, 1.05 and 1.75 GeV^2.

3. Multiparticle production region ($.8 < x < .2$), where the cross-section seems essentially independent of s and where dσ/dt is rather flat ($\sim e^{-4t}$) and varying slowly with s and M^2.

The mass dependence in the diffraction peak appears to be compatible with a 1/M^2 fall off:
1. The 200 GeV/c HBC expt. (Ref. 14)(see Fig. 10).
2. ACGHT group[16] at ISR find dσ/dM$^2 \propto$ (M^{-2})1.15 ± .1.
3. CHLM group[17] at ISR find dσ/dM$^2 \propto$ (M^{-2})0.98 ± .1.
4. Columbia-Stonybrook[17] at NAL find dσ/dM^2 compatible with M^{-2}.

342

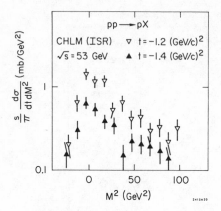

FIG. 20--Missing mass distribution at fixed t, for $\sqrt{s}$ = 53 GeV, as measured by the CHLM group at the ISR. Data is presented for t = 1.2 and 1.4 GeV^2.

region. The four histograms are the missing mass distributions measured by four different counters placed at different angles (near 90°) to the incident proton beam, and for an incident momentum of 260 GeV/c. Data were taken at 175, 260 and 400 GeV/c. The arrows on each histogram indicate the positions of known isobar which may be diffractively excited — N(1450), N(1560), N(1688), N(1780). A preliminary analysis of the data indicate the cross-section in the resonances region is independent of energy. In particular the cross-section in the 1400 MeV region exhibits a very steep t dependence, e^{-15t}, and that the NAL cross-section is the same as that measured at 20 GeV/c, to within 20%.

Similar observations are reported by a high resolution experiment by the Rutgers-Imperial College group.[21] Their resolution around masses of ∼2 GeV is ∼10 MeV, and for masses ∼7 GeV it is ∼50 MeV. Clear signals are observed for the production of N*(1688) and for N*(2190).

The π^-p[22] and pp HBC[23] experiments at 200 GeV/c both studied the

(This apparent agreement is perhaps a little puzzling in the light of the s- and t-dependence discussed above.)

It is also interesting to note that several high resolution investigations have found evidence for the reaction

$$pp \rightarrow pN^*$$

at high energies, where N* refers to well known nucleon isobars.

Figure 21 shows the missing mass spectrum observed in the NAL US-USSR collaboration experiment.[20] The experimental set-up is the same used to study the elastic p-p scattering,[8] employing solid state detectors to idenfy the recoil proton and a hydrogen gas jet as the target. The missing mass resolution is dominated by the angular resolution of the detectors and is typically ±100 MeV in the resonance

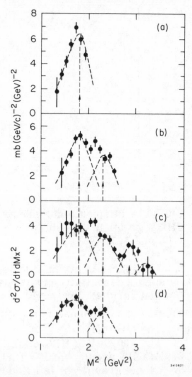

FIG. 21--Missing mass distribution in pp → pN* for an incident proton energy of 260 GeV/c.

exclusive reaction

$$\binom{\pi^-}{p} p \rightarrow \pi^+ \pi^- p \binom{\pi^-}{p}$$

The mass distribution for the $p\pi^+\pi^-$ system clearly shows evidence of the production of N(1450) and N(1700) resonances.

In summary then, there is good evidence for the production of low mass isobars in high energy collisions and that their cross-sections seem to roughly scale in M^2 and show steep t dependence.

E. Back to Momentum Transfer Studies

Above we had shown that there was evidence that the slope of the differential cross-section for the diffraction peak became flatter as the diffracted mass increased, and that the $d\sigma/dt$ for the whole peak (averaging over all masses) was exponential but with at least two slopes.

In Fig. 22 the s-dependence of the $d\sigma/dt$ is studied. The data comes from the Rutgers-Imperial College group[19] at NAL. For x = 0.87 the differential cross-section, $d\sigma/dt$, is shown for s = 108 and 752 GeV^2. Essentially no energy dependence is observed.

The $d\sigma/dt$ as measured by the Columbia-Stonybrook group[17] at NAL, for missing mass squared around 40 GeV^2 is shown in Fig. 23, together with data from Rutgers-Imperial College[19] and from the CHLM[15] group at ISR. Good agreement is observed between the measurements. A flattening of the cross-section is observed for small t values (t <.2 GeV^2). For smaller masses, this effect becomes a turnover in the very forward direction, with a maximum to the cross-section at t ~ 0.1 GeV^2, as shown in Fig. 24.

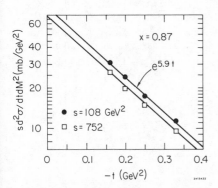

FIG. 22--Differential cross-section for pp → pX for x=0.87 and for s = 108 and 752 GeV^2.

Again the data comes from the Columbia-Stonybrook experiment.[17] Corrected data from a previous run by the same group at 200 GeV/c is also shown.[24]

Similar behavior is observed in some preliminary data from the (100 + 400) GeV/c HBC experiments at NAL.[25] In Fig. 25 and 26 the p_T^2 distribution is shown for small masses and large masses respectively. The low mass spectrum shows the same tendency to a forward turnover as the NAL counter experiment, whereas the distribution for large missing masses seems to be quite linear.

F. Multiplicity in Diffractive pp Collisions

As we noted earlier when discussing the structure of the low mass diffractive peak, these events are characterized by a smaller multiplicity, n, than the average. The NAL HBC experiments[11] report that the mean

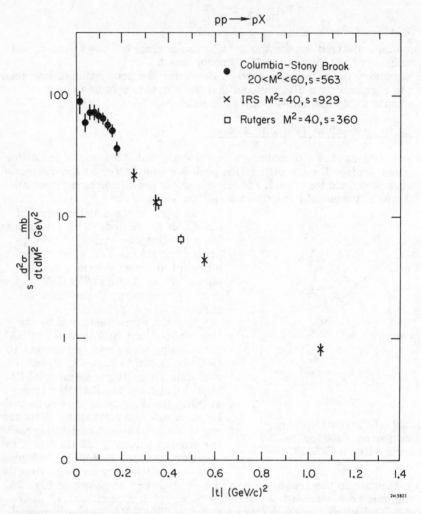

FIG. 23--Differential cross-section for pp → pX for missing mass squared ~40 GeV^2.

diffractive multiplicity, $\langle n_d \rangle$, is about half the total mean multiplicity.

$$\text{i.e.} \quad \langle n_d \rangle \sim \frac{1}{2} \langle n_{all} \rangle$$

At higher energies, the CHLM group[15] at the ISR report

$$\text{for} \quad x > 0.99 \qquad \langle n \rangle \sim 2.8 \pm .5$$

$$x \sim 0.8 \qquad \langle n \rangle \sim 6.7 \pm 1.0$$

is keeping with the NAL observation.

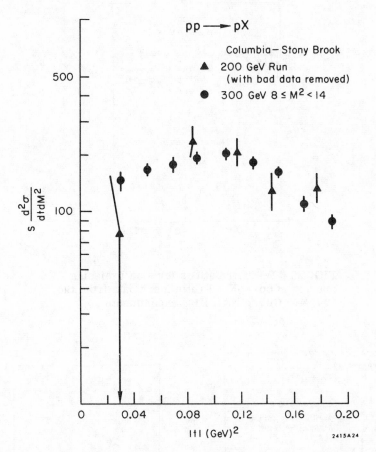

FIG. 24--Differential cross-section for pp→pX for $8 \leq M^2 \leq 14$ GeV^2.

We also noted earlier that the multiplicity increases as the mass in the diffraction peak increases. An interesting comment[14] on this increase is shown in Fig. 27 where the multiplicity in the breakup of the diffractive system is plotted against the mass squared of the system. The solid line is the total multiplicity in pp collisions plotted in such a way that the total energy in the pp collision is called M^2. This implies that the total multiplicity in proton-proton collisions and its energy dependence is similar to that in Pomeron-proton collisions.

PION DIFFRACTION

The first systematic study of high energy pion-proton collisions has been reported to this meeting by the Berkeley-NAL collaboration working on a

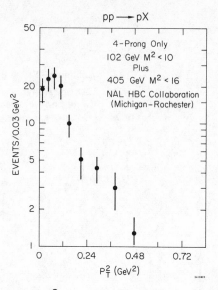

FIG. 25--P_T^2 distributions for small missing masses in pp → pX. Preliminary data from the 100, 400 GeV/c NAL HBC experiments.

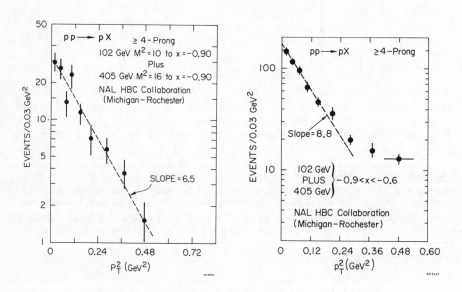

FIG. 26--(a,b) P_T^2 distribution for large missing masses in pp → pX. Preliminary data from the 100, 400 GeV/c NAL HBC experiments.

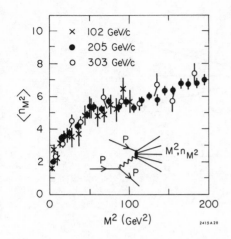

FIG. 27--Multiplicity distribution as a function of the mass of the diffracting system. The solid line is the total multiplicity distribution in pp collisions with the center of mass energy taken equal to M^2.

205 GeV/c π^-p exposure of the 30" NAL HBC.[22,26] Their results are briefly outlined below.

They have analyzed the exclusive process

$$\pi^- p \rightarrow \pi^- \pi^+ \pi^- p$$

and claim to have an event sample with less than 25% background. They see strong evidence of the pion diffracting into 3π, and the target proton diffracting into a ($p\pi^+\pi^-$) system, Fig. 28 and 29. The cross-section for both these processes is estimated to be 1.5 mb.

In addition, the diffraction of a $\pi \rightarrow \pi^*$ has been studied using the same technique as in the p-p HBC experiments. The pictures were scanned for events in which a slow recoil proton could be identified by ionisation. This selection works well for proton momenta up to 1.5 GeV/c.

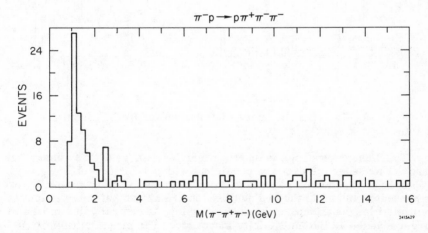

FIG. 28--The effective mass distribution of ($\pi^+\pi^-\pi^-$) from 200 GeV/c $\pi^- p \rightarrow \pi^+\pi^-\pi^- p$.

The missing mass distribution obtained from these events is shown in Fig. 30. A low mass peak is observed, extending out to $M^2 \sim 20$ GeV^2, associated with the diffractive excitation of the incoming pion.

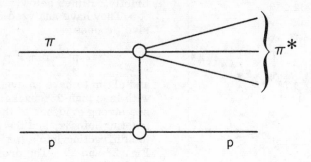

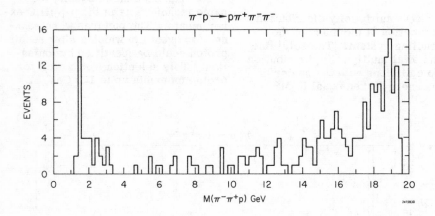

FIG. 29--The effective mass distribution for ($p\pi^+\pi^-$) from 200 GeV/c $\pi^-p \to p\pi^+\pi^-\pi^-$.

The mass dependence is shown in Fig. 31, where over a substantial range of masses, the data are consistent with a $1/M^2$ fall-off.

In Fig. 32, the composition of this low mass diffractive peak by topology is presented and as in the p-p studies, one remarks that only the lowest multiplicities contribute to the peak. Again, the central value moves to larger masses as the multiplicity increases. The mean multiplicity in the diffraction peak is about half that of the overall multiplicity ($<n_d>^{charged} \sim 4$, $<n_{all}>^{charged} \sim 8$) and increases with M^2.

The differential cross-section, $d\sigma/dt$, is shown, by topology in Fig. 33 and for two different mass regions in Fig. 34. No turnover in the forward direction is observed, nor any sizable mass dependence of the slope.

An interesting factorization test has been made possible by the study of the four body exclusive reaction in p-p and π^-p collisions at 205 GeV/c.[27]

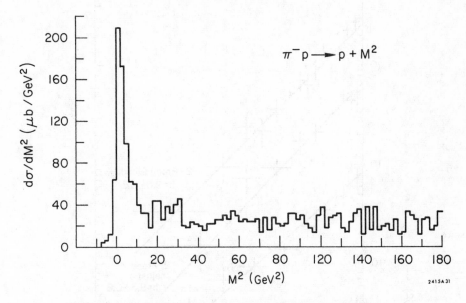

FIG. 30--The missing mass squared distribution for
$\pi^-p \to pX$ at 200 GeV/c.

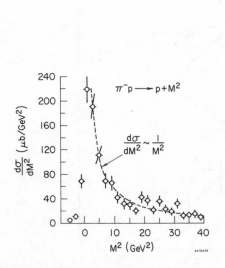

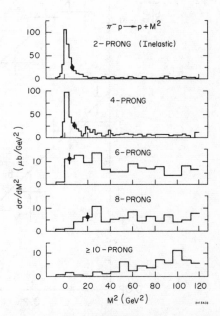

FIG. 31--The missing mass squared
distribution for $\pi^-p \to pX$ at 200 GeV/c.

FIG. 32--The missing mass squared
distribution, topology by topology,
for $\pi^-p \to pX$ at 200 GeV/c.

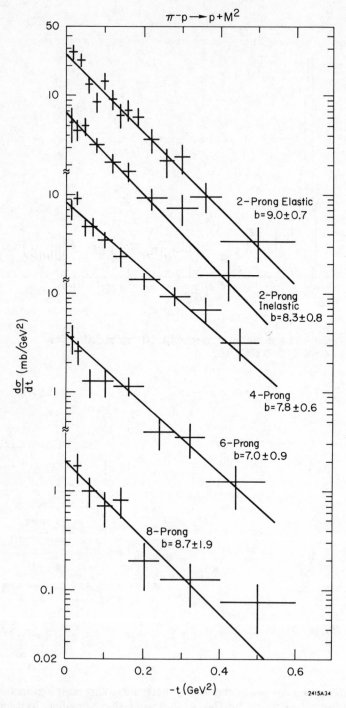

FIG. 33--The momentum transfer distribution, topology by topology, for $\pi^-p \to pX$ at 200 GeV/c.

The diffraction of the target proton into a $(p\pi^+\pi^-)$ system has been isolated—

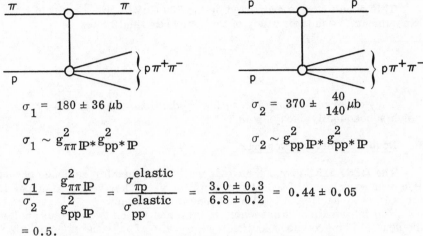

$$\sigma_1 = 180 \pm 36 \, \mu b \qquad\qquad \sigma_2 = 370 \pm \frac{40}{140} \, \mu b$$

$$\sigma_1 \sim g^2_{\pi\pi \, \mathbb{P}*} g^2_{pp*\mathbb{P}} \qquad\qquad \sigma_2 \sim g^2_{pp\,\mathbb{P}*} g^2_{pp*\mathbb{P}}$$

$$\frac{\sigma_1}{\sigma_2} = \frac{g^2_{\pi\pi\,\mathbb{P}}}{g^2_{pp\,\mathbb{P}}} = \frac{\sigma^{elastic}_{\pi p}}{\sigma^{elastic}_{pp}} = \frac{3.0 \pm 0.3}{6.8 \pm 0.2} = 0.44 \pm 0.05$$

$$= 0.5.$$

The factorization works remarkably well!

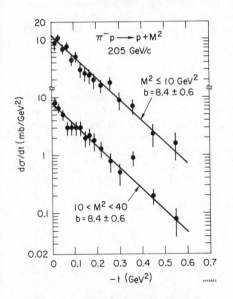

FIG. 34--The momentum transfer distribution for $\pi^- p \to pX$ at 200 GeV/c, for $M^2 < 10$ GeV^2 and $10 < M^2 < 40$ GeV^2.

OTHER COMMENTS

A. Strong Δ^{++} Production Observed at High Energies

The 300 GeV/c NAL HBC collaboration[28] have studied inclusive Δ^{++} production

$$pp \to \Delta^{++} X^0$$

and found a surprisingly large production cross-section. In fact between 6.6 GeV/c and 300 GeV/c the cross-section has only fallen by a factor of two—

$\sigma(pp \to \Delta^{++} X)$ at 6.6 GeV/c is (10 ± 1) mb

and at 300 GeV/c is (4.3 ± 5) mb.

Prompted by the above result the MIT HBC group[29] studied the process

$$\pi^- p \to \Delta^{++} X$$

at 15 GeV/c using the same technique for event selection as the 300 GeV/c pp experiment. In addition they studied the exclusive final states which gave rise to the Δ^{++} events. Their conclusion, summarized in Fig. 35, is that the Δ^{++} state is produced as a decay product of higher mass N* iso-bars which are produced diffractively.

This conclusion is supported by the 200 GeV/c pp,[23] and π^-p NAL HBC experiments,[22] in their study of the four body final states

$$pp \rightarrow p\pi^+\pi^-p$$

$$\pi^-p \rightarrow \pi^-\pi^+\pi^-p .$$

They observed strong diffractive production of the $(p\pi^+\pi^-)$ system which subsequently decays with $\Delta^{++}\pi^-$.

B. Double Pomeron Exchange

The DESY HBC group[30] have recently searched for evidence of double-Pomeron exchange in 24 GeV/c p-p collisions. They report an upper limit for the cross-section of such a process to be ≤ 30 μb.

New information is presented to this meeting on two careful studies of the double-Pomeron contribution to $\pi^-p \rightarrow \pi^-\pi^+\pi^-p$,[31] and pp $\rightarrow p\pi^+\pi^-p$[32] final states at 200 GeV/c. A few events are isolated with the correct charge ordering and large rapidity gaps between the dipion system and the projec-tile and target particles, which could be associated with this production mechanism (see Fig. 36). An upper limit of 50 μb cross-section is reported in both experiments.

C. Triple Regge Phenomenology

Analysis of the single particle distributions at high energies may be done through the application of triple-Regge theory. One wants to calculate the cross-section for processes of the type (a) in Fig. 37. Applying an equiva-lent of the optical theorem in 2 $\rightarrow$ 2 body scattering, the total cross-section is then given by the square of the forward scattering amplitude — so for processes of the type (a) we square the forward amplitude by multiplying by itself, shown diagramatically in Fig. 37(b). This is then approximated by the triple-Regge diagram — Fig. 37(c).

The cross-section obtained from this exercise is then written as

$$s\frac{d^2\sigma}{dtdM^2} = \sum_{1,2,3} \frac{R_{123}(t)}{s} \left(\frac{s}{M^2}\right)^{\alpha_1(t) + \alpha_2(t)} M^{2\alpha_3(0)}$$

$$= \sum_{1,2,3} \left(\frac{1}{s}\right)^{1-\alpha_3(0)} R_{123}(t) \left(\frac{s}{M^2}\right)^{\alpha_1(t) + \alpha_2(t) - \alpha_3(0)}$$

It is supposed that such a description should be valid for (s/M^2) and M^2 large.

One then tries to fit the data as a function of s, M^2 and t with an appro-priate selection of the trajectories α_1, α_2 and α_3 (see Fig. 37). For Pomeron exchanges, P, $\alpha(0)$ is taken to be 1, and for Regge terms, R,

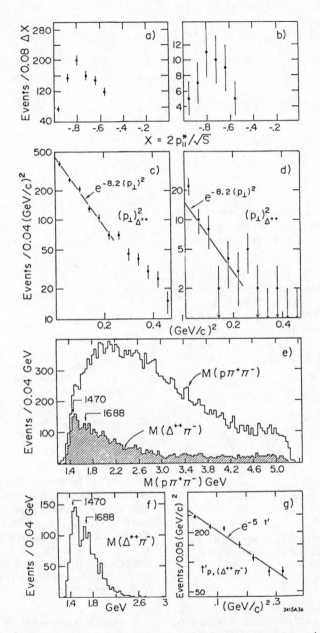

FIG. 35--Figures 2a and 2b compare the x distribution for Δ^{++} produced at 15 GeV/c and 303 GeV/c respectively. Figures 2c and 2d compare the $(P_T)^2_\Delta$ for 15 GeV/c and 303 GeV/c respectively. Figure 2e is the invariant mass of the $p\pi^+\pi^-$ system. The shaded area in the invariant mass of the $\Delta^{++}\pi^-$ system. Figure 2f displays the invariant mass of $\Delta^{++}\pi^-$ where the x of the π^- is between -0.2 and +0.05. Figure 2g is the t' distribution for the events in Fig. 2f.

354

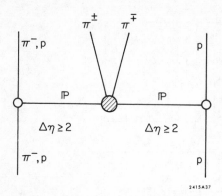

FIG. 36--Diagramatic representation of the Double Pomeron Exchange process for $\pi^-p + \pi^-\pi^+\pi^-p$ and $pp \to p\pi^+\pi^-p$.

$\alpha(0)$ is taken to be 1/2. Excluding interference terms, there are four leading terms to be used in fitting the data — PPP, PPR, RRP, and RRR. The s-dependence for fixed x and M^2-dependence of each is summarized in the table and in Fig. 38.

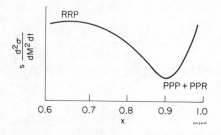

FIG. 38--A qualitative map of the s- and x-dependence of the four triple-Regge terms.

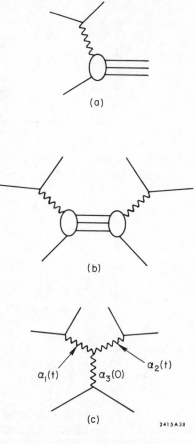

FIG. 37--The triple-Regge calculation of the single particle inclusive cross-section. (a) is the forward scattering amplitude for the single particle inclusive process, and (b) represents diagramatically the square of that amplitude. (c) is the triple-Regge generalization of diagram (b).

If the PPP contribution is not zero,[33] it is expected to dominate at large s and large M^2. Fits to the ISR data[34] show that the data is compatible with substantial PPP coupling, but important contributions from the other trajectories are also required and the fits are by no means unique.

The most systematic attempt to study the triple-Regge question has been performed by the Rutgers-Imperial College group at NAL.[17,35] Their data on the single particle inclusive cross-section spans a large range in the

Triple Regge Term	s-dependence (fixed x)	M^2-dependence, (x-dependence) (fixed s, t)	
PPP	constant	$1/M^2$,	$1/(1-x)$
PPR	$1/\sqrt{s}$	$1/M^3$,	$1/(1-x)^{3/2}$
RRP	constant	constant,	(constant)
RRR	$1/\sqrt{s}$	$1/M$,	$1/(1-x)^{1/2}$
		$M^2 = (1-x)s$	

important variables:

$$100 \leq s \leq 750 \ \text{GeV}^2$$
$$0.14 \leq t \leq 0.38 \ \text{GeV}^2$$
$$5 \leq s/M^2 \leq 12.5$$

and has already been discussed (see Fig. 14 and 15) with respect to the scaling behavior of the cross-section. The wide energy range available in this experiment allows a clean separation of the energy dependent terms, PPR and RRR, from the energy independent terms, PPP and RRP.

The data was divided into four t intervals — $0.14 < t < 0.18$, $0.18 < t < 0.22$, $0.22 < t < 0.28$, $0.28 < t < 0.38 \ \text{GeV}^2$, and fit to the triple-Regge cross-section formula given above, with the couplings being left free in each t interval.

Five fits were attempted: (1) in which the four leading triple-Regge terms were used with $\alpha_P = 1 + 0.25t$ and $\alpha_R = 0.5 + t$. This fit was quite poor, not reproducing the dip structure for $x \sim 0.88$. It is interesting to note that the PPP term exhibits a dip in the forward direction with a maximum at $t \sim 0.2 \ \text{GeV}^2$ — see Fig. 39; (2) which uses the same trajectories as in fit (1) but only fits the data for $x > 0.84$. This fit is much better but still not very good. The PPP term still shows the forward turnover; (3) in which the trajectory of the RRP terms is taken to be $\alpha = 0.2 + t$ (after Miettinen and Roberts)[36] to allow for the effects of lower lying trajectories. This provides a much better fit to the data, but now the PPP term has no forward turnover — see Fig. 39; (4) is very similar to fit (3) but an explicit parametrization is used for a $\pi\pi P$ term, (due to Bishari)[37], together with the four leading triple Regge terms with conventional trajectories. This gives a rather good fit to the data, and no forward structure to the PPP term; (5) in which the RRP term is replaced by an exponential e^{-cx}, as suggested by Capella et al.[38] This provides the steeper x-dependence required by the data and indeed this parametrization gives the best fit. Again, the PPP term shows no forward turnover — see Fig. 39.

It is interesting to note that despite the uncertainty and variation in the PPP term between the several fits tried, the energy dependent term — PPR — seems very stable, quite model independent and rather well determined.

In summary, a clear separation between the s-dependent and s-independent terms has been observed. For the s-dependent terms the RRR contribution is small and negligible, while the PPR contribution is well

356

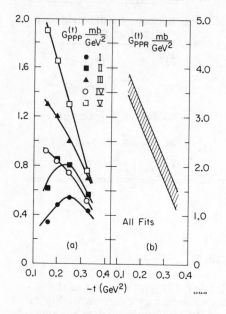

FIG. 39--Plot of G_{PPP} and G_{PPR} versus t for the five fits discussed in the text. For all fits $G_{PPR}(t)$ lies within the shaded band. The shape and magnitude of $G_{PPP}(t)$ depends on the fit assumption.

determined. The energy independent part requires both the PPP and RRP terms, and no unambiguous isolation of the PPP coupling seems possible at this time. Fits with conventional trajectories yielded a PPP coupling which peaked for $t \sim 0.2$ GeV^2 and turned over in the forward direction, while better fits to the data (with modified trajectories) had a quite structureless PPP t-dependence. Therefore not much light can be shed on the question of whether g_{PPP} vanishes at $t = 0$. To make more progress in studying the triple-Regge phenomenology and in particular to identify unambiguously the PPP contribution new data extending further into the diffraction peak, to x values nearer 1, are urgently required.

CONCLUSIONS

It has been interesting to see the new results from NAL providing detailed systematic data on high energy collisions and nicely complimenting the ISR data to give new and exciting insights on the structure of the proton.

The results on the s- and t-dependence of the elastic pp scattering and the s-dependence of the total cross section provide an interesting picture of the proton structure. It will be very interesting to see the total cross-section, elastic cross-section and real part measurements for K^+p scattering at NAL, where the features we have observed in pp scattering should also emerge.

The single particle inclusive studies have shown the existence of a large energy independent cross-section for the production of a low-mass peak. This process is assumed to be diffractive excitation of the target or projectile particle and has a cross-section almost equal to the elastic scattering cross-section, viz $\sigma_d \sim 6$ mb. At high energies the "low" mass peak in fact includes quite large masses (e.g., it extends up to masses of 5-7 GeV). This diffractive peak is made up mainly from the low multiplicity events, the mean multiplicity for events in the peak being about half the mean multiplicity for all events. The multiplicity increases with the mass of the diffracted system. Very similar properties are observed for the diffraction of pions or protons. The s-dependence and the x-dependence of the data is quite consistent with a strong PPP coupling, but no unambiguous determinations of the PPP properties has been achieved.

ACKNOWLEDGMENTS

I would like to thank Prof. F. Gilman and Dr. R. Cashmore for reading the manuscript and for their helpful comments.

REFERENCES

1. D.W.G.S. Leith, "Diffraction Dissociation" SLAC report no. SLAC-PUB-1141, Review talk presented at XVI International Conference on High Energy Physics, Batavia, Illinois; D.W.G.S. Leith "Diffraction Phenomena" SLAC report no. SLAC-PUB-1263; G. Kane "Phenomenology of Diffractive Reactions" Rutherford Preprint RPP/T/20; H. Lubatti, "Diffraction Dissociation of Hadrons", Washington University Preprint VTL PUB 9.
2. U. Amaldi, et al., Phys. Letters 44 B, 112 (1973).
3. S. R. Amendolia, et al., Phys. Letters 44 B, 119 (1973).
4. U. Amaldi and G. Bellettini, (private communication).
5. U. Amaldi, private communication on a comment by D.R.O. Morrison.
6. G. Barbiellini, et al., Phys. Letters B 39, 663 (1972) and Phys. Letters B 35, 355 (1971).
7. U. Amaldi, et al., paper submitted to the APS Division of Particles and Fields Meeting, Berkeley, August 1973.
8. V. Bartenev, et al., NAL Pub 73/54. Paper submitted to the APS Division of Particles and Fields Meeting, Berkeley, August 1973.
9. G. Giacomelli, Rapporteur's talk at XVI International Conference on High Energy Physics, Chicago-Batavia, 1972.
10. M. G. Albrow, et al., CERN preprint and submitted to the XVI International Conference on High Energy Physics, Chicago-Batavia, 1972.
11. There are four HBC pp experiments at NAL: (a) 102 GeV/c — Michigan-Rochester collaboration; (b) 205 GeV/c — ANL-NAL collaboration; (c) 303 GeV/c — NAL-UCLA collaboration; (d) 405 GeV/c — Michigan-Rochester collaboration.
12. From a compilation by J. Whitmore (private communication).
13. J. Vander Velde, (private communication).
14. S. J. Barish, et al., ANL/HEP 7338 and paper presented to the APS Division of Particles and Fields Meeting, Berkeley, August, 1972.
15. M. G. Albrow, et al., CERN preprint, Dec., 1972.
16. Aachen-CERN-Harvard-Genoa-Torino report, communicated by G. Goldhaber.
17. R. Schamberger, et al., Paper submitted to the APS Division of Particles and Fields Meeting, Berkeley, August 1973.
18. S. Childress, et al ., Paper submitted to the APS Division of Particles and Fields Meeting, Berkeley, August 1973.
19. K. Abe, et al., "Measurement of pp → pX between 50 and 400 GeV/c", paper submitted to the APS Division of Particles and Fields Meeting, Berkeley, August, 1973.
20. B. Bartenev et al., "Diffraction Excitation of Nucleon Resonances in p-p Collisions at Incident Proton Energies from 175 to 400 GeV/c," paper submitted to the APS Division of Particles and Fields Meeting, Berkeley, August, 1973.

21. K. Abe, et al ., "Measurement of N* Production in pp → pN* between 9 and 300 GeV/c", paper submitted to the APS Division of Particle Fields Meeting, Berkeley, August, 1973.

22. G. S. Abrams, et al., LBL-2112 and paper submitted to the APS Division of Particles and Fields Meeting, Berkeley, August, 1973.

23. M. Derrick, et al., ANL/HEP-7332 and paper submitted to the APS Division of Particles and Fields Meeting, Berkeley, August, 1973.

24. This data was originally presented in preliminary form at the Vanderbilt Conference on Inclusive Processes at High Energy, 1973. Corrections for instrumented failure have changed the cross-sections in the forward direction.

25. J. Vander Velde, (private communication).

26. F. C. Winkelmann, et al., LBL-2113 and paper submitted to the APS Division of Particles and Fields Meeting, Berkeley, August, 1973.

27. F. C. Winkelmann, (private communication).

28. F. T. Dao, et al., Phys. Rev. Letters 30, 34 (1973).

29. D. Brick, et al., submitted to Phys. Rev. Letters and to the APS Division of Particles and Fields Meeting, Berkeley, August, 1973.

30. V. Idschok, et al., Nucl. Phys. B 53, 282 (1973).

31. D. M. Chew, et al., talk presented at the APS Division of Particles and Fields Meeting, Berkeley, August, 1973.

32. M. Derrick, et al ., ANL/HEP-7339 and paper submitted to the APS Division of Particles and Fields Meeting, Berkeley, August, 1973.

33. Abarbanel, et al., Phys. Rev. Letters, 26, 937 (1971); Ellis, et al., Phys. Rev. D 6, 1347 (1972).

34. CERN-Holland-Lancaster-Manchester Group, M. G. Albrow, et al., CERN preprint; A. Capella, et al., SLAC report no. SLAC-PUB-1252. References to earlier work may be found in this paper.

35. K. Abe, et al., "Determination of Triple-Regge Coupling from a Study of Reaction pp → pX between 50 and 400 GeV/c", paper submitted to the II Aix-en-Provence International Conference on Elementary Particles, September, 1973.

36. H. I. Miettinen and R. G. Roberts, Rutherford Lab Preprint RPP/T/40 (1973).

37. M. Bishari, Phys. Letters 38 B, 510 (1972).

38. A. Capella, et al., Orsay Preprint 72/73.

DIFFRACTION DISSOCIATION IN 205 GeV/c $\pi^- p$ INTERACTIONS[*]

F. C. Winkelmann, G. S. Abrams, H. H. Bingham, D. M. Chew,
B. Y. Daugéras,[†] W. B. Fretter, C. E. Friedberg, G. Goldhaber,
W. R. Graves, A. D. Johnson, J. A. Kadyk, L. Stutte,
G. H. Trilling and G. P. Yost
Department of Physics and Lawrence Berkeley Laboratory
University of California, Berkeley, California 94720

D. Bogert, R. Hanft, F. R. Huson, D. Ljung,
C. Pascaud,[†] S. Pruss, W. M. Smart
National Accelerator Laboratory, Batavia, Illinois 60510

ABSTRACT

Pion and proton diffraction dissociation are observed
in $\pi^- p$ interactions at 205 GeV/c. The 2- and 4-prong final
states show evidence for N^* and A_1 production. Pion diffraction into masses up to ~ 6 GeV is observed in the
inclusive reaction $\pi^- p \rightarrow p + X$.

INTRODUCTION

We present data on pion and proton diffraction dissociation in
$\pi^- p$ interactions at 205 GeV/c in the NAL 30-inch hydrogen bubble
chamber. After a brief description of the experimental setup and
the processing of events, we investigate, in Sec. I, single diffraction dissociation in 2- and 4-prong final states. In Sec. II, we
discuss the characteristics of pion diffraction in the inclusive
reaction

$$\pi^- p \rightarrow p + X .$$

EXPERIMENTAL SETUP AND PROCESSING OF EVENTS

An unseparated 205 GeV/c negative particle beam was produced by
targeting 303 GeV/c protons from the NAL Synchrotron and was trans-
ported one km to the bubble chamber. Beam characteristics at the
chamber were as follows: a momentum spread of $\pm 0.1\%$, an angular
divergence of ± 0.25 mrad, and K^-, $\bar{p}$ and μ^- contaminations of
$1.4 \pm 0.2\%$, $0.16 \pm 0.1\%$ and $2.2 \pm 0.03\%$, respectively. The data presented
here are based on almost the complete data sample in an exposure of
48K pictures with an average of 7 beam tracks/frame. The film was
scanned with approximately lifesize projection in 3 separate views
by physicists and independently by professional scanners. Discrepancies were resolved using a scan table projecting 3.5X lifesize
images. The events accepted in the scan were restricted to a fiducial volume approximately 40 cm long in the beam direction. The
events were measured on film-plane measuring projectors. Bubble
density patterns were compared in each view in order to ensure
proper track matching. Geometrical and kinematic fitting were performed with the standard programs TVGP and SQUAW.

I.   DIFFRACTION DISSOCIATION IN 2- AND 4-PRONG INTERACTIONS

In this Section we discuss pion and proton single diffraction dissociation in the 2- and 4-prong final states. We examine first the exclusive reaction

$$\pi^- p \to \pi^- \pi^- \pi^+ p \tag{1}$$

and find evidence for pion diffraction into $\pi^- \pi^- \pi^+$ and proton diffraction into $p\pi^+ \pi^-$. We then consider 2- and 4-prong diffractive processes leading to neutrals in the final state.

I.1   The Reaction $\pi^- p \to \pi^- \pi^- \pi^+ p$

Events belonging to reaction (1) were obtained by requiring a four-constraint kinematic fit with $\chi^2 < 30$. Possible contamination from events with missing neutrals was studied by dropping all possible $\pi^+ \pi^-$ pairs from 6-prong events and refitting the resulting pseudo-4-prong events to reaction (1). Comparison of distributions of missing and invariant mass, transverse momentum imbalance,[1] and momentum transfer from real and pseudo-4-prong events yields a preliminary estimate that this contamination is less than 10%. A similar study of events with detected strange particles suggests that background from $\pi^- p \to K^- K^+ \pi^- p$ fitting reaction (1) is probably $< 5\%$, but could be as large as 20%. Neglecting this background but subtracting missing neutral background we find a cross section for reaction (1) of 0.6 ± 0.1 mb.

The momentum dependence of this cross section is shown in Fig. 1.[2] The cross section falls between 20 and 205 GeV/c with a $p_{LAB}^{-0.2}$ dependence, indicating that diffractive processes may be dominant.

Our subsequent discussion of this process is based on 128 fitted events within a restricted fiducial volume which provides at least 26 cm of path length for the measurement of fast forward tracks.

In Fig. 2, we show a two-dimensional histogram of the $\pi^- \pi^- \pi^+$ mass vs the lower of the two possible $p\pi^+ \pi^-$ masses. The striking features of this plot are:

(i) A clear grouping of low (< 3.2 GeV) $p\pi^+ \pi^-$ mass events, presumably involving nucleon diffraction,

$$\pi^- p \to \pi^- (\pi^- \pi^+ p) \ ;$$

(ii) Another clear grouping of low (< 3 GeV) $\pi^- \pi^- \pi^+$ mass events, presumably involving pion diffraction,

$$\pi^- p \to (\pi^- \pi^- \pi^+) p \ ;$$

(iii) Finally a few events which exhibit fairly high $p\pi^+ \pi^-$ and $\pi^- \pi^- \pi^+$ masses and perhaps do not belong in the two above categories. As discussed elsewhere these may be interpreted in terms of double-Pomeron exchange processes.[3]

Figures 3 and 4 show the $\pi^- \pi^- \pi^+$ and $p\pi^+ \pi^-$ mass distributions. The calculated errors in these fitted masses amount to about 50 MeV for $M(\pi^- \pi^- \pi^+)$ and 15 MeV for $M(\pi^- \pi^+ p)$ in the regions of the diffractive peaks and justify the finely binned histograms. Restricting the transverse momentum imbalance so as to further reduce the missing-neutral background yields the shaded region in Fig. 3.

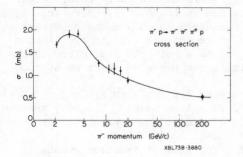

XBL738-3880

Fig. 1. P_{LAB} dependence of $\pi^- p \to \pi^- \pi^- \pi^+ p$
cross section.

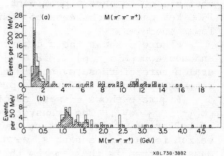

XBL738-3882

Fig. 3. $M(\pi^- \pi^- \pi^+)$ (a) 200 MeV bins; (b) 50
MeV bins. The shaded histograms have a
more restrictive cut on transverse
momentum balance (see text).

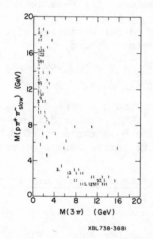

XBL738-3881

Fig. 2. $M^2(\pi^- \pi^- \pi^+)$ vs lower value of
$M^2(\pi^- \pi^+ p)$ for $\pi^- p \to \pi^- \pi^- \pi^+ p$.

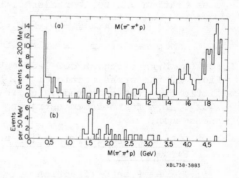

XBL738-3883

Fig. 4. $M(\pi^- \pi^+ p)$ (a) 200 MeV bins; (b) 50
MeV bins.

The $M(\pi^-\pi^-\pi^+)$ spectrum in Fig. 3b is dominated by a very clear peak at about 1100 MeV, presumably due to the A_1. If there are higher mass 3π diffractive states, they certainly do not become prominent at this energy. Similarly the $\pi^-\pi^+p$ state appears, within the limited statistics, to have a prominent peak at about 1550 MeV, close to the 1500 MeV peak which seems to dominate the $M(\pi^-\pi^+p)$ spectrum at much lower energies.

Figure 5 shows the t distributions for the π $[M(\pi^-\pi^-\pi^+) < 3$ GeV] and nucleon $[M(\pi^-\pi^+p) < 3.2$ GeV] diffractive peaks. The very peripheral nature of these events is quite evident and consistent with their interpretation as diffractive processes.

Figure 6 shows $\pi\pi$ mass spectra for pion diffraction events $[M(3\pi) < 3$ GeV]. The transverse momentum imbalance has been restricted to further reduce missing-neutral background. In order to search for $\pi^+\pi^-$ resonances, we have made the assumption that the $\pi^-\pi^-$ mass spectrum is the same as that of $\pi^+\pi_b^-$, where π_b^- is the "bachelor" π^-, and have subtracted it from the total $\pi^+\pi^-$ spectrum giving the residual distribution shown in Fig. 6c. This distribution appears to be dominated by the ρ peak with very little contribution from f, g or any higher-mass mesons.

Figure 7 shows $p\pi^+$ and $p\pi^-$ mass spectra for the nucleon diffraction events $[M(\pi^-\pi^+p) < 3.2$ GeV]. A prominent Δ^{++} peak as well as some Δ^0 are evident.

We complete this discussion by quoting our estimates of the pion dissociation and nucleon dissociation cross sections,

$$\sigma(\pi^- \to \pi^-\pi^-\pi^+) = 0.40\pm0.08 \text{ mb}, \quad M(\pi^-\pi^-\pi^+) < 3 \text{ GeV} ;$$

$$\sigma(p \to \pi^-\pi^+p) = 0.18\pm0.04 \text{ mb}, \quad M(\pi^-\pi^+p) < 3.2 \text{ GeV} .$$

For the $M(\pi\pi\pi)$ region 800-1200 MeV, which includes the A_1 peak in Fig. 3b, the cross section is 0.19 ± 0.04 mb. This number differs very little from the measured value in the same mass range at 20 GeV of 190 ± 30 μb,[2] further demonstrating the diffractive nature of the phenomenon.

I.2 2- and 4-Prong Diffractive Processes Leading to Neutrals in Final State

I.2.A Pion Diffraction

Considering first 2-prong interactions, we show in Fig. 8a, the spectrum of M^2, the mass squared recoiling against the proton (identified by ionization) for events which do not fit the elastic hypothesis. A large peak centered at $M^2 = 2$ GeV^2, of full width 4 GeV^2, and extending to about 20 GeV^2 is observed. The t distribution for the events in the peak is shown in Fig. 8b and is highly peripheral as expected. Just as in elastic scattering, there is a loss of events at very low t, so that the first bin in the distribution is not reliable.

We have estimated the cross section for the pion diffractive dissociation,

$$\pi^-p \to (\pi^- + \text{neutrals}) + p ,$$

taking into account (i) that 4% of the elastic events identified by

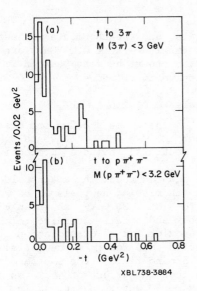

Fig. 5. t distributions: (a) π dissociation, (b) nucleon dissociation.

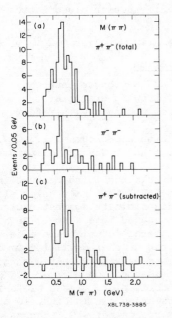

Fig. 6. M(ππ) spectra for pion dissociation [M($\pi^-\pi^-\pi^+$) < 3 GeV]; (a) M($\pi^+\pi^-$), (b) M($\pi^-\pi^-$), (c) difference of (a) and (b).

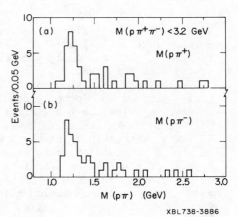

Fig. 7. M(πp) for nucleon dissociation; (a) M(π^+p), (b) M(π^-p).

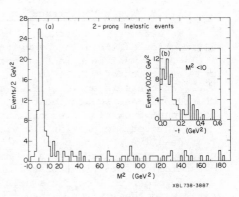

Fig. 8. (a) Spectrum of M^2 for 2-prong inelastic events with identified protons; (b) t distribution for $M^2 < 10$ GeV^2.

kinematic fitting have missing neutrals, and are therefore inelastic (see Ref. 1), and (ii) that some events with $|t| < 0.03$ GeV^2 are lost. Making no background subtraction under the mass peak in Fig. 8, and considering the diffraction region to extend to $M^2 = 20$ GeV^2 we obtain

$$\sigma(\pi^- \rightarrow \pi^- + \text{neutrals}) = 0.70 \pm 0.10 \text{ mb} .$$

This value is significantly larger than the cross section for dissociation into $\pi^-\pi^-\pi^+$, namely 0.40 mb for $M^2 < 9$ GeV^2. It seems likely, therefore, that the decay mode $(\pi^- + \text{neutrals})$ includes diffractive states with more than two π°.

Similarly, the spectrum of mass squared recoiling against identified protons in 4-prong processes with missing neutrals is shown in Fig. 9a, with the t-distribution for $M^2 < 20$ GeV^2 shown in Fig. 9b. We see here a broader low-mass peak and a tail extending to about 30 GeV^2. The estimate of the cross section for π^- dissociation into $(\pi^-\pi^-\pi^+ + \text{neutrals})$ is much less certain than for $(\pi^- + \text{neutrals})$ because of the smaller signal-to-background ratio. For the purposes of the present analysis we simply neglect background and take as our measure the event population below $M^2 = 30$ GeV^2. Again, adding on the contribution from the fits to reaction (1) we obtain

$$\sigma(\pi^- \rightarrow \pi^-\pi^-\pi^+ + \text{neutrals}) = 0.48 \pm 0.10 \text{ mb} .$$

The cross section for pion single diffraction dissociation into 2- and 4-prong events is then

$$\sigma[\pi^- \rightarrow \pi^*(2P,4P)] = 0.40 + 0.70 + 0.48 = 1.6 \pm 0.2 \text{ mb} .$$

I.2.B Nucleon Diffraction Dissociation

We attempt to separate in both 2- and 4-prong events the nucleon diffraction dissociation by using the following criteria:

(1) There must be a fast outgoing π^- of momentum within four standard deviations of 205 GeV/c.

(2) If there is an identified slow proton (momentum ≤ 1.5 GeV/c), the recoil mass squared must be greater than 30 GeV^2 to eliminate background from pion dissociation.

(3) The total energy of all visible tracks recoiling against the fast negative pion must be less than 15 GeV. This test helps eliminate background and is such as not to discriminate against nucleon dissociation into final states of mass squared less than 25 GeV^2.

In order to look for a highly peripheral contribution of events satisfying these tests we have plotted the angular deviation $\Delta\varphi$ in the plane perpendicular to the camera lens axis between the outgoing fast π^- and the beam particle, using an assumed momentum of 205 GeV/c to recalculate the direction of the outgoing pion. These plots for various classes of 2- and 4-prong events are shown in Figs. 10 and 11. These data all strongly populate the $\Delta\varphi$ region below 0.1 degree ($-t \lesssim 0.15$ GeV^2), and hence are in fact highly peripheral. Using $\Delta\varphi < 0.2^\circ$ as a definition of nucleon dissociation events, and making small corrections for inefficiencies in recognizing protons we obtain the following cross-section estimates[4]:

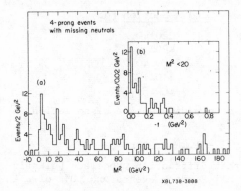

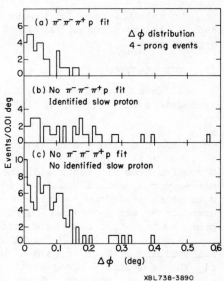

Fig. 9. (a) Spectrum of M^2 for 4-prong events with missing neutrals and identified protons; (b) t distribution for $M^2 < 20$ GeV^2.

Fig. 11. Distribution of $\Delta\varphi$ for 4-prong events.

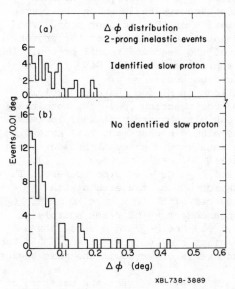

Fig. 10. Distribution of $\Delta\varphi$ for 2-prong events.

Dissociation	Cross Section (μb)
$p \rightarrow p$ + neutrals	220 ± 40
$p \rightarrow \pi^+$ + neutrals	420 ± 70
$p \rightarrow p\pi^+\pi^-$ + neutrals	170 ± 40
$p \rightarrow \pi^+\pi^+\pi^-$ + neutrals	440 ± 130
$p \rightarrow p\pi^+\pi^-$	180 ± 36

Thus the cross section for proton single diffraction dissociation in 2- and 4-prong events is,

$$\sigma[p \rightarrow p^*(2P,4P)] = 1.4 \pm 0.2 \text{ mb} .$$

To conclude Sec. I, we note that diffraction processes (elastic and inelastic) account for 90% of all 2-prong events and 50% of all 4-prong events.

II. THE REACTION $\pi^- p \rightarrow p + X$ AND PION DIFFRACTION DISSOCIATION

In this Section we discuss the data sample consisting of 1545 inelastic events of all multiplicities of the form

$$\pi^- p \rightarrow p + X , \qquad\qquad (2)$$

where the outgoing proton, identified by ionization, has momentum ≤ 1.5 GeV/c. Of particular interest are events in which the system X results from diffractive dissociation of the incident pion. The mass-squared, M^2, of X and the momentum transfer, t, to the proton were calculated from measurements of the beam and recoil proton. The error in M^2 was determined to be approximately ± 1.3 GeV^2 from 2-prong events which fit the elastic hypothesis.

Figure 12 shows the distributions in M^2 for charged particle multiplicity 2, 4, 6, 8, and ≥ 10 for reaction (2).[5] We note that: (1) The inelastic 2-prong events exhibit a sharply peaked, low-mass (≤ 10 GeV^2) enhancement. There is also a higher-mass tail extending to ~ 20 GeV^2. (2) The 4-prong events show a somewhat broader low-mass peak, which contains substantial $A_1 \rightarrow \pi^+\pi^-\pi^-$ (see Sec. I). Higher-mass excitation extending to ~ 30 GeV^2 is also present. The reaction $\pi^- p \rightarrow \pi^-\pi^-\pi^+ p$ accounts for 40% of the events with $M^2 < 10$ GeV^2, but for only 12% of the events with $10 < M^2 < 30$ GeV^2. (3) The 6-prong events show a broad enhancement which rises sharply at $M^2 \approx 0$ and extends to ~ 30 GeV^2. (4) The 8-prong events show a less-pronounced enhancement which rises slowly from $M^2 \approx 0$. (5) For ≥ 10 prongs, no well-defined structure is observed in the mass region below 30 GeV^2.

We interpret these enhancements as evidence for the presence of diffraction dissociation of the pion into masses up to ~ 30 GeV^2 in the 2-, 4-, 6-, and, possibly, 8-prong events. Combining the M^2 distributions for all multiplicities, we obtain the inclusive M^2 distribution shown in Fig. 13.

To estimate the cross section for pion single diffraction dissociation, we have taken an upper limit of $M^2 = 32$ GeV^2 for diffraction and have counted events above a hand-drawn background separately for each multiplicity. The background curves used are shown in Fig. 12. Table I gives the resulting cross sections for 2, 4, 6, 8, and ≥ 10 prongs. The errors shown are statistical only. We obtain an

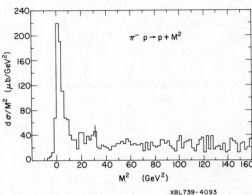

XBL739-4093

Fig. 13. (a) Inclusive M^2 distribution for
$\pi^- p \to p + X$.

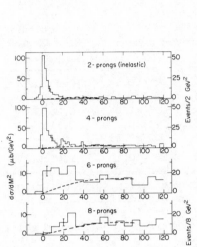

XBL739-4094

Fig. 12. Distribution in M^2 for $\pi^- p \to p + X$
for charged multiplicity 2, 4, 6, 8 and ≥ 10.

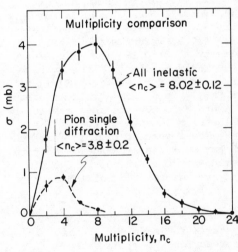

XBL739-4092

Fig. 14. Charged multiplicity distribution
for $\pi^- p \to$ anything (solid curve) and for
pion diffraction (dashed curve). The
curves have been drawn to guide the eye.

overall pion single diffraction dissociation cross section of 1.9 ± 0.2 mb for $M^2 < 32$ GeV^2. This is approximately 8% of the total π^-p cross section, 24.0 ± 0.5 mb, and is comparable to the elastic cross section, 3.0 ± 0.3 mb.

Table I. Cross sections for $\pi^-p \to p + X$.

Charged particle multiplicity	Overall inelastic cross section (mb)	$\pi^-p \to p + X$ cross section (mb), $P_{proton} < 1.5$ GeV/c		Pion single diffraction cross sections, $M^2 < 32$ GeV^2 (mb)
		All M^2	$M^2 < 32$	
2	1.76 ± 0.30	0.95 ± 0.20	0.70 ± 0.14	0.67 ± 0.14
4	3.45 ± 0.18	1.76 ± 0.12	1.00 ± 0.10	0.87 ± 0.08
6	3.79 ± 0.18	1.40 ± 0.10	0.38 ± 0.04	0.28 ± 0.05
8	4.05 ± 0.19	1.05 ± 0.08	0.18 ± 0.03	0.11 ± 0.03
≥ 10	7.88 ± 0.27	1.27 ± 0.15	0.03 ± 0.01	---
Totals	21.0 ± 0.5	6.43 ± 0.30	2.29 ± 0.18	1.93 ± 0.17

In Fig. 14 we show the charged particle multiplicity distribution for all events[6] (solid curve) and for pion diffraction (dashed curve). The average charged multiplicity for pion diffractive events is 3.8 ± 0.2, which is about half of the overall average charged multiplicity, 8.02 ± 0.12, for $\pi^-p \to$ anything.

The dependence of the average charged particle multiplicity, $\langle n_c\rangle$, on M^2 for reaction (2) is shown in Fig. 15. We observe that $\langle n_c(M^2)\rangle$ rises from a value of about 3.5 at $M^2 \approx 0$ to approximately 7.5 at $M^2 = 90$, and then remains nearly constant up to the highest value of M^2.

The insert of Fig. 16 shows the interpretation of reaction (2) in terms of the exchange of a system, $\tilde{P}$, which is expected to be predominantly the Pomeron in the pion diffraction region ($M^2 \lesssim 30$ GeV^2). The average charged multiplicity of the reaction

$$\tilde{P}\pi^- \to \text{anything} \qquad (3)$$

for $s = M^2$ is then $\langle n_c(M^2)\rangle - 1$, the average multiplicity of the system X for mass M^2. In Fig. 15 we compare the average multiplicity of reaction (3) with that of

$$\pi^-p \to \text{anything} . \qquad (4)$$

The comparison is made at the same center-of-mass Q-value for the two reactions. For reaction (3) we take $m_{\tilde{P}} = 0$, giving $Q = \sqrt{M^2} - m_\pi \approx M$. For reaction (4), $Q = \sqrt{s} - (m_{\tilde{P}} + m_\pi)$, where s is the center-of-mass energy squared. We observe that $\langle n_c\rangle_{\pi p \to \text{anything}}$ and $\langle n_c\rangle_{\tilde{P}\pi \to \text{anything}}$ are consistent with being the same over the range of Q^2 shown, and have a dependence on Q^2 of the form $A + B \log Q^2$, with $A \approx 0.3$ and $B \approx 1.3$.

The t-dependence of pion diffraction in the inelastic 2, 4, 6, and 8 prongs is shown in Fig. 17 for $M^2 < 40$ GeV^2 and $0.01 \lesssim -t \lesssim 0.6$ GeV^2. In this M^2 region t_{min} effects are negligible ($t_{min} \leq$

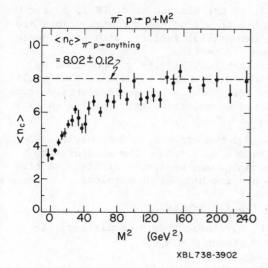

$$\pi^- p \to p + M^2$$

XBL738-3902

Fig. 15. Average charged multiplicity, $\langle n_c \rangle$ vs M^2 for $\pi^- p \to p + X$.

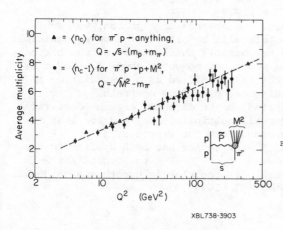

XBL738-3903

Fig. 16. Average charged multiplicity comparison for $\pi^- p \to$ anything (▲) and $\pi^- p \to p + X$ (●) at equivalent values of Q^2. To guide the eye, a dashed straight line has been drawn through the data points for $\pi^- p \to$ anything.

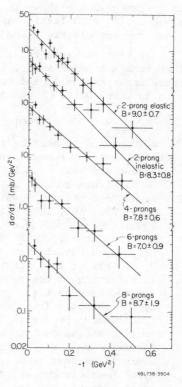

XBL738-3904

Fig. 17. $d\sigma/dt$ for inelastic 2-, 4-, 6-, and 8-prong events for $M^2 \lesssim 40$ GeV^2. For comparison, the elastic $d\sigma/dt$ is also shown. The data have been fitted to the form Ae^{Bt} for $0.02 < -t < 0.5$ GeV^2, yielding the exponential slopes indicated.

0.01 GeV^2). We also show in Fig. 17 the elastic $d\sigma/dt$ (Ref. 6) for comparison. For the t-range available all of these distributions are consistent with having a simple exponential falloff, with no evidence for a sharp turnover in the forward direction.

The exponential slope B for each multiplicity was obtained by fitting $d\sigma/dt$ to the form Ae^{Bt} for $0.02 < -t < 0.5$ GeV^2. The resulting values of B are shown in Fig. 17. For the inelastic events we find $B \approx 8$ GeV^{-2} with little dependence on multiplicity. This value is close to the elastic slope of 9.0 ± 0.7 GeV^{-2}.

It is a pleasure to acknowledge the effort put forth by the 30-inch bubble chamber staff, the hadron beam group, the accelerator operations personnel, and our scanning and measuring staffs. We also wish to thank G. F. Chew and R. Hwa for helpful discussions.

FOOTNOTES AND REFERENCES

*Work supported in part by the U. S. Atomic Energy Commission, the National Science Foundation, and French C.N.R.S.

†Permanent address: L.A.L., Orsay, France.

1. G. S. Abrams et al., LBL-2112 (1973).

2. J. H. Boyd et al., Phys. Rev. 166, 1458 (1968); S. U. Chung et al., Phys. Rev. 165, 1491 (1968); J. W. Lamsa et al., Phys. Rev. 166, 1395 (1968); C. Caso et al., Nuovo Cimento 57A, 699 (1968); M. L. Ioffredo et al., Phys. Rev. Letters 21, 1212 (1968); J. Ballam et al., Phys. Rev. Letters 21, 934 (1968).

3. D. M. Chew et al., LBL-2106 (1973).

4. In referring to the presence or absence of a proton, we have assumed here that the protons will be slow and hence recognizable by ionization. It is quite possible that in some of the baryon dissociation processes, a proton of momentum above 1.5 GeV/c is emitted and hence the event is classified as a dissociation of the form $p \rightarrow \pi$ + neutrals or $p \rightarrow 3\pi$ + neutrals.

5. Corrections have been applied to the data for proton identification inefficiency (10% for all multiplicities) and for loss of short, steeply-dipping protons (12% for 2-prongs, 5% for ≥ 4 prongs). In addition, a 25% correction has been applied to the inelastic 2-prong sample with $M^2 < 3$ GeV^2 to account for 2-prong inelastic events which fit the elastic hypothesis (see Ref. 1).

6. D. Bogert et al., NAL-Pub-73/57 (1973).

DIFFRACTION DISSOCIATION IN pp INTERACTIONS AT NAL

J. Whitmore

National Accelerator Laboratory, Batavia, Illinois 60510[*]

ABSTRACT

This report presents a brief summary of the study of diffractive fragmentation in pp collisions as observed in the NAL bubble-chamber experiments. Missing mass, effective mass, and secondary particle rapidity distributions permit a) the study of the multiplicity and t dependences of the diffractive process at high energy, b) the measurement of the cross section for the reaction $pp \rightarrow pp\pi^+\pi^-$, and c) an estimate of an upper limit for the double Pomeron exchange contribution to the $pp\pi^+\pi^-$ final state at 205 GeV/c.

Diffraction dissociation in pp interactions has been studied in four experiments using the NAL 30-in. bubble chamber. One of the methods available for studying proton diffraction is the effective mass technique which has been profitably employed by the ANL-NAL group[1,2] at 205 GeV/c in analyzing the 4-prong events, in particular, the reaction $pp \rightarrow pp\pi^+\pi^-$. The second method which has been used by all three groups, Michigan-Rochester[3] (102 and 405 GeV/c), ANL-NAL[4] (205 GeV/c), and NAL-UCLA[5] (303 GeV/c), is to study the missing-mass reaction:

$$pp \rightarrow \text{slow proton} + \text{anything}, \tag{1}$$

by measuring recoil protons with laboratory momentum below 1.4 GeV/c, a cut imposed by the requirement that the proton be identified visually by bubble density. Such a selection results in a bias against high missing mass (or x) as shown for the 205 GeV/c data[4] in Fig. 1. This scatter plot of x, the Feynman variable, versus P_T, the transverse momentum of the recoil proton, shows a strong elastic band near x = -1 and the circular boundary caused by the 1.4 GeV/c momentum cut. Following removal of the elastic 2-prong events, the missing mass squared (M^2) distributions are shown in Fig. 2 for various beam momenta.[3-7]

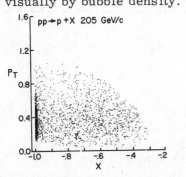

Fig. 1. Scatter plot of x vs P_T for the reaction $pp \rightarrow$ slow proton + anything at 205 GeV/c.

[*]Operated by Universities Research Association, Inc. under contract with the United States Atomic Energy Commission.

372

The dominant features of this figure are
     a) the large peak at low M^2,
     b) the relatively flat distribution at high M^2,
     c) the fall of the peak height as the beam momentum rises from 19 to 102 GeV/c, and the constant height of the peak for the data between 102 and 405 GeV/c, and
     d) the greater width of the low mass peak at the NAL energies. It should be noted that since the resolution in M^2 may be approximated by ± 0.7 GeV^2 $\times (P_{lab}/100$ GeV/c), this feature implies the observation of proton diffraction into states with masses up to 4 GeV.

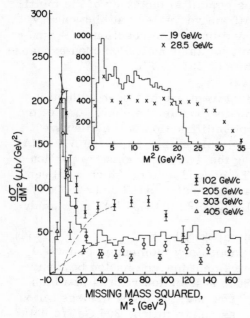

Fig. 2. Missing mass squared distributions for inelastic events in the reaction pp → slow p + X.

The data in Fig. 2 seem to be consistent with a "background" which falls (~1/s, see Fig. 4 below) and a low mass enhancement with a cross section for $M^2 \lesssim 20$ GeV^2 which is energy independent. In order to obtain cross sections for this this low mass peak, the ANL-NAL group has estimated the number of events above the hand-drawn background in Fig. 2. Using similar estimates for the shape of the background at each of the other energies, the resulting cross sections for single diffraction, σ_s, are

P_{lab}(GeV/c)	σ_s(mb)
19	2.15±0.30
28.5	1.70±0.30
102	2.50±0.35
205	2.60±0.30
303	2.15±0.25
405	2.05±0.25.

The cross section for low mass single diffraction thus appears to be relatively constant with a value ~2.2±0.5 mb.

To study the multiplicity dependence of this low mass peak, the missing mass squared distributions are shown in Fig. 3 for the individual topologies at 205 GeV/c (similar distributions are observed at the other energies) and indicate that (44±6)% of σ_s is due to the 2-prongs, (46±5)% to the 4-prongs, and (10±3)% to the 6-prongs.[4] A noticeable feature of Fig. 3 is that the position of the peak increases in M^2 as the charged multiplicity increases. There are no

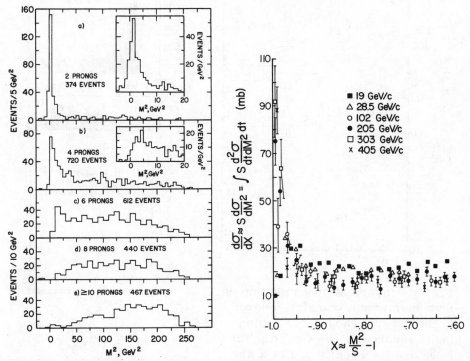

Fig. 3. Missing mass squared distributions at 205 GeV/c for various topologies.

Fig. 4. Inclusive proton differential cross sections as a function of x.

significant peaks for events with 8 or more prongs. Thus the cross sections quoted above represent lower limits on the diffractive fragmentation of the beam proton since it is hard to estimate contributions from diffractive processes leading to high M^2 states or yielding distributions that do not peak at low mass.

These slow proton data[3-7] may also be presented in terms of their x dependence as shown in Fig. 4 which indicates that for x $\lesssim$ -0.95 the cross section is rising with energy. For x $\gtrsim$ -0.95 there is perhaps a trend for a falling cross section as s increases up to NAL energies, although the cross section shows little energy dependence within the NAL region.

The t dependence of process (1) is further indication that the low mass peak is diffractively produced. Figure 5 shows the invariant cross section for several ranges of M^2 at 205 GeV/c.[4] Except for the regions affected by the kinematics at high M^2, all of the distributions can be well represented by an exponential t dependence.

The effective mass analysis has provided further information about the low mass peak. Figure 6(a) shows the missing mass

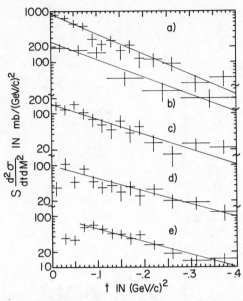

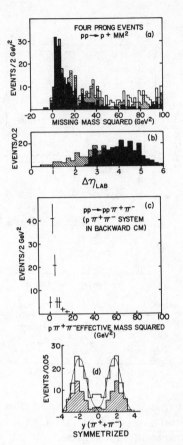

Fig. 5. Invariant cross section vs four-momentum transfer squared, t, for various ranges of missing mass squared at 205 GeV/c. The lines are the results of fits to the form $A \exp(bt)$. (a) $M^2 < 5$ GeV^2 $b = 9.1 \pm 0.7$ (GeV/c)$^{-2}$. (b) $5 \leq M^2 < 10$ GeV^2, $b = 8.0 \pm 1.1$ (GeV/c)$^{-2}$. (c) $10 \leq M^2 < 25$ GeV^2, $b = 6.1 \pm 0.7$ (GeV/c)$^{-2}$. (d) $25 \leq M^2 < 50$ GeV^2, $b = 5.8 \pm 0.7$ (GeV/c)$^{-2}$. (e) $50 \leq M^2 < 100$ GeV^2, $b = 5.8 \pm 0.6$ (GeV/c)$^{-2}$.

squared distribution for reaction (1) for the 4-prong sample at 205 GeV/c.[1] The shaded (cross-hatched) area shows the sub-sample of events in which just 3 (2) charged particles are in the forward c.m. hemisphere and in-dicates that most of the enhance-

Fig. 6(a). Missing mass squared distribution for 4-prongs at 205 GeV/c. (b) Distribution of the rapidity gap between the leading proton and its nearest neighbor for $M^2 \leq 50$ GeV^2. (c) $p\pi^+\pi^-$ effective mass squared distri-bution for the reaction pp → $pp\pi^+\pi^-$ at 205 GeV/c. (d) Center-of-mass rapidity distribution (after symmetrization) for the $\pi^+\pi^-$ system.

ment at low M^2 is associated with one backward c.m. proton and 3 forward c.m. charged particles. Since one might expect that dif-fractive events would show up in the ordered rapidity distribution with a large gap, associated with Pomeron exchange, Fig. 6(b) shows the distribution of the rapidity gap between the leading (i.e., slow) proton and its nearest neighbor, where the pseudorapidity $\eta = \ell n \tan(\theta_{lab}/2)$ has been used. The events with 3 forward c.m. particles have an average gap length of ~5 units, while those with 2 forward tracks usually have a smaller gap. Although having $M^2 \leq 50$ GeV^2, these latter events cannot be considered diffractive since this gap is the largest gap in the event for only 32 of the 58 events in the plot.

To further study the various contributions to the low M^2 peak in the 4-prong events, an effort has been made to determine those events consistent with the process

$$pp \rightarrow pp\pi^+\pi^-. \qquad (2)$$

By using those events in which there are 3 slow backward c.m. tracks and one forward c.m. charged track, a relatively clean sample, with an estimated 30% or less contamination, of events fitting (2) has been obtained. Derrick et al.[1,2] find a cross section for reaction (2) at 205 GeV/c of 0.85 $^{+0.09}_{-0.29}$ mb. The $p\pi^+\pi^-$ effective mass for these fitted events is shown in Fig. 6(c) and should be compared to Fig. 6(a). The peak due to $pp\pi^+\pi^-$ is confined to the low mass part of the total 4-prong peak and, furthermore, indicates that only ~35% of the 4-prong peak is due to reaction (2). This implies that the dominant contribution to the 4-prong peak is due to events with 5 or more particles in the final state. Further evidence of this is shown in Fig. 7 for those events in which three slow π's are identified in the backward c.m.[1] The rapidity, η_F, of the remaining charged track is plotted versus the rapidity gap, Δ, between this track and its nearest charged neighbor. The cluster of ~30 events with Δ ~ 5 and η_F ~ 6.5 is indicative of diffractive fragmentation of the target proton into high multiplicity states, such as $n\pi^+\pi^+\pi^-(m\pi^0)$ with $m \geq 0$.

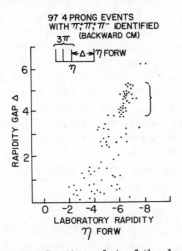

97 4 PRONG EVENTS
WITH $\pi^-\pi^-\pi^-$ IDENTIFIED
3π (BACKWARD CM)

Fig. 7. Scatter plot of the leading particle rapidity, η_F, vs the rapidity gap, Δ, between it and its closest neighbor for those 4-prongs with π^+, π^+, π^- identified by ionization.

Further rapidity analysis[2] has yielded an estimate for the double Pomeron (DP) exchange contribution to reaction (2). The dominant features of this reaction are a low $p\pi^+\pi^-$ effective mass enhancement, the strong production of $\Delta^{++}(1236)$ associated with the low mass $p\pi^+\pi^-$ peak,[9] and the peripherality of the $p\pi^+\pi^-$ system. For $p\pi^+\pi^-$ masses less than 3 GeV and $0 < |t| < 0.35$ (GeV/c)^2, the data are well represented by an exponential t dependence with slope b = 9.1±1.0 $(\text{GeV/c})^{-2}$.

To obtain the DP contribution, Derrick et al.[2] note that the effective mass of the $\pi^+\pi^-$ system tends to lie below the ρ mass, the helicity angular distribution of the 2π system is isotropic, and the rapidity of the 2π system has a double-peaked structure [Fig. 6(d)]. These features suggest that the 2π system results from the diffractive fragmentation of either the beam or target proton. Since any DP contribution would be expected to occur in the central 2 units of Fig. 6(d), an estimate of the events[9] above a fit with 2 gaussians [shown as the curve in Fig. 6(d)] yields an upper limit of $45\,\mu b$ for the the DP contribution. A similar result at 24 GeV/c[10] gave a $30\,\mu b$ upper limit for 2π effective masses less than 0.6 GeV. For a similar dipion mass cut [shown as the cross-hatched area in Fig. 6(d)], an upper limit of $35\,\mu b$ (7 events) is obtained at 205 GeV/c.[2]

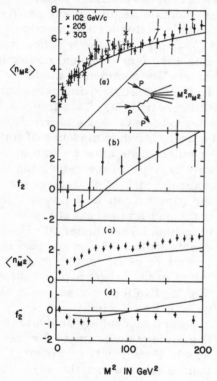

Finally, Fig. 8(a) shows[4] the average multiplicity $\langle n_{M2}\rangle$ for the charged particles recoiling against the slow proton in reaction (1) at 102, 205, and 303 GeV/c.[3-5] No strong dependence on beam energy is observed. The curve in Fig. 8(a) is obtained from a fit[11] to the s dependence of the charged particle multiplicity (in pp → n charged particles) with the result $\langle n\rangle = -4.8 + 2\ell n s + 10/\sqrt{s}$. For Fig. 8(a) the substitution $s = M^2$ has been made. Although the data lie systematically above the curve, they do show a remarkably similar energy dependence. Various other moments are also shown in Fig. 8.

It is tempting to suggest[4] that if reaction (1) proceeds via single particle exchange [insert in Fig. 8(a)], then studying $\langle n_{M2}\rangle$ as a function of M^2 is equivalent to studying exchanged particle-proton interactions as a function of s. It should be noted, however, that only for $M^2 \lesssim 20$ GeV^2

Fig. 8. Multiplicity moments of the charged system X in the reaction pp → slow proton + X plotted versus M^2. (a) $\langle n_{M2}\rangle$, (b) f_2, (c) $\langle n_{\overline{M}2}\rangle$ and (d) $f_{\overline{2}}$. The curve curves show the dependences on s of these quantities for real pp collisions.

can Fig. 8(a) be considered as describing Pomeron-proton collisions.

REFERENCES

1. M. Derrick et al., Diffraction Dissociation in Proton-Proton Interactions at 205 GeV/c, ANL/HEP 7332 (1973).

2. M. Derrick et al., An Estimate of the Double Pomeron Exchange Contribution to the Reaction pp → ppπ⁺π⁻ at 205 GeV/c, ANL/HEP 7339 (1973).

3. Michigan-Rochester collaboration, private communication from A. Seidl and J. VanderVelde.

4. S. J. Barish et al., Characteristics of the Reaction pp → p + X at 205 GeV/c, ANL/HEP 7338 (1973).

5. NAL-UCLA collaboration, private communication from F. T. Dao.

6. Scandinavian collaboration, private communication from H. Bøggild.

7. BNL-Vanderbilt collaboration, private communication from J. Hanlon.

8. The resolution in the $p\pi^+\pi^-$ effective mass squared is much smaller than 1 GeV^2, see Ref. 1.

9. Substantial Δ^{++} production in the 4-prong events has also been observed at 303 GeV/c, F. T. Dao et al., Phys. Rev. Letters 30, 34 (1973).

10. V. Idschok et al., DESY preprint, submitted to Nucl. Phys. B (1973).

11. D. M. Tow, Phys. Rev. D7, 3535 (1973).

The Reaction pp → p + X at 405 GeV/c.[*]

A. A. Seidl

The University of Michigan, Ann Arbor, Michigan 48104

ABSTRACT

Preliminary results on the reaction pp → p + X from an exposure of the NAL 30 inch liquid hydrogen bubble chamber are presented. Single particle inclusive distributions are discussed and compared with corresponding data at 102 GeV/c.

INTRODUCTION

I would like to present some preliminary results on the reaction pp → p + X at a beam momentum of 405 GeV/c. Table I lists the physicists contributing to this as well as to the similar experiment at 102 GeV/c.

Table I   List of Contributing Physicists

University of Rochester	University of Michigan
C. Bromberg	J. Chapman
D. Cohen	J. Cooper
T. Ferbel	N. Green
P. Slattery	B. Roe
	A. Seidl
	J. VanderVelde

DISCUSSION

We have identified events belonging to the reaction pp → p + X by the requirement that the observed ionization of the proton be consistent with its measured momentum. In order to insure a clean separation between p's and π's and K's we have used only protons whose laboratory momentum is less than 1.2 GeV/c. Due to the rapid fall off of the data as a function of the transverse momentum (the data when fitted to an exponential in p_T^2 have a slope of ~ 7.5 GeV^{-2}) the requirement that the laboratory momentum of the proton be less than 1.2 GeV/c does not bias distributions in $x = 2p_L^*/\sqrt{s}$ for x < 0.5. The variables p_L^* and $\sqrt{s}$ are respectively the longitudinal momentum and the energy in the center of the mass.

In order to separate elastically scattered protons from protons produced by inelastic reactions, we have fitted all two prongs to the four constraint reaction pp → pp. Since we cannot reliably measure the magnitude of the momentum of the fast tracks in the

30 inch bubble chamber, we have used the nominal beam momentum, 405 GeV/c, for both the beam track and the fast outgoing track with errors of ± 1 GeV/c on both. This effectively reduces the fits to two constraints. However we feel that the fit is an effective way of reducing the amount of elastic contamination in the inelastic sample.

In Figure la(lb) we plot $d\sigma/dx$ $(d\sigma/dM^2)$ for the inclusive reaction $pp \rightarrow p + X$. Except in the vicinity of $x = 0$, the mass squared recoiling against the observed proton is related to the x of the proton by $M^2 \simeq m_p^2 + s(1 + x)$, where m_p is the proton's mass. The data at 405 GeV/c are plotted as circles and, for comparison, the superimposed histograms are the data from 102 GeV/c.

The data displayed in Figure la, $d\sigma/dx$, exhibit two main features. First of all the data at 405 and 102 GeV/c scale (to within the statistical accuracy of the data) for $x > -0.9$. Secondly the peak in the cross section near $x = -1$ increases in size and narrows (so as to maintain approximately the same area) as the lab momentum increases from 102 to 405 GeV/c. The increase in the cross section at $x \approx -1$ is reflected in the approximate constancy of $d\sigma/dM^2$, Figure lb, for small values of M^2. In fact, on closer inspection, there appear to be three regions of variables with different scaling properties: the region $x \gtrsim -0.9$ in which $d\sigma/dx$ scales,

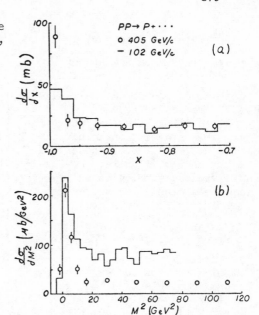

Fig.1. Inclusive distributions of a) $d\sigma/dx$ and b) $d\sigma/dM^2$.

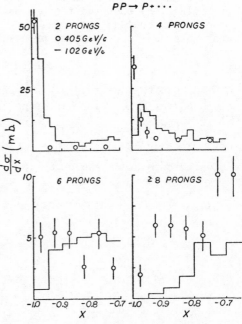

Fig. 2. Distributions of $d\sigma/dx$ versus charged prong multiplicity.

380

the region $M^2 \lesssim 10$ GeV^2 in which $d\sigma/dM^2$ scales, and an intermediate region in which both $d\sigma/dx$ and $d\sigma/dM^2$ fall with increasing s.

To illustrate that any possible elastic contamination does not effect these conclusions and to illustrate how the various topologies build up the inclusive cross section, we plot in Figures 2 and 3 $d\sigma/dx$ and $d\sigma/dM^2$ for various charged topologies. The peak for small M^2 ($x \approx -1$) comes mainly from the two and four prong topologies indicating that the major diffractive contribution is to low multiplicities. There is also some indication (although this could be affected by elastic contamination) that the two prong distributions are somewhat narrower than the four prong distributions.

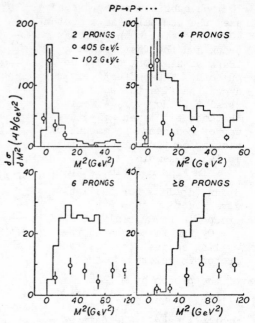

Fig.3. Distributions of $d\sigma/dM^2$ versus charged prong multiplicity.

CONCLUSION

We have observed evidence that there may be three distinct regions of variables with different scaling properties in the study of the reaction pp → p + X: x > -0.9 where $d\sigma/dx$ scales, $M^2 < 10$ GeV^2 where $d\sigma/dM^2$ approximately scales, and the intermediate region in which both $d\sigma/dx$ and $d\sigma/dM^2$ decrease with increasing s.

*Research supported in part by the U. S. Atomic Energy Commission

MEASUREMENT OF p + p → p + X BETWEEN 50 AND 400 GeV*

K. Abe, T. DeLillo, B. Robinson, F. Sannes
Rutgers University
New Brunswick, New Jersey 08903

J. Carr, J. Keyne, I. Siotis
Imperial College of Science
London SW7, U.K.

ABSTRACT

We have measured the s, t and x dependence of the invariant cross section for the inclusive reaction p + p → p + X in the region $108 < s < 752$ GeV^2, $0.14 < |t| < 0.38$ GeV^2 and $0.80 < x < 0.93$. The data were taken during the acceleration ramp of the National Accelerator Laboratory machine using the internal H$_2$ jet target facility.

We have studied the single-particle inclusive reaction

$$p + p \rightarrow p + X \quad (1 + 2 \rightarrow 3 + X) \tag{1}$$

(X = anything) at the National Accelerator Laboratory using the internal hydrogen jet[1] target at energies between 50 and 400 GeV. Recoil protons from Reaction (1) in the region $55° < \theta_{lab} < 65°$ with velocities $0.34 < \beta < 0.57$ pass through a scintillation counter telescope and stop in a total absorption scintillation counter. The experimental set-up is similar to that of an earlier experiment[2] in which the recoil proton momentum was determined by range in Al absorbers. In the present experiment the total absorption counter replaces the Al absorbers and the recoil momentum is determined by time of flight (TOF) over 186 cm. Both the TOF and the pulse height (PH) in the absorption counter are digitized and stored for each event. The scatter plot of TOF vs. PH has two distinct regions, one correspond-

*Development and operation of hydrogen jet target supported by the State Committee for Utilization of Atomic Energy of the USSR, Moscow. Research supported by the National Science Foundation and the Science Research Council, U.K.

ing to protons, the other to pions. The PH information
is used only to remove pions from the scatter plot.
The remaining events in each TOF interval are summed
over PH and represent the number of protons with a distinct momentum transfer squared t. This procedure avoids
the loss of proton events due to interactions in the
absorption counter which lead to inferior pulse heights.
A small t-dependent correction to our data was necessary
due to the higher probability of low momentum recoil
protons being scattered out of our spectrometer by the
forward counters than scattered in. This effect was
calculated by a Monte Carlo program and checked empir-
ically by varying the amount of material between the
target and absorption counter. The correction factor is
1.08 at $t = -0.16$ GeV^2 decreasing to 1.00 at $t = -0.33$
GeV^2.

Our results are expressed in terms of the invariant
cross section $sd^2\sigma/dtdM_X^2$ which is a function of the
three invariants

$$s \underset{\sim}{} 2mE_1 \tag{2a}$$

$$t = 2m(E_3 - m) \tag{2b}$$

$$x \underset{\sim}{} 1 - M_X^2/s \underset{\sim}{} (E_3 - p_3\cos\theta_3)/m \tag{2c}$$

where s is the total energy squared, t is the momentum
transfer squared, x is the Feynman variable $p_\parallel^*/p_{max}^*$, M_X^2
is the missing mass squared and m is the proton mass.
Typical full-width resolutions in these quantities are:
$\Delta s = 30$ GeV^2, $\Delta t = 0.05$ GeV^2 and $\Delta x = 0.01$.

We normalize our pp → pX data by monitoring the rate
of elastically scattered protons in a solid state detector[3] at θ(lab) = 85° $(t = -0.022$ GeV$^2)$, i.e., we measure
the ratio $sd^2\sigma/dtdM_X^2$(pp → pX):$d\sigma/dt$(pp → pp) and use the
known elastic cross section $d\sigma/dt$ to obtain $sd^2\sigma/dtdM_X^2$.
By the optical theorem the forward differential elastic
cross section is proportional to the square of the total
pp cross section $\sigma(s)_{tot}$. We extrapolate our measured
$d\sigma/dt(s)$ at $t = -0.022$ GeV^2 to $t = 0$ using the parameters determined by Bartenev et al.[4] and for $\sigma(s)_{tot}$ we
use the parametrization for this cross section of Bourrely
and Fischer[5]. Over our s range the square of the total
cross section increases by 8% while the increasing
elastic slope parameter causes a shrinkage of -3% so
that our measured ratio $sd^2\sigma/dtdM_X^2$(pp → pX):$d\sigma/dt$(pp→pp)
at $s = 752$ GeV^2 must be increased by 5% relative to the
ratio at $s = 108$ GeV^2 in order to obtain the correct
s-dependence of $sd^2\sigma/dtdM_X^2$. We estimate the uncertainty in our relative s normalization to be ±4% and
the uncertainty in the absolute normalization to be ±15%.

Our data at five s values and four t values are plotted as a function of x in Fig. 1. In our kinematic region, $0.14 < |t| < 0.38$ GeV^2, the t-dependence of the invariant cross section is well described by a simple exponential e^{bt} where b is not a function of s and depends only very weakly on x. Fits of the form

$$sd^2\sigma/dtdM_x^2 = A(x) \ e^{b(x)t}[1 + B(x)s^{-1/2}] \qquad (3)$$

to our data at fixed x and t show almost no variation of the parameter B in Eq. (3) with t. We therefore make an overall fit of the form (3) to our data at all values of s and t and arrive at the parameters given in Table I.

TABLE I

Table I. The coefficients A, B and b resulting from a fit of the form (3) to the data of this experiment.

$x = 1-M_x^2/s$	A (mb/GeV^2)	B(GeV)	b(GeV^{-2})
0.83	71 ± 7	1.9 ± 0.7	5.9 ± 0.3
0.85	64 ± 6	2.5 ± 0.7	5.9 ± 0.3
0.87	61 ± 5	3.0 ± 0.6	5.9 ± 0.3
0.89	62 ± 4	3.6 ± 0.5	6.0 ± 0.3
0.91	66 ± 3	4.3 ± 0.4	6.1 ± 0.3

The dip in the x-distributions of Fig. 1 near x = 0.88 is reflected in the A parameters of Table I which also have a minimum near x = 0.88. The b parameter, within errors, is constant with x while the B parameter increases significantly with x indicating a relatively stronger s-dependence at large x.

The authors are indebted to Professor B. Maglich for his support and valuable contributions throughout the experiment. We are grateful to the USSR-USA collaboration and the members of the Internal Target Laboratory for providing the H$_2$ jet target facility and to the Accelerator Section for their help and cooperation. We wish to thank Professor G. Cvijanovich, R. Stanek and J. Alspector for their contributions at various stages of the experiment and Professor A. Pagnamenta and S. D. Ellis for many useful discussions.

384

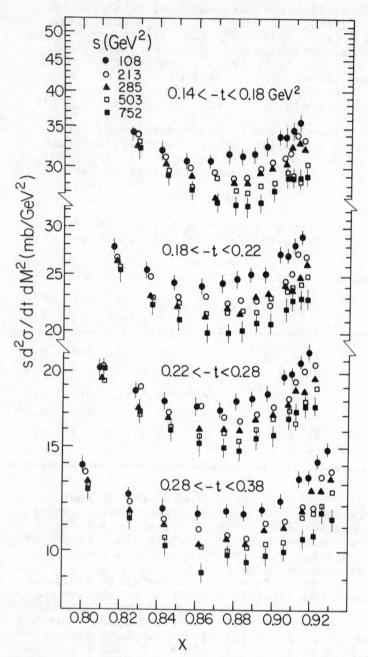

Figure 1.   Measured x-distributions at five values of s and four t ranges.

REFERENCES

1. V. Bartenev et al., Advances in Cryogenic Engineering $\underline{18}$ (1973).
2. F. Sannes et al., Phys. Rev. Letters $\underline{30}$, 733 (1973).
3. The signal from the elastic monitor was provided by the USA-USSR collaboration at NAL, authors of Ref. 1 and 4.
4. V. Bartenev et al., Phys. Rev. Letters $\underline{29}$, 1755 (1972).
5. Bourrely and Fischer, CERN Preprint TH.1652.
6. U. Amaldi et al., Phys. Letters $\underline{44B}$, 112 (1973); S. R. Amendolia et al., Phys. Letters $\underline{44B}$, 119 (1973).

PROTON DIFFRACTION DISSOCIATION DATA FROM THE CERN ISR[*]

G. Goldhaber[†]

Department of Physics and Lawrence Berkeley Laboratory
University of California, Berkeley, California 94720

In my talk I have discussed two experiments that have been carried out at the CERN ISR to measure proton diffraction dissociation. The first is by the CERN-Holland-Lancaster-Manchester collaboration (Albrow et al.) and the second by the Aachen-CERN-Harvard-Genova-Torino collaboration (Böhm et al.). Some details of these experiments follow herewith:

Single-Arm Forward Spectrometer
Inclusive Spectra

Resolution ~ 1%
Central θ set to 40 mrad - 150 mrad
p_T (protons)   0.7 to 1.2 GeV/c

CERN-Holland-Lancaster-Manchester

$$\sqrt{s} = 23, \ 31, \ 45 \text{ GeV}$$

- -

Double-Arm Spectrometer

Resolution ~ 2.5%
$\Delta\theta$ 20 - 92 mrad   each arm
$\Delta\varphi$ 2 radians   each arm
Angles fixed, auxiliary "jet" counters

Aachen-CERN-Harvard-Genova-Torino

$$\sqrt{s} = 31, \ 45, \ 54.3 \text{ GeV}$$

The experiments of Albrow et al. have shown clear evidence for the production of high masses up to about 7 GeV in the proton diffraction process. This data has already been reported in the literature.[1] In the written version of my talk I will thus confine myself to the discussion of the second experiment only, which is as yet not available in the literature.

The Double-Arm Experiment by the Aachen-CERN-Harvard-Genova-Torino Group[2]

In the double-arm magnetic spectrometer experiment on pp elastic scattering at the CERN ISR a short run was made (~ 24 hours) to study diffraction dissociation of the proton.

Figure 1 shows the experimental apparatus. The two magnetic spectrometers have an angular acceptance $\theta_i = 20$-92 mrad, $\Delta\varphi_i = 2$ rad, where θ_i, φ_i are the polar and azimuthal angles relative to the beam axis in arm i. Multiplicity information was provided by the scintillation counter hodoscopes A1 and A2, and by the counter telescopes (M1, M2) and (M3, M4). The hodoscopes A1, A2 each consist of

4 counters with full 2π azimuthal coverage for $\vartheta_i \cong 160-400$ mrad, and partial azimuthal coverage out to 590 mrad. These counters are covered by a 5-mm thick Pb-Al sandwich with a conversion efficiency for γ rays of 50%. The angular acceptance of the counter telescopes (M1, M2) and (M3, M4) is $\Delta\vartheta_i \cong 30-100$ mrad, $\Delta\varphi_i = \pi/2$.

The trigger was a four-fold coincidence between the scintillation counters S1, S2, S3 and S4, which ensured that at least one charged particle traversed each spectrometer. In each trigger the hit patterns of the hodoscopes A1, A2 and of the telescopes (M1, M2) and (M3, M4) were recorded. The four counters A and telescope M in each arm thus effectively constituted an "auxiliary 5-counter system" for recording jet multiplicities.

For all events particle trajectories in the magnetic spectrometer were reconstructed off-line with momentum and angle accuracy $(\Delta p/p)$ $\sim 2.5\%$, $\Delta\theta \sim 0.5$ mrad. The incident ISR beam momentum had a spread of $\sim 2\%$; this was reduced to $\sim 1\%$ by using the location of the individual event vertices together with the known "momentum compaction function."[*]

Five auxiliary counters were used to separate the data into 4 categories which give a <u>qualitative</u> description of the observed events:

(i) "Low" multiplicity: none of the auxiliary counters fire.

(ii) "Medium" multiplicity, single jet: one or two of the auxiliary counters fire in the other arm.

(iii) "High" multiplicity, single jet: three to five of the auxiliary counters fire in one arm. No auxiliary counters fire in the other arm.[**]

(iv) Double jet: one or more of the auxiliary counters fire in <u>each</u> arm.

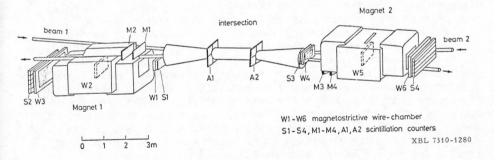

Fig. 1. Sketch of the double-arm spectrometer at the ISR.

---

[*] The "momentum compaction function" gives the beam momentum as a function of radial displacement from the central orbit.

[**] In half of the $\sqrt{s} = 53.4$ GeV data only the combined counter output was available in each arm. There thus is included a category which is: "medium to high" multiplicity single jet, and corresponds to (ii) and (iii) combined.

To illustrate the qualitative features of the data, Fig. 2a shows a plot of $e_2|X_2|$ versus $e_1|X_1|$, where X is the Feynman variable defined as $X_i = (P_i \cos \theta_i / P_{Bi})_{CM}$, e_i is ± 1 according to whether the charge of the particle in arm i is positive or negative and P_{Bi} is the beam momentum. The plot is for the median ISR energy studied here: $\sqrt{s} = 45$ GeV; the corresponding plots at $\sqrt{s} = 31$ GeV and 53.4 GeV are very similar. In Fig. 2a three distinct regions are clearly separated: $|X_1| \cong |X_2| \cong 1$, the elastic events; two bands $|X_1| \cong 1$, $|X_2| < 0.9$ and $|X_1| < 0.9$, $|X_2| \cong 1$ which we interpret as single diffraction dissociation, (SDD); and $|X_1| < 0.9$, $|X_2| < 0.9$, the pionization component of the inelastic cross section.

In Fig. 2c is shown the subset of events in category (i); elastic events have been removed by excluding collinear events. One notes that the central inelastic region has been strongly suppressed relative to the diffractive bands. This is a clear indication that SDD events have a very different multiplicity distribution than "pionization" events.

The "single jet" events in categories (ii) and (iii) are plotted in Figs. 2d and 2e respectively; here the subscript 2 indicates the arm containing the jet. One can note that there is now only one diffractive band $|X_1| \cong 1$, $|X_2| < 0.9$, confirming that the definition of SDD is valid; namely, the diffraction band disappears in the jet arm.

It is also clear in comparing Figs. 2d and 2e with 2c that the diffractive bands appear broader and that they have shifted to slightly lower X values. This shift implies that excitation to higher masses is involved since the missing mass M in the reaction, $p + p \to p + MM$ is related to X_1, through $M^2 \cong S(1 - X_1)$.

In Fig. 2b is shown category (iv); here a jet in each arm is required and, as expected, the diffractive bands have completely disappeared. One can also note that the requirement of a "single jet" only is very powerful in suppressing pionization events.

The missing mass distributions for the "single jet" events $p + p \to p + MM$ have been calculated. Elastic events were used for calibration of the measured momenta and for estimating mass resolution. For momentum calibration, the measured elastic peaks have been adjusted to the nominal central beam momenta given by the ISR operations group. This involved shifts in the measured momenta for single runs of at most 4%. The mass resolution was determined from the average of the missing mass against each proton in the elastic events. The resulting distributions in M^2/s are shown in Figs. 3 and 4 for the two extreme ISR energies $\sqrt{s} = 31.0$ GeV, and 53.4 GeV. The standard deviations, as determined by fitting a Gaussian to the elastic distributions, are $\sigma = 0.017$ and 0.022, corresponding to $\Delta M = 4$ GeV and 8 GeV at $\sqrt{s} = 31$ GeV and 53.4 GeV respectively.

The mass resolution in this experiment only allows the study of the "average" characteristics of the diffractive excitation spectrum. Certain features are readily apparent in Fig. 3. The diffractive peaks are shifted in M^2/s relative to the elastic peaks. Using the qualitative separation into multiplicity categories we furthermore note that these shifts increase with increasing multiplicity. Finally

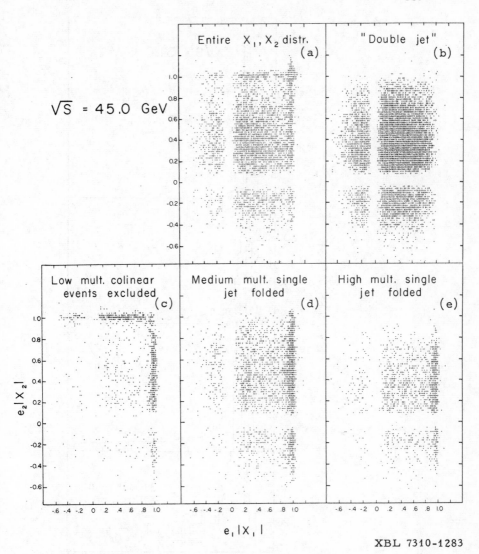

$\sqrt{S}$ = 45.0 GeV

XBL 7310-1283

Fig. 2. Illustration of the qualitative features of the data.
(a) shows the entire data; note the "elastic peak" at
$|X_1| \cong |X_2| \cong 1$, and the diffraction bands. For clarity
(a) includes only ~ 1/10 of the data. (b) to (e) show the
distributions for the various multiplicity cuts as discussed
in the text.

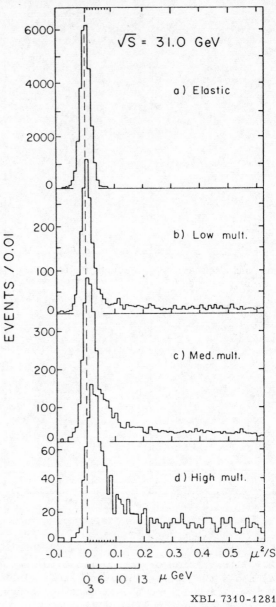

XBL 7310-1281

Fig. 3. M^2/s distributions for the
various cuts shown on the figure.

most of the diffractive peaks are asymmetric with a clear shoulder
on the high mass side.

To estimate the masses involved in these diffractive peaks the
shift of the center of each peak has been measured at half maximum
height relative to the elastic peak. It was found that masses M
occur ranging from 1.8 to 4.7 GeV for $\sqrt{s} = 31$ GeV, from 2.5 to 6.8
GeV for $\sqrt{s} = 45$ GeV and from 2.9 to 8.3 GeV for $\sqrt{s} = 53.4$ GeV,
with the mass always increasing with increasing multiplicity. One
must emphasize that the categories "low", "medium" and "high" multiplicity, as defined earlier describe only the relative multiplicity
at fixed s. Since the jet opening angle for fixed mass goes as $1/\sqrt{s}$,
the fixed angle auxiliary counters sample, for a given diffractive
mass, a different range of decay particles at different s.

The masses at the center of the shoulder are ~ 8.4 GeV, 9.3
GeV and 14 GeV for the three energies $\sqrt{s} = 31$, 45 and 53.4 GeV
respectively.

A more quantitative study of the mass distributions has been
made by fitting them with an invariant cross section of the form:

$$s \frac{d\sigma}{d^2 p_T dM^2} \propto \frac{s}{\{s(1 - X)\}} \nu \exp - [\Gamma/s(1 - X)] \qquad (1)$$

where Γ is a parameter related to X_p, the value of X at the peak of
the distribution, by $\Gamma = \nu s(1 - X_p)$, and ν is a parameter to be
determined from the data.

The mass region $M \gg m_o$ (threshold mass) on the high mass side
of the peak is the so-called "triple-Regge region"; in the Regge-
Muller approach

$$\nu = 2 \alpha_p(t) - 1 = 1 \qquad \text{for triple-Pomeron (PPP) coupling,}$$

and

$$\nu = 2 \alpha_p(t) - \frac{1}{2} = \frac{3}{2} \qquad \text{for PPf coupling}$$

(f indicates an effective meson trajectory with $\alpha_f(0) = 1/2$).

The fits to the data according to expression (1) and including
a background term, are shown in Figs. 5a, b and c. The points marked
(X) in Figs. 5 show the raw "uncut data." By use of the auxiliary
counters the "double jet" events were removed leaving the points
indicated by the vertical error bars ($|$). This data was fitted as
follows: A Gaussian resolution function, determined from the elastic
scattering data, was folded into expression (1). The curves labeled
"THEORY" correspond to expression (1). The resulting distribution
including a background term was then fitted to the data obtaining
"best fit" values for ν and Γ. These distributions are labeled "FIT"
in Figs. 5. Various assumptions on the background were tried and the
sensitivity to these background assumptions was explored. The curves
labeled "RESIDUAL BACKGROUND" shown in Figs. 5 correspond to the case
in which the shape of the background term was obtained from the
"medium" multiplicity data.

It is interesting to note that the full width at half height of
the curves labeled "THEORY," which in each case corresponds to the
best fit parameters, are $M = 3.2$, 5.2 and 6.4 GeV respectively at

392

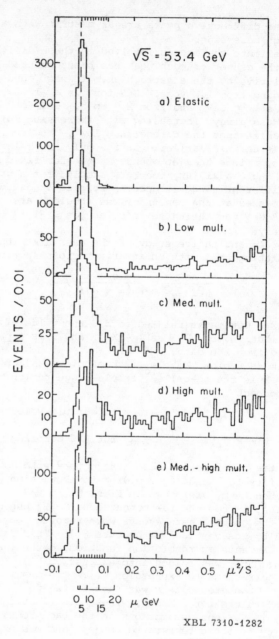

Fig. 4. M^2/s distributions for the
various cuts shown on the figure.

$\sqrt{s} = 31$, 45 and 53.4 GeV. These values are consistent with the ones obtained from the shifts of the peaks in Figs. 3 and 4 as described above. As for the best fit values the results at all three energies, $\sqrt{s} = 31$, 45 and 53.4 GeV were consistent, and give

$$\nu = 1.15 \pm 0.1 \ .$$

This indicates that the PPP coupling appears to be dominant, but that some PPf coupling may also be present.

General Remarks

The information gathered from the double-arm experiment differs from that of Albrow et al.[1] in that while the momentum resolution is poorer, thanks to the presence of the auxiliary counters and the correlation with the second spectrometer arm, one can isolate the events due to the diffractive diagrams. The main isolation of the diffractive events is obtained by eliminating the "double jet" events. The remaining small background is eliminated in the fit by allowing for a component essentially linear in M^2. The parameters in the fit are thus primarily determined both by the location of the observed diffractive mass peak and by the distribution in the shoulder region X approximately equal 0.85 to 0.95.

The P_T^2 range covered at the three energies for the leading proton in the diffractive region is shown in Figs. 5. While no cut on P_T^2 was applied to the data, in view of the typical slopes of $B = 3$ to 5 GeV^{-2} for the diffractive region this implies that the main contribution comes from the low P_T^2 end of the regions studied. The effective P_T^2 regions are thus $P_T^2 \approx 0.25 \pm 0.1$ (GeV)^2 at $\sqrt{s} = 31$ GeV, $P_T^2 \approx 0.35 \pm 0.15$ (GeV)^2 at $\sqrt{s} = 45$ GeV and $P_T^2 \approx 0.45 \pm 0.15$ (GeV)^2 at $\sqrt{s} = 53.4$ GeV.

A Monte Carlo acceptance calculation was performed and applied to the data at each energy. This had no appreciable effect in the diffractive regions under discussion. The fits were thus performed on the data as measured.

REFERENCES

*Work supported by the U. S. Atomic Energy Commission.
†Guggenheim Fellow at CERN, May 1972 to March 1973.
1. M. G. Albrow et al., Nuclear Physics B51, 388 (1973) and B54, 6 (1973).
2. A. Böhm, H. Bozzo, G. Diambrini Palazzi, G. de Zorzi, M. I. Ferrero, H. Foeth, G. Goldhaber, M. Hansroul, J. Jovanovic, A. Kernan, G. Maderni, P. Palazzi, J. Pilcher, C. Rubbia, G. Sette, A. Staude, P. Strolin, and L. Sulak (Aachen-CERN-Harvard-Genova-Torino Group at the ISR).

394

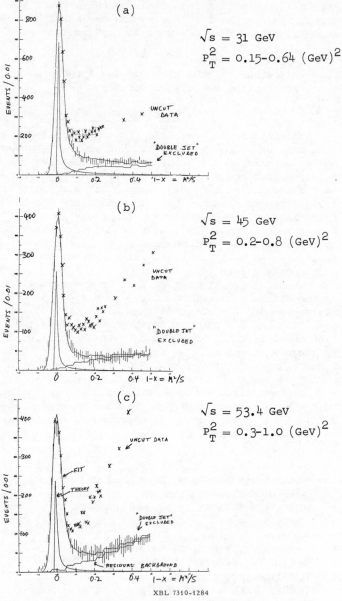

XBL 7310-1284

Fig. 5. Fits to the diffractive distributions
including all "single or no jet" multiplicity
categories. Curves are described in the text.

COMMENTS ON DIFFRACTION DISSOCIATION [*]

by

Juliet Lee-Franzini

State University of New York, Stony Brook, New York   11790

At this conference a whole day was devoted to the discussion of diffraction dissociation at high energies. There was no formal definition of "diffraction dissociation", but it was understood that a part of the inelastic cross section comes from the break up of the beam (or target) particle, hence involves relatively small momentum transfer and not too great masses. In the previous year the CHLM collaboration has observed a forward peak near $x = 1$ (where $x = 2 P_{\parallel}^{*}/\sqrt{s}$) at ISR energies. They have concluded that there is substantial diffractive production of masses up to 7 GeV, as their recoil mass distribution does not level off until approximately 50 GeV^2. One recalls that minimum four momentum transfer in the CHLM is about -.45, because the minimal approachable angle to the beam is 35 m radians. The momentum spread in the ISR beams of 2% was reduced in the analysis stage on the CHLM experiment to 0.7%, resulting in an M^2 resolution of approximately 9 GeV^2. Various bubble chamber experiments have claimed confirmation of the ISR results and estimate the diffractive dissociation cross section to be about 7-8 mb.

S. Childress this morning has presented our results from an experiment performed at NAL (S. Childress, P. Franzini, Columbia University; J. Lee-Franzini, R. McCarthy and R. Schamberger, Jr., State University of New York at Stony Brook), using 300 GeV incident protons. The reaction we studied was $P + P \rightarrow P + X$ where X is the quasi particle composed of all else excluding the recoil proton. We used a solid state hodoscope system to measure the recoil proton's kinetic energy (10-100 MeV) and laboratory angle (45°-90°), from which the four momentum transfer t ($|t| = 2 M_p T$) and missing mass squared M_X^2, can be computed. We used a polyethylene-carbon subtraction method to obtain the proton-free hydrogen cross sections. The discovery that deuterons and tritons are copiously produced simultaneously with the protons in the polyethylene and carbon targets enabled us to perform this subtraction with great accuracy. The use of the deuterons and tritons to normalize our polyethylene and carbon runs made us insensitive to beam characteristic variations, possible hydrogen depletion with exposure in the polyethylene target, etc. The t range in this experiment was $.019 < |t| < .168$, the missing mass squared range was $1 < M_X^2 < 60$ GeV^2. The mass square resolution was about 1 GeV^2, and can be seen directly in the following figure where the spectrum is displayed including the elastic events. One notes that $\sigma = .55$ GeV^2. The energy scale calibration was also checked using elastic events (340,000 in the experiment). One notes the very reasonable determination of the elastic slope of $10.6 \pm .7$ $(GeV/c)^2$. (Figure 2)

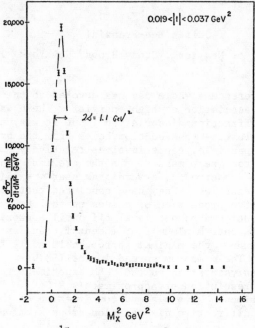

Figure 1. $S \dfrac{d\sigma}{dt dM_X^2}$ Vs M_X^2

for $.019 < |t| < .038$ $(GeV/c)^2$ including elastics

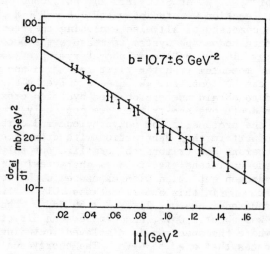

Figure 2. $\dfrac{d\sigma_{el}}{dt}$ Vs $|t|$

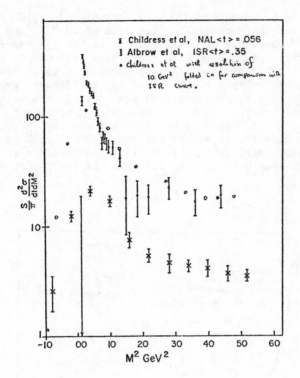

Figure 3. $\dfrac{S}{\Pi}\ \dfrac{d^2\sigma}{dt dM_X^2}$ Vs M_X^2

for $.019 < |t| < .094$ $(GeV/c)^2$ inelastic only

The invariant cross section $\dfrac{S}{\Pi}\ \dfrac{d^2\sigma}{dt dM_X^2}$ (S = total center of mass energy^2 = 563 GeV^2) vs M_X^2 for $|t|$ of .019 to .094 is seen in Figure 3. Also on the same graph is a plot of ISR data taken at $|t|$ = .35 and S = 929.5, for comparison. One notes that our M_X^2 spectrum has a sharp peak at M_X^2 = 2 GeV^2 (it is the N*(1400)), comes down steeply as M_X^2 increases, and has dropped to 1/20 of its peak value at M_X^2 = 16 GeV^2, thereafter the M_X^2 spectrum is approximately flat. This is in contrast with the ISR curve which has decreased only by a factor of five at a M_X^2 of 50 GeV^2. Note also that there the fall is gradual, approximately simulating $1/M_X^2$ dependence.

The main discussion was whether the difference is due to the two experiments looking at two different regions $< |t| > = .056$ Vs $< |t| >= .35$, or could be accounted for by resolution difference. We feel that it is primarily due to the latter since

398

1) the ISR curve has considerable area left of $M_x^2 = 0.0$, 2) we had
folded our curve with a resolution function of 10 GeV^2 and have obtained curves exceedingly similar to those of the ISR experiment
(circled points), i.e. a depressed peak, slow fall off as M^2 increa-
ses, and having a higher cross section because it is at lower $< |t| >$.
In conclusion, we feel the broadness of the ISR forward peak is due
to their resolution, not because they are looking at a much higher
$|t|$ region than we were. There are some differences in M_x^2 spectra
taken at different $|t|$ regions, but they are usually on details of
structure, for example, we do not see the $N^*(1400)$ peak in our
higher $|t|$ region data, $(.09 < |t| < .17)$, indicating a very sharp
t dependence, (slope b in e^{-bt} of the order of 18-20) for $N^*(1400)$
production.

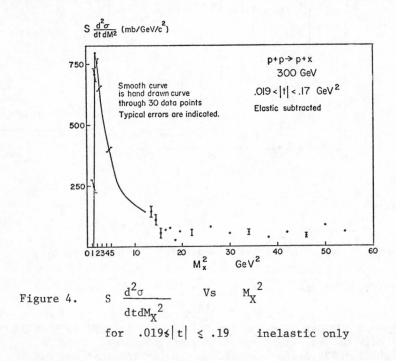

Figure 4. $S \dfrac{d^2\sigma}{dtdM_X^2}$ Vs M_X^2

for $.019 \leqslant |t| \leqslant .19$ inelastic only

Figure 4 gives our determination of the inelastic invariant
cross section $S \dfrac{d\sigma}{dtdM_X^2}$ for the whole t region of our experiment
$.019 < |t| < .17$. We can estimate the total cross section from
$1 < M_X^2 < 16$ GeV^2 to be $(2.35 \pm .2)$ mb using an average slope b of
4.3 determined from the same data. If one desires a lower limit of
the diffraction dissociation contribution, one should subtract from
this value the contribution due to whatever physical process is
responsible for the essentially constant cross section above M_X^2 of

16 GeV^2. If this background is assumed to extend down to $M_X^2 = 1$ with the same value observed in the interval $16 \geq M^2 \geq 60$ GeV^2, we obtain $\sigma(PP \rightarrow PX, 1 \geq M_X^2 \geq 16$ GeV^2, diffractive?) $= 1.6 \pm .2$ mb. Multiplying this value by 2 for the symmetry of the PP system we find the diffractive dissociation cross section is bounded by $3.2 \lesssim \sigma_{diff} \lesssim 4.7$ mb.

There was also considerable discussion on triple Regge fits, with claims made that the triple pomeron term dominates because the M_X^2 spectrum can be fitted with a $1/M_X^2$ dependence. Our data can not be so fitted because of its sharp drop as M_X^2 increases. We need a $1/M_X^3$ contribution; in triple regge terminology this corresponds to a pomeron-pomeron-reggeon term. Our best fit using only a pomeron-pomeron-pomeron ($\sim 1/M_X^2$), pomeron-pomeron-reggeon ($\sim 1/M_X^3$, reggeon-reggeon-pomeron term ($\sim$ constant as M_X^2) is

$$G_{PPP} = 1.43 \quad (mb/GeV^2) \quad at \ (t = -.1)$$

$$G_{PPR} = 5.48 \quad (mb/GeV^2) \quad at \ (t = -.1)$$

$$G_{RRP} = 51 \quad (mb/GeV^2) \quad at \ (t = -.1)$$

for a pomeron trajectory of $\alpha_P = 1 + .28 \ t$ and a reggeon trajectory of $\alpha_R = .5 + t$.

* Work supported in part by the National Science Foundation.

PARTICLE MULTIPLICITIES AND CORRELATIONS
AT NAL ENERGIES*

T. Ferbel[†]

University of Rochester, Rochester, N.Y.   14627

ABSTRACT

A summary is presented of the latest data concerning
particle multiplicities and correlations between particles
produced in pp collisions at high energies.

INTRODUCTION

The emphasis of this paper will be on the most recent data pertaining to measurements of charged-particle multiplicities and two-
particle correlations in pp collisions at high energies. I will also
make several remarks pertaining to single-particle inclusive data not
covered by the other plenary speakers at this Meeting. Much of what
I present on correlations comes directly from Carl Bromberg's summary
given in the parallel sessions.

INCLUSIVE CROSS SECTIONS

In Fig. 1 I present the latest compilation of inclusive cross
sections for the reactions[1]:

$$pp \rightarrow \Lambda^{o}/\Sigma^{o} + \text{anything} \qquad (1)$$

$$pp \rightarrow K_{s}^{o} + \text{anything} \qquad (2)$$

$$pp \rightarrow \pi^{o} + \text{anything} \qquad (3)$$

$$pp \rightarrow \pi^{-} + \text{anything} \qquad (4)$$

Cross sections for reactions (3) and (4) are shown reduced by a factor of 100. It is observed that by 400 GeV/c the K_{s}^{o} cross section,
after a rather dramatic rise for energies above 10 GeV/c, appears to
be approaching the sort of slow rate of increase which is more characteristic of π and Λ production.

Figure 2 displays the variation of the inclusive x-spectra for
reactions (1)-(3) as a function of incident energy ($x \equiv p_{\ell}^{*}/p_{o}^{*}$, with p_{ℓ}^{*}
and p^{*} being the longitudinal momentum and the incident momentum in
the $_{o}$CM frame). The data have been integrated over transverse momenta (p_{T}) and consequently reflect mainly the small-p_{T} behavior of
these cross sections[2]. (Reaction (3) is not really measured in the
NAL bubble chamber, what is observed is the process $pp \rightarrow \gamma + $anything. It
is assumed throughout that the cross sections for these two reactions

*Research supported by the U.S.Atomic Energy Commission. Invited
 paper presented at the Berkeley APS-DPF Meeting (1973).
†A. P. Sloan Fellow.

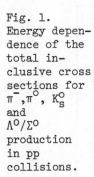

Fig. 1.
Energy depen-
dence of the
total in-
clusive cross
sections for
π^-, π^o, K_S^o
and
Λ^o/Σ^o
production
in pp
collisions.

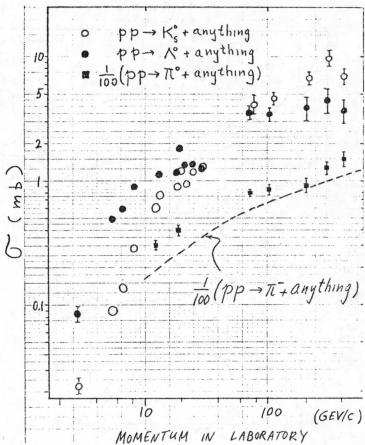

are related just by a factor of two.) All the data show rather clear
violation of scaling (i.e., the cross sections change) in the $\lesssim 400$
GeV/c momentum range at x=0. For larger x-values the statistics are
poor; however, above 100 GeV/c, the data in the proton fragmentation
regime are consistent with a faster approach to limiting behavior
than the data in the central region of particle production.

Figure 3 displays inclusive pion-production y-spectra for reaction (4) and for the π^+ channel:[3]

$$pp \rightarrow \pi^+ + \text{anything} \qquad (5)$$

Both π^+ and π^- production data are shown integrated over p_T (the y_{CM}
scale is for the 102 GeV spectra, with the rapidity defined in the
standard manner: $y = \frac{1}{2}\ln(E+p_\ell/E-p_\ell)$. The spectra for reaction (4)
appear to have reached their limiting form at $\lesssim 12$ GeV/c for $y_{LAB} \lesssim 0.5$.
At larger values of y_{LAB} we note substantial changes in the cross
sections. Similar remarks apply to reaction (5). The π^+/π^- production ratio changes from ~4 at $y_{LAB} = -0.5$ to ~1.2 at $y_{CM} = 0$ for both

402

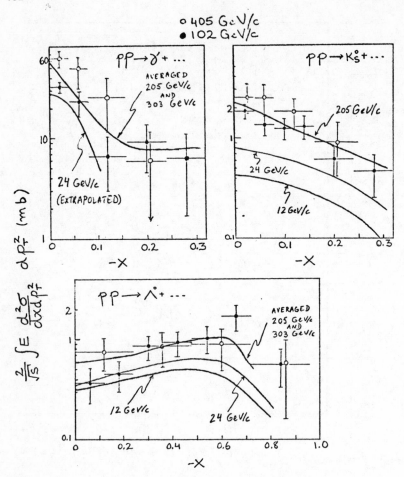

Fig. 2. Variation with incident energy of the invariant cross sections for γ, K_S^O and Λ^O/Σ^O production in pp collisions.

the 102 GeV/c and 205 GeV/c data; clearly, these spectra (particularly at $y_{CM}=0$) must be far from their limiting form. The energy dependence of reactions (1)-(5) at $y_{CM}=0$, when integrated over p_T, follows the $s^{-\frac{1}{4}}$ trend noted for similar data at lower energies.[4]

MULTIPLICITIES AND KNO SCALING

At the time of the last "Rochester" Conference at Chicago/NAL, Olesen and Slattery presented[5] astonishing evidence for the rapid onset of Koba-Olesen-Nielsen[6] scaling in the charged-particle multiplicities. This KNO semi-inclusive scaling, which was hoped for as an asymptotic dream, turned out to represent the data remarkably well between 50 GeV/c and 300 GeV/c. However, since Slattery's fit, the

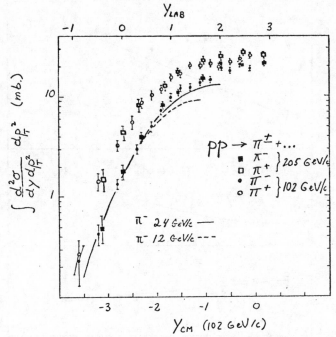

Fig. 3.
Variation with
incident momentum
of the invariant
cross section for
π^+ and π^- production in pp
collisions.

50 GeV/c and 303 GeV/c data have changed somewhat;[7] the 102 GeV/c
data have improved considerably;[8] and the 405 GeV/c data have become
available.[8] The present conclusions concerning the onset of KNO
scaling are that, at best, the limit is being approached slowly ($\sim\frac{1}{\langle n \rangle}$).

The most recent results pertaining to the lower moments of
charged-particle multiplicities observed in pp collisions at high
energies are shown in Fig. 4. Simple fits to these data are also
given. The average charged-particle multiplicity, $\langle n \rangle$, is consistent with a logarithmic dependence on the square of the energy in
the CM system(s) in the 50 GeV/c to 405 GeV/c momentum range[9]. It
should be remarked, however, that the fit to a $\ell n\ s$ form does not
yield an acceptable χ^2, indicating the presence of additional systematic errors in the individual experiments (higher order $\ell n\ s$ terms
do not substantially affect the quality of the fit). The Mueller f_2^-
moment[10], which prior to the availability of the 405 GeV/c data also
appeared to have a $\ell n\ s$ dependence, now definitely exhibits curvature,
which can be parameterized in terms of a sizeable $(\ell n\ s)^2$ term. The
f_3^- moment is at present consistent with a $\ell n\ s$ form.

Now, to investigate in more detail the question of the early
onset of KNO scaling, I present in Fig. 5 some relevant parameters
of the charged-particle multiplicity spectrum. If KNO semi-inclusive
scaling were valid at present energies then the multiplicity spectrum
would scale as follows:

$$\langle n \rangle \frac{\sigma_n}{\sigma_{INEL}} = \psi \left(\frac{n}{\langle n \rangle}\right) \tag{6}$$

404

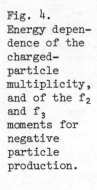

Fig. 4.
Energy depen-
dence of the
charged-
particle
multiplicity,
and of the f_2
and f_3
moments for
negative
particle
production.

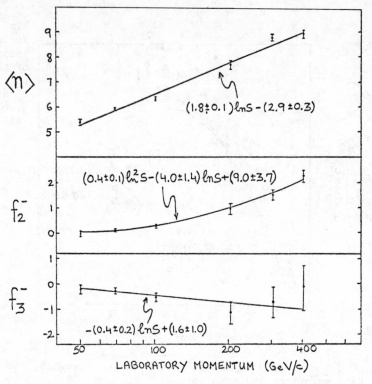

where σ_{INEL} and σ_n are the total inelastic and n-prong cross sections, and $\psi(\frac{n}{<n>})$ is the asymptotic scaling function. Equation (6), which embodies the KNO scaling prediction, can be expressed equivalently through the following sets of relationships relating the moments of the multiplicity spectrum:

$$<n^q> = C_q <n>^q \tag{7}$$

where the C_q are constants at high enough energies. Consequently, if KNO asymptopia had been reached in the 50-400 GeV/c momentum range, than the value of $\frac{<n>}{D}$ as well as $<n^2>/<n>^2$, $<n^3>/<n>^3$, etc. would all be constant. It is clear that the present data do not substan-tiate such a conclusion. Wroblewski has emphasized that all pp data (even down to energies of ~10 GeV) are consistent with a slow onset of KNO scaling (as ~ $\frac{1}{<n>}$)[11]. Wroblewski's phenomenological predic-tions for $\frac{<n>}{D}$ and for $\frac{<n^2>}{<n>^2}$ and $\frac{<n^3>}{<n>^3}$ are shown for comparison with the data. (Predictions are based on the observation that at lower energies D=0.58[<n>-1] and $\frac{\mu_3}{D^3} \equiv \frac{(n-<n>)^3}{D^3}$ and $\frac{\mu_4}{D^4} \equiv \frac{(n-<n>)^4}{D^4}$ appear

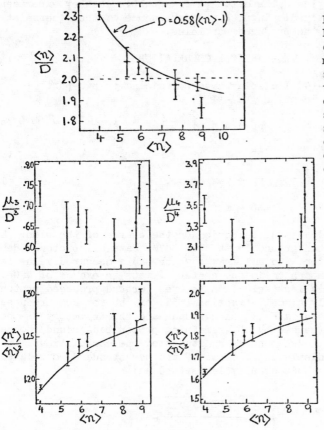

Fig. 5.
Parameters of the charged-particle multiplicity spectrum relevant to the question of the early onset of KNO scaling. The curves are based on Wroblewski's conjectures.

to be energy independent constants.) The trends suggested by Wroblewski are certainly supported by the new data. The implications of these results is that KNO scaling has not as yet been reached but is perhaps being approached as $1/\langle n \rangle$. (It is interesting to note that deviations from KNO scaling in the 405 GeV/c multiplicity data occur mainly for the higher charged-prong cross sections.)

Although KNO scaling has not as yet set in, it is clear that this form of approach to limiting behavior gives a surprisingly good overall description of the particle multiplicity spectrum. This is true not only for charged-particle data but also for π^0, K_s^0 and even Λ^0 production[12].

CORRELATIONS[13]

Extensive studies of two-particle correlations have recently been conducted at the ISR[14]. These have demonstrated the presence of substantial positive correlation among particles having small rapidity differences. Here I would like to present some recent results pertaining to correlations observed in the production of pions at NAL energies. The data are from bubble chamber experiments and can consequently distinguish the dependence of these correlations on the charges of the produced particles.

TWO-PARTICLE CORRELATIONS

In Figs. (6)-(9) I display data pertaining to two-particle correlations for the reactions (8)-(11):

$$pp \rightarrow \pi^c \pi^c + \ldots \tag{8}$$

$$pp \rightarrow \pi^+ \pi^- + \ldots \tag{9}$$

$$pp \rightarrow \pi^+ \pi^+ + \ldots \tag{10}$$

$$pp \rightarrow \pi^- \pi^- + \ldots \tag{11}$$

where the "c" indicates no selection on the charge of the pion. To minimize K and p background in the 102 GeV/c data all protons identifiable by ionization, and all tracks which had a measured value for the longitudinal momentum in the center of mass in excess of 4 GeV/c were removed. This last selection removed forward produced protons while removing only a small fraction (<5%) of the forward produced pions[13]. The remaining $K^{\pm}$, $\bar{p}$ backgrounds and the asymmetry in the positive spectra (caused by the remaining proton background) do not seriously affect the shapes or magnitudes of the correlations. The correlations are displayed in terms of the now standard correlated rapidity density. This density is defined as:

$$R_{12} = \frac{\sigma_{INEL} \frac{d^2\sigma}{dy_1 dy_2}}{\frac{d\sigma}{dy_1} \frac{d\sigma}{dy_2}} - 1$$

where $\sigma_{INEL} = 31.9 \pm 0.8$ mb is the total inelastic cross section for the 102 GeV/c data[8].

The smooth curves shown in Figs. (6)-(9) represent the results of a pion-production model calculated at 102 GeV/c, with the following properties:

(a) The a priori probabilities of each pion being a π^+, a π^-, or a π^0 are equal, as are those for each nucleon being a neutron or a proton. Charge and baryon conservation alone are used to determine which final states are possible. The probability for the production of any particular number of pions is obtained by constraining the resultant charged particle multiplicity for the model to agree with that observed for the data[8].

(b) The pions are produced with a cutoff transverse momentum distribution of the form $e^{-\alpha p_T^2}$, which is in approximate agreement with the data. The rapidity distribution of the generated pions is also chosen to be Gaussian in shape, with a variance which

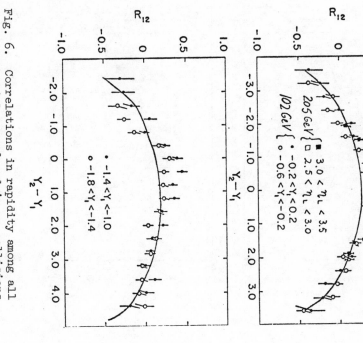

Fig. 6. Correlations in rapidity among all charged particles produced in pp collisions. For explanation of curves see text.

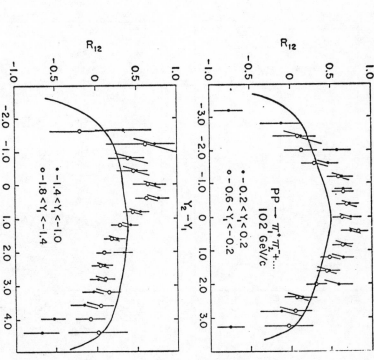

Fig. 7. Correlations between π^+ and π^- mesons produced in pp collisions. For explanation of curves see text.

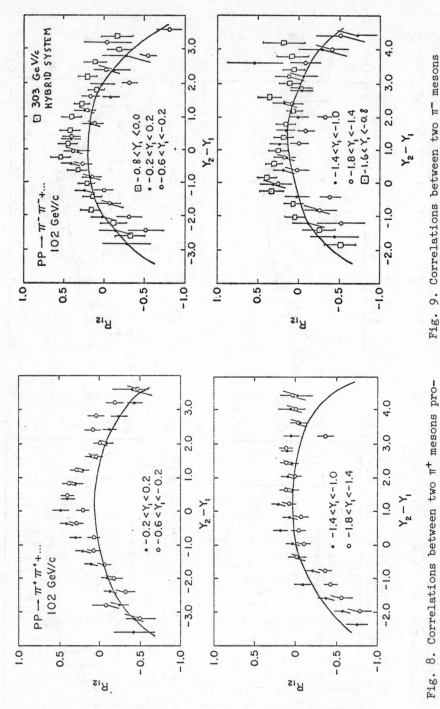

Fig. 9. Correlations between two π⁻ mesons produced in pp collisions. For explanation of curves see text.

Fig. 8. Correlations between two π⁺ mesons produced in pp collisions. For explanation of curves see text.

decreases with total pion multiplicity as $1/\sqrt{n}$ (also in approximate agreement with the data), and with an overall scale factor
which was chosen so that on the average the total energy carried
away by all of the pions in an event amounts to one half the
total center-of-mass energy.

The intent of the model was to compare the experimental data with a
"control sample" of the same general kinematic character. Although
the nature of this comparison can at best only be semi-quantitative,
the following general observations can be made:

(a) The R_{12} parameters for $\Delta y=0$ are consistently larger than expected
    on the basis of the model. This is true for all charge config-
    urations. In particular, the $\pi^+\pi^+$ and $\pi^-\pi^-$ correlations near
    $y_1 \approx y_2 \approx 0$ have $R_{12} \approx 0.4$; this is surprisingly large when com-
    pared to expectations from simple Mueller-Regge ideas[15].

(b) The magnitude of R_{12} for pions of all charge (Fig. 6a) agrees
    well with that observed for the central region of pion produc-
    tion at 205 GeV/c [16] and at ISR energies[14]. A similar statement
    can be made concerning the comparison of the results for $\pi^-\pi^-$
    correlations (Fig. 9a) at 102 GeV/c with data for the same pro-
    cess at 303 GeV/c [17]. Consequently, the maxima in R_{12} appear to
    be essentially energy independent.

(c) The model does not reproduce the magnitude or shape of R_{12}, par-
    ticularly for the $\pi^+\pi^-$ data, when the two particles are produced
    away from the most central region. (Data at 303 GeV/c for the
    $\pi^-\pi^-$ charge state also exhibit the peaking behavior in R_{12} at
    $\Delta y=0$ when both π^- are produced away from $y=0$.) The observed
    correlations for $\Delta y=0$ can be taken as evidence for additional
    particle clustering in the production process, a possibility
    not admitted in the model.

Transverse momentum correlations (the azimuth angles between
transverse momenta of two particles) are given in Fig. 10. The results are at 102 GeV/c for events with six or more charged prongs.
Again, I wish to note that the data for unlike-charged pions appear
to show more structure than for pions of same charge. Here, however,
momentum conservation requires some anti-correlation and, consequently,
the lack of correlation in reactions (10) and (11) and the reduced
correlation in reaction (9) for large rapidity gaps between the two
pions, would appear to have a dynamic origin[18]. The diminution in
the azimuthal correlation for large rapidity difference may be related to the nature of the Pomeranchuck trajectory[19].

FORWARD/BACKWARD CORRELATIONS IN THE CENTER OF MASS

The charge transfer distribution, i.e., half the difference between the charge moving in the forward direction (Q_F) and in the backward direction in the center of mass (Q_B) is shown in Fig. 11a.
(There is a very slight asymmetry in the data due to misidentifica-
tion of protons.) The variance of the distribution, $\langle U^2 \rangle = \frac{1}{4}\langle (Q_F - Q_B)^2 \rangle$
has important bearing on the nature of the production mechanism.
This variable has a weak dependence on laboratory momentum (Fig.11b),
and is more in line with predictions based on a multiperipheral mechanism than with those afforded by a fragmentation or fireball model[20].

410

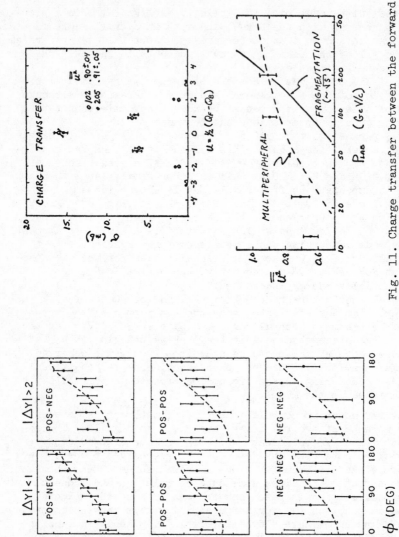

Fig. 11. Charge transfer between the forward and backward hemispheres in the center of mass. Curves for the prediction of the energy variation of the variance ($\overline{\overline{U}}^2$), normalized to the data at 205 GeV/c, have been privately communicated (C.Quigg and G.Thomas).

Fig. 10. Transverse correlations between charged particles produced in pp collisions at 102 GeV/c. For explanation of curves see text.

Figure 12 displays the average multiplicity in the forward hemisphere $\langle N_F \rangle$ as a function of the number of particles emitted backward in the center of mass frame (N_B). Note that there is a weak positive correlation for all multiplicities between N_B and $\langle N_F \rangle$; furthermore, the effect of the low-multiplicity diffractive contribution is discernible in the dips observed for $N_B = 1,3$ and perhaps $N_B = 5$. The data clearly do not exhibit a strong dependence on incident energy.

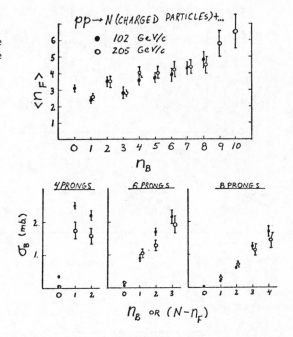

Fig. 12. Forward/Backward charge correlations in the center of mass frame.

POT POURRI

In this section I would like to make a remark pertaining to the growth of the large-p_T component in inclusive cross sections at yesteryear's high energies, that is, at incident momenta below 100 GeV/c. I would also like to make several observations pertaining to diffraction production at high energies. (The latter subject is discussed more fully by David Leith elsewhere in these Proceedings.)

Thus far I have presented bubble chamber data which were integrated over the p_T variable and consequently displayed characteristics of production processes at small p_T values. To remind you of the fact that inclusive p_T spectra at low incident momenta are not simply exponentials in p_T or p_T^2, I have plotted in Fig. 13 the average values of p_T, p_T^2 and the dispersion $(D=[\langle p_T^2 \rangle - \langle p_T \rangle^2]^{\frac{1}{2}})$ for inclusive π^- production in various incident channels as a function of the incident momentum[21]. The substantial growth of $\langle p_T \rangle$, $\langle p_T^2 \rangle$ and D with increasing energy gives another clear indication of the fact that Feynman scaling is being violated in inclusive pion production reactions at large p_T values. I expect that as the incident momenta increase the average values of the low-order moments of the p_T spectrum will start saturating, while ever higher order moments of p_T will continue to grow with energy (and again saturate at even greater incident momenta). The growth of the p_T moments is far stronger than

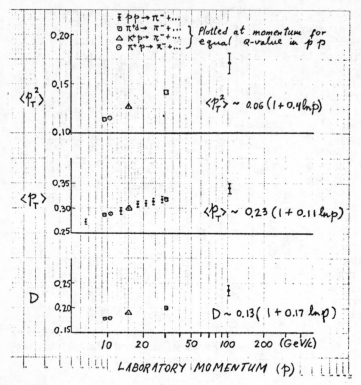

Fig. 13. Dependence on incident momentum of the low moments of the transverse-momentum spectrum for inclusive π^- production.

expected on the basis of just increasing phase space, and consequently may be related to conjectured substructure of hadronic matter[22].

Finally, I wish to present three ways of examining the reaction

$$pp \rightarrow p + \text{anything} \tag{12}$$

In Fig. 14 I display the cross section for reaction (12) integrated over p_T in terms of the mass (M) recoiling from the final-state proton[23]. The trend of the data with energy is quite clear. As the value of s increases the cross section for $s/2 > M^2 \gtrsim 16$ GeV^2 falls approximately as $1/s$ while the cross section for $M^2 \lesssim 16$ GeV^2 falls far less rapidly with energy and may, in fact, be approaching a limiting form. (The cross section for $M^2 < 16$ GeV^2 at 405 GeV/c is ~3.8 mb counting both target and projectile fragmentation.)

The same data can be displayed in terms of the x-variable for the proton ($x \sim 1 - M^2/s$). In Fig. 15 the cross section in x is compared between the 102 GeV/c data and the data at 405 GeV/c[23]. Here it is clear that for $x \gtrsim -0.9$ the cross section is s-independent to ~10% accuracy[24]. Also, the total cross section for $x < -0.9$ appears to be energy independent ($\sigma = 6.2 \pm 0.4$ mb counting both target and projectile excitation). However, the shape of the cross section near $x = -1$ changes drastically with energy indicating that reaction (12) does not scale near the kinematic boundary.

The last graph (Fig. 16) is another comparison between the

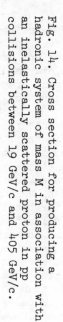
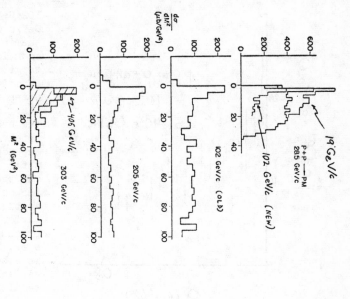

Fig. 14. Cross section for producing a hadronic system of mass M in association with an inelastically scattered proton in pp collisions between 19 GeV/c and 405 GeV/c.

$$\frac{d\sigma}{dM^2} \left(\mu b/GeV^2\right)$$

19 GeV/c

P + P → PM
285 GeV/c

102 GeV/c (NEW)

102 GeV/c (OLD)

205 GeV/c

303 GeV/c

405 GeV/c

M^2 (GeV²)

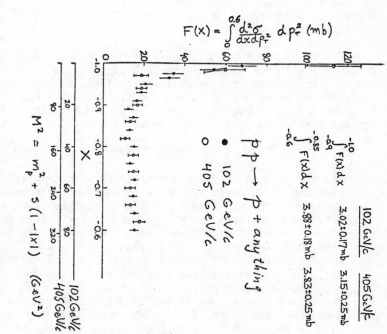

$$F(x) = \int_0^{0.6} \frac{d^2\sigma}{dx\,dp_T^2}\,dp_T^2 \ (mb)$$

$$pp \rightarrow p + anything$$

● 102 GeV/c
○ 405 GeV/c

	102 GeV/c	405 GeV/c
$\int_{-0.9}^{-1.0} F(x)\,dx$	3.02±0.17 mb	3.15±0.25 mb
$\int_{-0.6}^{-0.85} F(x)\,dx$	3.88±0.18 mb	3.83±0.25 mb

X

$M^2 = m_p^2 + 5(1-|x|) \ (GeV^2)$

102 GeV/c
405 GeV/c

Fig. 15. The x-spectra for inelastic proton production at 102 GeV/c and 405 GeV/c.

414

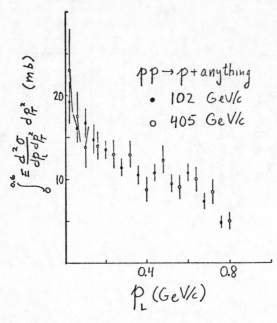

$pp \to p + anything$

$\bullet$ 102 GeV/c
$\circ$ 405 GeV/c

p_L (GeV/c)

Fig. 16. Inclusive proton-production data displayed in terms of the invariant cross section as observed in the rest frame of the incident proton.

102 GeV/c and the 405 GeV/c data, but this time the invariant cross section is examined in the target rest frame as a function of longitudinal momentum (p_ℓ). We note that in this rest frame the cross section appears to be energy independent! At asymptotic energies the x and the p_ℓ variable will become identical (as far as their limiting behavior is concerned) at present energies, however, it appears that p_ℓ is a better scaling variable than x^{25}. It remains to be seen whether at ISR energies these cross sections will also start scaling in x or whether they will stop scaling in $p_\ell{}^{26}$.

I wish to thank my colleagues at Michigan and Rochester for invaluable assistance in providing much of the data presented in this report. In particular I acknowledge the enthusiastic cooperation of C. Bromberg, D. Chaney, D. Cohen and P. Slattery. Finally, I thank G. Lynch and the organizing committee of the Berkeley DPF Meeting for inviting me to present this paper.

REFERENCES

1. The new data at 69 GeV/c are from the French-Soviet Collaboration report appearing in the Proceedings of the Vanderbilt Conference (1973) AIP Series No. 12, R. S. Panvini ed.; The 102 GeV/c data are from the Michigan-Rochester Groups Reports UMBC-73-20, UR-457; The 205 GeV/c data are from G. Charlton et al, Phys. Rev. Letters 30, 574 (1973); the data at 303 GeV/c are from F. Dao et al, Phys. Rev. Letters 30, 1151 (1973); The preliminary 405 GeV/c data are from the Michigan-Rochester Collaboration (to be published).

2. The K_s^0 and Λ data from 12 and 24 GeV/c are from the Bonn-Hamburg-Munich Group, H. J. Mück et al, DESY Report F1-72/1; the 6 GeV/c data are from a Michigan State preprint, B. Y. Oh et al. The 24 GeV/c extrapolated γ spectrum of Fidecaro et al, Nuovo Cimento 24, 73 (1962), is taken from the NAL-UCLA Report NAL 73/31, UCLA-1075.

3.   Data at 12 and 24 GeV/c are from H. J. Mück et al, <u>loc cit</u>. The data at 102 GeV/c are from the Michigan-Rochester Report UMBC 73-19, UR-460. The 205 GeV/c data are from a recent ANL-NAL-Stony Brook Report submitted to the Berkeley DPF Meeting (1973).

4.   T. Ferbel, Phys. Rev. Letters <u>29</u>, 448 (1972) and an update in Phys. Rev. <u>D</u> (in press).

5.   P. Olesen, Physics Letters <u>41B</u>, 602 (1972); P. Slattery, Phys. Rev. Letters <u>29</u>, 1624 (1972).

6.   Z. Koba, P. Olesen, H. B. Nielsen, Nuclear Physics <u>B40</u>, 317 (1972).

7.   French-Soviet Collaboration, Physics Letters <u>42B</u>, 519 (1972); NAL-UCLA Collaboration Report NAL 73/38, UCLA-1077.

8.   Michigan-Rochester Report UMBC 73-18, UR-459.

9.   This is only true for this "narrow" range of incident momenta; See, for example, T. Ferbel, Phys. Rev. <u>D7</u>, 925 (1973) for a discussion of a departure from a simple logarithmic form.

10.   The f_2 moment is defined in terms of the square of the dispersion $(D^2 = \langle n^2 \rangle - \langle n \rangle^2)$ as $f_2 = D^2 - \langle n \rangle$. For a discussion of the f moments see A. H. Mueller, Phys. Rev. <u>D4</u>, 159 (1971).

11.   A. Wroblewski in the Proceedings of the XIII Cracow School of Theoretical Physics (1973). For related phenomenological observations see P. K. Malhotra, Nucl. Phys. <u>46</u>, 559 (1963), and O. Czyzewski and K. Rybicki, Nuclear Physics <u>B47</u>, 633 (1972).

12.   See the papers of F-T. Dao and J. Whitmore, NAL preprint NAL-Pub-73/47-Exp, and D. Cohen, University of Rochester Report UR-449 (1973), and the review of T. Ferbel in Proceedings of the International Symposium on High Energy Physics at Tokyo (1973).

13.   The material presented in this section is based largely on the Michigan-Rochester report of C. Bromberg et al, UMBC 73-19, UR-460.

14.   See, for example, the early work presented by G. Bellettini in the Proceedings of the XVI International Conference on High Energy Physics, Vol.I, J. D. Jackson and A. Roberts eds.

15.   See, for example, the discussion of C. Quigg in Proceedings of the Vanderbilt Conference, AIP Series No. 12, R. S. Panvini, ed.

16.   See the report of J. Whitmore in the Vanderbilt Conference Proceedings, <u>loc cit</u>.

17.   See the report of the 30-inch bubble chamber Hybrid Spectrometer Group submitted to the Berkeley DPF Meeting (1973).

18.   For comparison with results at lower energies, see S. Stone et al, Phys. Rev. <u>D5</u>, 1622 (1972).

19.   See, for example, D. F. Freedman et al, Phys. Rev. Letters <u>26</u>, 1197 (1971), and references given therein.

20.   Private communication from C. Quigg and G. Thomas. The data at 12 and 24 GeV/c in Fig.11 are from the Bonn-Hamburg-Munich Group, the 205 GeV/c results are from J. Whitmore's summary at the Vanderbilt Conference.

21.   This was discussed previously by T. Ferbel at the Tokyo Symposium <u>loc. cit</u>.

22.   See, for example, the review by J. Gunion in the Proceedings of the Vanderbilt Conference (1973), <u>loc. cit</u>.

23.   The old data at 28.5 GeV/c, 102 GeV/c, 205 GeV/c and 303 GeV/c are from the review of P. Slattery in the Proceedings of the

Vanderbilt Conference, loc. cit.   The new 19 GeV/c results have been privately communicated to the author by H. Bøggild.   The new 102 GeV/c and preliminary 405 GeV/c data are from the Michigan-Rochester report UMBC-73-21, UR-458.

24.   The detailed energy dependence for a smaller range of x and t has been measured at NAL by the Rutgers-London (IC) Group.   See K. Abe et al, paper submitted to the Berkeley DPF Meeting (1973).

25.   A similar observation was made for the reaction $\pi^+ p \to \pi^- +$ anything at lower energies by T. Ferbel in the Proceedings of the III International Colloquium on Multiparticle Production (Zakopane, 1972), A. Bialas et al, eds.

26.   The CHLM Collaboration at the ISR has thus far only examined a small region of reaction (12); their data are most reliable for $|t| \geq 0.15$ GeV^2 and $M^2 \geq 6$ GeV^2, consequently they sample only a small fraction of the data between x = 0.9 and x = 1.0. See the report of D. Leith in these proceedings for more information.

INCLUSIVE EXPERIMENTS AT ISR-ENERGIES

Hans Bøggild

The Niels Bohr Institute
University of Copenhagen, Denmark

INTRODUCTION

Since the CERN-ISR came into succesfull operation
early 1971 and experiments came on the floor very soon
after, the range of available accelerator energies in
high energy hadron physics has got a considerable extension upwards. To day we hear PS and AGS experiments
classified as medium or even low energy physics. Fortunately the "ASYMPTOPIA", half expected, half feared to
be just around the corner has now been pushed further away
by the experimental findings of new and unexpected phenomena. The most exciting finding, however, i.e. the discovery of a new particle (a quark, a W, a ?) has not been
made (yet ?).

The many experiments and their many results have
been described, reported and reviewed many times and I
do not intend to give a complete account of everything here,
but rather try to concentrate on some of the most outstan-
ding (to my mind) and on the more recent results. Since
results from the ISR will be basis for most of this talk,
I will restrict the subject to proton-proton physics,
hoping that some other speaker will fill out the most "out-
standing holes".

I shall remind you that physics in this energy
region is explored by many experimental groups at many
accelerators and that in particular results from

Serpukhov and NAL play a very important role, both in
making a continuous energy scale available, in confir-
ming and elaborating results from difficult ISR-experiments <u>and</u> in doing experiments that have not been possible at the ISR.

Several regions of proton-proton physics have been
explored by ISR-experiments. In table I[*] a list of the
subjects and the names of the experimental groups involved is given (the abbreviations are used in the text
and on many figures).

As an introduction to the discussion of actual experimental results I shall briefly remind you what the
ISR is, and of what it can do (and <u>not</u> do). A more
complete description can be found in a recent review by
K. Johnsen[2]..

In the next section I will discuss the single particle inclusive spectra in terms of scaling, approach
to scaling, limiting fragmentation, central rapidity
plateau, particle composition etc.

A special interest has recently developed in the
study of events having particles of very high transverse
momenta. Such events seem to be much more abundant than
(naively) expected (by simple extrapolation from low p_T)
and there are strong indications of a marked s-dependence
(departure from Feynman-scaling). This will be discussed in the next following section.

At the end I will discuss some very recent results
concerning associated multiplicities and charge distri-

---

[*] The table comes from a recent review by J.C.Sens[1].

butions in the central region.

The many very interesting experimental results concerning total and elastic cross section, diffraction-like phenomena, correlations and multiplicity distributions will be discussed by other contributers to this conference and I will not comment on these results.

THE ISR MACHINE

The ISR consists of two slightly deformed rings intersecting in 8 regions. The layout is illustrated on fig. 1. By tuning the PS and the ISR to the same momentum a complete pulse of protons may be transferred into one of the ISR rings. The available phase-space allows the stacking of several hundreds of PS pulses in each ring resulting in beams consisting of typically $\sim 10^{14}$ protons (frequently quoted in Amperes: Current = 5-15 Amp). The cross section of the beams are $\sim 1 \times 6$ cm^2, which with a crossing angle of 15° gives a "diamond" shaped interaction region of $\sim 1 \times 6 \times 40 \ cm^3$. (Fig.2)

Under normal circumstances the interaction rate in such a region is $\sim 10^5 \ sec^{-1}$. During a typical run (~ 24 hours) the number of events has been 10^{10} so it is obvious that quite a lot can be done. On the other hand it is also clear that the ISR-rate is many orders of magnitude from conventional accelerators.

To keep 10^{14} protons circulating for hours it is understandable that a very good vacuum is needed, and it is indeed also supplied. At present a "typical" vacuum is better than 10^{-10} Torr (1 Torr = 1 mm Hg), and in intersection regions where background from beam collisions with residual gas must be depressed as much as possible, the pressure is often registered as "below 10^{-11} Torr" (10^{-11} Torr = 10 Fermi Hg!)

By having the two beams colliding with the same energy[*] instead of one of them colliding with a stationary target, a very large gain in CMS energy per $ is obtained. I list here the five frequently used ISR energies, with the corresponding values of momentum on a stationary target P_{INC}, and of $\sqrt{s}$:

P_{ISR} GeV/c	$\sqrt{s}$ GeV	s GeV^2	P_{INC} GeV/c
11.8	23.4	549	292
15.4	30.6	934	496
22.5	44.7	1996	1060
26.6	52.8	2784	1480
31.4[**]	62.8	3936	2100
(15x26[*]	∿ 40	∿1600	850)

A very important part of most ISR experiments is the normalization procedure. Mostly the so-called van der Meer method[3] has been used, but, especially in the measurements of total cross sections, other methods have been used also. These normalization procedures have been very thoroughly described by others (e.g. U. Amaldi), and I will not go into further details here.

---

[*] Running with two different energies has been tried a few times

[**] To get this an acceleration in the ISR has been necessary.

There are several important limitations in the possibilities for using the ISR. I list here the most important ones:

1) Only pp collisions can be studied
   (later on possibly $\bar{p}p$)

2) Limits in intensity

3) Lack of a really 4π device[*]

Because of these limitations it is extremely important to compare and combine the obtained results with conventional accelerator results, preferably at the same CMS energy. This has become possible recently at NAL and an important part of todays work is the comparison between the results from these two machines.

As an illustration of the experimental set-up at the ISR, fig. 3 gives an example, namely Intersection 2 which happens to be <u>very</u> crowded. Four different experiments have been on the floor at the same time namely:

1) A small angle spectrometer (CHLM)
   $\theta \sim 25$ -100 mr

2) A medium angle spectrometer (BCC)
   $\theta \sim 80$ -300 mr

3) A large angle spectrometer (BS)
   $\theta \sim 30$ -90°

   and

4) A large angle, large P_T muon spectrometer (B)

---

[*] Yet a streamer chamber being installed and the Split-Field Magnet facility are attemps to get "Pseudo"-4π devices.

INCLUSIVE SPECTRA

I would like to illustrate the recent history of the treatment of single particle inclusive spectra by the following graphs:

PEYROU

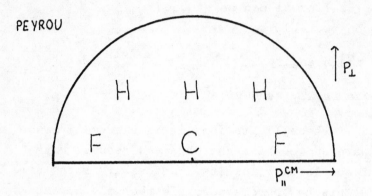

FEYNMAN
YANG ET AL

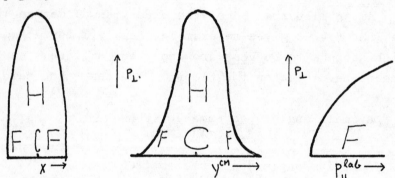

BJÖRKEN

. . . .

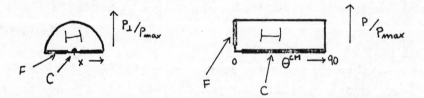

H : HIGH P_T C,F : CENTRAL, FRAGMENTATION REGION.

These graphs are supposed to illustrate how wise men during the recent times have helped us to use suitable representation of our data in the sense that new theories or conjectures hand in hand with new observed phenomena lead us (we hope) to better understanding. The Peyrou plot represents in a beautiful way the general characteristics of hadron-hadron collisions, The "Feynman-Yang" plots represent the concept of Feynman-scaling and limiting behaviour, and the "Parton" plots represent the point like behaviour of hadron matter giving very high transverse momenta. We will come back to these things soon.

To give an overall qualitative view on the single, charged particle production spectra let us look at fig. 4, which compiles[4] data at $p^{lab} \sim 1500$ GeV and $p_T = 0.4$ GeV/c on a x-scale. There are several things to note on this graph:

1) At $x \sim 0$ the production is dominated by pions, with a charge ratio close to 1, while K^+, K^- and p and $\bar{p}$ are suppressed by a factor ~ 10. The average charge is close to 0.

2) The $p/\bar{p}$ ratio is ~ 2 at $x \sim 0$, thus leaving room for a limited leading particle effect also at $x \sim 0$.

3) At large x the proton is the only abundantly produced particle.

4) At $x \sim 1$ there is a clear peak in the proton spectrum most likely corresponding to protons not being excited in the interaction (diffraction).

The next qualitative question to ask is how these spectra change with the CMS-energy and eventually approach a Feynman [5] scaling limit:

$$E \frac{d\sigma}{d\vec{p}} = f(x, p_T, s) \xrightarrow[s \to \infty]{} f_0(x, p_T)$$

where

$$x = P_{\shortparallel}^{CM} / P_{inc}^{CM} \sim 2p_{\shortparallel} / \sqrt{s}$$

Fig. 5a,b serves as a typical example from the CHLM experiment.[6] First it can be noted that the π^+-spectra ($pp \to \pi^+ +$ anything) at a fixed value of x and in the transverse momentum interval $0.4 < p_T < 1,2$ GeV/c seem to scale when s is varied between 47 and 2800 GeV^2. The same is not true for the proton and K$^+$ spectra, the proton spectra decrease and the K$^+$ spectra increase. Since a scaling spectrum corresponds to a fixed inelasticity (i.e. a fixed portion of the CMS energy) for the considered particle type, it is clear that not all spectra can increase(or decrease) at the same time. The figure gives an example of a simultaneus increase-decrease.

It is well known that Feynman scaling leads to a flat rapidity[*)] plateau, because at any finite value of y the invariant cross section becomes independent of s when s goes to infinity:

$$\frac{d^2\sigma}{\pi \, dy \, dp_\perp^2} = E \frac{d\sigma}{d\vec{p}} = \phi(x, p_\perp) = \phi\left(\frac{\sqrt{m^2 + p_\perp^2}}{\sqrt{s}/2} \sinh y, \; p_\perp\right) \xrightarrow[s \to \infty]{} \phi(0, p_\perp)$$

[*)] The longitudinal rapidity $y = \frac{1}{2}\log \frac{E + p_{\shortparallel}}{E - p_{\shortparallel}}$

This flattening is illustrated on fig. 6, which is another compilation of $p_T = 0.4$ GeV/c, now including four ISR-energies, and a comparison to PS (s = 47 GeV^2). Note that the scale is the rapidity measured in the projectile frame $y_{proj} = y_{beam} - y$, and that the spectra at the different energies seem to fall on smooth curves when plotted in this variable.

It is interesting to note that almost all spectra (except $\bar{p}$) scale at very low values of y and that an eventual limit seems to be approached from below, except for the protons. However, it is seen that none of the spectra are completely flat in rapidity. I will come back to that in a moment.

Two other nice illustrations of the scaling/non scaling aspect on more readable scales are seen on fig.7 and 8, comparing π^- spectra at 19 - 205 GeV/c[8] and 200 - 300 GeV[9]. It is clearly seen how scaling works very well for low values of y_{lab} (fragmentation region) and that it does not work for large values of y_{lab} (central region, small value of y^{CM}) **).

Scaling in fragmentation, or the equivalent Limiting Fragmentation[12] has been tested in a beautiful way by the PSB group[13], by comparing angular distributions in terms of $\eta = -\log\tan \theta/2$, which is a good approximation for rapidity (for relativistic particles *)). The data is obtained in three different running modes:

---

*) $y = \frac{1}{2}\log\frac{E+p''}{E-p''} \sim \frac{1}{2}\log\frac{p+p''}{p-p''} = \frac{1}{2}\log\frac{1+\cos\theta}{1-\cos\theta} = -\log\tan\frac{\theta}{2}$

**) The curve on fig. 8 is the gaussian distribution predicted by Landau[10,11]

$$\xrightarrow{\quad 15 \quad} \xleftarrow{\quad 15 \quad} GeV$$

$$\xrightarrow{\quad\quad 26 \quad\quad} \xleftarrow{\quad 26 \quad} GeV$$

$$\xrightarrow{\quad\quad 26 \quad\quad} \xleftarrow{\quad 15 \quad} GeV$$

and as seen on fig. 9 these data provide a beautiful confirmation of limiting fragmentation and factorization:
The spectrum of the fragments of one proton does not depend
on the energy of the other proton.

I will now concentrate on the behaviour in the central
region. Fig.10 illustrates the form and s-dependence of the
transverse momentum spectrum at $x = y = 0$[14]. There are
several interesting features on this graph:

1) Scaling seems to work in the ISR range, while as
   previously mentioned there is a factor two increase
   from PS to ISR energies.

2) There is a special change of form of the spectrum
   at very low values of p_T, the distribution seems
   to "sharpen" when the energy is increased. This
   last effect is going to be further investigated
   in the future.

The form and behaviour of the central rapidity distributions have been investigated by the BS group. The
preliminary results shown at the Batavia Conference last
year have now been further elaborated, more careful corrections have been made and now some interesting new
features stand out.

Fig. 11 is a typical example of the results[15], showing rapidity
distributions at 9 different values of p_T from 0.2 to 1.0 GeV/c for
$pp \to \pi^- + \ldots$ at $\sqrt{s} = 30.6$ and 52.8 GeV.

It is obvious that the "central flat rapidity plateau" is really <u>not</u> <u>flat</u>.

When a fit to the data of the type

$$E \frac{d\sigma}{d\vec{p}} = A (1 + \alpha y_{proj}) e^{-BP_T}$$

is tried the typical values of α come out as:

<u>Table 2</u>.

$\sqrt{s}$ =	30.6	52.8 GeV
α_{π^-}	0.18 ± 0.01	0.13 ± 0.01
α_{π^+}	0.15 ± 0.01	0.12 ± 0.01
β	0.16 ± 0.01	0.12 ± 0.01
ref.10,11: 0.18		0.15

The perhaps more natural fits to a gaussian $e^{-\beta y^2}$ give the average values of β shown above.

The value of the "rapidity-slope" seems to decrease slightly when the energy is increased and an approach to $\alpha=0$ at infinite energy is certainly possible.

Another interesting but not equally experimentally reliable effect is suggested on the figure namely the lack of energy dependence of these spectra, when plotted as functions of y_{proj}, which is a "fragmentation variable". It must however be noted, that the normalization uncertainly at each energy is $\pm 4\%$, thus giving a ratio between the yield at the two energies of $8 \pm 7\%$.

The corresponding spectra for $K^{\pm}$, p and $\bar{p}$ production[16] shown on fig. 12 and 13 indicate the same properties (but the proton spectrum does not rise).

It is clear that this rise of the cross section as a function of y_{proj} can have something to do with the rising total(inelastic) cross section but since the integral of these distributions is $\bar{n}\sigma_{IN}$ and we do not know $\bar{n}$ well enough it is not possible to make any quantitative comparison without strong assumptions. I will not try that here.

Before I turn to the problem of the observed effects and approach to scaling at very high transverse momenta I would like to show an example of production of a rare particle.[17] . Fig. 14 shows the spectrum at x=0 of antideuterons at $\sqrt{s}$ = 53 GeV. The ratio of $\bar{d}/\bar{p}$ is of the order of 10^{-3}, thus telling us that it is difficult to make a heavy particle. As we will see in a moment, it is also difficult to make a high transverse momentum particle. It is clear that these two effects are linked together and the spectra are perhaps better displayed on a scale which includes both mass and transverse momentum. The variable $m_L = \sqrt{p_T^2 + m^2}$ has been suggested by many authors[18] and fig. 15 shows the spectrum at x=0 and $\sqrt{s}$ = 53 GeV of pions,kaons,protons, antiprotons and antideuterons. It is remarkable how all these different spectra tend to "close up" when $\bar{m}_L$ is used instead of p_T.

It has also been possible to extract a sample of deuterons(although the background problem is very difficult) and a ratio of deuterons to antideuterons is obtained

$$d/\bar{d} \sim 3.5 \pm 1.4$$

This number may at first sight seem rather surprising since one(I) would expect the main source of deuterons to be pair production ($d\bar{d}$). On the other hand it is possible for a heavy baryon to _decay_ into a deuteron and an antinucleon:

$$N^{*+} \rightarrow d\ \bar{n}$$

while it requires another antibaryon to make an anti-deuteron this way, so perhaps this result is not so strange after all. It has also been suggested that this ratio ought to be:

$$d/\bar{d} = (p/\bar{p})^2 \cong 4$$

which is obviously in agreement with the observed value.

I would like to show a graph illustrating the possibilities for the rate of approach to an eventual scaling limit. On fig. 16[19] the invariant cross section for π^+ and π^- at $p_T = 0.4$ GeV/c and at $x=0$ is plotted for several energies on two scales, $s^{-\frac{1}{2}}$ and $s^{-1/4}$, which have often been suggested for the approach to scaling:

$$E\frac{d\sigma}{d\vec{p}} = \begin{cases} a + b\ s^{-\frac{1}{2}} \\ a + b\ s^{-1/4} \end{cases}$$

It is evident that if one requires the same number of π^+ and π^- at infinite energy the $s^{-1/4}$ behaviour is ruled out, while the $s^{-\frac{1}{2}}$ is possible.

HIGH TRANSVERSE MOMENTA

The observation of an apparent rapid approach to a scaling limit at low transverse momenta leads to the question, whether this is true for the whole spectrum, whether in the ISR energy range everything is settled and experimentalists should all retire and wait patiently for the theorists to explain why. "Fortunately" unexpected phenomena are still observed and experimentalists can still hope that they will be able to contribute to a better understanding of hadron physics.

One of these unexpected phenomena recently seen is the observation of a surprisingly large number of events with very high transverse momenta. Although these events still only contribute a minor part of the total sample, the numbers observed at very large p_T are many orders of magnitude above the exponential extrapolation of the low p_T distributions. This is indicating that there is more structure inside a proton than was generally assumed, and that effects involving small distances are important.

Another surprising observation has been that of a strong s-dependence of these high p_T spectra, i.e. when the energy increase the numbers at fixed p_T values increase.

All this is well illustrated on fig. 17, showing the invariant cross sections for π^0 production (CCR group) at x=0 for 5 different energies in the ISR range. The departure from the low transverse momentum behaviour and the energy dependence is very clear.

It has been pointed out that a parton picture, describing partons as point-like, leads to an expectation for the high transverse momenta.

$$ E \frac{d\sigma}{d\vec{p}} \propto \frac{1}{p_T^n} \quad f\left(\frac{p_T}{\sqrt{s}} \right) $$

where some authors expect[21] $n \sim 4$ (dimensional analysis) and some expect[22] $n \sim 8$

The CCR group has tried a fit to their data whith the following expression

$$E \frac{d\sigma}{d\vec{p}} = A \; p_T^{-n} \; e^{-b \; p_T / \sqrt{s}}$$

where A, n and b have been varied to get the best fit.

The values they obtain are the following:

$$A = (1.54 \pm 0.01) 10^{-26} \quad cm^2$$

$$n = 8.2 \pm 0.7 \qquad \left. \begin{array}{c} \\ \\ \\ \\ \end{array} \right\} \; \chi^2 = 140 \Big/ 88 \; deg. \, of$$

$$b = 26 \pm 5 \qquad\qquad\qquad\qquad freedom$$

This fit is shown on fig. 18, with $p_T^n \; E\frac{d\sigma}{dp}$ as function of $p_T / \sqrt{s}$, and although the $\sqrt{s} = 62$ GeV data seem to be a little off, it is remarkable how well a single function of $p_T / \sqrt{s}$ describes the data.

Since the π^o spectrum is obtained from the observed spectrum of γ-rays, assuming that the dominant source for γ-rays are π^o decays, it is important to compare these results with the spectra of charged pions. This is also done on fig. 17 where the average of the $\pi^{\pm}$ spectra from the SS-group are compared with the π^o-spectra from the CCR group. Although there seems to be a factor 2 difference in normalization the qualitative agreement is clear. This factor 2 may be partly accounted for by the very difficult normalization in the CCR experiment. The 6% error they claim for the momentum measurement results in at least a 50% uncertainly at the points at $p_T = 4$GeV/c.

Fig. 19 shows the p_T spectra for negative particles at y=0 and at $\sqrt{s}$ = 44 and 53 GeV measured by the BS group. Although these results indicate little s-dependence they are within statistics consistant with the results from the CCR-group. An interesting observation by the BS-group is that the p_T-dependence changes very little when the CMS angle is changed to 60°, corresponding to y~0.6, indicating that the high p_T spectra also have a "plateau".

Some preliminary π° spectra (γ-spectra converted to π°-spectra using the Sternheimer formula) have been produced at NAL[25] (and presented at this conference). By having a fixed spectrometer at a laboratory angle of 100 mr and a p^{lab} range of 50 - 375 GeV, they obtain spectra corresponding to CMS rapidities ranging from -0.6 to + 0.35 Assuming the presence of a central rapidity plateau they compare these spectra and observe a marked s-dependence above p_T~ 1 GeV/c , fig. 20. Using fits to the expression

$$E \frac{d\sigma}{d\vec{p}} = A e^{-(Bp_T + Cp_T^2)}$$

they can study the s-dependence and eventual departure from an exponential by studying the values of B and C as function of p^{lab}. This is illustrated on fig. 21, it is interesting to note that the values of B change very little, while C increases as p^{lab} increases.

Although these spectra and the results (through the "magic" formula) from the CCR group don't quite overlap in p_T and s-range I have not been able to resist the temptation to compare the results. To avoid normalisation problems I have compared the ratio of cross sections at p_T = 1.5 and 2.0GeV/c. As seen on fig. 22 the qualitative agreement is clear (in terms of a fit of the type the CCR group have used, the NAL results would correspond to a value of $n \sim 5.3$ instead of 8.2).

The BS group have also investigated[26] the particle composition of the high transverse momentum spectra (fig. 23). It is interesting to see how the heavy particle component increases.

It is interesting to investigate how these transverse momenta are correlated to the other particles produced in the same events.

As an introduction to this discussion I would like to show a graph[27] (fig. 24) showing the associated multiplicity for particles produced at the same and at the opposite side of the detected low p_T particle. On this graph it is seen that the associated multiplicity on the same side is decreasing when p_T is increasing while the multiplicity is increasing on the opposite side. This is a rather natural and expected feature. The higher the transverse momentum, the more compensation is needed and one way of compensation is to produce many particles with the "preferred" low transverse momenta.

In the next graph (fig. 25) a corresponding set of figures are shown for high transverse momentum π^0 (CCR group prelim.)[28] Again the multiplicity on the opposite side is increasing, but now the multiplicity on the same side starts increasing. This is clearly a dynamical and not a kinematical effect. It has been suggested that a parton picture giving rise to high transverse momenta would let the high p_T particle be accompanied by some more particles in the same direction and thus increase the multiplicity.

The CCR group has tried to investigate the rapidity distribution[28] on the same and opposite side requiring a π^0 with at least $p_T \gtrsim 3$ GeV/c.

On fig. 26 it is seen that indeed the distribution on the
same side has a peak in the rapidity distribution at the
same rapidity value as the triggering π^o. Although these
data are preliminary I find them very suggestive and look
forward to a confirmation.

Seeing that the multiplicity in the central region
is increasing with transverse momentum it is interesting
to know, what happens, if a heavy mass is produced. This
has been investigated by the BS-group[27]. They observe that
the multiplicity is definitely higher when a $p,\bar{p}$ is produced.
than if a pion is produced.

So far I have only discussed the high p_T spectra in
the central region. The CHLM-group has provided[29] a set of
spectra at x=0.6 at reasonably high transverse momenta
(up to ∿2 GeV/c). Their results indicate that up to 2
GeV/c Feynman-scaling is valid (no s-dependence) inside
the ISR energy range. Fig. 27 also shows a comparison with
PS energies and a departure from scaling. It must however,
be noted that at PS energies 2 GeV/c is not far from the
phase space boundary.

I would like to end this chapter by showing a graph
(fig. 28) that I find very suggestive. Taking the data
from the BS group it is possible to compare the average
charge per emitted charged particle.

It is seen that the number of positive particles become larger than the number of negative particles at high
p_T, but it looks as if <q> starts saturating when p_T becomes larger than 1 GeV/c. Now the question is why ? I
have a suggestion:

If an event has a very high p_T particle this
event is very inelastic, so inelastic that
all leading particle effects (at least what

charge is concerned) has disappeared. That means that the initial charge of 2 is spread out with no preferred direction. Since the average number of particles is ∿12 at this energy, the mean charge will be $<q> \cong 2/12=0.17$.

In a naive sense, imagining the high p_T particle as coming directly from collision between two constituents, it is clear that the observation of a positive excess puts some limits to the possible number of constituents, partons, in a proton. If this number was ∿∞ the average charge per constituent would be 0 and the mean charge for the emitted hadrons would be expected to be ∿0. It is also possible to make some wild speculations on the connection between the actual value of $<q>$ and the number of constituents. I will not comment further on this here but leave it as a game for the reader.

CONCLUSIONS

I think that the main conclusions have been made throughout the text and I will only make some general remarks on what is interesting and new.

Although Feynman scaling seems to work within ∿10% in the ISR range at low p_T, the plateau that was flat last year is now more curved and both a linear rise and a gaussian shape is possible (a gaussian shape was suggested already 1953 by Landau using a hydrodynamical model.)

Scaling in the fragmentation region seems to be very well established.

It is suggested that scaling is faster in the variable y_{proj}, but this really needs a confirmation and we have to wait for more data. It is in fact a generally interesting question: Although Feynman scaling and Limiting Fragmentation are asymptotically equivalent(except at x=0), in which frame is the approach faster ?

HIGH p_T

There seems to be no Feynman scaling in the central region,but it is possible to obtain good fit to the formula suggested by Blankenbecler, Brodsky and Gunion:

$$E \frac{d\sigma}{d\vec{p}} = \frac{A}{p_T^8} \ F \ (\frac{p_T}{\sqrt{s}} \ )$$

Scaling seems to work within errors at large p_T in the fragmentation region.

Heavy particles become relatively more abundant than at low p_T.

The associated multiplicities seem to increase with both increasing p_T and increasing mass.

FUTURE

Not all last year's asymptotic predictions seem to hold this year, we have got surprises, a rising total cross section, and unexpected high p_T behaviour etc. and we now see that we are not yet in an asymptotic regime. We begin seriously to think of building the next generation machines and to look forward to the results coming from these "dreams". Since ASYMPTOPIA seems to be pushed further away every time we get a new machine I would like to suggest the following new energy classification scheme:

SUGGESTION FOR NEW CLASSIFICATION SCHEME:

meV	:	LOW TEMPERATURE PHYS
eV	:	CHEMISTRY AND OPTICS
keV	:	X-RAY - OPTICS
MeV	:	NUCLEAR PHYSICS
GeV	:	LOW ENERGY PHYSICS
TeV	:	INTERMEDIATE ENERGY PHYSICS
?	:	HIGH ENERGY PHYSICS
$(\sqrt{s} \sim 10^{80} \text{GeV ?})$ ∞	:	ASYMPTOPIA

ACKNOWLEDGEMENTS

I am grateful for the kind invitation to come to this conference, and I would like to thank drs. Knud Hansen and Gunnar Damgaard for their help and advice preparing this manuscript.

438

1) J.C. Sens, Review of recent results from the European centre for nuclear research storage rings. Invited paper presented at the Conference on Recent Advances in Particle Physics. The New York Academy of Sciences.

2) Kjell Johnsen, Nucl.Inst. and Methods 108, 205(1973).

3) S. Van der Meer, CERN Internal Report ISR-PD/68-31(1968), unpublished.

4) D.R.O. Morrison, Review of inelastic Proton-Proton Reactions. Review Lecture given to the Royal Society meeting on Proton-Proton Scattering at Very High Energies, London 1973.

5) R.P. Feynman, Phys.Rev.Letters 23, 1415(1969).

6) ISR discussion meeting between experimentalists and theorists No.3 (ed.by M. Jacob).

7) J.V. Allaby et al., Proc. 4th International Conference on High Energy Collisions, Oxford 1972.

8) Y. Cho et al., Phys.Rev.Letters 31, 413(1973)
and references therein.
The 19 GeV/c data are private communication from the author.

9) Inclusive Spectra of Secondaries from 200 GeV/c Proton-Proton Interactions detected in the NAL 30-Inch Bubble Chamber Wide Gap Spark Chamber Hybrid System. Paper submitted to this confrence. 300 GeV/c data is private communication from B.Y. Oh.

10) L.D. Landau, Izv.Akad.Nauk. SSSR 17, 51(1953), English translation in Collected Papers of L.D. Landau ed. D. TerHaar (Gordon and Breach, New York, 1965) p.569.

11) P. Carruthers and M. Duong-Van, Phys.Lett. 41B, 597(1972).

12) J. Benecke, T.T.Chou, C.N. Yang and E. Yen, Phys.Rev.188 2159(1969).

13) G. Belletini et al., Phys.Lett. 45B, 69(1973).

14) 53 and 31 GeV data, private communication from the author.
13.8 GeV,(P_{INC} = 102 GeV/c), private communication from J. van der Velde.
6.1 GeV, private communication from the author.

15) B. Alper et al., Large angle inclusive production of charged pions at the CERN ISR with transverse momenta less than 1.0 GeV/c. Submitted to Phys.Lett.

16) B. Alper et al., Large angle inclusive production of protons, antiprotons and kaons, and particle composition of the CERN ISR. Submitted to Phys.Lett.

17) B. Alper et al., Large angle production of Particles heavier than the proton and a search for quarks at the CERN ISR. Submitted to Phys.Lett.

18) Data from the BS-group, compiled by E. Lillethun. It is perhaps interesting to note that the $\bar{p}$ and $\bar{d}$ spectra can be joined by the same line: $E \, d\sigma/d\vec{p} = 400 \, e^{-8.3m_L}$

19) Data from B. Alper et al., Paper presented by G. Jarlskog at the Int.Conf. on New Results from Exp. on High Energy Collisions, Nashville 1973 and from H.J. Mück et al., Phys.Lett. 39B, 303(1972).

20) F.W. Büsser er al., Observation of π^o mesons with large transverse momentum in high energy proton-proton collisions. Phys. Lett. 46B, 471 (1973).

21) R.M. Muradyan, Ebeltoft Summer School (1973) and V.O. Matveev, R.M. Muradyan, A.N. Tavkhelidse,JINR, D2-7110,(1973).

22) R. Blankenbecler, S.J. Brodsky and J.F. Gunion, Phys.Lett. 42B, 461(1972).

23) M. Banner et al., Phys.Lett. 44B, 537(1973).

24) B. Alper et al., Phys.Lett. 44B, 521(1973).

25) D.C. Carey et al., Large transverse momentum production of gamma rays of NAL, paper submitted to this conference.

26) B. Alper et al., paper submitted to the Aix-en-Provence Conference.

27) B. Alper et al., Preliminary results concerning two particle correlations and associated multiplicity at the CERN ISR. Submitted to the 2nd International Conference on Elementary Particle, Aix-en-Provence, 6.-12.Sept.1973.

28) Preliminary data represented at this conference by R.Cool.

29) Private communication from J.C. Sens.

TABLE 1

GROUP		DATA REPORTED
CERN–COLUMBIA–ROCKEFELLER	(CCR)	π°Spectra at 90° and $p_T \leqslant 9$ GeV/c Correlations associated with large p_T.
SACLAY–STRASBOURG	(SS)	Charged particle and π° spectra at 90° and $p_T \leqslant 5$ GeV/c
CERN–HOLLAND–LANCASTER MANCHESTER	(CHLM)	Particle spectra at small angles Diffraction dissociation. Correlations
BRITISH–SCANDINAVIAN	(BS)	Particle spectra at large angles
ARGONNE–BOLOGNA– CEN	(ABC) (BC)	Particle spectra at medium angles
CERN–ROME	(CR)	Elastic scattering Total cross-section
AACHEN–CERN–GENOVA – HARVARD–TORINO	(ACGHT)	Elastic scattering Total cross-section Diffraction dissociation
PISA–STONY BROOK	(PSB)	Total cross-section Correlations Large p_T
CERN–HAMBURG– ORSAY–VIENNA	(CHOV)	π° Spectra
CERN–HAMBURG– VIENNA	(CHV)	Charged/Photon Correlations

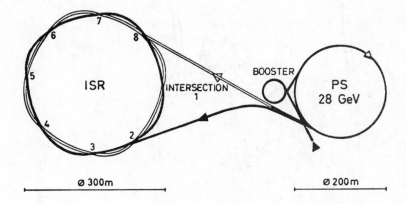

Fig. 1.   The CERN Intersecting Storage Rings.

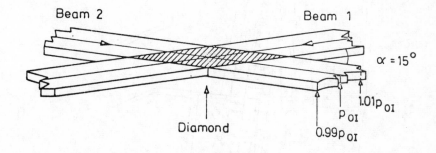

Fig. 2.   Sketch of the intersecting proton-beams at the ISR

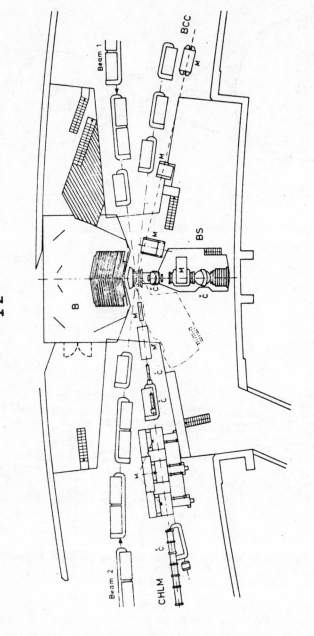

Fig. 3. The Intersection 2 at the ISR.

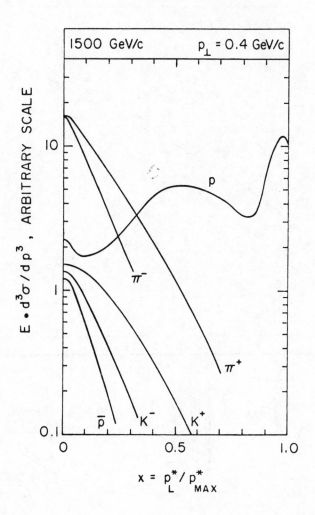

Fig. 4.   Compilation[4] of ISR data at p_T = 0.4 GeV/c.

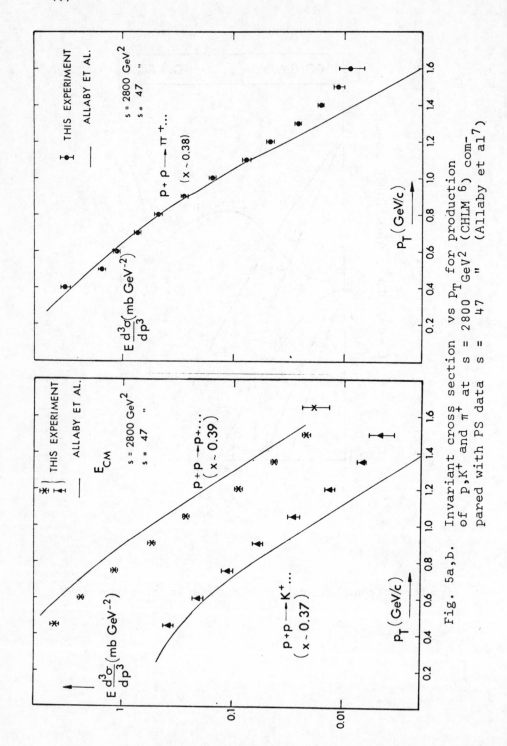

Fig. 5a,b. Invariant cross section vs p_T for production of P,K+ and π+ at s = 2800 GeV2 (CHLM 6) compared with PS data s = 47 " (Allaby et al7)

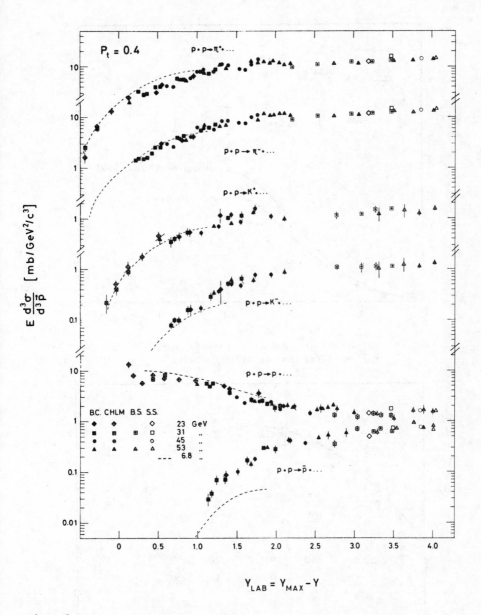

Fig. 6.
Compilation of data on the rapidity distributions,
in the beam proton rest frame, of pions, kaons, protons,
and anti-protons for a fixed transverse momentum
P_T of 0.4 GeV/c. (BS,BCC,CHLM and SS groups). The
dashed curves are from Allaby et al[7].

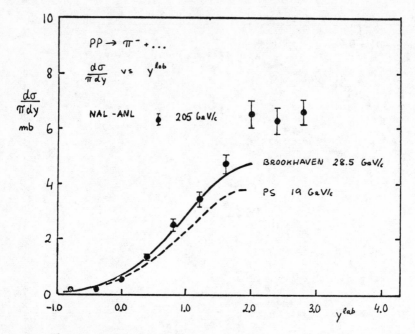

Fig. 7. The invariant cross section vs laboratory rapidity.
p^{lab} = 19,28.5 and 205 GeV/c (ref. 8).

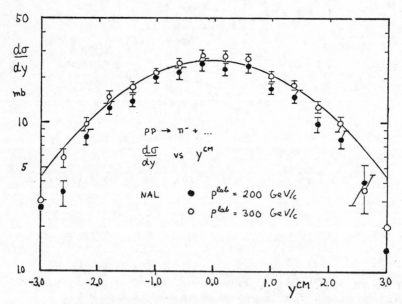

Fig. 8. The invariant cross section vs CMS rapidity at
p^{lab} = 200 and 300 GeV/c ref. 9. The curve is a
gausseau with width $\sigma = \sqrt{\ln\sqrt{s}/mp^2}$ (ref. 10,11).
normalised to the 300 GeV/c data.

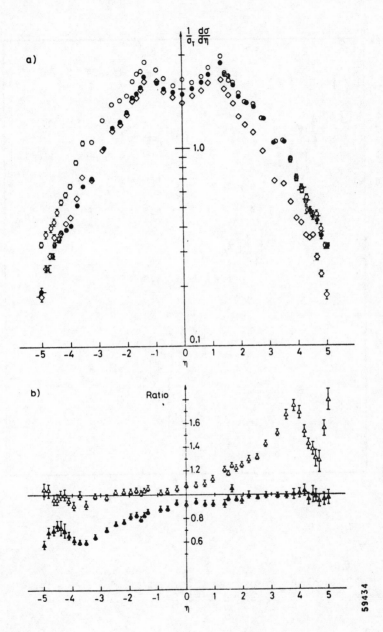

Fig. 9.
Single particle inclusive distributions $1/\sigma_T \, d\sigma/d\eta$
vs $\eta(= -\ln\tan\theta/2)$ for the three conditions
mentioned in the text.

448

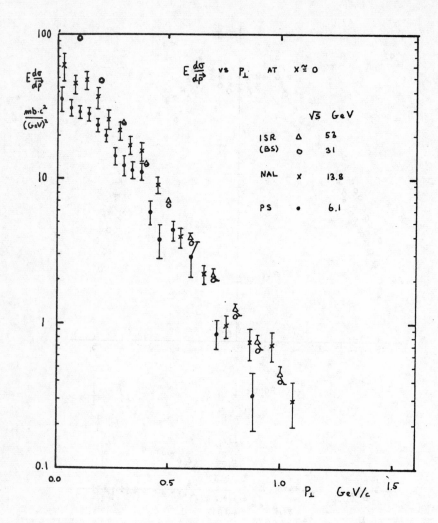

Fig. 10.
The Invariant cross section at X ∿0 vs p_T at $\sqrt{s}$ = 6.1, 13.8, 31 and 53 GeV (ref.14).

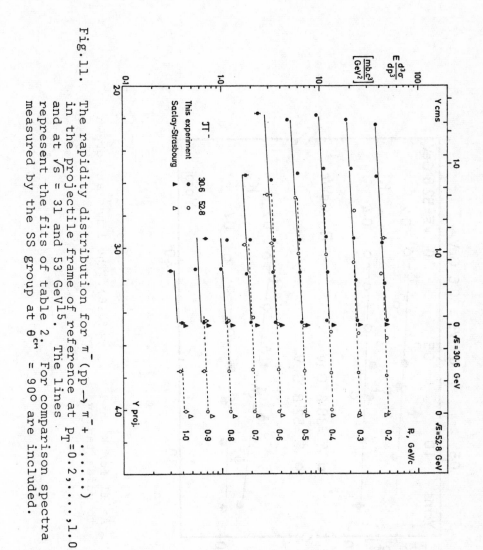

Fig.11. The rapidity distribution for π^- (pp $\rightarrow$ π^- + ...) in the projectile frame of reference at $P_T = 0.2, ..., 1.0$ and at $\sqrt{s}$ = 31 and 53 GeV15. The lines represent the fits of table 2. For comparison spectra measured by the SS group at θ^{cm} = 90° are included.

450

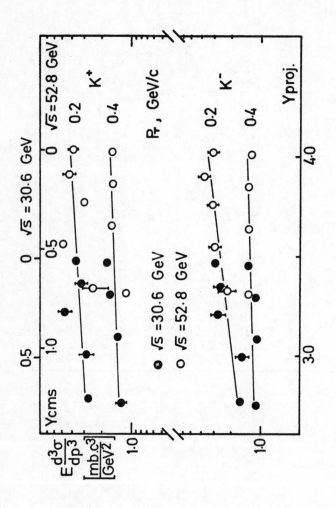

Fig. 12. As 11 for K⁺ and K⁻. (ref.16). The lines are drawn
to guide the eye.

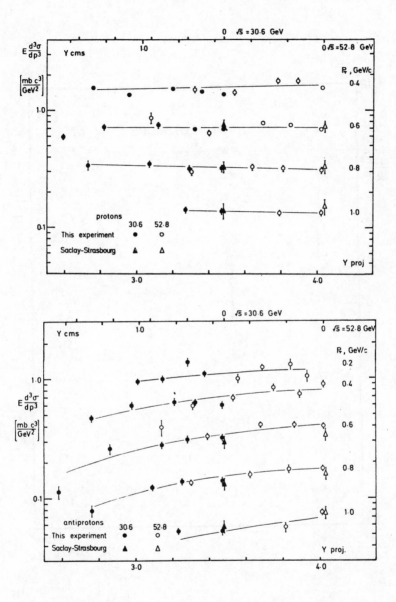

Fig. 13. As 12 for protons and antiprotons[16].

452

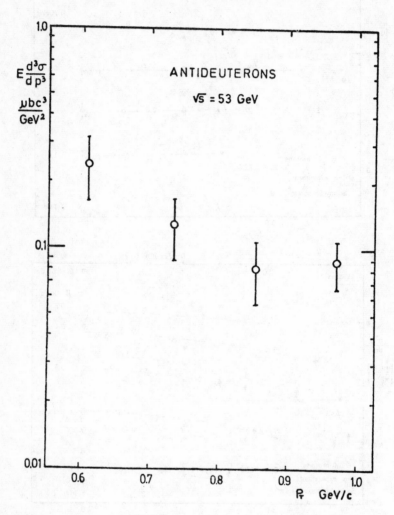

Fig. 14.

The invariant cross section for antideuteron production[17] at x ∿0 and √s = 53 GeV.

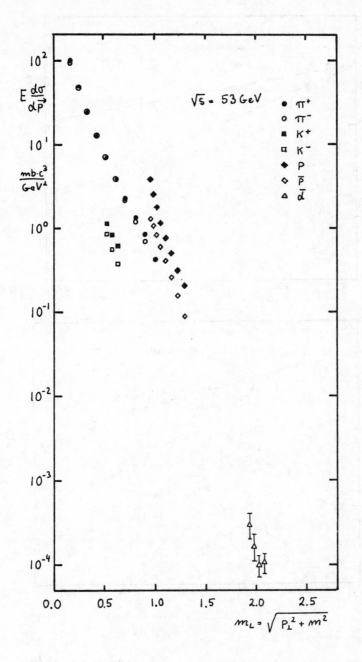

Fig. 15.

The Invariant cross section vs $m_L = \sqrt{m^2 + p_T^2}$ at $X \sim 0$ and $\sqrt{s}$ = 53 GeV.

454

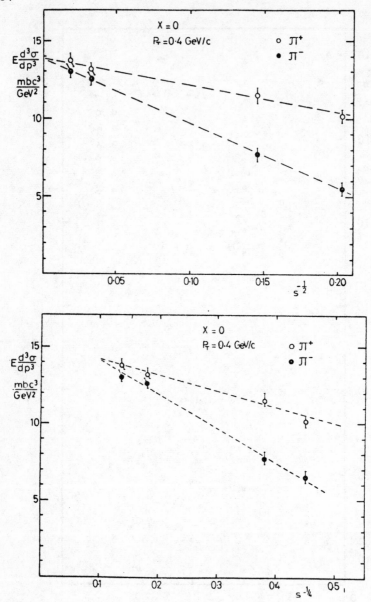

Fig. 16.

The Invariant cross section vs $s^{-\frac{1}{2}}$ and $s^{-1/4}$ at $X \sim 0$ and at $p_T = 0.4$ GeV (ref.19).

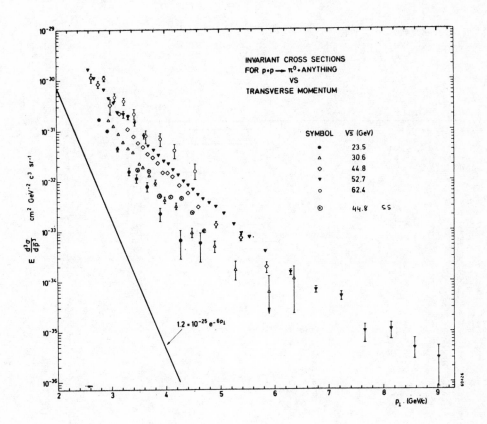

Fig. 17.

The Invariant cross section at $X \sim 0$ vs p_T for
π^0 production at $\sqrt{s}$ = 23,31,45,53 and 62GeV (CCR ref.20)

456

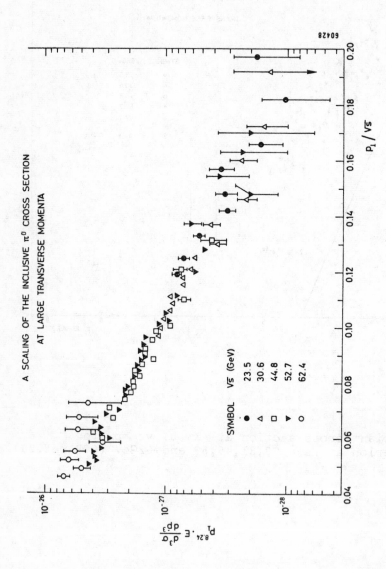

Fig. 18. $P_T^{8.2} E \frac{d\sigma}{d\vec{P}}$ vs $P_T/\sqrt{s}$, same data as on fig. 17, see comments in text.

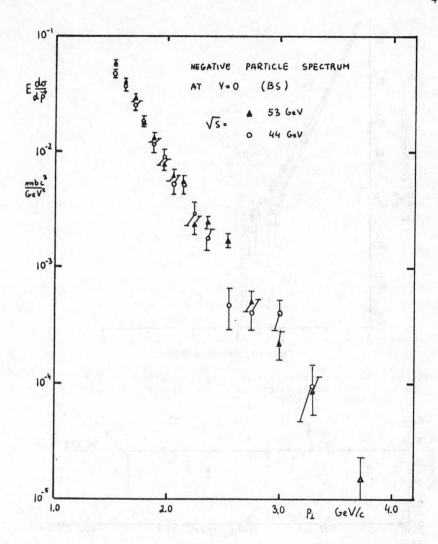

Fig. 19.

The Invariant cross section at X = 0 vs p_T, $\sqrt{s}$ = 44
and 53 GeV for negative particle production.

458

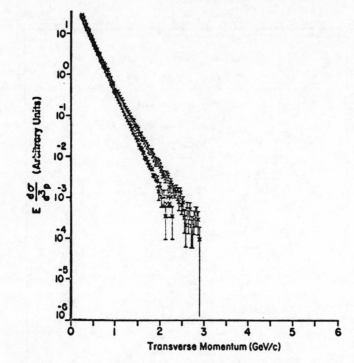

Fig.20. The Invariant cross section vs p_T at $\theta^{lab} = 100$ mr, (corresponding roughly to $y^{cm} = 0$) at $p^{lab} = 50$ and 375 GeV/c (ref.25).

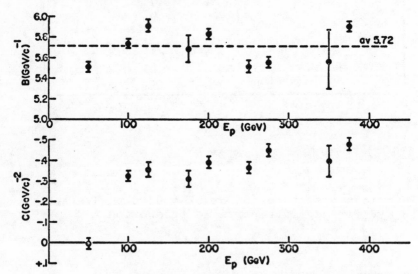

Fig. 21. The data from fig. 20, with more energies, represented by fits to $E\frac{d\sigma}{d\bar{p}} = \exp(-Bp_T - Cp_T^2)$. The values of B and C are given vs p^{lab}.

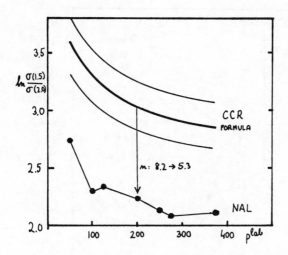

Fig. 22.

The ratio of invariant cross section at p_T = 1.5 and
2.0. The curve is from the CCR formula and
the points from the NAL experiment (fig.21).

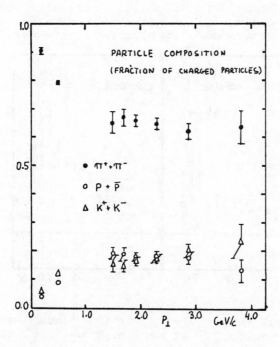

Fig. 23. Particle composition vs p_T.

460

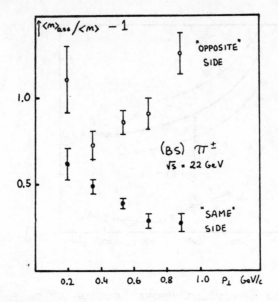

Fig. 24.

Associated multiplicity (represented by the quantity
$\langle n \rangle_{ass}$ /$\langle n \rangle$ -1, which is 0 if there are no correlations)
vs p_T at the "same" and "opposite" side with respect
to the particle, ($\pi^{\pm}$), which was identified and had
the momentum determined. (preliminary data ref.27).

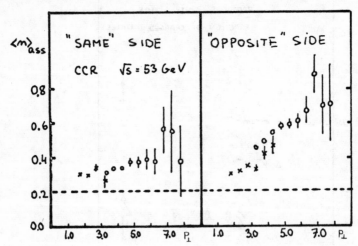

Fig. 25.

Associated multiplicity vs p_T at the "same" and
"opposite" side for π^o at very high p_T (preliminary
data ref. 28).

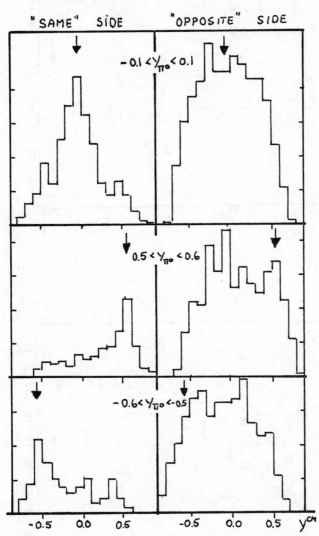

$\frac{dN}{dy}$ vs y WHEN $P_\perp (\pi^0) > 3$ GeV/c

CCR PRELIMINARY DATA

"SAME" SIDE   "OPPOSITE" SIDE

$-0.1 < Y_{\pi^0} < 0.1$

$0.5 < Y_{\pi^0} < 0.6$

$-0.6 < Y_{\pi^0} < -0.5$

-0.5 0.0 0.5 -0.5 0.0 0.5 y^{CM}

Fig. 26.

Associated rapidity distribution at the "same" and
"opposite" side, when a π^0 with $p_T \gtrsim 3$ GeV/c is required.

462

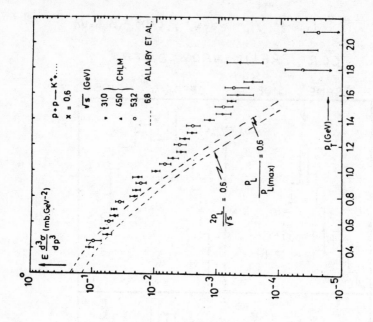

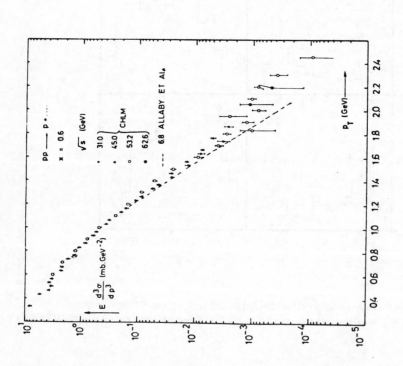

Fig. 27. The invariant cross section vs p_T at X = 0.6 (CHLM ref. 29).

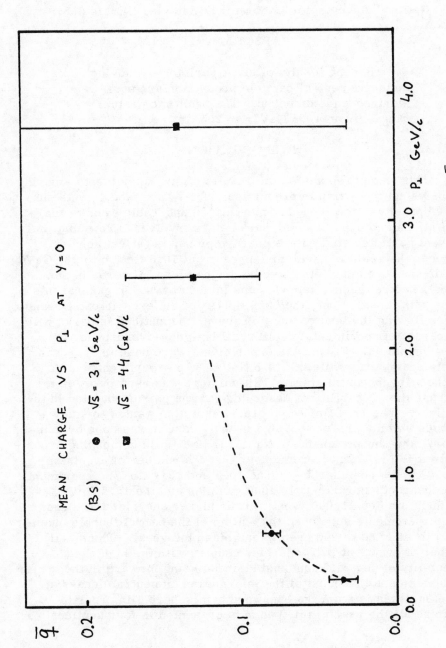

Fig. 28. Mean charge (of charged particles) vs p_T at $\sqrt{s}=31$ and 44 GeV.

EXPERIMENTAL INCLUSIVE γ, K^{o}, Λ, and $\overline{\Lambda}$ PRODUCTION

D. Ljung

National Accelerator Laboratory, Batavia, Illinois 60510

ABSTRACT

Recent results of six experiments studying inclusive neutral particle production are summarized and compared. The beam momentum ranges from 10.5 GeV/c to 205 GeV/c.

INTRODUCTION

This paper reports on the results of six experiments studying inclusive neutral particle production. These six experiments submitted papers to the Berkeley meeting[1-6] and Table I shows the institutions and experimental parameters involved. Note that the incident particles studied are positive pions, negative pions and protons; the beam momentum ranges from 10.5 GeV/c to 205 GeV/c; and the produced particles studied are gammas (pi zeros in some cases), neutral kaons, lambdas and lambda bars. In general this paper will consider only the "highlights" of the experimental results, and, following the lead of the six papers, theoretical remarks will be sparse. Experimental details will be ignored except for the following points. Five of the experiments were done in hydrogen bubble chambers, while the 10.5 GeV/c π^+p experiment was done in a neon-hydrogen mixture. This mixture was used in order to increase the probability of observing gamma pair production in the chamber. The 12.4 GeV/c pp experiment also wanted to study multiple gamma production, and in their case it was done by using a very large bubble chamber (the ANL 12-ft). In comparing experiments it is important to remember that the number of events observed varies considerably. The 10.5 and 12.4 GeV/c experiments both observed approximately 4000 gammas and the 18.5 GeV/c experiment studied 11,000 vees. At the higher energies the three NAL experiments scratched the bottom of the barrel (bubble chamber?) to find 400 to 900 events (gammas plus vees). The small number of events at NAL energies coupled with the high escape probability of neutral kaons and lambdas going forward in the center of mass means that most of the information on neutral decays at these energies is from the backward hemisphere. In order to organize all the results this paper is presented in four sections:

1) total inclusive cross sections
2) average number of neutral particles produced, $<n_o>$, per inelastic collision (as a function of the number of charged particles produced, n_{ch})
3) differential cross sections as a function of longitudinal momentum
4) differential cross sections as a function of transverse momentum, p_T.

TABLE I: Experiments Reported On

Institution	Momentum (GeV/c)	Beam	Produced Particles Studied
Duke University, University of North Carolina	10.5	π^+	π^o
IIT, ANL, SLAC, University of Maryland, Concordia Teachers College, NAL	12.4	p	π^o
Notre Dame University	18.5	π^+, π^-	$K_S^o, \Lambda^o, \overline{\Lambda}^o$
University of Michigan, University of Rochester	102	p	$\gamma, K_S^o, \Lambda^o, \overline{\Lambda}^o$
ANL	205	p	"
NAL, University of California, Berkeley, LBL	205	π^-	"

TOTAL INCLUSIVE CROSS SECTIONS

Each experiment has calculated $\sigma(a+b \to$ neutral $+ X)$. Remember that in inclusive cross sections there is a multiple counting of individual events. For example if one event produces two K_S then it is counted twice. Figure 1 shows the inclusive π^0 cross section for pp interactions as a function of laboratory momentum.[7] The 12.4 GeV/c point was calculated from events with two gammas fitting a pi zero, while the other points are just one half the experimental single gamma cross sections. The straight line[8] shows that the cross section appears to go as log p_{lab} in this energy region. The papers also remark that the relationship $\sigma(\pi^0) = 1/2 [\sigma(\pi^+) + \sigma(\pi^-)]$ holds in this energy range.

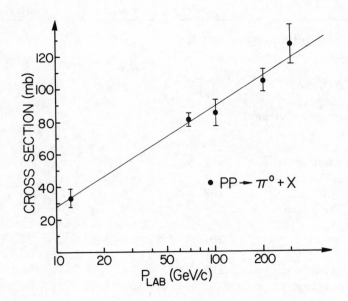

Fig. 1. Total inclusive π^0 cross sections for pp interactions.

Figure 2 shows the K_S^O, Λ^O, and $\overline{\Lambda}^O$ cross sections for pp interactions. Here note that above about 50 GeV/c the Λ^O (and possibly the $\overline{\Lambda}^O$?) cross section has leveled off while the K_S^O cross section appears to rise sharply.[9] Why should these cross sections behave differently? At this point your guess is as good as any. Note that above 10 GeV/c,

$$\sigma(\pi^O) >> \sigma(K_S^O) > \sigma(\Lambda^O) > \sigma(\overline{\Lambda}^O) \ .$$

The above inequalities as well as the increase in cross section in going from lower energies to NAL energies also hold for pion-proton collisions. In general π^- cross sections are slightly above π^+, and proton-proton cross sections are one to two times pion-proton cross sections at the same energy.

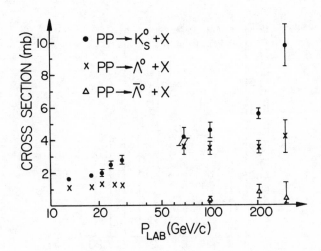

Fig. 2. Total inclusive K_S^O, Λ^O, $\overline{\Lambda}^O$ cross sections for pp interactions.

468

$<n_o>$ PER INELASTIC INTERACTION

In an attempt to discover correlations between the production of charged particles (mostly pions) and neutral particles (π^o's, K_S^o's or Λ's) several experiments have determined the average number of a particular neutral particle produced per inelastic interaction as a function of the number of charged particles produced. Figure 3 shows data on $<\pi^o>$ per inelastic pp interaction for three energies. Note that at 12.4 GeV/c the number of pi zeros produced shows almost no dependence on the number of charged particles. However at NAL energies, $<\pi^o>$ has a stronger dependence on n_{ch}. The exact dependence is not clear from the two proton experiments. Two possibilities are a linear increase as n_{ch} increases to six prongs and then a flattening off, or else a linear increase all the way to n_{ch} approximately 14 with a drop off due to total energy conservation.

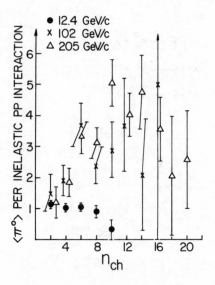

Fig. 3.   Average number of π^o's produced per inelastic pp interaction.

Figure 4 shows $<\pi^o>$ for pion-proton interactions. Again note the independence of $<\pi^o>$ from n_{ch} at low energy (at least for n_{ch} greater than two), and the strong dependence at NAL energies. Clearly, here the dependence favored is a linear increase all the way to n_{ch} of twenty. Figure 5 shows K_S^o production data. All

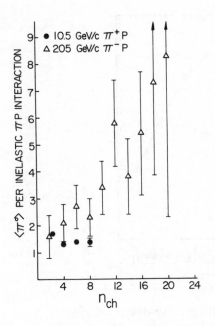

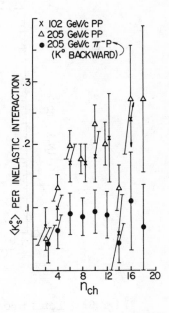

Fig. 4. Average number of π^o's produced per inelastic πp interaction.

Fig. 5. Average number of K^o's produced per inelastic interaction.

three experiments at NAL energies are consistent with $< K_S^o >$ being independent of n_{ch} except for a drop off in 2 and 4 prongs. This drop off could be related to the large amount of diffraction that is known to exist in low charged multiplicity events. Perhaps $< n_o >$ should be calculated per nondiffractive interaction. Data on lambda production indicate that $< \Lambda^o >$ is like $< K_S^o >$ in showing little dependence on n_{ch}.

The 10.5 GeV/c $\pi^+ p$ experiment was able to determine for the first time the total number of produced particles per event counting both charged and neutral particles. Figure 6 shows their cross sections as a function of total produced multiplicity. The curve is a Poisson fit to their data.

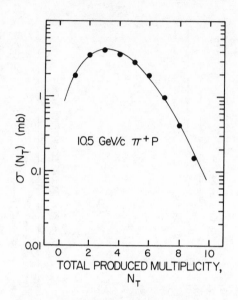

Fig. 6.   Total produced multiplicity distribution for
10.5 GeV/c π⁺p interactions.   The curve is
a Poisson fit.

The π⁻p experiment at 205 GeV/c compares their results with
the 205 GeV/c pp experiment. If one assumes one can "factorize"
an interaction into a forward part associated with the beam particle
and a backward part associated with the target, then the backward
results on particles produced per inelastic interaction for π⁻p at a
given momentum should be approximately the same as backward
results for pp interactions at the same momentum. Table II shows
the two experiments agree very well.

TABLE II: Comparison of Neutral Particles Produced Per
Inelastic Interaction for 205 GeV/c π⁻p and pp

Neutral Particle, n	$<n>$ π⁻p	$<n>$ pp
K_S^o (backward)	0.077 ± 0.014	0.085 ± 0.005
Λ (backward)	0.044 ± 0.11	0.055 ± 0.005
$\overline{\Lambda}$ (backward)	0.01 ± 0.01	0.013 ± 0.004

LONGITUDINAL MOMENTUM

The dependence of neutral particle production on the longitudinal momentum of the produced particle has also been studied. The following variables are most frequently used; the Feynmann scaling variable,

$$x \equiv \frac{2p_L}{\sqrt{s}}$$

and the invariant double differential cross section integrated over p_T^2,

$$F_1(x) \equiv \frac{2}{\pi \sqrt{s}} \int_0^\infty \frac{E\, d^2\sigma}{dx\, dp_T^2}\, dp_T^2 ,$$

where all quantities are calculated in the center of mass. In general the longitudinal distributions depend on the particle produced, sometimes depend on the energy (i. e. non-scaling), and sometimes depend on transverse momentum (i. e. non-factorization).

First, consider γ and π^0 production. Figure 7a shows the longitudinal momentum distribution for γ's produced by 12.4 GeV/c pp interactions. The exponential type drop-off seen here is typical of γ production. In this case the distribution was fit to a sum of three exponentials (the curve on Fig. 7a). This γ fit was transformed into a π^0 distribution as shown in Fig. 7b. For comparison,

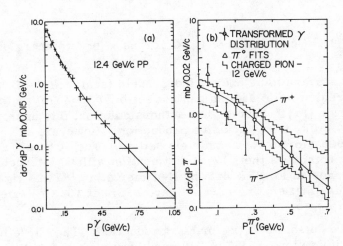

Fig. 7. (a) Longitudinal momentum distribution for γ's produced by 12.4 GeV/c pp interactions.
(b) Corresponding π^0 longitudinal momentum distribution.

the charged pion distributions are also shown, and the authors point out that the relation $\sigma(\pi^0) = 1/2[\sigma(\pi^+) + \sigma(\pi^-)]$ works for differential cross sections as well as total. Figure 8 shows the energy dependence of $F_1(x)$, by comparing 12.4 GeV/c and 205 GeV/c pp data.

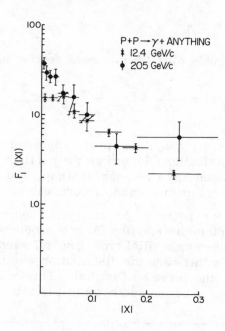

Fig. 8. Comparison of $F_1(x)$ versus x for two energies.

Note $F_1(x)$ appears to be energy independent (scale) in the fragmentation region while scaling has not set in at 12.4 GeV/c for the central region ($|x| < 0.05$). The authors point out this approach to scaling is similar to π^- inclusive production. However, the question of scaling behavior is not completely settled. The 102 GeV/c pp experiment compares their $F_1(x)$ distribution with an interpolation formula suggested for ISR data by Neuhofer et al. [10] (see Fig. 9a). They conclude that scaling may not have set in at 102 GeV/c even for $|x|$ up to 0.15.

Figure 9b shows $F_1(x)$ for K_S^o production. The curve is exponential with a slope of 4.7 ± 2.0, and is compatible with meson production data at higher energies. Finally, Fig. 9c shows an $F_1(x)$ distribution that is definitely not exponential. Lambda production is seen to occur in the fragmentation region.

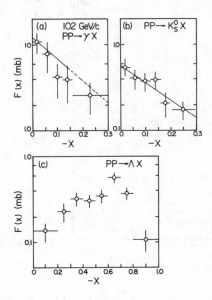

Fig. 9. $F_1(x)$ versus x for 102 GeV/c pp interactions.
The curves are described in the text.
(a) γ production
(b) K_S^O production
(c) Λ^O production.

Next consider factorization.   That is, can the differential
cross section be written as $f(x)g(p_T^2)$?   Figures 10 and 11 show
the 205 GeV/c pp $F_1(x)$ distributions for γ and K^O production.   The
γ data is clearly non-factorizable as shown by the difference in
slopes for different p_T regions, while the K^O data appears to be
factorizable.

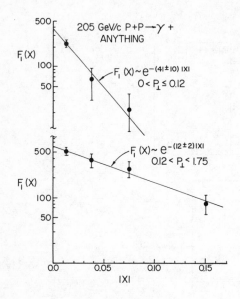

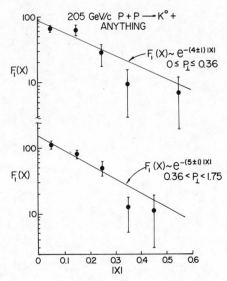

Fig. 10. Evidence for non-factorization of γ differential cross section at 205 GeV/c.

Fig. 11. Evidence for factorization of K_S^O differential cross section.

If one leaves the symmetry of the pp system and considers pion-proton interactions, one can get an asymmetry in the differential cross section about x = 0. Figure 12 shows 18.5 GeV/c $\pi^{\pm}$p data. For K^O production note the tendency to be produced in the forward direction (positive x, beam fragmentation), while Λ^O production is mainly backward (target fragmentation) and $\overline{\Lambda}^O$ production is possibly in the central region. The backward directions in $\pi^{\pm}$p for K^O and Λ^O production show similar behavior to the F(x) distributions for K^O and Λ^O production in pp interactions (compare Fig. 12 with Figs. 9b and 9c respectively).

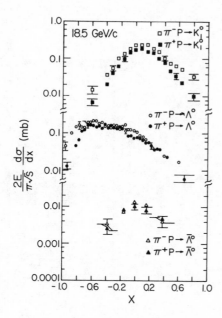

Fig. 12. x distributions for neutral particle
production at 18.5 GeV/c.

TRANSVERSE MOMENTUM

Unlike the situation for longitudinal momentum distributions
one finds an approximate exponential fall off in all cases for transverse momentum distributions. To study the dependence on transverse momentum one often calculates the invariant double differential cross section integrated over x,

$$F_2(p_T^2) \equiv \frac{2}{\pi \sqrt{s}} \int_{-1}^{+1} \frac{E \, d^2\sigma}{dx \, dp_T^2} \, dx \; .$$

Figure 13 shows the similarity of F_2 for γ production for pp interactions at two energies. Figure 14 shows the differential cross
sections as a function of p_T^2 for γ, K_S^0, and Λ^0 production with
102 GeV/c pp interactions. Note the flattening of the data points
as the mass of the produced particle increases. This flattening

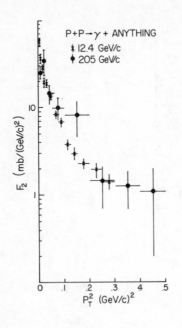

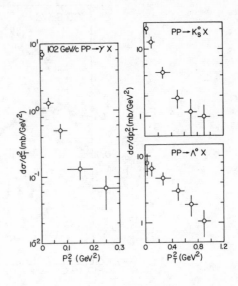

Fig. 13. Comparison of $F_2(p_T^2)$ versus p_T^2 for two energies.

Fig. 14. p_T^2 distributions at 102 GeV/c for γ, K_S^O and Λ^O production.

reflects itself in an increase in average p_T, $<p_T>$, as the mass of the produced particle increases. At 102 GeV/c the values of $<p_T>$ are 0.175 ± 0.020, 0.424 ± 0.043, and 0.541 ± 0.060 GeV/c for γ, K_S^O, and Λ production respectively. This increase in $<p_T>$ was also observed in the 18.5 GeV/c $\pi^{\pm}p$ experiment. In fact, this latter experiment also found a variation in $<p_T>$ for K^O production with the number of charged prongs (see Fig. 15).

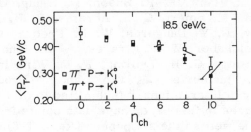

Fig. 15. Average transverse momentum as a function of
number of charged prongs at 18.5 GeV/c.

In conclusion, the study of inclusive neutral particle production has yielded a nice variety of experimental facts. One has just
about all combinations of independence and dependence occurring
among the various variables such as energy, beam   particle,
target particle, produced particle, x, and p_T. It seems all this
information is just waiting for some theory to explain it.

REFERENCES

1.   M. E. Binkley, J. R. Elliot, L. R. Fortney, J. S. Loos,
     W. J. Robertson, C. M. Rose, W. D. Walker, W. M. Yeager,
     G. W. Meisner, and R. B. Muir, "π^0 Multiplicities in $\pi^+ p$
     Interactions at 10.5 GeV/c," (submitted to this conference).
2.   D. Swanson, C. Fu, H. Rubin, K. Jaeger, G. Charlton, R. G.
     Glasser, D. Koetke, and J. Whitmore, "Study of Inclusive π^0
     Momentum Spectra in 12.4 GeV/c Proton-Proton Interactions,"
     (submitted to this conference).
3.   P. H. Stuntebeck, N. M. Cason, J. M. Bishop, N. N. Biswas,
     V. P. Kenney, and W. D. Shephard, "Inclusive Production of
     K_1^0, Λ^0, and $\overline{\Lambda}^0$ in 18.5 GeV/c $\pi^\pm p$ Interactions," (submitted
     to this conference).
4.   J. W. Chapman, J. Cooper, N. Green, B. P. Roe, A. A. Seidl,
     J. C. Vander Velde, C. M. Bromberg, D. Cohen, T. Ferbel,
     and P. Slattery, "Production of γ, Λ^0, K_S^0, and $\overline{\Lambda}^0$ in pp
     Collisions at 102 GeV/c," (submitted to this conference).
5.   K. Jaeger, J. Rest, D. Colley, L. Hyman, and J. J. Phelan,
     "Production of Strange Particles and of γ-Rays in Proton-
     Proton Interactions at 205 GeV/c," (submitted to this conference).

6.   D. Bogert, R. Hanft, F. R. Huson, D. Ljung, C. Pascaud, S. Pruss, W. M. Smart, G. S. Abrams, H. H. Bingham, D. M. Chew, B. Y. Daugeras, W. B. Fretter, C. E. Friedberg, G. Goldhaber, W. R. Graves, A. D. Johnson, J. A. Kadyk, L. Stutte, G. H. Trilling, F. C. Winkelmann, and G. P. Yost, "Inclusive γ, K_S^0, Λ^0, and $\overline{\Lambda}^0$ Production by 205 GeV/c π^-p Interactions," (submitted to this conference).

7.   Various figures in this paper have data points from the following papers as well as the six papers (Refs. 1-6) being summarized here. B. Y. Oh and G. A. Smith, "Inclusive Study of Λ^0 and $\Sigma^\pm$ Hyperons Produced in Proton-Proton Collisions from 6.6 to 28 GeV/c," (submitted to XVI International Conference on High Energy Physics, Batavia, 1972).

        France-Soviet Union Collaboration, "Photon, Neutral Kaon, and Lambda Inclusive Production in 69 GeV/c pp Interactions," (AIP Conference Proceedings No. 12 - Vanderbilt).

        F. T. Dao et al., Phys. Rev. Letters 30, 1151 (1973).

8.   The five data points fit $\sigma(\pi^0) = (61.5 \pm 4.1) \log p_{lab} - (33.7 \pm 7.5)$ with a 74% probability.

9.   During this talk Tom Ferbel stated that preliminary results on the 405 GeV/c pp experiment indicate that the K_S^0 cross section at 405 GeV/c is lower than the 303 GeV/c point. Thus it is not at all clear what is happening.

10.   G. Neuhofer et al., Phys. Letters 38B, 51 (1972).

UNDERGROUND MUON DATA COMPARED TO HADRONIC
SCALING PREDICTIONS FROM 2 To 1000 TeV*

J. W. Elbert[†], G. K. Ashley II, H. E. Bergeson, J. W. Keuffel,
M. O. Larson, G. H. Lowe, and J. L. Morrison

University of Utah, Salt Lake City, Utah 84112

and

G. W. Mason

Brigham Young University, Provo, Utah 84602

The Utah cosmic ray detector has
recorded extensive data on underground muons
resulting from the early stages of hadronic
cascades in the atmosphere. The measured
quantities are sensitive to the hadronic interaction characteristics in the 2-1000 TeV range.
The charge ratio of muons has been measured and
also calculated semi-analytically by assuming
scaling and using fits to accelerator data for
production of mesons in hadron-nucleus collisions.
In addition, a Monte-Carlo program which uses the
same assumptions has been developed to calculate
rates of observation of multiple muons for comparison with the data. It is observed that the
data are consistent with the scaling model calculations up to laboratory energies in excess of 1000
TeV.

I.   Introduction.   The advent of the NAL and ISR machines, together
with the development of the scaling and limiting fragmentation ideas,
makes it especially interesting now to look for cosmic ray measurements
sensitive to the features of hadronic interactions in the ultra-high
energy region.

This paper presents results recently obtained by comparison of
observations of ultra-high energy collision products (underground
muons) with scaling model calculations based on inclusive particle
production cross sections obtained in accelerator experiments. The
events were observed with the Utah underground muon detector. Some of
these results have been reported elsewhere[1,2] and this paper describes

*Research Supported by the National Science Foundation.
†Presented by J. W. Elbert.

the present activity and observations in this subject area by the Utah
cosmic ray group.

A first test of a general feature of scaling models is provided
by the cosmic ray muon charge ratio. A simple result of the scaling
hypothesis is that the charge ratio is approximately independent of
muon energy if the composition and spectrum of the primary cosmic rays
does not change in the appropriate energy range, and this constancy
of the charge ratio has been investigated for underground muons resulting from primaries up to 40 TeV.

A second, more detailed test is available from rates of muon events
of different multiplicities detected underground. These muons result
from the decay of pions and kaons produced in hadronic collisions in
the upper atmosphere. The events having one or two muons result mainly
from the first and second generation collisions and therefore are rather
direct sources of information about the high energy interactions. A
detailed Monte-Carlo computer program has been written which uses the
scaling assumption and predicts rates of muon events for the various
zenith angles, rock depths, and the number of muons, n_D, seen in the
80 m^2 aperture of the Utah detector. The calculation has shown that
primary particles of median energies from 10 TeV up to more than 1000
TeV are involved in the available range of detected multiplicity and
rock depth.

II. Apparatus and Analysis. The detector has been described in some
detail previously.[3-7] Briefly, it consists of 600 cylindrical spark
counters arrayed in 15 vertical planes, each 6 x 10 m^2, as shown in
Fig. 1. A trigger is provided by water-filled Cherenkov counters.
The spark counters resemble oversized Geiger counters, 15 cm dia. x 10 m
long, but operated in a pulsed mode at a higher pressure so that the
discharge is a sharply localized corona spike which is detected by means
of a sonic ranging system.

Muon trajectories through the detector are reconstructed using a
computer pattern recognition program. The efficiency of the recognition
program ranges from greater than 99% for single muon events to 85-90%
for events which contain 5 muons in the detector. Multiple muon rates
are adjusted by calculated correction factors (small in all cases) to
correspond to rates for a fiducial area of exactly 80 m^2.

The cosmic ray muon charge ratio measurements are done by analysis
of the deflection of muons in the two 5 x 8 m^2 x 60 cm planes of mag-
netized iron shown by the dark shading in Fig. 1. The basic principle
of the measurement is unique in that the muon momentum at production in
the atmosphere is determined by the slant range of rock traversed by
the muon on its way to the underground detector. The sign of the muon
charge may then be determined by magnetic analysis of the underground
muons, which have a local energy spectrum with a relatively low mean
energy.

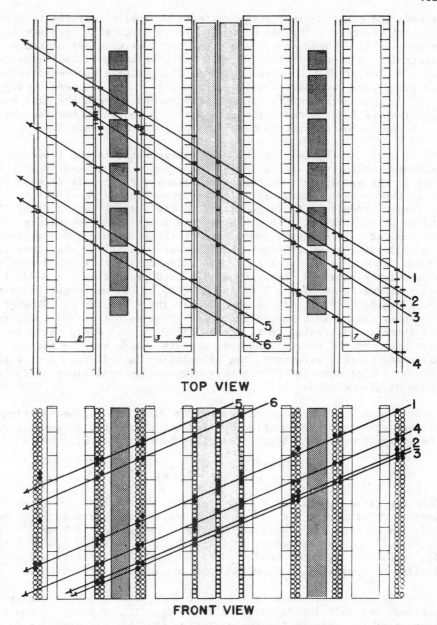

Fig. 1. Plot of an event containing 6 muons. The
coordinates of the sparks on the top view are obtained
from the time delays of the acoustical pulses.

III. Muon Charge Ratio Predictions and Results. The muon charge
ratio predictions (and the Monte-Carlo predictions for rates of
multiple muons treated in sec. IV) were based on the scaling assumption
and the use of inclusive distributions for protons, kaons, and pions
observed in accelerator experiments. In order to include intranuclear

cascade and other nuclear target effects we applied scaling to production cross sections for mesons and nucleons produced by protons incident on air nuclei. These production cross sections were calculated by interpolating between extensive 19.2 GeV p-Be and p-Al collision results.[8] The production cross sections for positive and negative kaons and pions were each fitted with functions of the type given by Boggild et al.[9] This parameterization was very successful and the fits agreed with the available accelerator data within 5 to 10% in the regions in which the inclusive spectra were not insignificantly small.

Basic discussions of the muon charge ratio in the framework of hadronic scaling are available.[10-12] An important general result is that in the atmospheric diffusion equations for particle fluxes, the steep cosmic ray primary particle spectrum gives extra weight to particles produced with large values of the scaling parameter x. The effect of uncertainties in the structure function at low values of x (as implied by the energy dependence of the structure function for p-p collisions between 20 GeV and ISR measurements) is therefore reduced. In any case, our fits to inclusive data with x > 0.3 give low x behavior similar to that seen at ISR (and presumably our $d\sigma/dx$ for meson production would be high compared to 20 GeV measurements in the low x region). It is also observed that the K/π ratio at ISR energies is higher than that observed at 20 GeV. The mean kaon multiplicity was therefore increased in the calculation to give a K/π ratio in agreement with the ISR results. Because of this change and the observations discussed in this paragraph, the calculation is believed to be a satisfactory approximation of the very high energy collisions producing the underground muons.

For a cosmic ray primary spectrum $dN/dE \propto E^{-\gamma}$, the relationship between the structure function F_{ab} and the charge ratio is manifest in the energy independent quantities given by Frazer et al.[10]

$$Z_{ab} = \pi \int_0^1 dx \int_0^\infty dP_T^2 \, F_{ab} \, (x, P_T) \, x^{\gamma-2}$$

Each Z_{ab} gives a ratio of a flux of produced particles (b) to an incident flux (of particle a) at the same energy after each incident particle has undergone a single interaction. Using $\sigma_{in} = 275$ mb,[13] $\gamma = 2.7$,[14] and our structure functions F_{ab}, we obtained $Z_{p\pi}^+ = 0.0564$, $Z_{p\pi}^- = 0.0386$, $Z_{pK}^+ = 0.0062$, and $Z_{pK}^- = 0.0022$. A fit to proton production data gave $Z_{pp} = 0.20$ and a proton inelasticity of 0.58.

If one considers only the pions from primary proton-air interactions, the calculated charge ratio is $Z_{p\pi}^+/Z_{p\pi}^- = 1.46$. Muons from kaons tend to increase the charge ratio, and hadronic cascades in the atmosphere tend to decrease it, as do neutrons present in primary nuclei.

We assumed that the structure functions for production of charged kaons were related by $F_{nK}^\pm = F_{pK}^\mp$ like the relation $F_{n\pi}^\pm = F_{p\pi}^\mp$ obtained for pions from isotopic spin symmetry with a charge symmetric target. Use of an extreme opposite assumption, $F_{nK}^\pm = F_{pK}^\pm$, would increase our charge ratio predictions by about 0.03 at 0.05 TeV and

0.07 at 5 TeV. The muon charge ratio depends on the fraction of α-particles and heavier nuclei in the primary beam. The charge excess $(N_\mu^+ - N_\mu^-)/(N_\mu^+ + N_\mu^-)$ of muons is nearly proprotional to the proton excess $(N_p - N_n)/(N_p + N_n)$ of primaries when incident nuclei are treated as made of free nucleons. We used a primary proton excess of 0.81. This was calculated from a proton to alpha ratio (at a given energy/nucleon) of 22.5 obtained by averaging the two measurements at energies above 50 GeV/nucleon[14,15] and from the ratios of other primaries at 10 GeV/nucleon.[16]

The calculations show that even with the constant Z values which result from scaling, there are small changes of the charge ratio with energy and angle. These result from changes in the probabilities of muons coming from different generations of the hadron cascade and from increases in the fraction of muons from kaons with increasing energy or decreasing zenith angle. These changes are caused by the approach to high energy limits of the effects of competition between meson interaction and decay into muons.

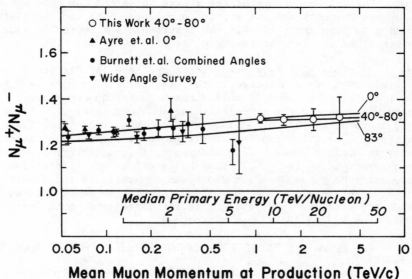

Fig. 2. Scaling predictions compared to
measurements for the muon charge ratio.

Predicted curves resulting from our calculations of the charge ratio are compared in Fig. 2 to the charge ratio of Ashley et al.[1] and of others referred to in that paper.[17-24] The agreement is good for muons produced with energies from 50 GeV up to 4.5 TeV.

The Utah points, at the highest energies, are in satisfactory agreement with the curve labeled 40° - 80°. It was drawn through the predictions made for the four data points, which occur at different average zenith angles. Uncertainties in the primary spectrum exponent, γ, and more important, statistical uncertainties arising in the fits to the structure functions could shift the predicted curves up or down by

484

0.07 - 0.11 but the value of $\gamma = 2.7$ and the best values of the fitted parameters gave the curves that are shown. The good agreement of the calculations with the low-energy points indicates that the fitting errors are in fact small.

The muon charge ratio is insensitive to the presence of an energy-dependent cross section factor if the x and P_T dependences of all the inclusive distributions are not significantly changed. However, we have considered interaction models which do not exhibit limiting fragmentation and have found a wide range of possible results, even when the average fraction of the energy and charge of the proton which is transferred to the mesons was held constant.

The observed nearly constant charge ratio is simple to understand as a result of scaling behavior of hadronic interactions. If deviations from scaling are present, they must be cancelled over almost two decades of energy by compensating effects such as a changing primary composition. The near constancy of the charge ratio and the good agreement between measurements and our predictions support the applicability of scaling to pion production in the intermediate x region of hadronic interactions for laboratory energies up to 40 TeV.

IV. <u>Multiple Muon Rate Predictions and Results</u>. In order to see how multiple muon evens observed in the Utah detector may be used to study the properties of hadronic collisions high in the atmosphere, it is useful to consider the schematic diagram shown in Fig. 3. A primary (say a proton of 10^{15} eV) strikes the atmosphere and initiates a hadronic cascade. A certain fraction of the pions (and kaons) in the cascade decay to produce muons before undergoing further interactions. The decay probability is $P_D \sim (90 \text{ GeV}/E_\pi) \sec \theta$ at one interaction length down into the atmosphere and decreases inversely as the density of the air at lower levels. The rock above the Utah detector acts as a muon range analyzer; by looking in different directions, muon energy thresholds from 0.5 to 20 TeV may be imposed.

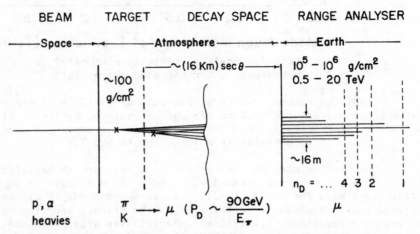

Fig. 3. Schematic diagram of the high energy muon component of an energetic cosmic ray event.

The quantities actually observed are (a) the rates $J(n_D,h,\theta)$ of events where n_D muons traverse the 80 m^2 fiducial area of the detector at a rock slant depth h and a zenith angle θ, and (b) the distribution in the separations of the muons.

The Monte-Carlo predictions for multiple muon events were done using the same inclusive fits used for the charge ratio calculations. A Monte-Carlo technique was developed which conserves energy precisely in individual events and generates particles which follow the desired multiplicity distributions and inclusive particle spectra with high accuracy.

In the development of hadronic cascades in the atmosphere, mesons frequently become the incident particles in secondary collisions. A quark model has suggested that forward hemisphere particle distributions in meson-proton collisions are related to those in p-p collisions.[25] The model has been extended to define a procedure to relate meson-air collisions to proton-air collisions. The validity of the procedure does not depend on the validity of the quark model which suggested it, and the scaling assumption assures its validity at all energies.

The total inelastic p-air cross section was based on the result of Yodh et al.[26] Their analysis of unaccompanied protons at various depths in the atmosphere indicates that the total cross section may rise from a value of 275 mb at 10-20 GeV to an extrapolated value in excess of 400 mb at 10^7 GeV. Alpha particles, when used as the initiator of the atmospheric cascade, were assumed to fragment into individual nucleons in the first interaction. The number of projectile nucleons which participate in the interaction was selected from a theoretical distribution given by Faeldt et al.[27] Nuclei heavier than alpha particles were allowed to break up into heavy fragments, alpha particles, free nucleons, and interacting nucleons in collisions with the air. The same primary composition was used in this Monte-Carlo calculation as was used in the charge ratio calculation. The proton spectrum was assumed to steepen abruptly to $dN/dE \propto E^{-3.3}$ at 10^{15} eV. A similar steepening of the spectrum of primary alpha particles and heavier nuclei was assumed to occur at 0.5×10^{15} eV/nucleon.

One of the results of the Monte-Carlo calculation is the determination of the median energies for events of detected muon multiplicity, n_D, for different rock depths. Table 1 shows these results for proton-induced showers.

TABLE I. Median primary energies giving rise to underground muon events.

Depth 10^5 g/cm^2	$n_D = 1$	Median Primary Energies (TeV)			
		2	3	4	5
2.4	10	80	350	900	1100
3.2	15	125	900	2200	3000
4.8	30	220			
7.2	65				
10.0	140				

One may note that the effects of a primary particle of a given energy appear as singles (n_D = 1) at a particular depth and as higher multiples at successively shallower depths, as might be expected from Fig. 3. The Monte-Carlo calculations also show that the median x-value for the parents of the muons in events with n_D = 5 is 0.10, compared to 0.23 for singles. The calculations confirm that a considerable fraction of the muons in the low-multiplicity events come from the first or second collisions of the primary (90% for singles, 79% for doubles, in one example).

In Fig. 4 are shown the results of a fit of the scaling model calculations to the Utah underground muon rates. The experimental results are given for different rock depths and the curves are the calculated rates for events with n_D observed muons. There were two free parameters in the fit, the normalization and slope, γ, of the primary proton spectrum below 10^{15} eV. The spectral slope for alpha particles and heavier nuclei below 0.5 x 10^{15} eV/nucleon was assumed to be equal to γ, also. The values obtained from the fit for the normalization and slope (we obtained γ = 2.73 ± .08) agreed within 8% and 1% respectively with results given by Ryan et al.[14] from balloon flight measurements of the primary cosmic ray spectrum. The results of Ryan et al. were for primary particles of much lower energy (< 1 TeV). The χ^2 for the fit was reasonable (15.3 for 19 degrees of freedom). The depth, multiplicity, and angular dependence of the experimental data were all reproduced by the Monte-Carlo calculation.

The results displayed in Fig. 4 were obtained using a scaling model and reasonable assumptions about the behavior of the primary spectrum. All the interaction model parameters used were obtained from the literature before comparisons to the data were made. We see in the success of the predictions support for the ideas of scaling and a "conventional" primary spectrum and composition over the wide ranges of primary energy and event rates considered.

Compared to constant cross sections, the use of increasing total hadron-air cross sections with increasing energy (as indicated by Yodh et al.[26] for proton-air collisions) produced only a small change in the rate of singles at a given depth and angle (the single muons come predominantly from relatively low energy collisions). With larger cross sections the collisions occur farther away from the detector. The muons consequently spread out more and the rate of doubles compared to singles is decreased by 20-25% at depths of 2.4 and 3.2 x 10^5 g/cm^2 and an angle of 47.5°. For higher detected multiplicities, the effect of the greater relative hadron decay probabilities at higher altitude apparently overcomes the effect of the greater muon separations and the rates for higher multiplicities are increased by an increasing cross section.

The distributions of separations of muons in the Utah detector are being studied in order to extract information concerning the inclusive transverse momentum distributions of the particles which decay to give muons. The mean muon pair separations estimated from the distribution of separations observed in the detector (up to 11

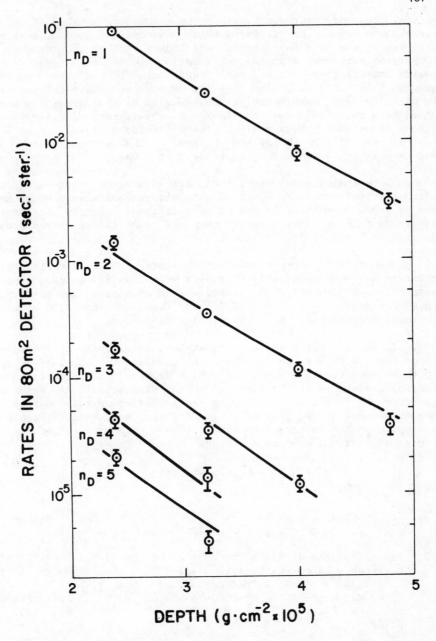

Fig. 4. Calculated and observed rates $J(n_D,h)$ in an 80 m^2 detector as a function of rock slant depth, h. The median primary proton energies are given in Table I and range from 10 TeV at $n_D = 1$ and 2.4×10^5 g/cm^2 up to 3000 TeV at $n_D = 5$ and 3.2×10^5 g/cm^2.

meters) are crudely proprotional to the assumed mean value of the transverse momentum of the particles which produced the muons. Preliminary analysis of the muon pair separations indicates that they are very roughly in agreement with the Monte-Carlo calculations using mean transverse momenta seen at accelerator energies. It should be pointed out, however, that this comparison may not be very sensitive to rare high P_T particles and that the collision energies of the parent hadrons are often very much lower than the energy of the primary cosmic rays producing the shower. Nevertheless, the collision energies are at least in the range of tens of TeV and the bulk of the muon-producing hadrons have a mean P_T value of roughly the expected value.

Data analysis and predictions are in progress for the rates at which pairs of muons are observed with wide separations underground (up to about 50 meters) by use of an additional detector located in an adjoining tunnel. These measurements are sensitive to hadron production at high transverse momenta.

Recently, the event information storage of the detector has been enlarged and near vertical events with more than 100 muons in the detector have been observed. These events originate from primary cosmic rays of energies in the 1000-10,000 TeV range. Monte-Carlo simulations of these events will soon be available, also.

Work is in progress to evaluate the sensitivity of the Monte-Carlo results to various possible violations of the scaling assumption at these very high energies. If a high degree of sensitivity to certain scaling violations is revealed by the calculations, it may be possible to determine that these violations are supported or ruled out by the measurements. At the present stage of comparison, however, the scaling assumption seems in agreement with a rather extensive set of very high energy underground muon measurements.

References

1. G. K. Ashley II, J. W. Elbert, J. W. Keuffel, M. O. Larson, and J. L. Morrison, (to be published).

2. Papers published in the Proceedings of the 13th International Conference on Cosmic Rays (Denver, 1973): G. K. Ashley II, et al., Vol. 3, p. 1828; H. E. Bergeson et al., Vol. 3, p. 1721; G. W. Mason and J. W. Elbert, Vol. 3, p. 2348; J. L. Morrison and J. W. Elbert, Vol. 3, p. 1833; G. H. Lowe, et al., Vol. 3, p. 1878.

3. H. E. Bergeson and C. J. Wolfson, Nucl. Inst. and Meth. 51, 47 (1967).

4. G. L. Cassiday, D. E. Groom, and M. O. Larson, Nucl. Inst. and Meth. 107, 509 (1973).

5. L.K. Hilton et al., Nucl. Inst. and Meth. 51, 43 (1967).

6. J. W. Keuffel and J. L. Parker, Nucl. Inst. and Meth. 51, 29 (1967).

7. J. W. Keuffel, paper presented at the Frascati Conference on Instrumentation for High Energy Physics, May 1973.

8. J. V. Allaby et al., CERN Report 70-12 (1970).

9. H. Boggild, K. H. Hansen, and K. Suk, Nucl. Phys. B27, 1 (1971).

10. W. R. Frazer, C. H. Poon, D. Silverman, and H. J. Yesian, Phys. Rev. D5, 1653 (1972).

11. Z. Garaffo, A. Pignotti, and G. Zgrablich, Nucl. Phys. B56, 419 (1973).

12. G. Yekeutieli, Nucl. Phys. B47, 621 (1972).

13. G. Bellettini et al., Nucl. Phys. 79, 609 (1966).

14. M. J. Ryan, J. F. Ormes, and V. K. Balasubramanian, Phys. Rev. Lett. 28, 985 (1972).

15. N. L. Grigorov et al., Proc. 12th Int. Conf. on Cosmic Rays (Hobart, 1971), Vol. 5, p. 1760.

16. V. K. Balasubramanian and J. F. Ormes, Goddard Space Flight Center preprint X-661-72-447.

17. T. H. Burnett et al., Phys. Rev. Lett. 30, 937 (1973).

18. C. A. Ayre et al., J. Phys. A 5, L53 (1972) and private communication.

19. A. M. Aurela, P. K. Mackeown, and A. W. Wolfendale, Proc. Phys. Soc. (London) 89, 401 (1966).

20. O. C. Allkofer et al., Proc. 12th Int. Conf. on Cosmic Rays (Hobart, 1971), Vol. 4, p. 1319.

21. R. W. Flint and W. F. Nash, ibid., p. 1346.

22. Y. Kamiya et al., ibid., p. 1354.

23. Z. Fujii, S. Iida, and Y. Kamiya, Lett. al Nuovo Cimento 1, 16 (1969).

24. N. S. Palmer and W. F. Nash, Can. J. Phys. 46, S313 (1968).

25. J. W. Elbert, A. R. Erwin, and W. D. Walker, Phys. Rev. D3, 2042 (1971).

26. G. B. Yodh, Y. Pal, and J. L. Trefil, Phys. Rev. Lett. 28, 1005 (1972).

27. G. Faeldt, H. Pilkuhn, and H. B. Schlaile, Karlsruhe preprint TKP 24/72 (1972).

PROTON INTERACTIONS IN HEAVY NUCLEI AT 200 GEV*

Joseph R. Florian, L.D. Kirkpatrick,
J.J. Lord, and James Martin
University of Washington, Seattle, Washington 98195

Robert E. Gibbs
Eastern Washington State College,
Cheney, Washington 99004

Peter Kotzer
Fairhaven College, Bellingham, Washington 98225

Robert Piserchio
San Diego State College, San Diego, California 92115

ABSTRACT

Nuclear track emulsions were exposed to 200 GeV protons at the National Accelerator Laboratory. One of the
emulsion plates was loaded with granules of Tungsten. Interactions in the
emulsion and with the Tungsten granules were located and angular measurements were made on the shower particles.
The average number of charged evaporation particles produced on Tungsten
was found to be 29.4 ± 4.3, which is
much larger than expected. Moreover,
the average multiplicity of shower
particles is 16.8 ± 3.8, about twice
as large as that for p-p interactions.
The corresponding values for the emulsion are 7.2 ± 0.5 and 13.9 ± 0.6 for
the multiplicity of evaporation and
shower particles, respectively. The
angular distribution of shower particles produced on Tungsten was compared to that for p-p interactions.
These data are in qualitative agreement with recent calculations by Fishbane and Trefil.

INTRODUCTION

Recently there has been renewed interest in the
nature of intranuclear cascading resulting from collisions of hadrons with heavy nuclei. This is in part
due to the belief that the study of the inclusive dis-

tributions in such reactions may allow one to distinguish between various classes of models for particle production on individual nucleons. In order to make such distinctions with nucleon targets, one must study the correlations among the produced particles.

Fishbane, Newmeyer, and Trefil[1] have discussed the possibility of inferring the character of the p-p interaction by measuring the multiplicity and the production angular distribution produced by protons on nuclei both as a function of the incident momentum and of the atomic number of the nucleus. In this paper we would like to present some initial data obtained during a recent exposure of nuclear emulsions (one of which was loaded with granules of tungsten) to 200 GeV protons at the National Accelerator Laboratory and compare these data with the theoretical predictions made by these authors.

Fishbane and Trefil[2] have divided the current models for multiparticle production into two classes: (1) coherent production models (CPM) in which an intermediate excitation propagates through the nucleus before it decays, and (2) incoherent models (IPM) in which the secondaries are produced directly. In the latter case, the secondaries can interact with other nucleons in the nucleus producing an intranuclear cascade. In either case, the nuclear part of the interaction is considered to be incoherent and therefore a summation is performed over all final nuclear states.

Both calculations are based on an extension of the Glauber theory. In the case of the IPM, the model chosen for the p-p interaction was of the multiperipheral type. The CPM calculation was based on a nova model. Further information about the details of these calculations has been published[2-3] by these authors.

The qualitative results of the calculations for both models can be summarized as follows:

    i)   The rapidity distribution in the projectile region is approximately the same as for p-p collisions.

    ii)   In the target region, the rapidity distribution exceeds that for p-p collisions.

    iii)   The multiplicity is predicted to be larger than for proton targets.

The models differ in their prediction of the magnitude of the average charged shower particle multiplicity $\langle n_s \rangle$

(although they do not differ much for certain energies)
and in the dependence of the multiplicity on the total
center of mass energy (s) and on the atomic number (A)
of the target. The IPM calculation predicts[4]

$$\langle n_s \rangle = E + F \ln s$$

where E and F are independent of A for values of A greater
than 10. The CPM calculation predicts[4]

$$\langle n_s \rangle = \tfrac{1}{2}(C\ A^{\frac{1}{3}} + 1)\ \langle n \rangle_H$$

where $\langle n \rangle_H$ is the multiplicity on a hydrogen target and C
has a value close to $\tfrac{1}{2}$.

EXPERIMENTAL PROCEDURE

One of the nuclear track plates (Ilford G-5) was
prepared with a dispersion of tungsten powder in the
emulsion. The use of small granules made it possible
to observe nearly all of the tracks produced in a given
collision. For example, the collision shown in Fig. 1
took place near the middle of an irregular piece of tungsten, yet all but the shortest recoil track can readily
be seen.

After preparation, the plates were exposed to the
200 GeV proton beam at the National Accelerator Laboratory until an intensity of about 100,000 tracks per
square centimeter had been obtained. The emulsion plates
were scanned by following proton tracks. The tungsten
plates were area scanned. Each event was examined to
insure that it had an incoming track pointing in the
direction of the beam. For tungsten events, the emitted
tracks were required to project back to an origin within
a tungsten granule. Spacial measurements were made on
each track in order to determine the production angle of
each particle. These emitted tracks were grouped according to the usual criterion:

    i)   Tracks with an ionization less than 1.4
           times that of a minimum ionizing track
           were classified as shower particles, n_s.
    ii)   Tracks with an ionization greater than
           this were classified as evaporation, or
           heavy tracks, N_h.

During the scanning of the plate loaded with tungsten
powder, 25 possible events were located. Eight of these

493

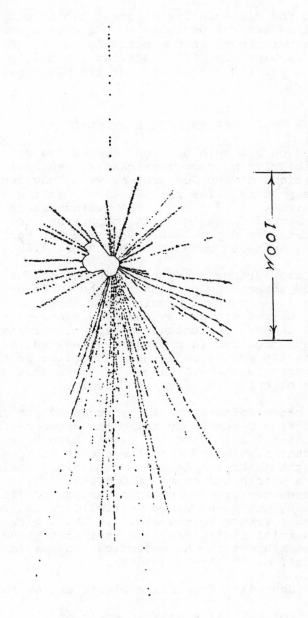

Fig. 1. Collision of 200 GeV proton with a tungsten nucleus. A total of 66 tracks radiate from a common center within the tungsten powder target located in the nuclear emulsion. 18 of the tracks were classified as shower particles.

satisfied the criteria for an event taking place on tungsten. Since several possible events with a small number
of tracks were found in the scanning, we do not believe
that our results are biased against low multiplicity
events. A partial second scan of the plate reinforces
this belief.

EXPERIMENTAL RESULTS

Based on a sample of eight events, we find the average multiplicity of shower tracks $<n_s>$ to be 16.8 ± 3.8
for collisions of 200 GeV protons with Tungsten nuclei.
The corresponding value for 181 events taking place in
the emulsion is 13.9 ± 0.6. The quoted errors correspond
to one standard deviation. In comparison, the average
multiplicity for p-p collisions at 205 GeV has been measured[5] in a hydrogen bubble chamber to be 7.65 ± 0.17.

One can further study the A dependence of the multiplicity by attempting to separate the emulsion events
occurring in silver and bromine from those in the carbon,
nitrogen, oxygen group. By assuming cross-sections proportional to $A^{2/3}$, one calculates that 10 of the events
should have occurred in hydrogen, 45 events in the CNO
group, and 126 events in Ag-Br. Secondly, we have assumed
that hydrogen events all have $N_h = 0$ and that all events
of $N_h > 8$ occurred in silver on bromine.

One can eliminate the 10 hydrogen events from the
sample of $N_h = 0$ events by using the known p-p multiplicity of 7.65 ± 0.17. Since 64 events have $N_h > 8$, 62
events must be selected from the events of $N_h < 8$ to include in the Ag-Br sample. The remaining unselected
events are attributed to the CNO group. While this selection process can proceed under a variety of different
assumptions, the Ag-Br group multiplicity can be determined within rather narrow limits. The limits on the
CNO group multiplicity are less stringent since all CNO
events are subject to the selection process (as opposed
to only half of the Ag-Br events).

The input data for this analysis are as follows:

i)   for all 181 events in emulsion,

$$<n_s> = 13.9 \pm 0.6$$

ii)   for 171 non-hydrogen events,

$$\langle n_s \rangle = 14.3 \pm 0.6$$

iii)   for 64 events with $N_h > 8$

$$\langle n_s \rangle = 18.4 \pm 1.1$$

iv)   for 107 non-hydrogen events with $N_h \leq 8$

$$\langle n_s \rangle = 11.8 \pm 0.5$$

Quoted errors are one standard deviation.

The "best estimate" of the Ag-Br and CNO multiplicities was obtained by plotting the N_h distribution for $N_h > 8$ and smoothly extrapolating it through the $N_h < 8$ region such that exactly 62 events were contained in the extrapolation region. This gave the number of events of each N_h value to be included in the Ag-Br sample. Events of each N_h value were than assigned a multiplicity equal to the average for all events of that N_h. (Thus, the assumption was that for a particular $N_h < 8$ the average multiplicities are equal for Ag-Br and CNO events.) The values obtained are:

$$\langle n_s \rangle = 15.4 \pm 1.0 \qquad \text{for Ag-Br}$$

$$\langle n_s \rangle = 11.2 \pm 1.5 \qquad \text{for CNO}$$

The errors quoted are a subjective estimate based on the sample standard deviations given earlier and a feeling for possible systematic errors based on the analysis to follow.

If it is assumed that the CNO average multiplicity cannot exceed (except by force of statistics) that for Ag-Br one calculates the maximum CNO multiplicity and the minimum Ag-Br multiplicity by forcing them to be equal. The value so obtained is $\langle n_s \rangle = 14.3 \pm 0.6$ which is quoted above for 171 non-hydrogen events. Similarly the (not too realistic) lower limit for the CNO multiplicity is the p-p multiplicity, 7.65 ± .17. This assumption leads to an upper limit for the Ag-Br multiplicity of 16.7 ± ∿.5. Operating under either of these limiting assumptions, one must select Ag-Br events with $N_h < 8$ in such a way that the resulting N_h and n_s distributions for the CNO and Ag-Br groups are skewed unreasonably.

Fig. 2 is a compilation of the above results in which the average multiplicity of charged particles is plotted

496

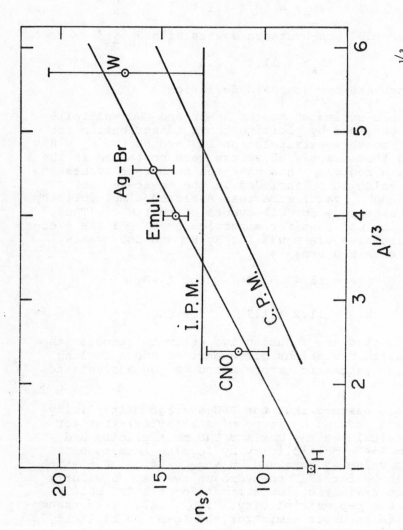

Fig. 2. Average charged particle multiplicity plotted against $A^{1/3}$ for 200 GeV proton interactions in hydrogen, emulsion, and tungsten. Furthermore the emulsion data have been separated into silver-bromine group and carbon-nitrogen-oxygen group events.

against $A^{\frac{1}{3}}$. Data for pure hydrogen, CNO and Ag-Br groups in emulsion, all non-hydrogen events in emulsion and tungsten events are included. Theoretical curves for IPM and CPM calculations are shown[2,3]. These predictions are expected to be good to within ∿10%. In spite of large experimental uncertainties several important conclusions are evident. First, the data seem incompatible with A independence. Only by stretching the statistics to their limits can one claim A independence. Secondly, the multiplicities are systematically higher than CPM predictions. However, the slope (within broad limits) is compatible with CPM. Furthermore, it is possible to extrapolate a linear $A^{1/3}$ dependence to include the pure p-p data.

The large value of the average evaporation prong number for tungsten events, $<N_h> = 29.4 \pm 4.3$, can be interpreted as a further indication that the intranuclear cascade process is A dependent. By comparison, all emulsion events have $<N_h> = 7.2 \pm 0.5$ while for non-hydrogen emulsion events $<N_h> = 7.6 \pm 0.5$. Subjecting the emulsion N_h distribution to the same selection process indicated earlier for shower particle multiplicities, one calculates the maximum possible evaporation prong multiplicity for the Ag-Br group to be $<N_h> = 10.1 \pm .6$. The ratio of $<N_h>$ in tungsten to that for Ag-Br, $R = 2.9 \pm 0.5$, seems too large to be explained by the ratio of nuclear charges $Zw/Z_{Ag-Br} = 1.8$. In emulsion the shower particle multiplicity is linearly related to N_h[6], so that large values of either N_h or n_s are indicative of cascading. By similar reasoning it would seem that since tungsten nuclei are fragmented to a much larger degree than silver or bromine nuclei there must be more secondary cascading interactions involved.

Analysis of the angular distribution is best made in terms of the rapidity. This requires a knowledge of the $\beta (\equiv v/c)$ of the emitted tracks, which we did not determine. However, our ionization criterion for the classification of a track as a shower track requires that β be close to one. If we set $\beta = 1$, the rapidity is given by

$$r = -\ln \tan(\theta/2),$$

where θ is the production angle of the track in the laboratory frame of reference.

The histogram in Fig. 3 shows the angular distribution for those events which occurred on tungsten. The comparison data for pure p-p interactions[6] are shown by the points. These have been normalized so that the rel-

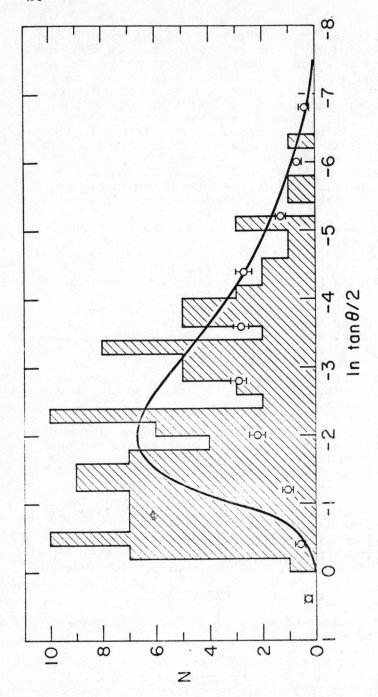

Fig. 3. Angular distribution of emitted particles produced by 200 GeV protons.
The histogram is for collisions with tungsten nuclei; while the points
are for p-p interactions.[7] The solid curve is a theoretical prediction
by Fishbane and Trefil[2].

ative number of tracks corresponds to the relative multiplicities. The solid curve is the prediction of the IPM calculation by Fishbane and Trefil[2]. It has been normalized to their predicted value of 13 for the multiplicity.

We see that the theoretical curve is in qualitative agreement with the experimental data. It is in quantitative agreement for large values of rapidity. Namely, the p-p data and the p-nucleus data agree for small angle tracks. However, in the region of very small rapidity, there exists a considerable excess in the experimental data.

ACKNOWLEDGEMENTS

We express our gratitude to Drs. Lundy and Voyvodic as well as the N.A.L. staff for making this experiment possible. The special tungsten loaded plates were prepared by Douglas Lord.

* Work supported in part by the Atomic Energy Commission under contract AT(45-1)-2225.

1.   P.M. Fishbane, J.L. Newmeyer, and J.S. Trefil, Phys. Rev. Lett. <u>29</u> 685 (1972)

2.   P.M. Fishbane and J.S. Trefil, SUNY preprint ITP-SB-73-15 (to be published in Nucl. Phys.)

3.   P.M. Fishbane and J.S. Trefil, SUNY preprint ITP-SB-73-36 (to be published in Phys. Rev.)

4.   P.M. Fishbane and J.S. Trefil (private communications)

5.   G. Charlton, Y. Cho, M. Derrick, R. Engelmann, T. Fields, L. Hyman, K. Jaeger, U. Mehtani, B. Musgrave, Y. Oren, D. Rhines, P. Schreiner, H. Yuta, L. Voyvodic, R. Walker, J. Whitmore, H.B. Crawley, A. Ming Ma, and R.G. Glasser, Phys. Rev. Lett. <u>29</u> 515 (1972)

6.   R.E. Gibbs, J.J. Lord, and E.R. Goza, Proc. of the VI Interamerican Seminar on Cosmic Rays, Vol. <u>40</u> 639 (1970)

7.   G. Charlton, Y. Cho, M. Derrick, R. Engelmann, T. Fields, L. Hyman, K. Jaeger, U. Mehtani, B. Musgrave, Y. Oren, D. Rhines, P. Schreiner, H. Yuta, L. Voyvodic, R. Walker, J. Whitmore, H.B. Crawley, Z. Ming Ma, and R.G. Glasser, <u>Proceedings of the XVI Intl. Conf. on High Energy Physics</u> 1 225 (1972)

THE NAL 30-INCH BUBBLE CHAMBER-WIDE GAP SPARK CHAMBER HYBRID SYSTEM*,**

Argonne National Laboratory
Iowa State University
University of Maryland
National Accelerator Laboratory
Michigan State University

Presented by G. A. Smith

ABSTRACT

We describe the physical characteristics of the Experiment 2B hybrid spectrometer now operating at NAL, consisting of the 30-inch bubble chamber and wide-gap optical spark chambers. Details of the equipment and operating conditions are presented. Further details of track reconstruction and bubble chamber/spark chamber hookup software are presented, along with results for 15-200 GeV/c tracks.

---

*Work supported in part by the U.S. Atomic Energy Commission and the National Science Foundation.

**Paper submitted to the Berkeley meeting of the DPF, American Physical Society, 13-17 August, 1973.

The NAL 30-inch bubble chamber-wide gap spark chamber hybrid system was approved for construction and data-taking approximately two years ago. Since that time, wide gap spark chambers and basic counter trigger apparatus have been tested at the Argonne ZGS and installed at NAL in a configuration upstream and downstream of the 30-inch bubble chamber. To date, a total of 192,000 bubble chamber pictures with corresponding spark chamber pictures have been taken, primarily in a parasitic mode with other approved "bare" bubble chamber experiments. At this time, a considerable number of bubble chamber photographs, primarily from 200 and 300 GeV proton-proton exposures, have reverted to the hybrid group and analysis of those photographs is under way. In the next year 450,000 pictures will be taken by the hybrid group (Experiment 2B). These runs include 200 and 400 GeV/c p-p, 100 and 200 GeV/c π^--p and 100 GeV/c π^+-p.

The physical layout of the Experiment 2B hybrid spectrometer now operating at NAL is shown in Figure 1. In this configuration the 30-inch bubble chamber is used as a detector of the event vertex and for measuring the momentum and angles of low momentum tracks (< 15 GeV/c) and the wide-gap optical spark chambers are used to measure the momentum and angles of the forward, high momentum secondary tracks.

The downstream apparatus consists of four dual wide-gap (8 inches) optical spark chambers each with an active area of 30 x 40 inches (horizontal x vertical). The chambers are approximately one meter apart and the most upstream chamber is approximately four meters from the center of the bubble chamber. Each of the four chambers is fired by a ten-stage Marx generator producing typically a 280 KV pulse with a width of 60 nanoseconds. With such a pulse as input and chamber termination of 100-150 ohms, track widths of 2-3 millimeters in space are achieved. In Figures 2 and 3 we show a plot of track width in space versus delay from coincidence and track width in space versus Marx voltage respectively. Although the indicated voltage and termination conditions, as well as film, are not those in use currently, the trend and scale of the data in Figure 2 are typical of current conditons, namely a chamber life-time of ~5 microseconds. Similarly, Figure 3 shows the sensitivity of track width versus Marx voltage for single tracks. For multitrack events of interest at NAL, 28 KV per stage typically produces 3 mm tracks.

In Figure 4 we show a plot of the single gap efficiency, defined as the ratio of the number of times the first or second gap fires less the number of times the first gap does not fire but the second gap does, divided by the number of times the first or second gap fires, versus the observed track multiplicity, averaged over the four chambers. The efficiencies are quite high (> 97%) and only weakly dependent on multiplicity.

The chambers and optical recording system can be multipulsed easily with a cycle time of 200 milliseconds. It is further possible to fire the chambers in pairs to photograph two triggers during each beam burst (typically 200 microseconds). Two radiation lengths of lead have been inserted between the last two chambers to detect forward gamma rays.

Photography is done with two 35 millimeter Flight Research cameras using GAFSTAR film. Each frame contains three views of the tracks: (1) a direct view (2) a 90-degree mirror view and (3) a 10-degree mirror view. The direct and 10-degree views are photographed at f/11 with a demagnification of ~50 and the 90-degree views are photographed at f/8 with a demagnification of ~60. Comparing reconstructions using the three view-pairs removes ambiguities one normally gets from simple two-view reconstruction.

The trigger for the spark chambers is also shown in Figure 1. A trigger is generated if an incoming beam track either produces two or more forward secondary tracks as detected in a set of three dE/dx counters or is deflected from a normal beam trajectory as detected by two sets of aligned counters, one upstream and one downstream of the bubble chamber. The dE/dx counters are each 8 x 14 x 1/16 inches and are viewed at two ends of RCA 8575 photomultiplier tubes. Each of the three counters is required to produce a signal larger than the minimum signal produced by the simultaneous passage of two minimum-ionizing particles. The upstream and downstream counters divide the beam into three 0.6 and 0.75 inch vertical slices respectively, the difference in size being such as to compensate for beam divergence and multiple scattering. Logic is used to determine whether a given particle stays in the appropriate slice. If not, a trigger is generated. The two triggering systems compliment each other in two respects: (1) the dE/dx trigger efficiency increases with increasing beam momentum, whereas the beam deflection trigger efficiency falls somewhat with increasing beam momentum; (2) the dE/dx trigger has high efficiency for high multiplicity events, whereas the beam deflection trigger has high efficiency for low multiplicity events (particularly elastic and quasi-elastic two-prong events). Typical efficiencies, depending on the particular choice of the trigger, range from 70% to 95% as measured at 200 GeV/c.

A typical event is shown in Figure 5. The bubble chamber view shows two slow tracks and six forward tracks which are detected and photographed in the spark chambers. Only the upstream chambers are shown in the figure. Immediately adjacent to and on each side of the data box one sees the direct view of the two upstream chambers, with the 10-degree view overlaid (short track segments). The 90-degree view of the two upstream chambers is furthest from the data box. As can be seen, each camera-based optical system has many fiducials. Survey measurements give the relative coordinates of the fiducials in space. Subsequent film measurements and fits to the fiducials give spatial X-Y R.M.S. deviations of ~150 microns in the direct views and ~400 microns in the 90-degree views.

The bubble chamber magnet (typically 30 Kg) deflects particles vertically and the direct views measure this deflection. For a 200 GeV/c track the deflection from the center of the bubble chamber to the centroid of the spark chambers is ~9 millimeters.

The software system for the Experiment 2B NAL Hybrid spectrometer has three basic components: (1) reconstruction in the bubble chamber; (2) reconstruction in the spark chambers, and (3) the track hookup between the two detectors. Reconstruction in the bubble chamber is done with the standard program TVGP.

In Figure 6 we show a block diagram of the logic flow in the spark chamber reconstruction program. The film plane measurements are first transformed to the ideal film plane in much the same way that TVGP does for the bubble chamber. Then each direct view track is paired with the 90-degree mirror view tracks and each resulting view-pair reconstruction is rejected unless there is a corresponding 10-degree mirror view track image. This procedure is continued until all tracks have been reconstructed without ambiguities. Figures 7 and 8 show point scatter (FRMS) distributions in space for a sample of beam tracks. The direct views (Figure 7) measure the momentum determining coordinate (y) and the indirect views (Figure 8) measure the equivalent of the bubble chamber depth (z) coordinate. Since each dual gap spark chamber has a separate 90-degree mirror view, this process is repeated four times and the four resulting track segments are subjected to a least square fit to obtain a best determination of the physical quantities of interest for each track. These quantities are: (1) two angles corresponding to azimuth and the dip in the usual bubble chamber terminology, and (2) two transverse beam-coordinates, all calculated at a fixed value of x, the coordinate along the beam direction.

Pursuant to the hookup with the bubble chamber, the track coordinates and angles are then transformed to the bubble chamber coordinate system. The matrix used to carry out this tranformation is obtained from a sample of magnet-off, straight-through tracks. Figure 9 shows, for example, the distribution of the difference between the y coordinate in the spark chamber system and the bubble chamber y coordinate extended to the spark chamber system for a sample of magnet-off tracks. The width of this distribution is understood in terms of the straight forward propagation of bubble chamber errors to the spark chambers.

The track hookup program now combines the bubble chamber and spark chamber results. Figure 10 shows a block diagram of the logic flow of this program. Each bubble chamber track with angles and momentum approximately consistent with the spark chamber acceptance is propagated to the no field region using a Runge-Kutta stepping method, then drifted to the point x_0 at which the spark chamber coordinates and angles are known. At this point, one of two options is elected: (1) if there is no track candidate in the region of acceptability the track is completed with only the bubble chamber information for it; or (2) if there is a track candidate, then the program proceeds to iterate angles and momentum repeating the bend-drift until a best fit is obtained.

We have measured forward tracks with the spark chamber-bubble chamber hybrid system having momenta between 15 GeV/c and 200 GeV/c. The momentum distribution for a sample of 200 GeV/c beam tracks is shown in Figure 11. We note that the FWHM of the distribution is 25 GeV/c, considerably smaller than the ~90 GeV/c value obtained with the bubble chamber data alone in the same film. We show similar results in Figure 12 for 300 GeV/c beam tracks. These results are consistent with the fact that the percentage error on momentum scales as the momentum.

In Figure 13 we show a $\pm \Delta p/p$ vs. p scatterplot for a sample of secondary tracks as measured in the bubble chamber alone and as measured in the combined hybrid system. The straight line indicates our early expectations for the system, with a form

$$\frac{\Delta p}{p} (\%) = 0.07 \; p \; (GeV/c) \tag{1}$$

Our results indicate a more realistic representation of the form

$$\pm \frac{\Delta p}{p} (\%) \approx 0.04 \; p \; (GeV/c) \tag{2}$$

At all values of momentum the accuracy of the hybrid system is vastly superior to that of the bubble chamber alone.

FIGURE CAPTIONS

Figure 1 - Schematic layout of the Experiment 2B hybrid spectrometer system at NAL.

Figure 2 - Measured spark chamber track width versus time delay from coincidence.

Figure 3 - Measured spark chamber track width versus Marx voltage for single tracks.

Figure 4 - Single gap efficiency versus track multiplicity in the spark chambers. See text for definition of efficiency.

Figure 5 - An eight-prong event, photographed in the bubble chamber and upstream spark chambers at 200 GeV/c.

Figure 6 - Flow diagram used in spark chamber track reconstruction.

Figure 7 - Point scatter (FRMS) results on beam tracks in the direct view.

Figure 8 - Point scatter (FRMS) results on beam tracks in the 90-degree view.

Figure 9 - Distribution of transverse coordinate of bubble chamber track (extended to spark chambers) around same coordinate of spark chamber track for beam tracks with no magnetic field.

Figure 10 - Flow diagram used in bubble chamber-spark chamber hookup.

Figure 11 - Distribution of fitted beam momentum for known 200 GeV/c beam.

Figure 12 - Distribution of fitted beam momentum for known 300 GeV/c beam.

Figure 13 - Scatter plot of $\pm \Delta p/p$ versus p for secondary tracks from 15 to 200 GeV/c based on (a) bubble chamber alone (open circles) and (b) hybrid system (closed circles).

NAL 30-INCH BUBBLE CHAMBER-WIDE GAP
SPARK CHAMBER HYBRID SYSTEM
(EXPERIMENT 2-B)

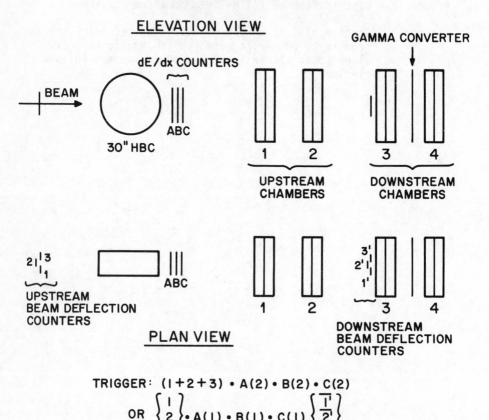

ELEVATION VIEW

TRIGGER: $(1+2+3) \cdot A(2) \cdot B(2) \cdot C(2)$

$\underline{OR}$ $\left\{\begin{matrix} 1 \\ 2 \\ 3 \end{matrix}\right\} \cdot A(1) \cdot B(1) \cdot C(1) \left\{\begin{matrix} \overline{1'} \\ \overline{2'} \\ \overline{3'} \end{matrix}\right\}$

APPARATUS SCHEMATIC AND TRIGGER

FIGURE 1

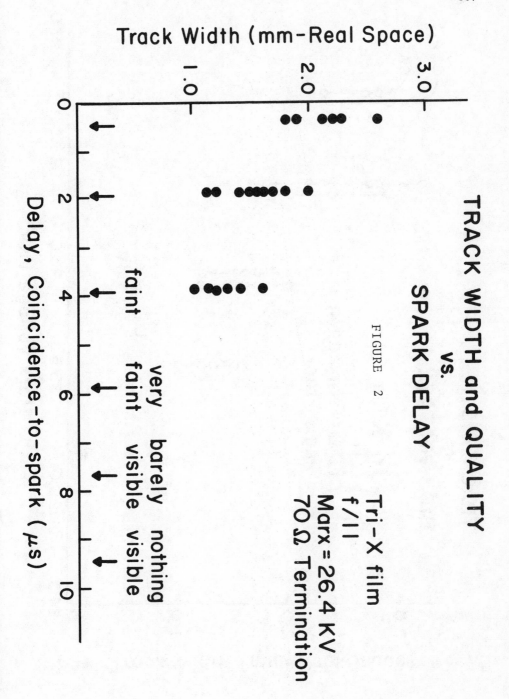

FIGURE 2

TRACK WIDTH and QUALITY
vs.
SPARK DELAY

Tri-X film
f/11
Marx = 26.4 KV
70Ω Termination

FIGURE 3

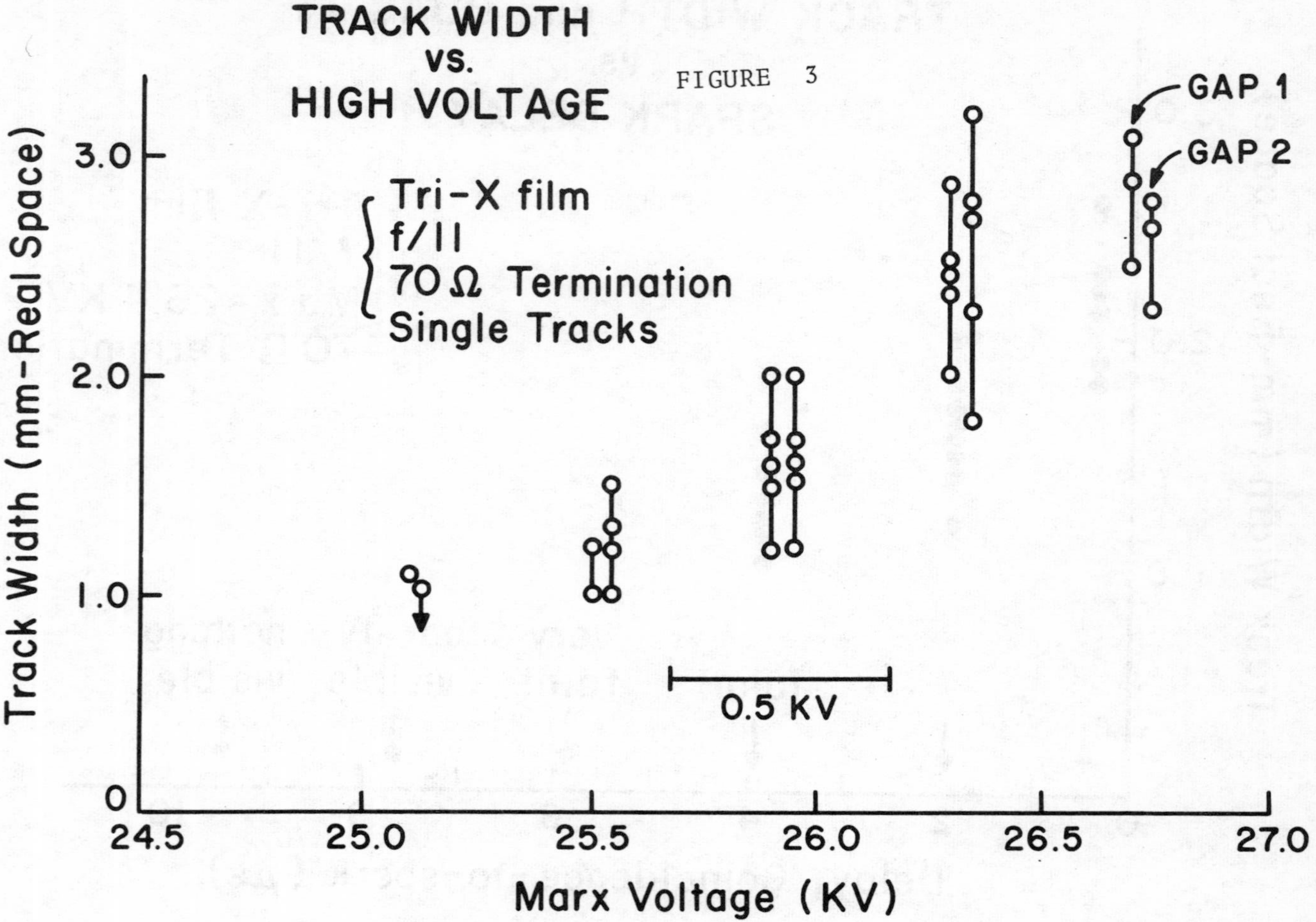
TRACK WIDTH
vs.
HIGH VOLTAGE
Tri-X film
f/11
70 Ω Termination
Single Tracks
GAP 1
GAP 2
0.5 KV
Track Width (mm-Real Space)
3.0
2.0
1.0
0
24.5
25.0
25.5
26.0
26.5
27.0
Marx Voltage (KV)

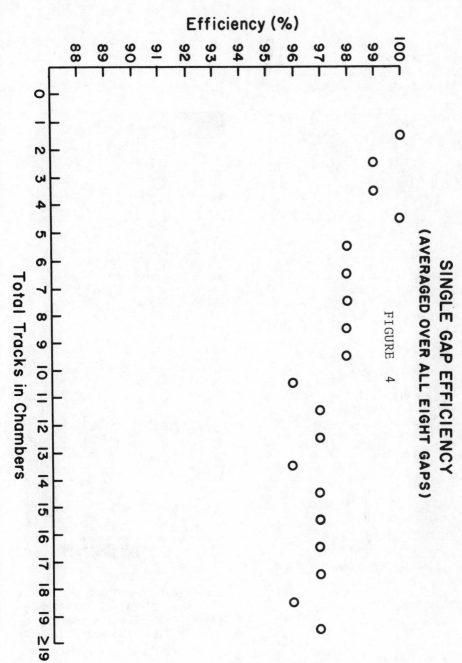

SINGLE GAP EFFICIENCY
(AVERAGED OVER ALL EIGHT GAPS)

FIGURE 4

510

Experiment 2B-200 GeV p-p
Nov. 27-28, 1972
(Eight Prong Event As Seen
in Wide-Gap Spark Chambers)

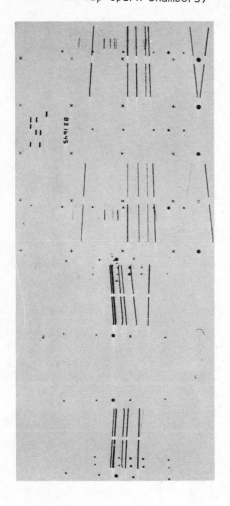

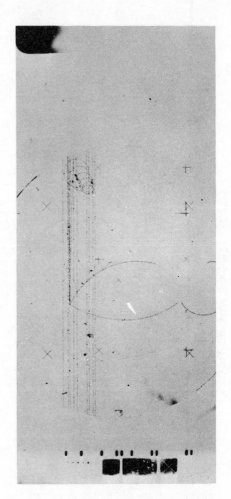

Experiment 2B-200 GeV p-p
Nov. 27-28, 1972
(Eight Prong Event AS Seen
in Bubble Chamber)

FIGURE 5

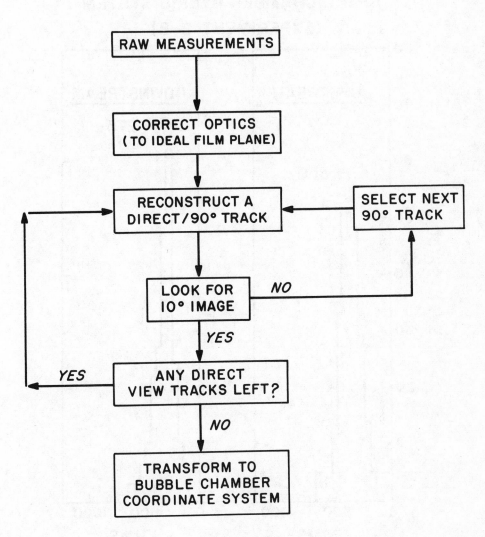

FIGURE 6

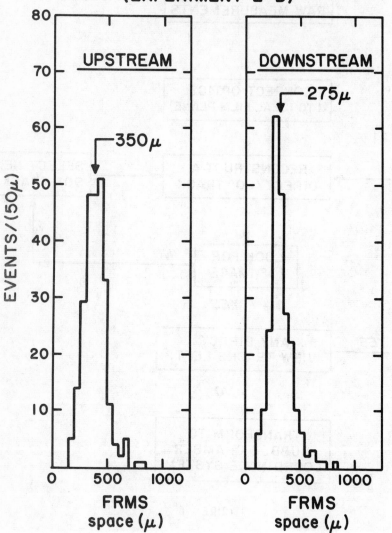

NAL 30-INCH BUBBLE CHAMBER-WIDE GAP
SPARK CHAMBER HYBRID SYSTEM
(EXPERIMENT 2-B)

SPARK-CHAMBER POINT SCATTER (FRMS)
(DIRECT VIEW)

FIGURE 7

NAL 30-INCH BUBBLE CHAMBER-WIDE GAP SPARK CHAMBER HYBRID SYSTEM (EXPERIMENT 2-B)

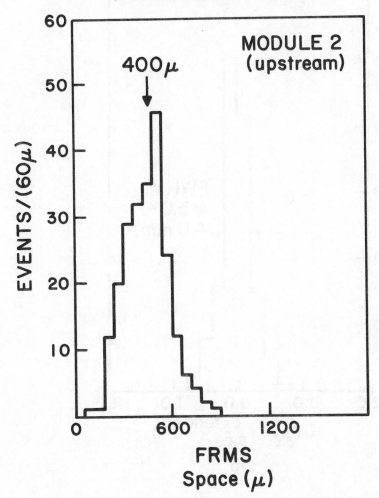

SPARK-CHAMBER POINT SCATTER (FRMS) (90-DEGREE VIEW)

FIGURE 8

NAL 30-INCH BUBBLE CHAMBER-WIDE GAP SPARK CHAMBER HYBRID SYSTEM (EXPERIMENT 2-B)

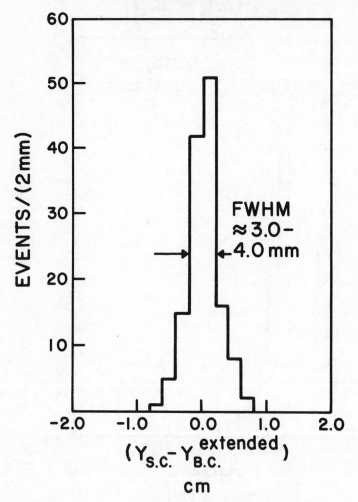

BUBBLE CHAMBER – SPARK CHAMBER
HOOK-UP MEASUREMENT

FIGURE 9

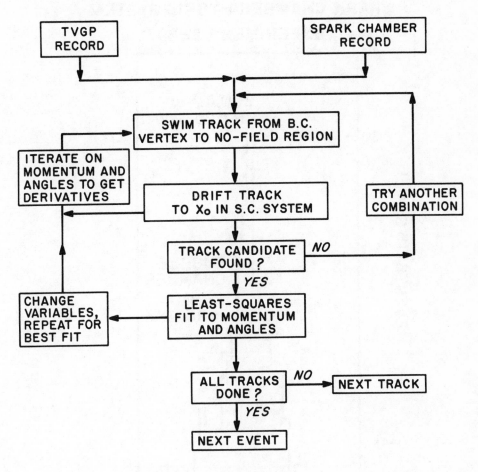

FIGURE 10

NAL 30-INCH BUBBLE CHAMBER-WIDE GAP SPARK CHAMBER HYBRID SYSTEM
(EXPERIMENT 2-B)

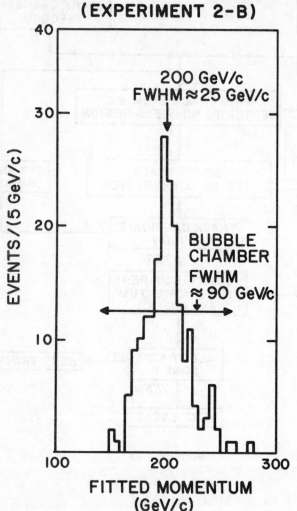

FITTED BEAM MOMENTUM USING
BUBBLE CHAMBER – SPARK CHAMBER
HOOK-UP DATA

FIGURE 11

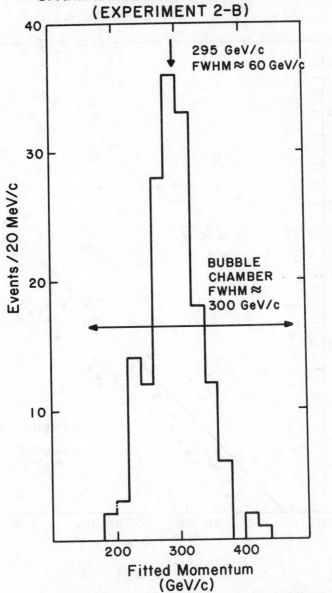

NAL 30-INCH BUBBLE CHAMBER-WIDE GAP
SPARK CHAMBER HYBRID SYSTEM
(EXPERIMENT 2-B)

Fitted Beam Momentum using Bubble-
Chamber-Spark Chamber Hook-up data

FIGURE 12

NAL 30-INCH BUBBLE CHAMBER–WIDE GAP
SPARK CHAMBER HYBRID SYSTEM
(EXPERIMENT 2–B)

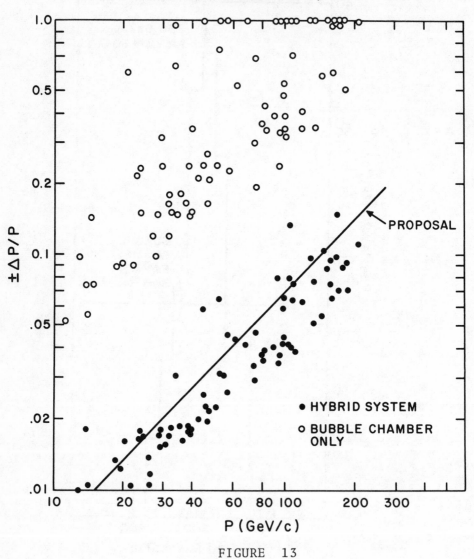

FIGURE   13

Chapter IV
Theoretical Aspects of Strong
Interactions at High Energies

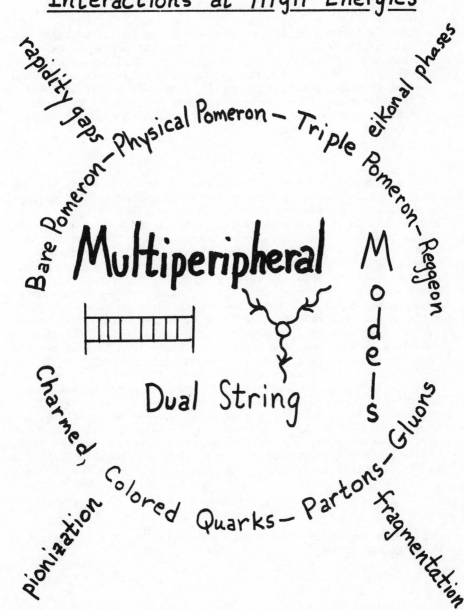

WHAT HAVE WE LEARNED FROM HIGH ENERGY EXPERIMENTS?

C. Quigg*
Institute for Theoretical Physics
State University of New York
Stony Brook, Long Island, New York 11790

ABSTRACT

A survey is given of the lessons to be learned from
first-generation strong-interaction experiments at the
National Accelerator Laboratory and the CERN Intersecting
Storage Rings. A program to study the properties of diffraction dissociation is urged for the NAL bubble chamber
experiments. Throughout, the emphasis is placed upon conclusions of a general nature rather than those which depend
on details of models.

INTRODUCTION

As a representative of the generation which is participating for
the first time in the opening of a new energy regime, I feel impelled
to begin with an observation that will be old hat to many of you,
namely that it is very stimulating to be around when a new accelerator is turned on. Although early experiments at NAL and ISR have not
(yet) confronted us with any sharply-drawn puzzles nor revealed
strikingly different phenomena which would completely change our perception of hadron physics, we have seen some surprises (rising total
cross sections, high-mass diffraction, etc.), and we seem much nearer
a conceptual understanding of multiple production than we were before.
It is an exciting time for the study of high-energy collisions!

My inventory of important topics appears in Fig. 1. With the
exception of the last item, each could serve (and has) as the title
of a mini-conference[1], so it is evident that I cannot hope in an hour
to do justice to the extensive experimental information now available.
What I will try to do is to describe how each piece of information
contributes to our evolving view of high-energy reactions. The
pressure of time, desire for a somewhat orderly presentation, and the
knowledge that they have received considerable attention from others
at this meeting conspire to force me to omit any discussion of large
transverse momentum phenomena. Apart from that omission, the list
in Fig. 1 serves as an outline for the body of my talk.

* Research supported in part by the National Science Foundation under
Grant No. GP-32998X.

SCALING AND THE APPROACH TO SCALING

A concept basic to the study of inclusive reactions is that of scaling or limiting fragmentation, first brought to wide attention by Feynman[2] and by Benecke, Chou, Yang, and Yen[3]. This prediction, long ago noticed as a consequence of the multiperipheral model[4] but only in recent times appreciated in its generality, holds that (for example)

$$\underset{s \to \infty}{\text{Lim}} \quad \frac{1}{\pi} \frac{d\sigma(s; y, p_\perp^2)}{dy \, dp_\perp^2} \quad \to \quad \rho_1(y, p_\perp^2), \tag{1}$$

or, in words, that the invariant cross section will, when expressed in terms of suitable variables, become energy-independent at high energies. As Bøggild[5] and Ferbel[6] have just reminded you, this expectation has been confirmed in impressive, though still qualitative, fashion. A representative data compilation[7] is shown in Fig. 2. It demonstrates that at $p_\perp$=0.4 GeV/c, limiting behavior is approached for copiously-produced particles, whereas for antiproton production there is a marked increase with energy. These features are reflected in Fig. 3 which shows the energy dependence of the mean multiplicities for individual species, here defined as

What Have We Learned?

1. Limiting fragmentation (scaling) for one- and two-particle inclusive spectra.

2. Two-particle correlations.

3. Rising total cross section and related observables.

4. Diffraction to high masses?

5. Large transverse momentum behavior.

6. Evidence for clustering effects.

Fig. 1. An inventory.

$$\langle n_i \rangle \equiv (1/\sigma_{\text{inelastic}}) \int (d^3p/E) d\sigma_i / (d^3p/E), \tag{2}$$

where $d\sigma_i / (d^3p/E)$ includes inelastic events only.

The energy dependence of the "central plateau" is shown in more detail in the data of the British-Scandinavian Collaboration[5] on the reaction

$$p + p \to \pi^+ + \text{anything}, \tag{3}$$

presented in Fig. 4. Scaling is confirmed very nicely, but as Bøggild has emphasized, the "plateau" isn't flat. However, the same Mueller-Regge analysis[8] that leads to the asymptotic prediction of a flat central plateau also prescribes the approach to that asymptotic simplicity. Furthermore it links the energy-dependence and the rapidity-dependence of the inclusive cross section[9]. The connection is a systematic one:

522

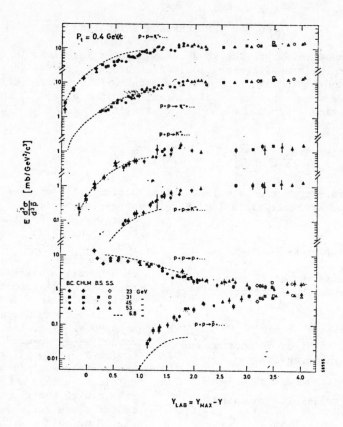

Fig. 2. The invariant cross sections plotted versus laboratory rapidity y_{lab} at $p_\perp = 0.4$ GeV/c for pion, kaon, proton, and antiproton production in pp collisions.

       If $d\sigma/dy$ at zero center-of-mass rapidity approaches its asymptotic limit from below (above), the rapidity distribution should be concave downward [i.e. peaked at $y^*=0$] (upward [i.e. minimal at $y^*=0$]).

Rather remarkably, this pattern is reproduced by the data. Looking again at Fig. 2 we notice that the invariant cross section for

$$p + p \rightarrow p + \text{anything}, \qquad (4)$$

which approaches its apparent asymptopia from above, is the only one to be concave upward as a function of rapidity. This is one of many surprising relations suggested by the Mueller-Regge analysis of inclusive spectra, which has proved to be a remarkably successful description of the gross features of multiple production. We should not however lose sight of the desirability of gaining an understanding in microscopic, exclusive terms of the manner in which these inclusive properties come about. That is, the Mueller approach,

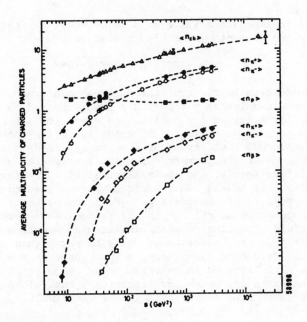

Fig. 3. The average multiplicities of various species of produced particles plotted as functions of s. Dashed lines are fits to the form $\langle n \rangle = A + B\ln s + C/\sqrt{s}$. [From Ref. 7]

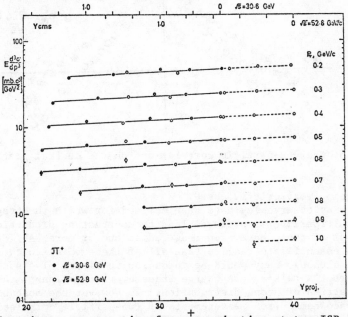

Fig. 4. Invariant cross section for π^{+} production at two ISR energies, for several values of transverse momentum. [From Ref. 5]

524

while of indispensable value as a guide, does not tell us the how and
why -- which we want ultimately to discover.

TWO-PARTICLE CORRELATIONS

In addition to the exploratory experiments mounted at the new
facilities, considerable effort has been expended on a well-defined
program, involving in its outline and execution a large number of people, the goal of which is to determine the basic character of multiple production. Most often the problem is posed in terms of a distinction between the geometrical view, represented by diffractive
fragmentation models, and the analytical view, represented by the
multiperipheral model. That program has now been carried out, and
with the support of considerable convincing evidence we can say that
the fragmentation model[10-12] in any recognizable form[13] is ruled out
as a picture of inclusive reactions at high energies. With less cer-
tainty --it is far harder to use data to prove than to disprove an
idea-- the data come down strongly in support of the multiperipheral
picture. This is such an important conclusion [it inevitably influ-
ences the lines of future investigations] that although I have previously reviewed some of the evidence at Vanderbilt[14], I will summarize

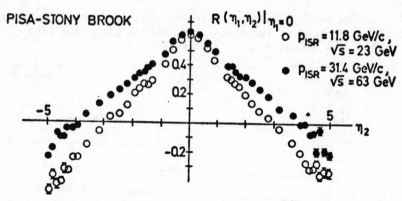

Fig. 5. Charged-particle correlations on the central plateau [19].

it again, very briefly, here.
Many observables have been defined for which the fragmentation
and multiperipheral pictures lead to contrasting predictions, and
several of these have been measured at one or more NAL/ISR energies.
It is essential to realize that all of these point to the same verdict, although many would be inconclusive alone. Two such, mentioned
in Ferbel's talk[15], are charge transfer fluctuations[16] and front-back
asymmetries of prong distributions[17]. However the most definitive
evidence comes from measurements of two-particle correlations in
rapidity. While the data are still rather crude and incomplete, they
exist for a wide range of energies and for several different species.

This suffices to distinguish between the multiperipheral and fragmentation alternatives, although we shall need more details to flesh out the multiperipheral skeleton.

In analogy with the statistical mechanical description of density fluctuations in a liquid, we define a correlation function[18]

$$C(y_c, y_d) \equiv \frac{1}{\sigma} \frac{d^2\sigma}{dy_c dy_d} - \frac{1}{\sigma^2} \frac{d\sigma}{dy_c} \frac{d\sigma}{dy_d} . \tag{5}$$

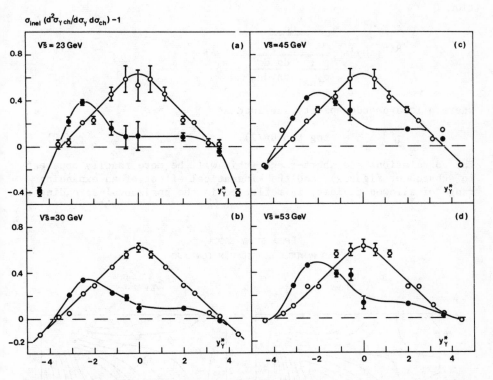

$\sigma_{inel} (d^2\sigma_{\gamma\,ch}/d\sigma_\gamma\, d\sigma_{ch}) - 1$

Fig. 6. Correlations between charged particles and photons [20]. The two sets of points are for $y^*_{ch}=0$ (O) and $y^*_{ch}=-2.5$ (●).

It is related to the "correlation moment"

$$f_2 = \int dy_c dy_d C(y_c, y_d) = \langle n(n-1) \rangle - \langle n \rangle^2, \tag{6}$$

but -- being more differential -- has more capacity to distinguish between models. In particular, the multiperipheral and fragmentation pictures lead to definite and very different expectations. In a simple multiperipheral model one finds[18,9] the characteristic short-range correlation behavior

$$C(y_c, y_d) = A \exp[-|y_c - y_d|/L], \tag{7}$$

526

with the correlation length $L \simeq 2$, and the coefficient A independent (at high energies and on the central plateau) of the incident energy. In contrast, a caricature fragmentation model[12] leads to long-range correlations, with

$$C(0,0) \propto +\sqrt{s} . \tag{8}$$

New data from the Pisa/Stony Brook ISR experiment[19] are shown in Fig. 5. The quantity displayed is the normalized correlation function

$$R(\eta_1, \eta_2) \equiv \frac{\dfrac{d\sigma}{d\eta_1 d\eta_2}}{\dfrac{1}{\sigma_{inel}} \dfrac{d\sigma}{d\eta_1} \dfrac{d\sigma}{d\eta_2}} - 1, \tag{9}$$

where η is a pseudorapidity, defined as

$$\eta = -\log \tan(\theta*/2). \tag{10}$$

The correlations are short-range (this will be more readily apparent in subsequent figures), and the kinematical effect of an expanding range of allowed rapidity is reflected in the horizontal spreading of

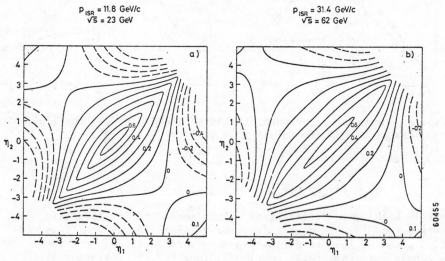

PISA-STONY BROOK

TWO PARTICLE CORRELATION CONTOURS

$P_{ISR} = 11.8$ GeV/c
$\sqrt{s} = 23$ GeV

$P_{ISR} = 31.4$ GeV/c
$\sqrt{s} = 62$ GeV

Fig. 7. Contour plots of the normalized correlation function for all charged particles [19]: (a) $\sqrt{s} = 23$ GeV; (b) $\sqrt{s} = 62$ GeV. The plots are derived in part from the data shown in Fig. 5.

the correlation function with increasing energy. Very important is the energy-independence of $C(0,0)$. The same features are present in the data of the CERN-Hamburg-Vienna Collaboration[20], shown in Fig. 6, on photon-charged particle correlations. The energy-independence of $C(0,0)$, which is supported by bubble-chamber data[15] as well, contradicts (8) and so disproves the fragmentation hypothesis.

A convenient way to exhibit the principal features of the correlation function in its dependence upon two variables is to plot contours of equal correlation (isopleths) in the η_1-η_2 plane. The Pisa/Stony Brook data, partially contained in Fig. 5, are displayed in this fashion in Fig. 7. In the central region [$|\eta_1|$, $|\eta_2| < 2$], the dependence on $|\eta_1-\eta_2|$ and independence of energy are clearly shown, and as Fig. 8 indicates more explicitly, the $|\eta_1-\eta_2|$ dependence is quite compatible with the multiperipheral expectation (7). Additional interesting effects[21] including long-range correlations apparently tied to the kinematical boundaries are present as well. These are at least qualitatively understood in the two-component (multiperipheral plus diffraction dissociation) picture.[18,22,23] Certainly we have only begun to apprehend the wealth of information contained in rapidity correlations.

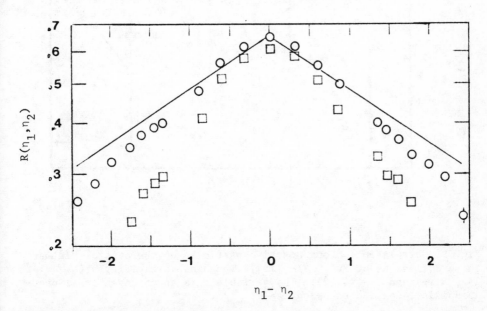

Fig. 8. A semilog plot of the data shown in Fig. 5. The total cm energy $\sqrt{s}$ is 23 GeV (□) or 63 GeV (O). From Ref. 19. The line is proportional to $\exp[-\Delta\eta /2]$.

A Mueller-Regge description of the short-range correlation component leads to definite expectations for the relative strengths of correlations among specific species of produced particles.[22,24] In

528

the high-energy limit,

$$C(y_c, y_d) \sim \quad (11)$$

$$\sim \sum_x \quad (12)$$

where the two sets of Mueller diagrams are equivalent through duality. It is then a natural first expectation that the coefficient of

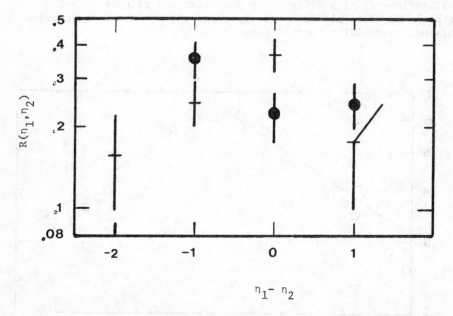

Fig. 9. Correlations among negative particles on the central plateau in pp collisions at 205 GeV/c [15]. The bins in rapidity are $2 < \eta_1 < 3$ (+) and $3 < \eta_1 < 4$ (○). The variable η is an unconventional pseudorapidity, defined as $-\log \tan(\theta_{Lab}/2)$.

the $L \approx 2$ short-range correlation will vanish if the combination $(\overline{cd})$ has exotic quantum numbers. For example, this would mean the absence (or, more conservatively, the smallness) of $(L \approx 2)$ short-range correlations between $\pi^- \pi^-$. If this were so, any long-range correlations would be plainly visible. The two-component description anticipates long-range correlations and explains their existence in elementary terms.

The basic assumption of the two-component scheme is that the inelastic cross section can be split into distinct multiperipheral and diffractive events, so that

$$\sigma_{inelastic} = \sigma^M + \sigma^D .$$ (13)

The inclusive cross sections will then be

$$\frac{d\sigma}{dy} = \frac{d\sigma^M}{dy} + \frac{d\sigma^D}{dy} ;$$ (14)

$$\frac{d^2\sigma}{dy_1 dy_2} = \frac{d^2\sigma^M}{dy_1 dy_2} + \frac{d^2\sigma^D}{dy_1 dy_2} .$$ (15)

With the understanding that σ refers to the inelastic cross section, and the notation $\alpha = \sigma^D/\sigma$, we may express the correlation function (5) as

$$C(y_1,y_2) = (1-\alpha)C^M(y_1,y_2) + \alpha C^D(y_1,y_2)$$

$$+ \alpha(1-\alpha)\left[\frac{1}{\sigma^M}\frac{d\sigma^M}{dy_1} - \frac{1}{\sigma^D}\frac{d\sigma^D}{dy_1}\right]\left[\frac{1}{\sigma^M}\frac{d\sigma^M}{dy_2} - \frac{1}{\sigma^D}\frac{d\sigma^D}{dy_2}\right] .$$ (16)

The first two terms give the weighted average of the correlations for the two separate components. But even if each component produced uncorrelated particles [$C^M=0=C^D$], the last term would give rise to a long-range correlation with factorized dependence upon y_1 and y_2.

With a very literal interpretation of the hypothesis that diffraction occurs only to low-mass, low-multiplicity states, it is plausible that on the central plateau

$$\frac{1}{\sigma^M}\frac{d\sigma^M}{dy} > \frac{1}{\sigma^D}\frac{d\sigma^D}{dy} .$$ (17)

Likewise C^D would be insignificant on the central plateau. In any situation in which C^M vanished, one would therefore expect to see a positive, long-range correlation in the central region. In other words, having found one particle in the central region, one can be reasonably sure (within this picture) that the event was multiperipheral. This increases the probability of finding a second particle in the central region and so implies a positive correlation.

The Argonne / NAL / Stony Brook collaboration has reported data to this conference[15] on correlations between two positive or two negative tracks from the 205 GeV/c pp exposure. The normalized correlation function (9) is shown in Fig. 9 for negative-negative combinations. With a little poetic license [which I invoke in order to make the following illustrative point, and not because of any Muelleristic preconceptions], one may interpret the correlation as small (0.2 to 0.3), positive, and roughly independent of the rapidity difference. Therefore it has the properties we expect of the long-range correlation in a two-component description.

For the normalized correlation function we have, in analogy with the last term of (16),

$$R_{--}(y_1, y_2) \simeq \alpha/(1-\alpha), \tag{18}$$

where in deriving (18) we have neglected $(1/\sigma^D)d\sigma^D/dy$ compared with $(1/\sigma^M)d\sigma^M/dy$. For the data of interest, if
(i) $R_{--} = 0.2$, then $\alpha = 0.17$ and $\sigma^D \simeq 5.3$ mb; if
(ii) $R_{--} = 0.3$, then $\alpha = 0.23$ and $\sigma^D \simeq 7.4$ mb.
These estimates of the diffractive inelastic cross section derived from the tentatively-identified long-range correlations between like charges are in good qualitative agreement with the diffractive cross sections estimated from the inelastic proton spectrum listed in Table I, and with the results of fits to the multiplicity distributions.[29] The consistency speaks well for the two-component interpretation.

Table I. Estimates of the Diffractive Cross Section

Group	Technique	$s, (\text{GeV})^2$	σ^D, mb
Michigan/Rochester [25]	BC	193	6.8 ± 1.0
NAL/UCLA [26]	BC	569	$\begin{cases} 8.4 \pm 0.7 \\ 5.6 \pm 0.8 \end{cases}$
Columbia/Stony Brook [27]	Counter	569	$3.2 < \sigma^D < 4.7$
CHLM [28]	Spectrometer	530	5.4 ± 1
		929.5	5.0 ± 1

The two-component model also makes rather definite predictions for the behavior of the so-called correlation moments. The first three of these are defined as

$$f_1 \equiv \langle n \rangle = (1/\sigma) \int dy \, d\sigma/dy, \tag{19}$$

$$f_2 \equiv \langle n(n-1) \rangle - \langle n \rangle^2 = (1/\sigma) \int dy_1 dy_2 \, C(y_1, y_2), \tag{20}$$

$$f_3 \equiv \langle n(n-1)(n-2) \rangle - 3\langle n \rangle\langle n(n-1) \rangle + 2\langle n \rangle^3 = \dots \tag{21}$$

Using an obvious notation, we may express the two-component equivalents of these as

$$f_1 = \alpha f_1^D + (1-\alpha)f_1^M, \tag{22}$$

$$f_2 = \alpha f_2^D + (1-\alpha)f_2^M + \alpha(1-\alpha)[f_1^D - f_1^M]^2, \tag{23}$$

$$f_3 = \alpha f_3^D + (1-\alpha) f_3^M + 3\alpha (1-\alpha) [(f_2^D - f_2^M)(f_1^D - f_1^M)]$$
$$+ 2\alpha (1-\alpha) (\tfrac{1}{2}-\alpha) [f_1^D - f_1^M]^3 . \tag{24}$$

In each case the first two terms give the weighted average of the correlation moments for the two components. The conventional possibility is

$$f_q^D \sim \text{constant,} \tag{25}$$

$$f_q^M \sim Y = \log[s/m^2]. \tag{26}$$

Therefore the dominant asymptotic behavior of the correlation moments will be

$$f_1 \sim Y, \tag{27}$$

$$f_2 \sim \alpha (1-\alpha) Y^2, \tag{28}$$

$$f_3 \sim -2\alpha (1-\alpha)(\tfrac{1}{2}-\alpha) Y^3 . \tag{29}$$

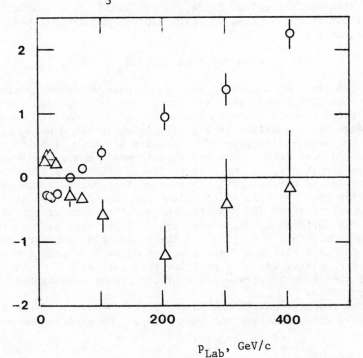

Fig. 10. Energy dependence of the correlation moments for negative particles produced in pp collisions: f_2^- (O); f_3^- (△).

In the two latter cases the dominant asymptotic behavior comes from the interference term involving the mean multiplicities. This scheme predicts that asymptotically

$$f_2 > 0, \ f_2 \leq 0.25 \ <n>^2 ,$$

(30)

$$f_3 \left\{ \begin{array}{l} < 0, \ \alpha < \tfrac{1}{2} \\ > 0, \ \alpha > \tfrac{1}{2} \end{array} \right\}; \quad |f_3| \leq 0.096 \ <n>^3 .$$

(31)

Since the parameter α is surely less than $\tfrac{1}{2}$ in the kinds of models we are discussing ($\tfrac{1}{4}$ to 1/6 is a typical range), the conventional two component pictures require $f_3 < 0$ asymptotically. The data up to 405 GeV/c are collected in Fig. 10. It appears that f_2, after an excursion into negative values at low energies, is on its asymptotic path, whereas f_3 seems still in the midst of low-energy wiggles at 405 GeV/c. Ferbel has quoted a fit to f_2 which has the leading behavior

$$f_2^- = (0.4\pm0.1)\log^2 s - (4\pm1.4)\log s + \ldots \sim (0.8\pm0.2)<n_->^2 .$$

(32)

It is two early to write off the two-component model on the basis of this underdetermined fit, but let us take notice of the conflict between the fitted coefficient of $\log^2 s$ and the bound (30). Evidently this is a situation to watch as the data improve and are extended to still higher energies.

TOTAL CROSS SECTIONS AND SUCH

One of the exciting surprises in the new energy regime is the discovery by the CERN/Rome[30] and Pisa/Stony Brook[31] Collaborations that the pp total cross section increases by 10% over the ISR energy range. The data are summarized in Fig. 11, which is based on a figure in Amaldi's thorough review paper[32]. The data lie very close to a "lower bound" deduced from cosmic ray experiments[33] under the assumption that Glauber theory, in the form tested at AGS/PS energies, holds at energies of several TeV. This is an interesting consonance, but I think few would be willing to adduce the cosmic ray measurement as strong support for the ISR results. A source of more direct support may be the forthcoming NAL measurements of the real part of the forward elastic scattering amplitude. The preëxisting data are shown in Fig. 12, together with the results of two dispersion relation calculations. The observation of a positive real part at NAL would be an important independent corroboration of the trends established by the ISR experiments.[35]

Unitarity imposes constraints on the mutual behavior of the total and elastic cross sections and the slope of the diffraction peak

$$b \equiv \left. \frac{\partial(\log \, d\sigma/dt)}{\partial t} \right|_{t=0} .$$

(33)

One restriction of some interest (because the data closely approach the bound) is the MacDowell-Martin lower bound[36] on the slope. Under

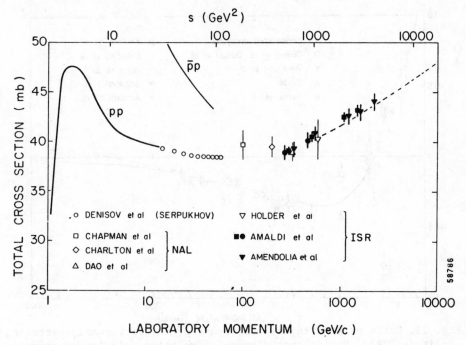

Fig. 11. Compilation of data on the pp and p̄p total cross sections [after Ref. 32]. The dashed line is the cosmic ray "lower bound."

the assumptions that (i) only a single spin amplitude contributes and (ii) the real part of the amplitude is negligible, the bound takes the form

$$b \gtrsim (\sigma_{total})^2/18\pi\sigma_{elastic}. \tag{34}$$

The experimental situation in pp scattering is shown in Fig. 13 as a plot of $\sigma_{total}/16\pi b$ versus $\sigma_{elastic}/\sigma_{total}$. The trends at AGS/PS energies are the same for all combinations of beam and target[38]. While it is instructive to give a detailed interpretation[37] of this plot, I wish only to make two points. First, the MacDowell-Martin bound is nearly saturated at the highest energies. If the bound were exactly satisfied [this is really rather utopian; "exactly" means in the sense that two analytic functions are identical] one would know precisely the partial-wave structure of the scattering amplitude in terms of a parametric equation[39]

$$\text{Im } a_\ell = \alpha - \beta\ell(\ell+1) \geq 0, \tag{35}$$

where α and β are determined by the observables. To be merely close to the bound is not terribly constraining; but it is useful to have in mind where the data may be tending. Second, the asymptotic situation contemplated in the impact picture[40] corresponds in Fig. 13 to the circled point at $(\frac{1}{2},\frac{1}{2})$. I am not prescient enough to know

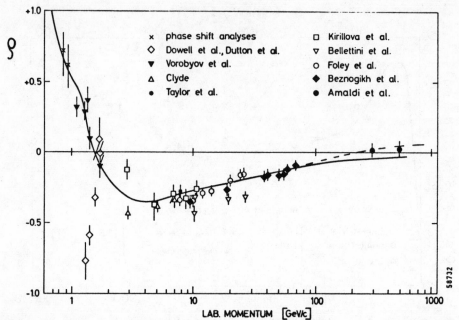

Fig. 12. Ratio of real to imaginary part of the pp forward scattering amplitude [32]. Solid line: dispersion relation calculation assuming $\sigma_{total} \equiv 40$ mb; dashed line, same assuming the ISR total cross sections.

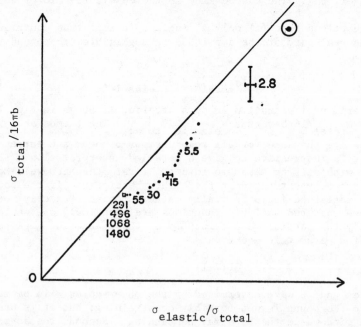

Fig. 13. Relation among observables in pp scattering [from 37].

what will happen as s→∞, but it is evident that if the impact picture is asymptotically a correct one, we are still very far from asymptopia. Alternatively, if in spite of appearances the impact picture is relevant at present energies, we must try to understand why.

A final remark on this general topic pertains to the ISR results on the near-forward differential cross section[41], typified by the data in Fig. 14. The deviation from an exponential shape has generated much interest and hundreds of explanations[42], and as Kane[43] has told us, one can use the Fourier-Bessel transform of this cross section as the basis for an elaborate description of two-body scattering. All this attention may be deserved, but in my rôle as sheepdog[44] I feel obliged to mention another less exciting possibility. It is unquestionably true (provided the data are correct) that a single exponential anchored to the forward data fits very badly for -t > 0.2

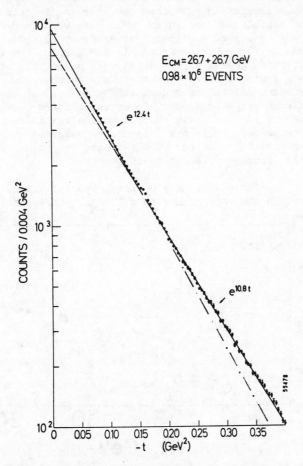

Fig. 14. Angular distribution of proton-proton elastic scattering at a squared cm energy s = 2800 GeV². [From Ref. 41]

536

(GeV/c)^2. [Notice the dash-dotted line in Fig. 14.] There are, however, five spin amplitudes for pp scattering, and it would be rather
miraculous if four of them vanished identically. Furthermore, the
magnitude of the difference between the forward [exp(12.4t)] exponential and the data is very small (starting from zero at t=0). The
difference has in fact just the shape one expects from the square of
a spinflip amplitude. I find it amusing that ancient [45] Regge pole
fits to sub-30 GeV/c data displayed curvature similar to what is now
observed at the ISR, and that the curvature derived from a Pomeron
contribution to a spinflip amplitude, the possibility we have just
raised.

PROPERTIES OF DIFFRACTION DISSOCIATION

Recent experiments[46] at NAL and ISR raise the possibility that
diffraction dissociation can occur not only to discrete resonances
but also to a high-mass continuum. The very unsettled experimental
situation was described admirably yesterday by Leith[47]. I have nothing to add to (or subtract from) his discussion; the issues are
well-appreciated and the experimental work needed to settle them is
understood. I wish instead to concentrate on some general features
of hadron-hadron collisions and on the evidence just beginning to
accumulate that suggests a much closer resemblance between diffractive scattering and "ordinary" hadron-hadron collisions than we
might have expected. This new information suggests an extensive
new type of investigation for bubble chamber experiments at NAL,
which I will describe at some length.

It now appears that to a good first approximation, particles
are produced in the same manner in all hadron-hadron collisions,

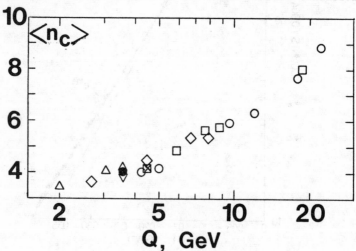

Fig. 15. Mean charged multiplicity per inelastic collision versus
$Q \equiv \sqrt{s} - M_a - M_b$ for pp (O), $\bar{p}p$ ($\triangle$), $\pi^+ p$ ($\square$), $\pi^- p$ ($\diamondsuit$), $K^- p$ ($\triangledown$),
$K^+ p$ ($\bullet$), and $\pi^- N$ ($\boxtimes$) collisions.

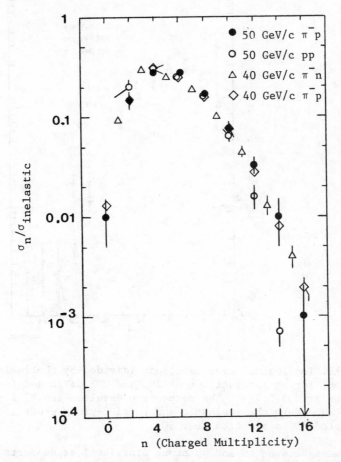

Fig. 16. Topological cross sections for several channels at approximately equal values of Q [8.6, 7.9, 7.6, and 7.6 GeV].   Data are from Ref. 49.

independent of the incoming particles. For example, as Fig. 15 indicates[48], the mean multiplicity of charged particles appears to depend only upon the energy available in the collision,

$$Q = \sqrt{s} - M_a - M_b \qquad (36)$$

where M_a and M_b are the masses of the incoming (and therefore leading) particles. Indeed, it is likely that at high energies the prong distribution

$$P_n \equiv \sigma_n / \sigma_{inelastic}, \qquad (37)$$

and not merely its first moment, is "universal" and Q-dependent. Data which bear on this observation are available. at $Q \simeq 8$ GeV, collected in Fig. 16, and at $Q \simeq 18$ GeV, collected in Fig. 17.   The

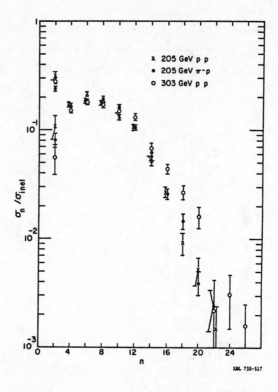

Fig. 17. Topological cross sections (divided by the inelastic cross section) for pp interactions at 205 and 303 GeV/c and for π⁻p interactions at 205 GeV/c. The respective Q-values are 17.5, 21.9, and 18.3 GeV. Both the inelastic and total 2-prong cross sections are indicated. Data are from Ref. 50.

agreement between πN and pp prong distributions supports the idea of a "universal" mechanism for particle production.

We may summarize this aspect of the data by means of a greatly simplified mnemonic:

by which we understand the following average statements. In the cm frame (of e.g. pp collisions) the incident particles enter with energies $\frac{1}{2}\sqrt{s}$ and depart as leading particles having deposited half of their incident energy but no hint of their identity. The amount of energy left behind which goes into particle production is

$$K \simeq \frac{1}{2}\sqrt{s}. \tag{38}$$

Let us now shamelessly apply the same kind of reasoning to the diffractive reaction

$$p + p \rightarrow p + [\text{missing mass}] \mathcal{M}. \tag{39}$$

That is, we shall <u>assume</u> that diffractive scattering is basically similar to the whole of particle production. This leads to the mnemonic

in the cm, and thus to

in the missing mass rest frame. In drawing the final picture I have assumed that the target proton acts just as it always does in "ordinary" collisions, but that there is no leading particle associated with what is up to now identified only as a broken line. This suggests that in reaction (39) the amount of energy (on the average) which goes into particle production is

$$K' \approx 3\mathcal{M}/4. \tag{40}$$

Because the rate of particle production seems not to depend on projectile or target, we are led to expect that

$$\langle n_c : p+p \rightarrow p+\mathcal{M} \rangle = \langle n_c : p+p \rightarrow \text{anything}(s=9\mathcal{M}^2/4) \rangle, \tag{41}$$

i.e. that the mean multiplicity observed in (39) should be the same as that observed in unrestricted pp collisions at equal available energies $K = K'$. Moreover, the mean multiplicity should depend only on $\mathcal{M}$, and not upon s. The NAL bubble chamber results are collected in Fig. 18. They do indeed indicate a dependence on $\mathcal{M}^2$ only. The agreement of the curve (41) with the data solidly supports our basic assumption that diffractive events are essentially similar to nondiffractive ones. The secondary assumption that no leading particles are associated with the energy carrier (the dashed line) is tested only casually. [I hope it is apparent that the bad argument just reviewed was invented after I saw the data; it is simply a primitive vehicle for the underlying assumptions. Other bad arguments[51] serve about as well to illustrate the same viewpoint. In specific regions of phase space, triple-Regge perturbative-Pomeron models lead to the same sort of results I have obtained here by handwaving.[52] I have chosen the heuristic approach in order to emphasize assumptions over formalism.]

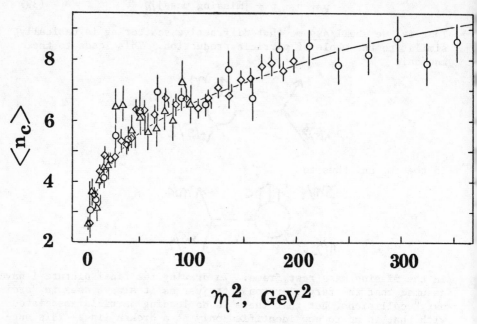

Fig. 18. Mean charged multiplicities observed[46] in the reaction $p + p \rightarrow p + \mathcal{M}$ in NAL experiments at 102 ($\triangle$), 205 ($\diamondsuit$), and 303 (O) GeV/c. The recoil proton is counted as an observed track.

It may be that the data are telling us that what matters is the energy delivered to the collision, and not the guise in which it appears. In this regard there is a connection with recent work on particle production in nuclei and emulsions. The very low multiplicities observed in complex nuclei are inconsistent with (at least) a naïve application of most popular models because any intranuclear cascade will, in Malthusian fashion, give rise to large (and strongly A-dependent) multiplicities. The trends are indicated in Fig. 19 which shows Echo Lake data on

$$R_C \equiv <n_{ch}>_{pC}/<n_{ch}>_{pp} , \qquad (42)$$

together with schematic predictions of models in which (i) only leading particles participate in intranuclear cascade [LP] and (ii) leading particles and the first generation of secondaries are allowed to cascade [LP+SMC]. A novel model in which the local energy flux is of key importance [EFC][54], on the other hand, is in good agreement with the data. Similar measurements of multiplicities in emulsions are shown in Fig. 20. The problem of nuclear multiplicities is a challenging one in its own right [Gottfried's paper[54] contains a nice summary of most of the data and the recent theoretical

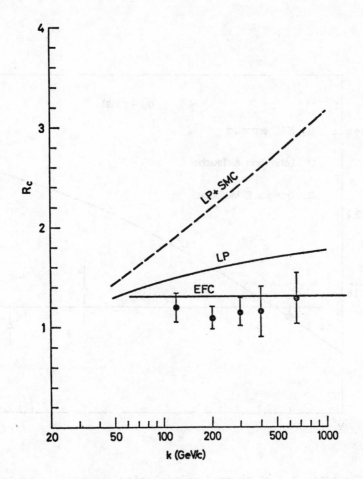

Fig. 19. The ratio R_c of charged multiplicity observed in proton-^{12}C interactions to that observed in proton-proton interactions as a function of the incident proton momentum. The curves are explained in the text. Data are from Ref. 53.

work] but of more immediate interest to us is the possibility that it may teach us something highly relevant to our own pursuits. Specifically, it may be worthwhile to contemplate what might be learned from a heavy-liquid filling of the 30" chamber at NAL

AN ELECTROPRODUCTION ANALOG

In order to set out and motivate a systematic program to probe the properties of diffraction, I think it helpful to lean on the crutch of an analogy with electroproduction. Let me make it clear that there are profound differences in the physics of diffractive scattering and deeply-inelastic electron scattering. The parallel

542

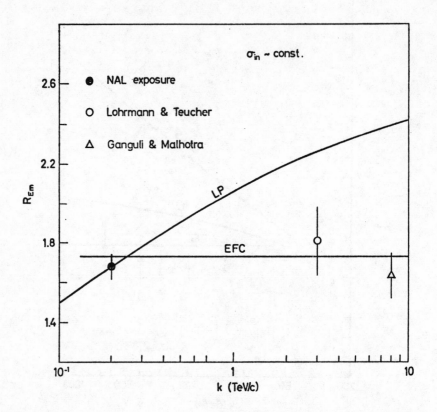

Fig. 20. The ratio R_{Em} of charged multiplicity observed in emulsion experiments to that observed in hydrogen as a function of the incident momentum [from Ref. 54]. The calculations assume an asymptotically constant pp total cross section. Data are from Ref. 55.

I want to draw lies in the kinematics and observables, and not in the dynamics. Consider the reactions

$$e+hadron \rightarrow e+hadrons \qquad (43) \qquad\qquad p+hadron \rightarrow p+hadrons. \qquad (44)$$

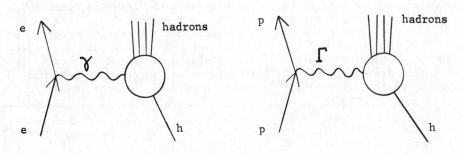

From the viewpoint of inclusive reactions, it is meaningful to regard the electron in (43) as a source for the virtual photon, $\gamma(Q^2)$. Likewise, let us think of the proton in (44) as the source of a virtual something, which we call $\Gamma(t)$.

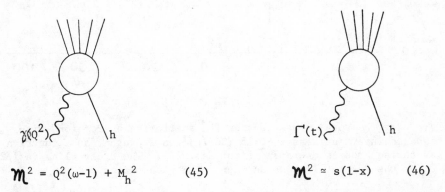

$$\mathcal{M}^2 = Q^2(\omega-1) + M_h{}^2 \qquad (45) \qquad\qquad \mathcal{M}^2 \simeq s(1-x) \qquad (46)$$

Having complete knowledge of γ (if QED holds), we seek to probe the structure of the target hadron through its interactions with γ.	With only partial knowledge of the structure of h (derived from hadron-hadron collisions), we seek to discover the nature of Γ through its interactions with h.

Observables

$$\gamma(Q^2)+h \rightarrow anything \qquad (47) \qquad\qquad \Gamma(t)+h \rightarrow anything \qquad (48)$$

In electroproduction, the total cross section is specified in terms of the structure functions W_1 and W_2.	In diffraction dissociation, the corresponding experiment is the measurement of a total cross section as a function of the energy, $\mathcal{M}$. Since Γ ought to carry the quantum numbers of the vacu-

um, it is natural to anticipate that

$$\sigma_{\Gamma p} = \text{constant} \cdot \sigma_{\pi N[I=\frac{1}{2}]} \cdot \tag{49}$$

Kaidalov and collaborators[56] have attempted to extract a "Pomeron"-proton total cross section from data on reaction (39). This is an extremely delicate task. M. B. Einhorn independently undertook the exercise and concluded that especially for $\mathbf{m}^2$ in the resonance region the uncertainties associated with unfolding s- and $\mathbf{m}^2$-dependent resolution are crippling. It therefore seems prudent to regard the "data" of Kaidalov, et al.[56], shown in Fig. 21, as very tentative.

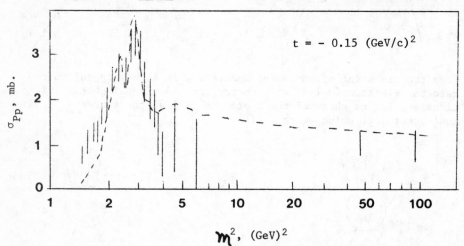

Fig. 21. The total cross section for scattering a "Pomeron" with squared invariant mass t=-0.15 (GeV/c)^2 on a proton, as a function of the squared cm energy $\mathbf{m}^2$ [from Ref. 56]. The broken line is 1/20 times the I=$\frac{1}{2}$ total cross section for πN scattering.

The general trends are however in good agreement with our guess (49). This is tantalizing enough to encourage further work on the measurement of Γp total cross sections. Obviously one wants to ask about Γ-hadron cross sections all the standard questions familiar in the hadron-hadron case. One of the most basic is whether factorization holds, i.e. that

$$\frac{\sigma_{\Gamma\pi}}{\sigma_{\Gamma p}} = \frac{\sigma_{\pi p}}{\sigma_{pp}}, \tag{50}$$

etc.

$$\gamma(Q^2)+h \rightarrow c+\text{anything} \tag{51} \qquad \Gamma(t)+h \rightarrow c+\text{anything} \tag{52}$$

The basic observable is the single particle inclusive cross section, normalized to the total cross sec-   The basic observable is the single particle inclusive cross section, normalized to the total cross section   tion

$$\frac{1}{\sigma_{\gamma(Q^2)h}} \cdot \frac{d\sigma}{dy_c} \cdot \qquad (53)$$

$$\frac{1}{\sigma_{\Gamma(t)h}} \cdot \frac{d\sigma}{dy_c} = \qquad (54)$$

$$\frac{d\sigma/dtd(\mathfrak{M}^2/s)dy_c}{d\sigma/dtd(\mathfrak{M}^2/s)},$$

for which our previous discussion suggests two features: (1) There should be no leading particles associated with Γ [a prejudice which may well be wrong]; (2) Outside the Γ-fragmentation region, the inclusive cross section should be "ordinary" i.e.

$$\frac{1}{\sigma_{\Gamma(t)h}} \cdot \frac{d\sigma(\Gamma+h\to c+anything)}{dy_c} =$$

$$\frac{1}{\sigma_{h'h}} \cdot \frac{d\sigma(h'+h\to c+anything)}{dy_c} . \qquad (55)$$

The latter expectation is, I believe, a safer one. It should be possible to explore these hypotheses in the NAL bubble chamber experiments. In addition, since data exist for both $h=p,\pi$, other obvious checks of factorization present themselves.

Two-Photon Processes   Doubly-Diffractive Processes

$e+e\to e+e+hadrons \qquad (56)$ $p+p\to p+p+hadrons \qquad (57)$

Extending to this case the argument leading to (41), we may expect the mean charged multiplicity in doubly-diffractive events to be

$$\langle n_c : p+p\to p+p+\mathfrak{M}\rangle = \langle n_c : p+p\to anything(s=4\mathfrak{M}^2)\rangle. \qquad (58)$$

Two additional remarks will bring the present discussion to a close. Interpreting the reaction

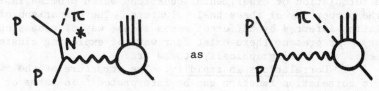

as

results in a misassignment of missing mass (i.e. a miscomputation of the invariant mass of the Γh system). Some Monte Carlo calculations may help in understanding how great a problem this is likely to be in practice. The triple-Regge connection gives a prescription for the dependence of observables upon t and M^2/s, so it may help in certain kinematical regions in identifying Γ with a specific Regge trajectory. Let us only go so far as to note that the correspondence is between

$$p+h \rightarrow p+M \qquad \text{and}$$

and between

$$p+h \rightarrow p+c+\text{anything and}$$

My remarks here have been rather diffuse, and I fear that the theoretical interpretation of this experimental program is a priori a bit vague. Yet I feel certain that there are discoveries to be made in this area, whether or not we can frame the questions sharply now.

CLUSTERING EFFECTS

If it is correct that particle production is basically multiperipheral in character, it is of clear importance to discover what this means in microscopic, exclusive terms. In the usual argot the question is, what are the primitive links in the multiperipheral chain? I am not sure that this question is answerable -- or even meaningful -- in any precise sense, but we may still learn something from an "average" answer. An important task in the months ahead will be the formulation of experimental questions which promise insight into the properties of these basic clusters. The comparison of characteristics inferred by different means is one way of assessing consistency. At present there exist four ways of exploring clustering phenomena. Very telegraphically, these are:

1. Correlations in rapidity. The structure of the two-particle correlation function can be interpreted[57] in terms of the independent emission of clusters of approximately four pions, with masses of about $1 - 2$ GeV/c^2.

2. <u>Charged-particle – neutral-particle correlations.</u> The variation of the mean number of neutral pions per event with the number of charged particles observed requires that charged and neutral pions be emitted together in clusters.[58]

3. <u>Charge-transfer fluctuations.</u> Ferbel has already mentioned[6] the data on mean-squared fluctuations in the charge transferred from one cm hemisphere to the other. A more stringent test of the hypothesis that clusters are emitted independently is provided by measurements of charge fluctuations with respect to arbitrary boundaries in rapidity between "forward" and "backward." The experimental results are in good agreement with the cluster picture.[59]

4. <u>Front-back multiplicity correlations.</u> Cluster production can give rise to dependence of

$$\langle n_{forward}(n_{backward})\rangle$$

upon $n_{backward}$ if products of a single cluster are mobile enough to populate both the forward and backward regions. By varying the definitions of these regions, one should be able to "measure" a mobility parameter and thereby to infer very roughly the mass of an "average" cluster.

ACKNOWLEDGEMENTS

I thank the Organizing Committee, Harry Bingham, Michel Davier, and Gerry Lynch for their kind invitation to prepare this report. The Theoretical Studies Division at CERN provided me with generous support and a stimulating environment in which to ponder what I should say. During my stay there I have been influenced in my choice of topics by informative conversations with U. Amaldi, E. Berger, G. Finocchiaro, G. Fox, K. Gottfried, P. Grannis, M. Jacob, C. Michael, and others. I am also pleased to acknowledge with thanks the contributions of R. Engelmann, R. McCarthy, and J. Whitmore. Lastly, I am grateful to the staff of the Cowell Memorial Hospital for timely assistance.

REFERENCES

1. For additional details see the famous "unpublished" ISR discussion meeting notes, newly revised and issued as summer school notes by M. Jacob, CERN-TH-1683; reports from the parallel sessions of this meeting; and the proceedings of the Stony Brook Conference (to appear shortly).

2. R. P. Feynman, Phys. Rev. Letters 23, 1415 (1969).

3. J. Benecke, T. T. Chou, C. N. Yang, and E. Yen, Phys. Rev. 188, 2159 (1969).

4. For example, S. Fubini, in Strong Interactions and High Energy Physics, ed. R. G. Moorhouse (New York: Plenum Press, 1964), p. 259; K. G. Wilson, Acta Phys. Austriaca 17, 37 (1963).

5. H. Bøggild, these proceedings.

6. T. Ferbel, these proceedings.

7. This compilation is due to M. Antinucci, A. Bertin, P. Capiluppi, G. Giacomelli, A. M. Rossi, G. Vannini, and A. Bussière, in Experiments on High Energy Particle Collisions - 1973, ed. R. S. Panvini (New York: AIP), p. 235.

8. A. H. Mueller, Phys. Rev. D2, 2963 (1970).

9. H. D. I. Abarbanel, Phys. Letters 34B, 69 (1971) and Phys. Rev. D3, 2227 (1971) derived these results in terms of imposing-looking variables.

10. R. C. Hwa, Phys. Rev. Letters 26, 1143 (1971).

11. M. Jacob and R. Slansky, Phys. Rev. D5, 1847 (1972); E. L. Berger and M. Jacob, Phys. Rev. D6, 1930 (1972); E. L. Berger, M. Jacob, and R. Slansky, ibid., p. 2580.

12. C. Quigg, J.-M. Wang, and C. N. Yang, Phys. Rev. Letters 28, 1290 (1972).

13. K. Kajantie and P. V. Ruuskanen, to be published.

14. C. Quigg, in Experiments on High Energy Particle Collisions - 1973, ed. R. S. Panvini (New York: AIP), p. 375.

15. See also R. Engelmann, et al., Argonne preprint ANL/HEP 7341, contributed to this conference.

16. T. T. Chou and C. N. Yang, Phys. Rev. D7, 1425 (1973); C. Quigg and G. H. Thomas, ibid., p. 2752.

17. S. Nussinov, C. Quigg, and J. M. Wang, Phys. Rev. D6, 2713 (1972).

18. The first to stress the usefulness of the correlation function (in modern times) was K. G. Wilson, Cornell preprint CLNS-131 (1970, unpublished).

19. S. R. Amendolia, et al., Phys. Letters (to be published).

20. H. Dibon, et al., Phys. Letters 44B, 313 (1973).

21. G. Belletini, in High Energy Collisions - 1973, ed. C. Quigg (New York: AIP, to be published).

22. W. R. Frazer, R. D. Peccei, S. S. Pinsky, and C.-I Tan, Phys. Rev. D7, 2647 (1973).

23. A very elementary and experimentally oriented discussion of two-component models is contained in my lectures at the 1973 Canadian Institute for Particle Physics Summer School. I know of no proper review.

24. J. R. Freeman and C. Quigg, Phys. Letters (to be published).

25. P. Slattery, in Experiments on High Energy Particle Collisions -1973, ed. R. S. Panvini (New York: AIP), p. 1; C. M. Bromberg, et al., Michigan preprint UMBC #72-14; Rochester preprint #416.

26. F. T. Dao, et al., NAL-Pub-73/22-EXP, June, 1973; NAL-Pub-73/38-EXP, June, 1973.

27. J. Lee-Franzini, these proceedings.

28. M. G. Albrow, et al., Phys. Letters 44B, 207 (1973); Nucl. Phys. B54, 6 (1973); Nucl. Phys. B51, 388 (1973).

29. K. Fiałkowski, Phys. Letters 41B, 379 (1972); K. Fiałkowski and H. Miettinen, Phys. Letters 43B, 61 (1973); H. Harari and E. Rabinovici, Phys. Letters 43B, 49 (1973); C. Quigg and J. D. Jackson, NAL report NAL-THY-93 (1972, unpublished); L. van Hove, Phys. Letters 43B, 65 (1973); J. Lach and E. Malamud, Phys. Letters 44B, 474 (1973). See also Ref. 22.

30. U. Amaldi, et al., Phys. Letters 44B, 112 (1973).

31. S. R. Amendolia, et al., Phys. Letters 44B, 119 (1973).

32. U. Amaldi, CERN NP-Internal Report 73-5.

33. G. B. Yodh, Y. Pal, and J. S. Trefil, Phys. Rev. Letters 28, 1005 (1972); University of Maryland Technical Report 73-114.

34. C. Bourrely and J. Fischer, CERN-TH-1652.

35. N. N. Khuri and T. Kinoshita, Phys. Rev. 137, B720 (1965).

36. S. W. MacDowell and A. Martin, Phys. Rev. 135, B960 (1964).

37. A. W. Chao and C. N. Yang, Stony Brook preprint ITP-SB-73-27.

38. A. W. Chao, private communication.

39. S. M. Roy, Phys. Reports 5C, 125 (1972).

40. H. Cheng and T. T. Wu, Phys. Rev. Letters 24, 1456 (1970); Phys. Letters 34B, 647 (1971); Phys. Letters 36B, 357 (1971).

41. G. Barbiellini, et al., Phys. Letters 39B, 663 (1972).

42. For a sampling, consult Ref. 32.

43. G. L. Kane, these proceedings.

44. Compare C. Lovelace, in Proc. XVI Int. Conf. on High Energy Physics, ed. J. D. Jackson and A. Roberts (Batavia: NAL, 1972), vol. 3, p. 73.

45. D. Austin, W. Greiman, and W. Rarita, Phys. Rev. D2, 2613 (1970); D. Austin and W. Rarita, ibid., D4, 3507 (1971).

46. See refs. 25-28 and F. Sannes, et al., Phys. Rev. Letters 30, 766 (1973); J. Whitmore, these proceedings.

47. D. W. G. S. Leith, these proceedings.

48. J. Lach, private communication.

49. For pp collisions at 50 GeV/c, V. V. Ammosov, et al., Phys. Letters 42B, 519 (1972); for 50 GeV/c $\pi^- p$ collisions, ABCILMSV Collaboration, contribution #484 to the XVI Int. Conf. on High Energy Physics; for 40 GeV/c πN collisions, BBCDHSSTT(U-B)W Collaboration, in Proc. 4th Int. Conf. on High Energy Collisions, ed. J. R. Smith (Chilton: RHEL, 1972), vol. 2, p. 162.

50. For 205 GeV/c pp collisions, G. Charlton, et al., Phys. Rev. Letters 29, 515 (1972); for 205 GeV/c $\pi^- p$ collisions, D. Bogert, et al., in Experiments on High Energy Particle Collisions - 1973, ed. R. S. Panvini (New York: AIP), p. 60; for 303 GeV/c pp collisions, F. T. Dao, et al., Phys. Rev. Letters 29, 1627 (1972). The figure is from J. D. Jackson, in Experiments on High Energy Particle Collisions - 1973, op. cit., p. 404.

51. J. Whitmore, these proceedings; F. Winkelmann, these proceedings.

52. W. R. Frazer and D. R. Snider, Phys. Letters 45B, 136 (1973);
W. R. Frazer, D. R. Snider, and C.-I Tan, San Diego preprint UCSD-
10P10-127 (1973).

53. L. W. Jones, et al., Proc. 11th Cosmic Ray Conference, Budapest,
1969.

54. K. Gottfried, CERN-TH-1735.

55. NAL data: BBBBLLMNOPQRV Collaboration, contribution to the 5th
Int. Conf. on High Energy Physics and Nuclear Structure; S. N. Gan-
guli and P. K. Malhotra, private communication to K. Gottfried;
E. Lohrmann and M. W. Teucher, Nuovo Cimento 25, 957 (1962).

56. A. B. Kaidalov, V. A. Khoze, Yu. F. Pirogov, and N. L. Ter-Isaakyan, Leningrad Nuclear Physics Institute preprint #44, May, 1973.

57. P. Pirilä and S. Pokorski, CERN preprint; E. L. Berger and G. C.
Fox, CERN-TH-1700.

58. E. L. Berger, D. Horn, and G. H. Thomas, Phys. Rev. D7, 1412
(1973); F. T. Dao and J. Whitmore, NAL-Pub-73/47-EXP.

59. ABCLV Collaboration, CERN preprint D.Ph.II/PHYS 73-18 [K⁻p
collisions at 10 and 16 GeV/c]; R. Engelmann, T. Kafka, and M. Pra-
tap, private communication [pp collisions at 205 GeV/c].

SOME OFF-BEAT ASPECTS OF PROTON-PROTON
PRODUCTION PROCESSES*

Dennis Sivers
Stanford Linear Accelerator Center
Stanford University, Stanford, Calif. 94305

ABSTRACT

We discuss four aspects of the phenomenology of high energy
production processes: the approach to scaling, the relation between inclusive cross-sections and total cross-sections, the rapidity charge density, and left-right multiplicity distributions.
The goal of the discussion is to provide a slightly different slant
on important features of the data.

INTRODUCTION

In the absence of a solid theory, the quest for an adequate description of
the data frequently involves casting for relations among unfamiliar quantities. The following describes some recent efforts in which the author has
been involved to find an empirical understanding of production processes.

THE APPROACH TO SCALING

At a gathering like this, it's often important to reflect on subjects which
are no longer fashionable. Sometimes the decrease in interest in a certain
topic masks a good deal of valuable physics. That seems to be true in the
case of the subject of the approach to scaling of the inclusive process

$$f^c_{ab}(s, \vec{p}_c) = \sigma^{-1}_{ab} E_c \, d^3\sigma/d^3p_c \, . \tag{1}$$

The flurry of papers[1-2] concerning various exoticity conditions (ab, a$\bar{c}$, ab$\bar{c}$,
etc.) represented an important attempt to carry over into Mueller-Regge
analysis ideas about duality which proved valuable in 2-2 and 2-3 body reactions.[3] The effort was not a success in that most of the simple ideas did
not work. For example, the fact that all the produced particles (as opposed
to the leading particles) in pp collisions approach scaling from below is
just the opposite of the naive dual prediction that the secondary contributions
to inclusive cross sections — just like those in total cross sections — should
be positive.[2]
The energy sum rule[4]

$$\sqrt{s} = \sum_c \int \frac{d^3\vec{p}_c}{E_c} (E_c) \, f^c_{ab}(s, \vec{p}_c) \tag{2}$$

---

*Work supported by the U. S. Atomic Energy Commission.

has implications for the approach to scaling in that the behavior of the energy fraction

$$\eta_c(s) = \int \frac{d^3\vec{p}_c}{E_c} \; \frac{E_c}{\sqrt{s}} \; f_{ab}^c(s, \vec{p}_c)$$

$$= \frac{1}{2} \int dx \, d^2\vec{p}_T \, f_{ab}^c(x, \vec{p}_T, s) \tag{3}$$

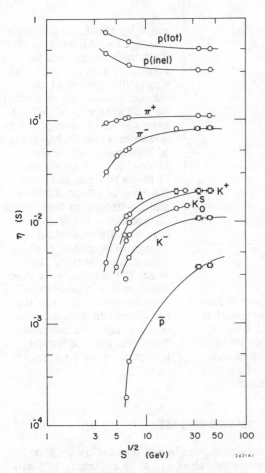

describes the "average" approach the asymptotic behavior of the inclusive cross section. Data[5] on energy fractions in pp collisions is shown in Fig. 1. The figure illustrates how the fall of the leading proton spectrum is balanced by the rise of the produced particles. It turns out not necessary to invoke Muller-Regge ideas to describe the behavior of the energy fractions. Although a dual scheme consistent with the energy sum rule can be constructed, [6] the behavior of the data is fairly well described in terms of kinematic reflections of the known dyamical mechanisms.[5] This is illustrated for the case of $pp \rightarrow \pi$ and $pp \rightarrow \bar{p}$ in terms of a prediction of a simple "phase-space" model[5,7] in Fig. 2. The same model describes the approach to scaling of $K\bar{K}$ and the large p_T component of inclusive distributions. It's not necessarily surprising that phase space effects are important. What is surprising is that within the framework of duality it should prove so awkward to incorporate the simple kinematic consequences of well known dynamic effects in Mueller-Regge models.

FIG. 1--Taken from Ref. 5; this figure displays the average fraction of cm energy carried off by different final particles and the relation of the energy fraction through the sum rule (2) to the approach to scaling.

TOTAL CROSS SECTIONS

The fact that the sudden rise in the cross section for producing $\bar{p}$ [illustrated in Figs. 1 and 2] takes place at the same energy

554

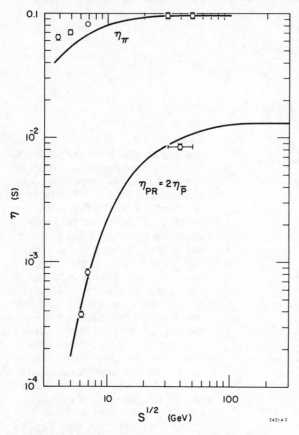

where structure is seen in the total pp cross section has caused speculation that these two effects might be connected.[8,9]

Neglecting multiple production of baryon-antibaryon pairs, the cross section

$$\sigma_{B\bar{B}} \cong \langle n_{\bar{B}} \rangle \, \sigma_{inel} \qquad (4)$$

rises by about 6 millibarns through the ISR region.[10] This information can be combined with the fact that, within the context of the eikonal model, there should be a drop in σ_{tot} of 2-3 mb over the same energy range due to increased shadowing of high mass diffractive channels.[11] A combination of these two mechanisms— the rise in $B\bar{B}$ production and the growth of high mass diffraction — might therefore be able to explain the energy dependence of the total cross section. However, it remains to be seen whether this type of description would provide the peripheral increase in the overlap integral indicated from analyses of the differential cross section.[12]

FIG. 2--A simple phase space model calculation of the behavior of the energy fraction as a function of s is compared with data on $\bar{p}$ and π production. The calculation demonstrates that the late rise in the $\bar{p}$ yield can be understood as a kinematic reflection of well-known dynamic features. Taken from Ref. 5.

RAPIDITY CHARGE DENSITY

One simple thing that can be done with single particle inclusive distributions is to combine the inclusive spectra $ab \to c_1$, $ab \to c_2$, etc., to form a charge density,

$$\delta Q^{ab}(s, \vec{p}) = \sigma_{ab}^{-1} \sum_i Q_i \left[E_i \frac{d^3\sigma}{d^3 p_i}^{ab \to c_i}(s, \vec{p}) \right]. \qquad (5)$$

Because charge is conserved, the integral over invariant phase space of the charge density must, of course, be given by the charge in the initial state[13]

$$\int \frac{d^3p}{E} \; \delta \; Q^{ab}(s, \; p) = \sum_i Q_i <n_i(s)> \; = Q_a + Q_b \; . \tag{6}$$

In Fig. 3 the charge density in pp inelastic collisions for 4 different energies[14] is integrated over transverse momentum and plotted as a function of laboratory (or target) rapidity, $y = \sinh^{-1}(p_L/(m^2 + p_T^2)^{1/2})$,

$$\delta \; Q^{ab}(y, \; y-Y) = \int d \; \vec{p}_T \; \delta \; Q(s, \; \vec{p}) \; . \tag{7}$$

In Eq. (7), $Y = \cosh^{-1}(s^{1/2}/m_p)$ is the rapidity of the beam in the target rest frame.

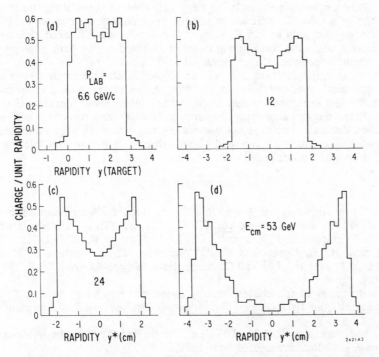

FIG. 3--The average charge per unit rapidity in the final state of a pp collision. Taken from Ref. 14.

Because the R.H.S. of (6) only contains the initial particle's charge, the charge density provides a convenient tool for the study of what has come to be called the leading particle effect. As emphasized by Morrison,[15] the term "leading particle effect" applied to inclusive data represents a correlation between the properties of the initial particles and those of final particles.

Mueller-Regge analysis connects this effect to the types of correlations we see in 2-particle inclusives in the central region. It is therefore not surprising that the "initial-particle-final particle charge correlation" found in the charge density is of short range as is the correlation found in $pp \to \pi\gamma$ and $pp \to \pi\pi$ in the central region. The indication is that the double-Regge expansion valid in the central region continues smoothly into the single-Regge expansions valid in the experimental region. Here is a place where Mueller-Regge ideas work well.

LEFT-RIGHT MULTIPLICITIES

A left-right multiplicity distribution consists of data on the number of charged particles going left (backward) and going right (forward) in the cm system of a production process.[16] It is an interesting exercise to see how coarse-grained data of this type can prove to be quite a sensitive test of models for the production process. Because the pomeron has I=0 and cannot contribute to charge transfer, pomeron exchange will only be important in those cross sections which have an odd number of particles in each hemisphere. This property proves to be very valuable in separating the two components of a hybrid, diffraction plus short range order, model. Figure 4 shows cross-sections at 205 GeV/c,[17] for producing different charge configurations when the total prong number is fixed. The data support the two component concept quite emphatically.[18]

Left-right multiplicities and related experimental quantities such as the average number of particles in the right hemisphere with a fixed multiplicity in the left hemisphere can also provide interesting factorization tests. Since data of this type are comparatively easy to obtain and since calculations indicate that it is not necessary to go to very high energies to get important information, it would be valuable if more data on left-right multiplicities were made available.

REFERENCES

1. See, for example, Chan Hong-Mo, C. S. Hue, C. Quigg and Jiunn-Ming Wang, Phys. Rev. Letters 26, 672 (1972). J. Ellis, J. Finkelstein, P. H. Frampton and M. Jacob, Phys. Letters 35 B, 227 (1971). M.B. Einhorn, M. B. Green and M. A. Virasoro, Phys. Letters 37 B, 292 (1971). S. -H. H. Tye and G. Veneziano, Phys. Letters 38 B, 30 (1972).
2. A good review of the subject can be found in Chan Hong-Mo, in Proceedings of the 1972 Oxford Conference, (Rutherford Lab, England, 1972).
3. See, for example, R. J. N. Phillips, "High Energy Two-Body Phenomenology," Rutherford Report (1972).
4. T. T. Chou and C. N. Yang, Phys. Rev. Letters 25, 1072 (1972).
5. D. Sivers, ANL/HEP 7308, Phys. Rev. D (to be published).
6. S. -H. H. Tye and G. Veneziano, Nuovo Cimento 14 A, 711 (1973), and references contained.
7. D. Sivers and G. H. Thomas, Phys. Rev. D 6, 1961 (1972).
8. D. Sivers and F. von Hippel, ANL/HEP 7323.
9. T. K. Gausser and C. -I. Tan, Brown preprint, July 1973.
10. M. Antinucci, et al., Nuovo Cimento Letters 6, 121 (1973).

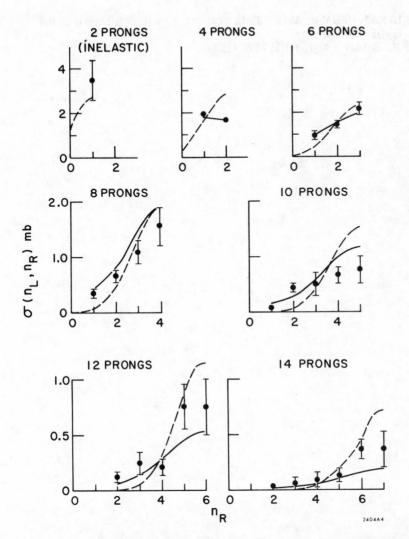

FIG. 4--Cross sections for left-right multiplicity configurations.
The solid curve represents a 2-component model and the dashed
curve a gas analog model explained in Ref. 16.

11. R. Blankenbecler, J. R. Fulco and R. L. Sugar, SLAC report no.
    SLAC-PUB-1281; R. Blankenbecler, SLAC report no. SLAC-PUB-
    1282.
12. R. Henzi and P. Valin, McGill preprint (1973).
13. C. DeTar, D. Z. Freedman and G. Veneziano, Phys. Rev. D 4, 906
    (1971).
14. D. Sivers, ANL/HEP 7313, Phys. Rev. to be published.
15. D.R.O. Morrison, in Proceedings of 1972 Oxford Conference (Ruther-
    ford Lab, England, 1972).
16. D. Sivers and G. H. Thomas, SLAC report no. SLAC-PUB-1308.

558

17. ANL-NAL Collaboration. Data presented by J. Whitmore at the Nashville Conference.
18. D. R. Snider, ANL/HEP 7326 (1973).

ONE DIMENSIONAL MODELS AND WHAT CAN BE LEARNED ABOUT THEM FROM NAL AND ISR DATA*, [1]

Gerald H. Thomas
High Energy Physics Division
Argonne National Laboratory, Argonne, Illinois 60439

Abstract: The one dimensional language is employed in the description of some of the data recently available from the NAL and ISR. To illustrate the phenomenological value of such a description, left-right multiplicity data are discussed in some detail. In addition to the more orthodox, a few non-standard suggestions are made for presenting data based on the one dimensional ideas.

INTRODUCTION

Correlation data presented at the Vanderbilt Conference gave strong support for the Multiperipheral picture, and for the present, effectively defeated the Fragmentation picture.[2] Hopefully I may be excused therefore for adopting the Multiperipheral point of view in this talk to the exclusion of all others. For the most part, only Regge poles are presumed to be present, although this may be dangerous since even in two-body phenomenology, Regge cuts are known to be important. No important distinction will be drawn between the Multiperipheral picture or the use of generalized optical theorems as proposed by Mueller.[3] Indeed, there is recent evidence that these two approaches are mathematically equivalent.[4] Also note that calculations using Independent Emission Models are in the multiperipheral spirit, though not simply relatable.[5] There are large classes of models satisfying the above simple constraints, though in general they are still too complicated to use in any simple discussion of data. A great simplification occurs by reducing the models to one-dimension by integrating out the transverse momentum dependence. Since the average transverse momenta are observed small, no essential loss of information is expected. For multiperipheral models, this expectation has been found to be valid.[6]

The class of multiperipheral type models, which remains in this

---

*Work performed under the auspices of the U. S. Atomic Energy Commission.

one-dimensional approximation, is still quite large and certainly indicative of what one might expect generally in the multiperipheral picture. For example, the conflict between pure short range order models versus "two component" models can be expressed in this one dimensional language (for details q.v. Ref. 7). Further support for using this language is given by the Fluid Analog, [8] which contains as a special case, the one dimensional multiperipheral type models. Within the fluid analog, it is possible to generalize the multiperipheral concepts. For example, it has been proposed that observed multiplicity distributions at NAL and higher energies are considerably broader than Poisson due to the fluid analog displaying critical (long-range) fluctuations. [9]

Now that we have defined in some detail the one-dimensional class of models from which we can choose a description, we turn to the more interesting question of which data can give useful information. Although all data are of some use, it is obvious that certain data are more useful than others. Already, we have learned that charged particle multiplicity data can give unexpected results (viz. the large positive f_2 values);[9] single particle distributions $d\sigma/dy$ have not approached scaling as expected;[10] two particle correlation functions display multiperipheral type correlation lengths at precociously small rapidity separations. [10] (For a further list of references, see e.g. Ref. 7.) As more statistics are gathered, and as more of present data are analyzed, it becomes possible to compute more finely grained distributions and therefore ask more sophisticated questions. The point to emphasize is that these questions can be as important to any ultimate description of high energy data, as were the initial broad questions such as "Do data follow a Fragmentation or Multiperipheral picture." In this context, we shall now illustrate what might be learned from measuring left-right multiplicity distributions as suggested first by Nussinov, Quigg and Wang. [11]

LEFT-RIGHT MULTIPLICITIES

Define the cross section $\sigma(n_L, n_R)$ as that for n_L charged particles in the left or backward cm hemisphere and n_R charged particles in the right or forward cm hemisphere. Data on such cross section exist at 102[12] and 205[13] GeV/c as well as at lower energies.[14] The 205 GeV/c data, when summed over n_R ($\sigma(n_L, \text{tot})$ plotted in Fig. 1) show a dip for $n_L = 2$. There is moreover a tendency for odd n_L points to lie above even n_L points. A similar systematics is apparent in the average number of right movers for a fixed number of left movers $\langle n_R \rangle_L$ (Fig. 2). Moreover in the latter distributions at NAL and at

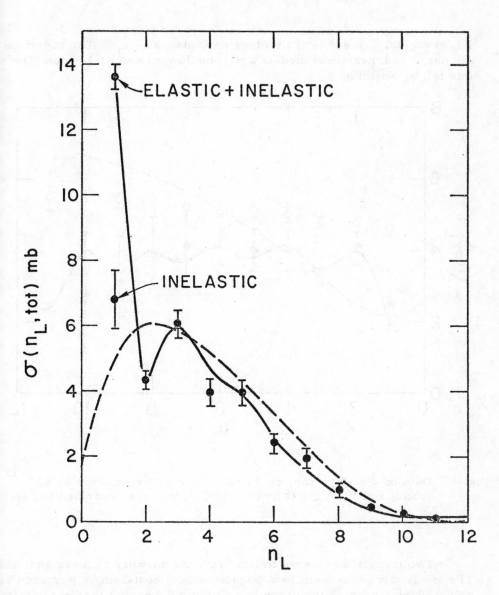

Fig. 1. Preliminary data on $\sigma(n_L, \text{tot})$ from the ANL/NAL collaboration at 205 GeV/c.[13] The dashed curve is the prediction of the critical point fluid model[9] (Eq. 5') and the smooth curve is a two-component model (Eq. 2).

ISR energies, [15] there is little other dependence on n_L. The questions for our one-dimensional models are "Should we expect this" and "Does this tell us anything."

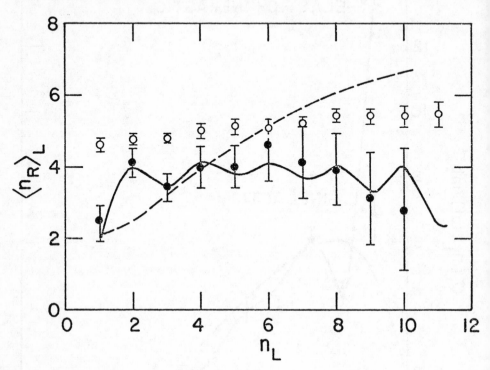

Fig. 2. Data on $\langle n_L \rangle_R$ from the bubble chamber experiment at NAL, [13] (solid) and ISR [15] (open). The curves are described in Fig.

Two models may serve to illustrate the answers to these question The one is a two-channel Chew-Pignotti Model containing a Pomeron an a Secondary Meson; [16] the other is a fluid model having long range inter actions. [17] Although neither model is very realistic, nor is either free from conceptual difficulties, both models can be easily calculated and both represent certain features which could be expected more generally Moreover, for left-right multiplicity data, the models represent certai extremes.

The two-channel Chew-Pignotti model when treated in a practical manner is a precise expression of the two-component idea (q. v. Wilsor By "practical manner" I mean the Pomeranchuk pole is not allowed to b exchanged more than once, the assumption being that the strength of the exchange, $g_{ppp} \ln s$, is small at present energies (for more details and suitable references Cf. Ref. 7). When this manner is followed, the cross section $\sigma(n_L, n_R)$ has the form

$$\sigma(n_L, n_R) = A_{n_L} A_{n_R} + B_{n_L} B_{n_R} , \tag{1}$$

where A_n is the sum of a short range (Poisson) distribution plus a "high mass diffraction" (approximately Poisson) distribution. The distribution B_n contains all the low mass (including elastic) diffraction contributions. Approximating B_n by $1/n^2$, a fit to the 205 GeV/c data in this model is given by

$$\sigma(n_L, n_R) \propto \left(\frac{1}{n_L^2} \frac{1}{n_R^2} + 4.8 \frac{e^{-4} 4^{n_L}}{n_L!} \frac{e^{-4} 4^{n_R}}{n_R!} \right) \tag{2}$$

As has been pointed out by Snider,[16] the first term in the above cross section is sensible only if no charge is exchanged between hemispheres, otherwise the term should be zero. As an approximation, this means n_L or n_R must be mostly odd; n_L even must be charge exchange processes. The difference between even n_L (Figs. 1-2) in the data is then explained.

Besides understanding the oscillatory nature of $\sigma(n_L, \text{tot})$ and $\langle n_R \rangle_L$ by means of the two-component model, we also see that one would expect a noticeable dip in the $\sigma(n_L, \text{tot})$ cross section for $n_L = 2$, somewhat enhanced by the exclusion of diffraction from $\Delta Q \neq 0$ events. It remains to be seen whether or not the dip is real, but if it were, it would provide the first direct empirical evidence for the two-component concept. An independent test of this concept, among others, is to observe the energy dependence of $\langle n_R \rangle_L$ at $n_L = 1$. As can be shown,[7] the two-component model predicts

$$\begin{aligned} \langle n_R \rangle_L &\to \text{const} & n_L &= 1 \\ &\to \ln s & n_L &\geq 2 \end{aligned} \tag{3}$$

Data at ISR could give information on this point, as long as diffractive events were not rejected by the measuring apparatus.

The above two-component model departs from a simple Poisson distribution by the addition of an extra term to the cross section. Another way to depart from

$$\sigma_P(n_L, n_R) = \frac{(gY)^{n_L}}{n_L!} e^{-gY} \frac{(gY)^{n_R}}{n_R!} e^{-gY} \qquad (4)$$

where $Y = \ln s$, is to incorporate for each (n_L, n_R) an extra <u>factor</u> representing an average or mean value approximation to effects such as final state interactions which might be reasonably expected to be multiplicative. Such averaging is sensible for long range forces (e. g. final state diffractive scattering between all pairs of particles), and based upon the fluid analog, is expected to have the form[9]

$$\sigma(n_L n_R) \sim \sigma_P(n_L n_R) e^{an^2/Y} , \qquad (5)$$

where $a > 0$, $n = n_L + n_R$, and an^2/Y represents the mean value of a strength (a/Y) times the number of pairs $\binom{n}{2} \sim n^2$. Perhaps the exponential should be thought of as an eikonalization of some basic interaction;[18] the exact connection to hadron dynamics has not yet been clarified.

The alert listener will note that for large n, (5) gives arbitrarily large cross sections. The problem is that we have been a little too quick in writing the model down. We have ignored the repulsive correlations which should have been incorporated into the Chew-Pignotti model (4) due to t-channel thresholds. For σ_n, the change is $Y^n/n! \rightarrow \theta(Y - nb)(Y - nb)^n/n!$, and for (4) the change is

$$\sigma_P(n_L, n_R) \rightarrow \sigma_{h.c.}(n_L, n_R) \approx \frac{g^n(\frac{Y}{2} - n_L b)^{n_L}}{n_L!} \frac{(\frac{Y}{2} - n_R b)^{n_R}}{n_R!}$$

$$\theta(\frac{Y}{2} - n_L b) \theta(\frac{Y}{2} - n_R b) e^{-\beta Y} . \qquad (4')$$

(For a more correct evaluation of $\sigma_{h.c.}$ see Ref. 7.) The parameters a, b, β, and g can be determined from the total charged multiplicity distribution and are found to be approximately $a = 27/64$, $b = 1/8$, $\beta = 1$ and $g = 0.695\ldots$. The model is now well defined for calculating $\sigma(n_L, n_R)$ and is

$$\sigma(n_L, n_R) = \sigma_{h.c.}(n_L, n_R) e^{an^2/Y} . \qquad (5')$$

Taking this model at face value, it provides a description of $\sigma(n_L, n_R)$ which is orthogonal to the two-component model. The results are presented in Figs. 1-2 along side those for the two-component model.

Note that in Fig. 2, $\langle n_R \rangle_L$ shows a linear dependence on n_L, except for effects due to thresholds in the model which cause $\langle n_R \rangle_L$

to go to zero for sufficiently large n_L. (Experimental values for $\langle n_R \rangle_L$ are made using only a subsample of $\sigma(n_L, n_R)$; if the theory were plotted from this same subsample, it would give a curve more nearly like the data.) Except for small oscillations (and at $n_L = 1$), the two-component model predicts $\langle n_R \rangle_L$ independent of n_L.

The distinction is general and of some importance. In general, if there are no long range (inclusive) interactions, meaning the inclusive correlation length is finite, then $\sigma(n_L, n_R)$ will be the product of two factors, $a(n_L)$ and $a(n_R)$. [7] On general grounds, if the Pomeranchuk singularity factorizes in the t-channel in the usual sense, which it is expected to do if it is a pole or a "hard" singularity, then one can also expect $\sigma(n_L, n_R)$ to be $a(n_L) a(n_R)$. The short range part of the two-component model is thus expected to give such a behavior for $\sigma(n_L, n_R)$. The diffractive piece appears to cause some problems of consistency since in the version we use (2) is not in a factorized form, and $\langle n_R \rangle_{n_L}$ behaves differently for $n_L = 1$ and $n_L \neq 1$. The difficulty is related to the more well known problems of the Pomeron; if we iterated the Pomeron, we would have no difficulty with factorization, but would then violate the Froissart bound. [19]

If the correlation length is infinite, as it is in the long-range fluid model, then $\sigma(n_L, n_R)$ will not factorize and the Pomeranchuk singularity can be expected to be more complicated than a pole. For these reasons, it would be quite spectacular to find evidence that $\langle n_R \rangle_L \sim n_L$ irrespective of the simple models discussed here.

Because of the lack of time, only one test of factorization has been discussed ($\langle n_R \rangle_L$ independent of n_L). There are obviously many more and these are discussed in Ref. 7. It is also obvious that left-right multiplicities are not the only kinds of data giving information on one-dimensional models. Charge Transfer, proton missing mass distributions and, of course, completely differential (one-dimensional) exclusive distributions $d\sigma_n/dy_1 \dots dy_n$ are ultimately useful. I shall next discuss a systematic way in which more information than is presently known can be obtained concerning these quantities.

DENSITIES AS FUNCTIONS OF MULTIPLICITIES

Data on inclusive rapidity distributions can be most easily supplemented by data on the corresponding exclusive distributions. Even for single particle distributions, the problem is how to present the data in a way which can be easily compared with theory. Based upon the generating function approach, [20] which has been shown to be extremely useful for all the one-dimensional models considered here (but not limited to just those), there is an obvious set of quantities to plot. [21] Consider the cross section σ_n and the associated generating function

$$Q(z, Y) = \sum_n \sigma_n(Y) z^n \qquad (6)$$

A plot of $Q(z, Y)$ vs. z using experimental numbers for $\sigma_n(Y)$ contains the same information as plotting $\sigma_n(Y)$ vs. n. Asymptotically significant in one-dimensional models are the related quantities

$$p(z, Y) = \frac{\ln Q(z, Y)}{Y} \qquad (7)$$

$$\rho(z, Y) = \sum_n n \, \sigma_n(Y) z^n / Q(z, Y) \qquad (8)$$

It is clear that $Q(z, Y)$ vs. z at fixed Y is equivalent to $p(z, Y)$ vs. $\rho(z, Y)$. The latter relation has a proven value in statistical mechanics as being the equation of state of the fluid. Taking σ_n to be the experimental charged multiplicity distributions, the hadron equation of state is shown in Fig. 3. It shows nothing not already known in other ways; but also leaves nothing out. The motivation for using such quantities is that the idea can be extended to all inclusive distributions without introducing any "new" correlation functions.

For example, the single particle density as a function of "z" is

$$\rho_1(y, z, Y) = \sum_n \frac{d\sigma_n(Y)}{dy} z^n / Q(z, Y) \, , \qquad (9)$$

and the two-particle distribution density is

$$\rho_2(y_1, y_2, z, Y) = \sum_n \frac{d^2\sigma_n(Y)}{dy_1 \, dy_2} z^n / Q(z, Y) \qquad (10)$$

allowing a correlation function to be defined as usual

$$C(y_1, y_2, z, Y) = \rho_2(y_1, y_2, z, Y) - \rho_1(y_1, z, Y) \rho_1(y_2, z, Y) \, . \qquad (11)$$

This correlation function is a natural way to plot the dependence of correlation on prong number: i. e. to plot correlation vs. z. The definition is natural in terms of the fluid analog, or natural in the sense of being suggested by the generating function technique. The main ambiguity in the above definition is whether to include or not include the elastic scattering contribution. Either way, the above equations hold, and the choice is still a matter of taste; experimentalists and some theorists prefer only inelastic σ_n, whereas Mueller-Regge analysis would seem to demand including the elastic (q. v. Ref. 10).

Before leaving this subject, I would like to say a few words about what might be expected. At small z only low multiplicities matter and the correlation will be characteristic of diffractive events. For example, we expect to see long range correlations between particles in opposite hemispheres due in part just to energy momentum conservation. At z = 1, the correlations are by definition the usual ones. For z > 1, the correlations will depend upon the model. Assuming large attractive correlations between particles for high multiplicity events, the height of C may well increase for a while as z increases. The correlation <u>length</u> might decrease however if some region around z = 1 showed abnormally large correlations.[9] The behavior of C will be closely connected to the behavior of its integral $f_2(z, Y)$ which can be obtained from Fig. 3 through

$$\frac{1}{Y} f_2(z, Y)/\rho(z, Y) = \left(\frac{\partial p}{\partial \rho}\right)^{-1} - 1 \tag{12}$$

Seeing that $\partial p/\partial \rho < 1$ for fairly large ρ (and hence z), we have reason for believing the positive correlations are due mainly to high multiplicity events. Ultimately, however, $\partial p/\partial \rho > 1$ and we expect (due to phase space effects) a large negative correlation to set in.

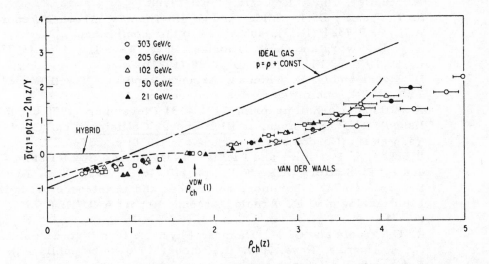

Fig. 3. The analog "equation of state" p(z, Y) (Eq. 7) vs. $\rho(z, Y)$ (Eq. 8) for z = 0.2, 0.3, ..., 2. The figure is taken from Ref. 21.

Whatever the behavior, it is clear that the above way of presenting inclusive distributions is worth exploring, and I hope to see such distributions presented in the future.

568

CONCLUSIONS

I have tried to give detailed reasons for using the language of one-dimensional models based primarily on the Multiperipheral picture. Left-right multiplicities provide a nice example of the usefulness of such models. Finally, a suggestion is given for making a more serious use of the one-dimensional ideas than has been done to date. It is hoped that in analyzing the vast amount of information which has been and will be obtained, the above comments will prove of some use.

FOOTNOTES AND REFERENCES

1. The written version here is an expansion of a short talk on Left-Right Multiplicities given at the Berkeley 1973 APS Conference.
2. For a fair presentation of this point, see the invited talk of C. Quigg, Experiments on High Energy Particle Collisions 1973 (American Institute of Physics, N. Y., 1973) p. 375.
3. A. Mueller, Phys. Rev. $\underline{D2}$, 2963 (1970).
4. S. S. Pinsky, D. R. Snider and G. H. Thomas, Argonne Report ANL/HEP 7331 (1973), submitted to this conference.
5. E. g. D. Sivers and G. H. Thomas, Phys. Rev. $\underline{D6}$, 1961 (1972).
6. C. E. DeTar, Phys. Rev. $\underline{D3}$, 128 (1971).
7. D. Sivers and G. H. Thomas, Argonne Reports ANL/HEP 7321, 7328 (1973), submitted to this conference.
8. K. Wilson, Cornell preprint CLNS-131 (November, 1970 unpublished); R. P. Feynman, in High Energy Collisions, ed. C. N. Yang et al. (Gordon and Breach, N. Y. 1970) p. 237; J. D. Bjorken, in Particles and Fields - 1971, ed. A. C. Melissinos and P. F. Slattery (AIP, N. Y.) p. 110; T. D. Lee, Phys. Rev. $\underline{D6}$, 3617 (1972). For more references and an introduction to the Fluid Analog q. v. R. Arnold, Argonne Report ANL/HEP 7317 (1973).
9. R. C. Arnold and G. H. Thomas, Phys. Letters $\underline{B}$ (to be publish G. H. Thomas, Phys. Rev. $\underline{D}$, October 1973 (to be published).
10. For a detailed comparison of single and two particle correlations versus Mueller-Regge model expectations, see S. S. Pinsky and G. H. Thomas, Argonne Report ANL/HEP 7345 (1973). A less detailed version is given in Ref. 2.
11. S. Nussinov, C. Quigg and J. -M. Wang, Phys. Rev. $\underline{D6}$, 2713 (1972).
12. T. Ferbel, C. Bromberg, private communication.
13. ANL-NAL Collaboration q. v. J. Whitmore in Experiments on Hig Energy Particle Collisions - 1973, (AIP, N. Y. 1973), p. 14.
14. 12 and 24 GeV/c, Bonn-Hamburg-Munchen Collaboration; V. Blo

et al., Hamburg preprint (1973).

15. G. Belletini et al., Pisa-Stony Brook Collaboration, see C. Quigg's review talk, this conference.

16. This model for left-right multiplicities is discussed in detail by D. R. Snider, Argonne Report ANL/HEP 7326 (1973). See also Ref. 7.

17. The model is that of Ref. 9 and is applied to left-right multiplicities in Ref. 7.

18. R. C. Arnold and J. Steinhoff, Phys. Letters 45B, 141 (1973).

19. J. Finkelstein and K. Kajantie, Phys. Letters 26B, 305 (1968); Nuovo Cimento 56, 659 (1968).

20. See e. g. A. H. Mueller, Phys. Rev. D4, 150 (1970); B. R. Webber, Nucl. Phys. B43, 541 (1972); W. Frazer, R. D. Peccei, S. S. Pinsky, and C. -I. Tan, Phys. Rev. D7, 2647 (1973).

21. The idea has been applied to multiplicities by R. C. Arnold and G. H. Thomas, Argonne Report ANL/HEP 7325 (1973); suggested for one- and two-particle distributions by the same authors (unpublished); and applied to these distributions by W. Shephard, private communication.

A Survey of Developments in Strong Interaction Theories[*]

HENRY D. I. ABARBANEL

National Accelerator Laboratory[†], Batavia, Illinois 60510

I. APOLOGIES AND INTRODUCTION

Strong interaction theories cover a broad and interesting range of ideas and phenomena. Although we all in our logical hearts expect that we will someday know from the same physical theory the explanation of why, say, the observed baryons come in octets and decimets <u>and</u> why the intercept of secondary Regge trajectories have $\alpha(0) \approx 1/2$, at this point in time the views on these and other topics are at best fragmented. In order to present today a finite discussion of some ideas in hadronic physics, I have been forced to choose among a large selection of fascinating subjects. I propose, then, to address three questions during this talk:

1. Rising total cross sections and theories which attempt to understand this.

2. Gauge theories of strong interactions and the possible relevance of such field theories to scaling.

3. Dual String Models.

Obviously I have left out vast numbers of worthwhile topics; I trust that my distinguished colleagues speaking in other sessions will cover them in depth.

---

[*]Invited paper presented at the 1973 meeting of the Division of Particles and Fields of the APS, Berkeley, California, August 1973.

[†]Operated by Universities Research Association Inc. Under Contract . with the United States Atomic Energy Commission.

II. RISING TOTAL CROSS SECTIONS

There can be no doubt that the most interesting new phenomenon to have been observed in hadronic physics during the last year is the ~ 10% rise in the proton proton total cross section over the range of CERN-IRS energies,[1] $400 \, (GeV)^2 \leq s \leq 3000 \, (GeV)^2$. I show a casual picture of this in Fig. 1 which I borrowed from the nice review talk of M. Jacob.[2]

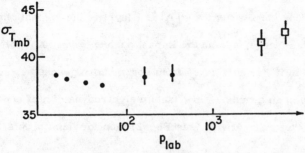

Fig. 1. A representation of the Serpukhov, NAL, and CERN-ISR data on the proton-proton total cross section.

Two basic views of this rise in σ_T^{pp} can be taken:

(a) It is an indication of a real trend for σ_T to continue to rise probably saturating the Froissart bound. This is supported primarily by the "eikonal school" although occasionally a bootstrap theorist is found in this corner.

(b) The rise in σ_T is a transient phenomenon. At larger energies (alas, not yet available) σ_T will settle into its real asymptotic behavior which is

(i) σ_T decreases as a very small power of s or

(ii) σ_T eventually goes to a constant.

Let's discuss these ideas in order. The theories which yield σ_T saturating the Froissart bound usually begin with the eikonal form of the elastic scattering amplitude[3]

$$T_{el}(s,t) = i s \int d^2 b \, e^{i \underset{\sim}{\Delta} \cdot \underset{\sim}{b}} [e^{i X(s, \underset{\sim}{b})} - 1] , \qquad (1)$$

where $\underset{\sim}{\Delta}$ is a two vector momentum transfer in the x, y plane when the beam comes in along the z-axis; $t = - |\underset{\sim}{\Delta}|^2$. $X(s, \underset{\sim}{b})$ is the eikonal phase as a function of the energy, s, and the impact parameter $\underset{\sim}{b}$. X, which has the dynamics in it, is calculated from some "born graphs" or some infinite set of Feynman graphs.[4] In quantum electrodynamics if one takes certain sets of tower graphs (see Fig. 2) then for fixed $\underset{\sim}{b}$, $X(s, \underset{\sim}{b})$ behaves as

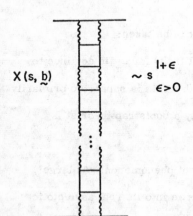

$$X(s, \underset{\sim}{b}) \sim s^{1+\epsilon} \quad \epsilon > 0$$

Fig. 2. Tower graphs summed in quantum electrodynamics to give an eikonal phase $X(s, \underset{\sim}{b})$ which grows as $s^{1+\epsilon}$, $\epsilon > 0$.

$$X(s, \underset{\sim}{b}) \sim s^{1+\epsilon}, \; \epsilon > 0 \tag{2}$$

and the b dependence is rather like

$$X(s, \underset{\sim}{b}) \sim e^{-\mu b} \tag{3}$$

where μ is some characteristic mass. The T-matrix as a function of s and b then is very close to a Θ function

$$e^{iX(s, \underset{\sim}{b})} - 1 = T_{el}(s, \underset{\sim}{b}) \approx \Theta\left(r_o \log s - |\underset{\sim}{b}|\right), \tag{4}$$

and this gives

$$T_{el}(s, t) = 2\pi i \, s \, (r_o \log s)^2 \left[\frac{J_1(\sqrt{-t} \, r_o \log s)}{\sqrt{-t} \, r_o \log s}\right], \tag{5}$$

so

$$\sigma_T(s) = \pi r_o^2 (\log s)^2. \tag{6}$$

This exactly saturates the Froissart bound

$$\sigma_T(s) \leq (\log s)^2, \tag{7}$$

and is to be thought of as the leading approximation to an expansion of $\sigma_T(s)$ in decreasing powers of log s. Indeed according to Jacob[2] a fit to the pp data can be achieved by

$$\sigma_T(s) = 38\text{mb} + 0.68\text{mb} \log^2\left(\frac{P_{lab} \text{ in GeV/c}}{100}\right). \tag{8}$$

Some comments are in order. First, it must not be thought that this $(\log s)^2$ is a firm prediction of quantum field theory. The specific form for the eikonal phase is a choice abstracted from a summation of leading behaviors of selected Feynman graphs - if σ_τ does not behave as $(\log s)^2$, one does not throw away field theory - only perhaps some field theorists. Second, in these same models the average multiplicity $\bar{n}(s)$ of produced particles grows as a small power times $\log s$. Third, because the leading singularity in the J-plane is more complicated than a pole, one expects long range correlations yielding integrated correlation functions f k (s) which behave as

$$fk(s) \sim (\log s)^k \tag{9}$$

and finally, in these models the diffraction peak in t of $\dfrac{d\sigma_{elastic}}{dt}$ shrinks as $(\log s)^2$ as one sees directly from Eq. (5). This last point is not a feature of present pp elastic data. [2]

The same structure for $T_{el}(s, t)$ comes from a marriage of the absorption model with the multiperipheral model. [5] Of course, the same critical comments apply if one substitutes for "abstractions from field theory" the phrase "conjectures from a presumed self consistent theory of diffraction scattering."

To saturate the Froissart bound and have total cross sections rising slowly forever has a definite aesthetic appeal. The details of the theories which yield $\sigma_\tau \sim (\log s)^2$ are less appealing. One must deal with the observations made above, especially the shrinkage of the elastic diffraction peak, and one must provide some understanding for the unusually large energies at which the $(\log s)^2$ growth sets in; note the scale setting factor of 100 GeV/c in Eq. (8).

Now to the view that the rise in σ_τ is a transient phenomenon. Basically there are two schools of thought. The first says that what we are seeing is just the effect of two or more Pomeron cut exchange (Fig. 3) which is emerging as the contributions of secondary Regge

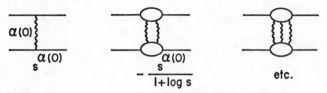

Fig. 3. The Pomeron pole and absorptive Pomeron cuts which lead to total cross sections which rise logarithmically to a constant.

trajectories with $\alpha(0) = 1/2$ disappears into the noise. One would expect $\sigma_\tau(s)$ to take the form

$$\sigma_\tau(s) = \sigma_0\left(1 - \frac{a}{b+\log p_{lab}}\right) + 0\left(\frac{1}{\sqrt{p_{lab}}}\right) \qquad (10)$$

Indeed, a fit to the ISR data of the form[2]

$$\sigma_\tau = 60\text{mb}\left(1 - \frac{3\text{mb}}{3+\log(p_{lab} \text{ in GeV/c})}\right) , \qquad (11)$$

seems acceptable, if not compelling. From either a theoretical or a phenomenological point of view there is little one can say to fault this attitude. It is true that no one has yet produced a consistent, well formulated theory of diffraction scattering which yields (10) without having other ghastly features.[6]

The second school of thought attributes the rise in $\sigma_T(s)$ to the contribution of the triple Pomeron coupling in T_{el}.[7] The triple Pomeron coupling is thought to give a contribution to $\sigma_T(s)$ of the form[8]

$$\sigma_{Tp}(s) = \frac{g_p(0)}{16\pi\alpha'} \, \log\left(1 + \frac{2\alpha'}{b} \log s\right) \qquad (12)$$

where α' is the slope of the Pomeron trajectory $\alpha p(t) = 1 + \alpha' t$, $g_p(0)$ is the triple Pomeron coupling appropriately normalized, and b is a slope parameter associated with $g_p(t)$

$$g_p(t) = g_p(0)e^{bt}. \qquad (13)$$

It is argued that when $(2\alpha'/b)\log s$ is small, then the triple Pomeron formula gives an effective log s rise to σ_T and later flattens off to the essentially irrelevant log (log s).

The major question associated with this explanation of the rise in σ_T would appear to be numerical. In order for this argument to be viable

$$\frac{2\alpha'}{b} \log s \ll 1 \qquad (14)$$

If $\alpha' \approx 1/2$ and b is a fairly normal slope of 10 in $(GeV)^{-2}$, then we may use this idea for

$$\log s \le 10, \tag{15}$$

which does cover the ISR range. However, to match the 4mb rise in σ_τ as log s varies from about 4 to 8, one needs quite a sizeable $g_p(0)$. So large, in fact, that it is likely to be inconsistent with the values of $g_p(0)$ one infers from the peaking of the X distribution in pp → p + anything near X = 1 at ISR energies[2] - a phenomenon which is generally considered to be the only convincing evidence for the existence of a triple Pomeron coupling.

Numerical questions aside one may raise theoretical eyebrows at the use of the triple Pomeron. The original reaction to the log (log s) growth in σ_τ arising from the triple Pomeron coupling was that it was not a virtue, but required $g_p(0)$ to vanish.[8] This led to a variety of disasters about vanishing Pomeron couplings, the most striking of which was the decoupling of the Pomeron from total cross sections themselves,[9] thus removing the rationale for a Pomeron with $\alpha(0) = 1$ in the first place. By taking an attitude that makes a virtue out of disaster, it seems to me that one has really postponed the difficult and interesting issue of how $\sigma_\tau(s)$ really behaves. Only the Berkeley school which advocates $\alpha(0) < 1$ has a logical answer to the hard question. Eventually σ_τ must go to zero as a small power after the amusing, but transient, effect of the triple Pomeron rise wears itself out.

578

Another objection altogether is raised by Blankenbecler and his collaborators[3] who argue that the triple Pomeron contribution to the Feynman graph like Fig. 4, say Fig. 5, contributes not $+ g_p \log (\log s)$

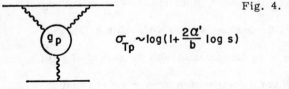

$$\sigma_{Tp} \sim \log \left(1 + \frac{2\alpha'}{b} \log s\right)$$

Fig. 4. The triple Pomeron contribution to the elastic scattering amplitude. The contribution of this to the total cross section is proportional to log (log s).

Fig. 5. A Feynman graph representation of the triple Pomeron amplitude.

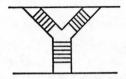

to σ_T but $-g_p \log (\log s)$ and, never mind orders of magnitude or detailed fits, this has the wrong sign to explain a rise in σ_T. This objection harks back to the ancient controversy over the sign of the two Pomeron cut to which the triple Pomeron piece of T_{el} is one contribution. The Feynman graph view says that when one takes Im T_{el} from the Y-graph of Fig. 5 to find its contributions to σ_T, only one of these, Fig. 6a, is connected with the triple Pomeron coupling usually measured in inclusive processes. There are two other cuts of Fig. 5 which contribute to Im T_{el} looking Fig. 6b and they yield an amount $-2g_p \log (\log s)$ to σ_T.

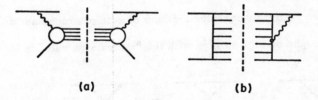

(a)   (b)

Fig. 6. Two cuts of Fig. 5 which contribute to Im T_{el} and, therefore, σ_T.
   6a. Yields the inclusive cross section near the edge of phase space
       and thus the usual triple Pomeron result.
   6b. Another cut which is the eikonal model serves to change the
       sign of Fig. 6a.

Let's look into this argument a bit more. It is clear that we

cannot stop with the Y-graph of Fig. 5 since we will eventually have a

negative σ_T. So we must sum up whole sets of contributions to Im T_{el}

to find a positive σ_T. Call $\tilde{g}_p$ the triple Pomeron coupling defined by

Fig. 5; it is a coupling in a model only and isn't the physical g_p measured

in inclusive reactions. Call β the elastic coupling coming, say, from the

ordinary ladder, as in Fig. 7. Now representing the ladders by a

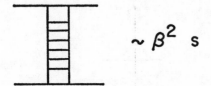

Fig. 7. A ladder graph
   representation of the $t = 0$
   Pomeron exchange with
   factorizable residue β^2.

580

wiggly line (bare Pomeron) consider the sum of sets of graphs as in

Fig. 8. The graphs of Fig. 8a give with the "minus sign rule" a

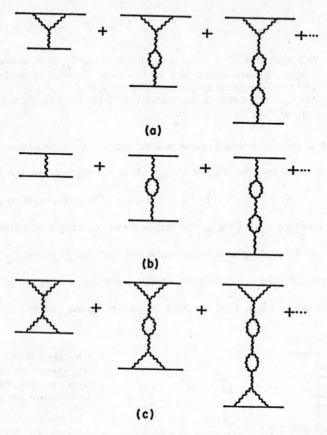

(a)

(b)

(c)

Fig. 8. Various sets of Reggeon graphs which are summed up in the
text with the eikonal sign for Pomeron cuts.

contribution to σ_τ of

$$\sigma_\tau(s) \sim \frac{-\beta^3 g_p \log (\log s)}{1 + g_p^2 \log (\log s)} : \qquad (16)$$

Those of Fig. 8b give

$$\sigma_\tau(s) \sim \beta^2 / [1 + g_p^2 \log (\log s)], \qquad (17)$$

and from Fig. 8c we have

$$\sigma_\tau(s) \sim \frac{\beta^4 g_p^2 [\log (\log s)]^2}{1 + g_p^2 \log (\log s)} . \qquad (18)$$

Adding these contributions we find a net σ_τ from triple Pomeron diagrams to be positive for large $\log (\log s)$ and to behave as

$$\sigma_\tau \sim \beta^4 \log (\log s). \qquad (19)$$

Does one infer then that $\beta \neq 0$, since to produce $\log (\log s)$ even in the simplest diagram of Fig. 8 we had to require $\alpha(0) = 1$ for the input ladder? I think not. Probably one is forced to the conclusion that without some rather more consistent theory of diffraction, the Feynman graph argument only dents but does not yet destroy the triple Pomeron couplers. That they have enough trouble on their own, we have already pointed out.

I think that a fair conclusion from the foregoing discussion is that the origin of the rise in σ_τ and its non-transient implications for hadronic theories remains an open and fascinating question.

III. GAUGE THEORIES FOR STRONG INTERACTIONS

What I wish to discuss in this section are ideas which involve a certain level of speculation but are so exciting that no one ought to ignore them. As a fallout of the intense interest focused on renoralizable gauge theories of the weak and electromagnetic interactions it has been suggested that non-Abelian gauge field theories, of which the ancient Yang-Mills theory is a classical example, may also be relevant to hadronic physics.[10] In particular a rather recent development involving detailed properties of the renormalization group for these non-Abelian gauge theories has raised the amusing prospect[11] that one may be able to understand the scaling properties observed in deep inelastic electron scattering at SLAC.

It is not my purpose to turn us all into giant experts on the renormalization group in twenty minutes, but to briefly draw attention to the new ideas which are around and some problems associated with them.

What the renormalization group enables one to do is give a compact discussion of the behavior of various Green functions as the momenta involved approach large spacelike values. Then there are constraint equations on the Green functions which were derived by Callan and Symanzik[12] several years ago. These express how the masses and coupling constants of the field theory presumed to govern the interactions underlying the Green function may be varied.

A typical equation of this form reads

$$\left[m \frac{\partial}{\partial m} + \beta(g)\frac{\partial}{\partial g} - n\gamma(g) \right] G^{(n)}_{Asy} (p_i) = 0, \tag{20}$$

where m and g are the renormalized mass and coupling constants of the field theory, $\beta(g)$ and $\gamma(g)$ are finite functions of g alone and $G^{(n)}_{Asy}$ is the asymptotic form of an n-point Green function. The functions β and γ are known only in perturbation theory for all but the most special models.

The key observation is that zeroes of $\beta(g)$ where the slope of β is negative govern the asymptotic behavior of $G^{(n)}$. (See Fig. 9). For

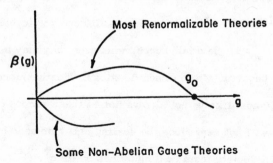

Fig. 9. The behavior of the coupling constant function $\beta(g)$ in most renormalizable field theories and in many non-Abelian gauge theories. The zeroes of $\beta(g)$ where $\beta' < 0$ govern the asymptotic behavior of Green functions in field theory.

example, if $\beta(g)$ has a simple zero at g_o and $d\beta/dg\big|_{g_o} < 0$, then for all momenta in $G^{(n)}$ going simultaneously to space-like infinity $p_i = \xi k_i$, $\xi \to \infty$, $G^{(n)}$ behaves as

$$G_{Asy}^{(n)} \sim \xi^{4-n} \times \xi^{-n\gamma(g_o)} \times f^{(n)}(g_o), \tag{21}$$

where ξ^{4-n} is just reminding us of the normal dimensions of $G^{(n)}$, $\xi^{-n\gamma(g_o)}$ is a measure of the "anomalous dimensions" due to the renormalization procedure, and $f^{(n)}(g_o)$ is some finite function of g_o. If $\gamma(g_o)$ were zero by some miracle, then there would be no anomalous dimensions and the theory would be scale invariant: that is, all quantities have only naïve dimensions.

Very little is known in general about the zeroes of $\beta(g)$. By its definition it turns out that $\beta(0) = 0$, but for almost all renormalizable field theories $d\beta/dg\big|_{g=0} > 0$. So other zeros, wherever they may be govern the asymptotic behavior of the Green functions. Furthermore, the functions $\gamma(g)$ will, most likely, not also vanish at these zeroes of $\beta(g)$ and such theories will not reproduce the scaling behavior seen at SLAC; indeed, they will deviate from scaling by powers of q^2.

Now for the good news. In a large class of non-Abelian gauge theories it has been found that[11]

$$\beta(g) = -\beta_0 g^3 + O(g^5), \quad \beta_0 > 0. \tag{22}$$

This means that the value of the couplings of the underlying field theories which govern the asymptotic behavior of Green functions is zero coupling. That is, free field theories give the asymptotic behavior and corrections to those asymptotic values are calculable by perturbation theory. Furthermore, for free field theories $\gamma(g)$ vanishes since there are no anomalous dimensions for a free field.

The detailed results of these renormalization group studies are that there are still logarithmic deviations from exact scaling in most instances and in general the approach to scaling is only logarithmic. For example, it is still true that for an underlying field theory of vector bosons (the gauge fields) and fermions the ratio $R = \sigma_L / \sigma_T$ of longitudional over transverse photon cross sections for deep inelastic electron scattering goes to zero in the Bjorken limit but

$$\lim_{\substack{q^2 \to \infty \\ X \text{ fixed}}} R(X = \frac{-q^2}{2m\nu}, q^2) \sim \frac{1}{\log q^2}. \tag{23}$$

And in electron-positron annihilation one finds

$$\frac{\sigma_{e^+e^-} \to \text{hadrons}}{\sigma_{e^+e^-} \to \mu^+\mu^-} \underset{q^2 \to \infty}{\sim} \sum_i Q_i^2 \left(1 + 0\left(\frac{1}{\log q^2}\right)\right), \tag{24}$$

where q^2 is now the energy of the e^+e^- system and Q_i are the charges of the constituents of the hadrons.

Of course, these theories are not without their problems. First
of all, they are stuck, so far, on logarithmic approaches to scaling. If
this is verified by the muon scattering experiments at NAL or by e^+e^-
annihilation experiments at SPEAR, one will, of course, not regard this
as a problem. Second, in order to give the vector bosons entering these
theories some non-zero mass, one conventionally introduces some scalar
(Higgs) bosons which develop non-zero vacuum expectation values, break
the underlying gauge symmetry, and yield up masses for the gauge bosons.
So far it has not been possible to carry this out completely without
destroying the key result that $\beta'(g=0) < 0$. So activists in gauge theories
have pinned their hopes on another mechanism, invented by Coleman and
E. Weinberg, [13] which takes advantage of the infrared singular behavior
of theories involving massless bosons and fermions to dynamically
break the gauge symmetry and produce masses for the particles in the
physical spectrum of the initial Lagrangian. There is also the hope that
the infrared behavior is so singular that the physical spectrum resulting
from solving the bound state problem will not resemble the underlying
fields ("quarks" and bosons)and one will not be faced with the usual
embarrassment of "keeping the quarks in." Because of our less than
dramatic success in solving the bound state problem in less singular
field theories, one must view this as a strong hope indeed. Finally,
there is the problem of which gauge group to use for the basic field
theory. Hints from experiment will only come as the detailed nature of

the predicted logarithmic approach to scaling is seen; that is, the powers of $\log q^2$ can yield up significant information. Clearly, however, the practical problems are quite non-trivial. Nevertheless, I regard this whole scheme as an attractive prospect for really learning something concrete about hadronic interactions; whether we will at the same time learn all we want to know, I hesitate to conjecture.

IV. DUAL STRING MODELS

The third and final subject I propose to consider today is that of the string picture in dual theories. You will recall that the spectrum of the dual resonance model was noted some years ago by Nambu and Susskind[14] to be identical to the excitation spectrum of a string in one dimension at every point of which there is attached a four vector $X_\mu (\sigma, \tau)$ as the actual space-time displacement vector of the constituents of the hadron-infinite in number and thus continuously distributed in α. (See Fig. 10.) To reproduce the dual spectrum is then the requirement

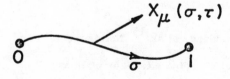

Fig. 10. A picture of the one dimensional string stretching from 0 to 1 in the σ parameter space. A vector $X_\mu (\sigma, \tau)$ is attached to each point at each time τ. It is supposed to represent the displacement in real space-time of the string taken to be a hadron.

that $X_\mu (\sigma, \tau)$ obey the wave equation

$$\left(\frac{\partial^2}{\partial \sigma^2} - \frac{\partial^2}{\partial \tau^2} \right) X_\mu (\sigma, \tau) = 0. \tag{25}$$

588

To achieve this one builds an action out of X_μ and its derivatives and imposes constraint conditions reflecting the invariances of the action, if any, so that the classical Euler-Lagrange equations of motion for the independent components of X_μ are just (25).

The action which has been most thoroughly studied is that proposed by Nambu.[14] in which it is taken to be proportional to the invariant two dimensional area swept out by the string as it extends in σ and moves in time τ. This action is

$$A = - \frac{1}{2\pi\alpha'} \int_0^1 d\sigma \int_{\tau_i}^{\tau_f} dt \left\{ \left(\frac{\partial X_\mu}{\partial \tau} \frac{\partial X^\mu}{\partial \sigma} \right)^2 - \left(\frac{\partial X_\mu}{\partial \sigma} \right)^2 \left(\frac{\partial X_\mu}{\partial \tau} \right)^2 \right\}^{\frac{1}{2}}, \quad (26)$$

where the constant is conventional and the "length" of the string in parameter space has been chosen to be one. (See Fig. 11). The most care-

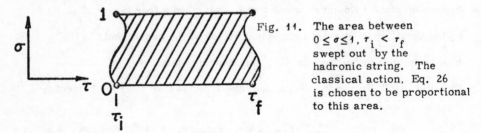

Fig. 11. The area between $0 \le \sigma \le 1$, $\tau_i < \tau_f$ swept out by the hadronic string. The classical action, Eq. 26 is chosen to be proportional to this area.

ful study of this action has been by P. Goddard, et al.[15] Noting the invariance of the action under the general coordinate transformations

$$\sigma \to f(\sigma, \tau), \quad (27)$$

and

$$\tau \to g(\sigma, \tau), \quad (28)$$

they choose as auxiliary conditions on X_μ

$$\frac{\partial X_\mu}{\partial \sigma} \cdot \frac{\partial X^\mu}{\partial \tau} = 0, \qquad (29)$$

and

$$\left(\frac{\partial X_\mu}{\partial \sigma}\right)^2 + \left(\frac{\partial X_\mu}{\partial \tau}\right)^2 = 0. \qquad (30)$$

These guarantee that the independent components of X_μ satisfy (25).

When one is willing to work in d space-time dimensions, then the two fold invariance of the action means that precisely d-2 components of the space-time displacement vector $X_\mu(\sigma, \tau)$ are independent. This has the consequence that the first excited state created from the vacuum by the normal mode operators of X_μ has only d-2 degrees of freedom, and since this is one less than the normal number (one degree of freedom always being lost essentially through a mass-shell constraint), the first excited state must be massless. In terms of the Regge intercept of the leading trajectory of the dual spectrum, this implies $\alpha(0) = 1$, and further that the ground state (vacuum) is a tachyon with $\alpha' m^2 = -1$; α' is the universal slope of the dual model. All theories based on an action like (26) with "too much" symmetry suffer from this disease.

More detailed analysis shows that when one takes this action very seriously and requires that the geometrical generators of the Lorentz group which seems manifest in Eq. 26 have the commutation relations required by Lorentz symmetry, then there is a restriction on the number of space-time dimensions of the theory to d = 26. Physics, one recalls, takes place in d = 24.

There are two attitudes to take at this point: (1) the model action is a disaster and must be replaced by one with less symmetry or (2) the model action with all its faults is an interesting prototype theory for what a "real" theory in four dimensions must look like and deserves further intensive study. I think both points of view are correct in the usual spirit of inquiry. Clearly one needs a better action; nevertheless one may use (26) to learn a great deal about any future, more realistic string models.

The most significant contribution to this latter point of view has been by Mandelstam.[16] By studying the functional integral formulation of the quantum theory of the string with (26) as a classical action, he is able to reproduce the n-point amplitudes of the dual resonance model and to justify the attractive, if picturesque language, of imagining strings in space-time coming together and splitting. The basic dual vertex consists of one string splitting into two (Fig. 12) and higher point functions are

Fig. 12. One string (hadron) splits into two strings (hadrons) to form the basic dual vertex.

similarly described. Mandelstam is also able to explicitly demonstrate the role that space-time dimension 26 plays in guaranteeing the Lorentz covariance of the theory.

Although the string model is as yet rather an unphysical entity (tachyons and d=26 just smell peculiar), it still holds an attractive allure and both ought and will be the subject of study for its improvement, perhaps to a physically realistic model.

ACKNOWLEDGMENTS

I am very grateful to R. J. Crewther, M. B. Einhorn, S. D. Ellis and S. Nussinov for patiently helping me to learn about the subjects covered in this brief. survey.

REFERENCES

[1] U. Amaldi, et al., Phys. Letters 44B, 112 (1973) and S. R. Amendolia, et al., Phys. Letters 44B, 119 (1973).

[2] M. Jacob, "Multi-Body Phenomena in Strong Interactions," CERN Theory Preprint No. 1683.

[3] A recent, more or less complete, mini-review of this subject is provided by R. Blankenbecler, J. R. Fulco, and R. L. Sugar, "An Eikonal Primer," SLAC-Preprint, July 1973. A more pedagogical formulation may be found in my lectures at the International Summer Institute on Theoretical Physics in Kaiserslautern 1972, Vol. 17, Lecture Notes in Physics, Edited by W. Ruhl and A. Vancura, p. 146-173. Also T. Neff, (unpublished), June 1973.

[4] H. Cheng and T. T. Wu, Phys. Rev. 186, 1611 (1969) or S. Auerbach et al., Phys. Rev. D6, 2216 (1972) and references therein.

[5] J. R. Fulco and R. L. Sugar, Phys. Rev. D4, 1919 (1971); J. Finkelstein and F. Zachariasen, Phys. Letters 34B, 631 (1971); L. Caneschi and A. Schwimmer, Nucl. Phys. B44, 31 (1972).

[6] Some of the most convincing efforts have been made by Gribov and his collaborators. This work can be traced back from V. N. Gribov, et al., Zh. Eksp. Theor. Phys. 59, 2140 (1970) Sov. Phys. JETP 32, 1158 (1971). The bad features are the various "decoupling theorems" for the Pomeron which I will not discuss here.

[7]A. Capella, et al., SLAC preprint No. 1241 (May, 1973), G. F. Chew, Phys. Letters. 44B, 169 (1973), W. R. Frazer, et al., UCSD preprint No. 10P10-127 (June 1973), and M. Bishari and J. Koplik, Phys. Letters 44B, 175 (1973), and probably others.

[8]L. M. Saunders, et al., Phys. Rev. Letters 26, 937 (1971).

[9]R. Brower and J. Weis, Phys. Letters 41B, 631 (1972).

[10]A thorough summary is given by B. W. Lee in Proceedings of the XVI International Conf. on High Energy Physics, Vol 4, p. 249 (National Accelerator Laboratory, 1973, A. Roberts and J. D. Jackson, editors.)

[11]H. D. Politzer, Phys. Rev. Letters 30, 1346 (1973); G. t'Hooft, unpublished; D. J. Gross and F. Wilczek, Phys. Rev. Letters 30, 1343 (1973).

[12]C. G. Callan, Phys. Rev. D2, 1541 (1970) and K. Symanzik, Comm. Math. Phys. 18, 227 (1970). In the form given here these renormalization group equations were known many years ago by the Soviets: V. Osviannikov, Doklady ANSSSR 109, 1112 (1956).

[13]S. Coleman and E. Weinberg, Phys. Rev. D7, 1888 (1973).

[14]Y. Nambu, report presented at the International Conf. on Symmetries and Quark Models, Wayne State University, June, 1969; L. Susskind, Phys. Rev. Letters 23, 545 (1969).

[15]P. Goddard, et al., CERN Theory Preprint No. 1563, October 1972.

[16]S. Mandelstam, U. C. Berkeley Preprint, May 1973.

594

THE EIKONAL APPROACH TO HIGH ENERGY SCATTERING*

R. L. Sugar
Department of Physics, University of California
Santa Barbara, California 93106

ABSTRACT

The eikonal approach to high energy scattering
and particle production is reviewed. The energy
dependence of the eikonal phase is discussed. The
effect of the fragmentation of the incident particles
on the energy dependence of cross sections is considered.
It is pointed out that the opening of diffractive
channels leads to a decrease in the total cross section
for a wide class of Feynman diagram models.

I would like to briefly review the present status
of the eikonal approach to high energy scattering and
particle production. I shall not attempt to make a
comprehensive survey of the subject, but shall instead
concentrate on a few topics which I think are of
particular importance. This talk is based upon a paper
by Blankenbecler, Fulco and myself[1] which contains a
broader discussion of the material presented here.

Undoubtedly the main virtue of the eikonal method
is that the geometrical constraints of s-channel unitarity are automatically enforced. In fact it has been
possible to construct eikonal models for which the
scattering operator satisfies full multiparticle unitarity in the direct channel.[2-4] The approach is
general enough to allow one to study a variety of
production mechanisms; however, this generality is also
a disadvantage since all of the specific predictions
are quite model dependent and can be changed by
altering the assumptions about the underlying dynamics.
A second drawback is that the constraints of t-channel
unitarity are not automatically incorporated, and in
general it appears to be difficult to include them.

Let me start by considering the simple eikonal
picture in which the incident particles retain their
identity throughout the scattering process and do not
make significant changes in their energies or longitudinal momenta. This is obviously an oversimplifi-

*Work supported by the National Science Foundation

cation of the leading particle effect, and I shall later return to the important question of introducing effects associated with the fragmentation of the incident particles. Since the incident particles are assumed to travel through the interaction region in a straight line, the scattering operator is diagonal in the impact parameter representation, and it is convenient to write the invariant elastic scattering amplitude in the form

$$M(s,t) = 4\pi i s \int_{0}^{\infty} b\,db \ J_{0}(b\sqrt{-t})[1 - e^{i\chi(b,s)}] \quad (1)$$

where the complex eikonal phase, $\chi(b,s)$, is the sum over all connected graphs involving the exchange of an arbitrary number of mesons as shown in figure 1[5]. By connected graphs I mean that the circles in figure 1 represent connected t-channel scattering amplitudes. Disconnected graphs arise from the expansion of the exponential.

It is probably best to regard eq.(1) as a simple ansatz which automatically takes into account the constraints of s-channel unitarity. This equation can be "derived" from Feynman graphs of the type shown in figure 1[5] provided one considers only contributions in which the incident particles retain their large momenta throughout the scattering process.[6] There are classes of Feynman diagrams for which the contributions from the eikonal paths do give the leading asymptotic behavior, for example, the exchange of an arbitrary number of non-interacting vector mesons[7] or Quantum Electrodynamic (QED) towers,[8] and the exchange of one or two φ^3 ladders.[9] However, one can also find classes of diagrams, such as the exchange of scalar mesons, for which the eikonal paths do not give the leading asymptotic behavior.[10] In the case of ladder exchange, the eikonal picture holds only if one treats the ladders in the leading log approximation. There are non-leading log contributions which correspond to two or more intermediate particles sharing the large incident momentum.[9] A similar result undoubtedly holds for the exchange of QED towers.

In general the circles in figure 1 can correspond to $n \rightarrow m$ meson scattering amplitudes; however, in all of the work that I am aware of only diagonal ($n \rightarrow n$) contributions to χ have been taken into account, and I shall limit myself to them. It is then convenient to write

$$i\chi(b,s) = \sum_{n=1}^{\infty} i^n d_n(b,s) \, s^{[n(\alpha-1) + a(n)]} e^{-n\mu b} \tag{2}$$

Here n is the number of mesons being exchanged, μ is their mass and α is their spin. Since couplings between the various meson channels are being neglected, the nearest t-channel singularity in the n-meson amplitude is at $t = (n\mu)^2$. As a result, one expects $d_n(b,s)$ to go to a constant for large b and fixed s. One also expects that for large s, a(n) can be chosen so that $d_n(b,s)$ varies with s at most like a power of ℓn s.

Cheng and Wu have suggested that in QED terms in eq. (2) which correspond to the exchange of three or more mesons can be neglected at large values of the impact parameter because of their more rapid fall off. Let us therefore start by considering the first two terms in eq. (2). In general d_1 is real, a(1) = 0, Re $d_2 > 0$, and a(2) > 0. As a result, for large values of s and b, the tower graphs always dominate the single particle exchange terms for vector exchange. They also dominate for scalar exchange provided a(2)>1. If one retains only the contributions to χ arising from the tower graphs, then for vector exchange $e^{i\chi(b,s)}$ goes to zero at large s for $b \lesssim [a(2)/2_\mu] \ell n$ s $\equiv R_o \ell n$ s, and goes to 1 for $b > R_o \ell n$ s. In the present normalization, the total and elastic cross sections at high energies are given by

$$\sigma_T = 4\pi \int_0^{\infty} bdb \, \mathrm{Re}[1 - e^{i\chi(b,s)}], \tag{3}$$

$$\sigma_{e\ell} = 2\pi \int_0^{\infty} bdb \, \left| 1 - e^{i\chi(b,s)} \right|^2. \tag{4}$$

So for vector exchange[11]

$$\sigma_T = 2\sigma_{e\ell} \simeq 2\pi(R_o \, \ell ns)^2. \tag{5}$$

A similar result holds for scalar exchange when a(2)>2[12], in other words when the asymptotic behavior of $\chi(b,s)$ is dominated by a Regge pole with intercept greater than one. Eq. (5) of course corresponds to scattering from a black disc of radius $R_o \ell n$ s.

Whether the contributions to χ arising from the exchange of three or more mesons can actually be

neglected for large values of the impact parameter
depends upon the behavior of $a(n)$ as a function of n.
In models which include the checkerboard graph diagrams
shown in figure 2, $a(n)$ grows like $\frac{1}{2}n(n-1)$[4,13], so these
terms obviously cannot be neglected. This behavior
for $a(n)$ is not hard to understand. The particles
represented by dashed lines in figure 2 give rise to
attractive forces among the exchanged mesons. Since the
number of "two body potentials" increases like $\frac{1}{2}n(n-1)$,
it is hardly surprising that the binding among the
mesons does also. In these models one finds that for
most values of the input parameters the total and
elastic cross sections fall like a power of the energy
as s goes to infinity. The calculation of the checkerboard diagrams has been carried out in a model satisfying
full s-channel unitarity in which the Born term, the
amplitude for production from a single chain, was
patterned after the multiperipheral model,[4] and in a
Feynman diagram model involving massive vector and
scalar mesons.[13] To my knowledge the corresponding QED
diagrams have not been calculated. It would be particularly interesting to know the asymptotic behavior of the
QED diagrams corresponding to three photon exchange. An
example is shown in figure 3. If the checkerboard graph
calculations are an accurate guide, then these diagrams
should give a contribution to $\chi(b,s)$ which is important
out to larger impact parameters than the tower graph
contribution, and the tower dominance hypothesis would
not be correct.

To summarize the behavior of $a(n)$ in relativistic
field theories remains an open question. If it grows
less rapidly than n, then only one and two meson exchange contributions are important at large b. As a
result, for vector exchange there is always appreciable
scattering out to b of order R_0 $\ln s$, and eq. 5 holds.
On the other hand, if $a(n)$ grows linearily with n or
faster, then all terms in the series for χ must be
retained and a detailed calculation is necessary to
determine the high energy behavior of the total cross
section. This case is further complicated by the fact
that couplings between the various meson channels,
which are required by t-channel unitarity, are likely
to be important.

The high energy behavior of $\chi(b,s)$ depends
critically on the mechanism for producing particles in
the central region. Particle production can be introduced into the eikonal framework by treating $\chi(b,s)$ as
an operator.[2-4] In general it is a functional of
the creation and annihilation operators of the produced
particles. In the work of reference 4, where the form

of $\chi(b,s)$ is taken from the multiperipheral model, $\chi(b,s)$ turns out to be an unbounded operator for most values of the input parameters. It is then hardly surprising that one must take into account all powers of the operator χ in computing the eikonal phase of the elastic scattering amplitude. However, it is also possible to construct reasonable models in which χ is a bounded operator.[4,14] In these models it is possible to adjust the input parameters so that the tower dominance hypothesis holds. It is also possible to arrange for any desired energy dependence of the total cross section.

As I mentioned earlier, the simple eikonal picture that I have been discussing can not be the entire story. If the incident particles never lost a significant fraction of their incident momenta, then all of the produced particles would have to come off in the central region. Experimentally one knows that the incident particles often fragment into two or more secondaries which share the large incident momentum. Such effects are present in the Feynman diagram models I have mentioned once one goes beyond the leading log approximation. Fragmentation effects can be included in the general eikonal picture provided the invariant mass of the fragments of each particle is small compared to the total center of mass energy.[3,15] The only detailed eikonal model that I am aware of in which such effects have been taken into account is the work of Skard and Fulco.[15]

It is convenient to divide both the intermediate and final states into two classes: those in which there are no large rapidity gaps and those in which there is at least one large gap. For simplicity let us consider explicitly only those final states in which there is at least one large gap. Then the scattering amplitude can be written in matrix form[16]

$$M_{k\ell}(x,t) = 4\pi i s \int_0^\infty dbd \ J_0(b\sqrt{-t}) \ [1 - e^{i\chi(b,s)}]_{k\ell} \qquad (6)$$

where the subscripts label the various states with at least one large rapidity gap. They consist of the incident state and all states to which it can be diffractively excited. Typical diagrams are shown in figure 4. The matrix χ, which is represented by a wavy line in figure 4, is itself a sum of diagrams in which none of the intermediate states have large rapidity gaps. It is convenient to write χ in the form

$$i \ \chi_{k\ell}(b,s) = -A_{k\ell}(b,s), \qquad (7)$$

Then assuming that the nondiffractive intermediate states produce absorption in all eigenchannels, A will be a positive definite hermitian matrix which can be diagonalized by the unitary matrix $G(b,s)$:

$$[G^{-1}(b,s)\ A(b,s)\ G(b,s)]_{k\ell} = \delta_{k\ell}\ a_k(b,s). \qquad (8)$$

The scattering amplitude then takes the form

$$M_{k\ell}(s,t) = 4\pi i s \int_0^\infty bdb\ J_0(b\sqrt{-t}) \sum_m G_{km}(b,s)$$

$$\qquad (9)$$

$$[1 - e^{-a_m(b,s)}]\ G^{-1}_{m\ell}(b,s).$$

It is instructive to consider a few special cases. Suppose there are N discrete eigenvalues of A which are very large out to an impact parameter of order b_0 (perhaps $b_0 = R_0\ \ell ns$) and that all of the eigenvalues decrease rapidly to zero for $b > b_0$. Then

$$\sigma_T^k = \frac{1}{s} I_m M_{kk}(s,o)$$

$$\simeq 4\pi \int_0^{b_0} bdb \sum_{m=1}^N |G_{km}(b,s)|^2 \qquad (10)$$

$$\sigma_{e\ell}^k = 2\pi \int_0^\infty bdb\ |(1 - e^{-A})_{kk}|^2$$

$$\simeq 2\pi \int_0^{b_0} bdb \sum_{m,m'=1}^N |G_{km}(b,s)|^2 |G_{km'}(b,s)|^2 \qquad (11)$$

and

$$\sigma^{k\ell} = 2\pi \int_0^\infty bdb\ |(1 - e^{-A})_{k\ell}|^2$$

$$\qquad (12)$$

$$\simeq 2\pi \int_0^{b_0} bdb \sum_{m,m'=1}^N G_{km}(b,s)\ G^*_{\ell m}(b,s)\ G^*_{km'}(b,s)$$

$$G_{\ell m'}(b,s).$$

In the simple black disc models in which fragmentation is neglected, all total cross sections become equal at high energies because R_o does not depend on the coupling to the external particles (it depends on a(2) but not on d_2). However, from eq. (10) one sees that as long as there is more than one diffractive channel, the total cross sections do not have to become equal at high energies. Furthermore since G is a unitary matrix, $\sigma_{e\ell}/\sigma_T \leq \frac{1}{2}$ instead of being exactly $\frac{1}{2}$ as in the simple black disc models. However, defining the diffractive cross section by

$$\sigma_{dif}^k = \sigma_{e\ell}^k + \sum_{\ell \neq k} \sigma^{k\ell} \tag{13}$$

one finds that[15]

$$\sigma_{dif}^k = \frac{1}{2}\sigma_T^k \tag{14}$$

There are two special cases of interest. First if all of the eigenvalues of A are large out to $b \approx b_o$, then using the unitarity of G one finds $\sigma_T^k = 2\sigma_{e\ell}^k = 2\pi b_o^2$ and $\sigma^{k\ell}/\sigma_T^k \approx 0$. These are just the results of the one channel model. Going to the opposite extreme consider the case in which only one eigenvalue of A is large out to $b \approx b_O$. This is equivalent to taking A to be separable so let us write

$$A_{k\ell}(b,s) = G_k(b,s) \, a(b,s) \, G_\ell(b,s) \tag{15}$$

This is a crude version of the model of Skard and Fulco.[15] Writing $\sum_k G_k^2(b,s) = I(b,s)$ the scattering amplitude takes the form

$$M_{k\ell}(s,t) = 4\pi is \int_0^\infty bdb \, J_o(b\sqrt{-t}) \, \frac{G_k(b,s) \, G_\ell(b,s)}{I(b,s)}$$

$$[1 - e^{-I(b,s) \, a(b,s)}]. \tag{16}$$

On the basis of the one channel models, one expects a(b,s) to grow like a power of s for fixed b. I(b,s) will also increase with s since new diffractive channels are continually being opened, but it is not expected to grow nearly as rapidly as a(b,s). Furthermore, G_k and I are expected to be slowly varying functions of b. As a result, the value of b_O is only slightly effected by the presence of the diffractive channels; however, the factor of $I(s)^{-1}$ under the integral in eq. (14) tends to decrease $M_{k\ell}(s,t)$. In other words the opening of new diffractive channels makes the disc more transparent. This effect has also been pointed out by Kirby and Fried in a paper submitted to this meeting.[17]

In the work of Skard and Fulco[15] fragmentation effects are treated in a manner similar to the diffractive model.[18] They find that I grows like $(\ln s)^\eta$, where η is constrained to vary between 0 and 2 by self consistency requirements. Therefore, in this model the disc is no longer black and the total cross section behaves like $(\ln s)^{2-\eta}$. The point to be emphasized is that the high energy behavior of the total cross section depends sensitively both on the production mechanism in the central region which determines the behavior of $a(b,s)$ and on the production mechanism in the fragmentation region which determines the behavior of $I(b,s)$.

Finally, let me consider the effects of fragmentation and diffraction in a multiperipheral-like model. The simplest graphs that contribute to the eikonal phase are shown in figure 5a.[5] Cutting these diagrams one can divide the intermediate states into those with no large rapidity gaps and those with one or more such gaps. Examples are shown in figures 5b and 5c respectively. The wavy lines represent ladders whose high energy behavior is assumed to be dominated by a Regge pole with intercept close to or equal to one. For the graphs in figure 5b these Regge poles give rise to absorptive corrections to the basic multiperipheral production amplitude. The graphs containing these absorptive corrections interfere destructively with the graph obtained by cutting the simple ladder. The graph in which the Reggeon is attached to the incoming lines and the one in which it is attached to the outgoing lines both contribute to the two Reggeon cut. Each of these graphs is equal in magnitude, but opposite in sign to the AFS graph (the first one in figure 5c) which has one large rapidity gap. This is the origin of the well known result that in the eikonal model the two-Reggeon cut makes a negative contribution to the total cross section. The same sign reversal holds for the term linear in the triple Regge vertex which also makes a negative contribution to the total cross section. As is well known, this term grows like $\ln \ln s$ if the Pomeron has intercept one and the triple Pomeron vertex does not vanish at zero momentum transfer. This does not mean that the total cross section becomes negative at high energies. When the full contribution

of the Y graph is included in the eikonal phase one
finds that the total cross section falls like $(\ln \ln s)^{-1}$
unless the triple Pomeron vertex vanishes. In the latter
case it approaches a constant. Higher order diffractive
contributions will certainly change the rate of fall of
the total cross section, but this simple example indicates the importance of treating shadowing and
absorption in the triple Regge region.

The close connection between the Mandelstam cut and
the triple Regge contribution is illustrated in figure 6.
If no rungs are allowed on the bottom ladder, this
diagram is exactly the Mandelstam graph. In both cases
the sign obtained in the eikonal model is in agreement
with that obtained in Gribov's Reggeon calculus,[19] but
in disagreement with that obtained in the standard
multiperipheral model. The differences can be traced to
the forms of the production amplitudes in these models.
In the multiperipheral model, one assumes that all
production comes from a single chain as in the first
diagram of figure 5 b. In the eikonal model model one
includes absorptive corrections to the simple multiperipheral chain as well as production from more than
one chain. As I have already mentioned, the terms
containing absorptive corrections play a crucial role in
the sign flip. The arguments for including them are
that they are present in simple Feynman diagrams, and
they arise naturally in models with s-channel unitarity.

The model just outlined provides an example of an
interesting result recently obtained by Blankenbecler.[20]
He has studied the effect of the opening of new channels
on total cross sections. It is well known that in
potential scattering a closed channel gives rise to an
attractive effective potential. Since this "potential"
becomes large near inelastic thresholds, cross sections
tend to rise as new channels are opened. This result
holds for hermitian potentials. However, Blankenbecler
has shown that for anti-hermitian potentials cross
sections fall as new channels are opened. He has also
shown that a similar result holds in a quite general
class of Feynman diagram models. For a diffractively
produced channel, Pomeron exchange is equivalent to an
anti-hermitian potential. As a result, Blankenbecler
argues that the opening of such a channel will lead
to a decrease in the total cross section. The difference in sign between this result and the multiperipheral calculations can again be traced to the fact
that the Feynman diagram model includes absorptive
corrections to the production amplitude while the multiperipheral model does not.

REFERENCES

1. R. Blankenbecler, J. R. Fulco and R. L. Sugar, SLAC - PUB 1281.

2. G. Calucci, R. Jengo and C. Rebi, Nuovo Cimento 4A, 330 (1971); 6A, 601 (1971).

3. R. Aviv, R. Blankenbecler and R. Sugar, Phys. Rev. D5, 3252 (1972).

4. S. Auerbach, R. Aviv, R. Blankenbecler and R. Sugar, Phys. Rev. Lett. 29, 522 (1972); Phys. Rev. D6, 2216 (1972); R. Sugar, Phys. Rev. D (to be published); S. Auerbach (U. C. Berkeley Preprint).

5. For every diagram shown in this paper one must add a sum over all possible ways of attaching the exchanged mesons to the world lines of the incident particles.

6. H. M. Fried, Phys. Rev. D3, 2010 (1971).

7. S. J. Chang and S. Ma, Phys. Rev. Lett. 22, 1334 (1969); Phys. Rev. 188, 2385 (1969); A. Cheng and T.T. Wu, Phys. Rev. 186, 1611 (1969); H. D. I. Abarbanel and C. I. Itzykson, Phys. Rev. Lett. 23, 53 (1969).

8. H. Cheng and T. T. Wu, Phys. Rev. D1, 2775 (1970).

9. B. Hasslocher et al., Phys. Rev. Lett. 25, 1591 (1970); G. Cicuta and R. Sugar, Phys. Rev. D3, 970 (1971); B. Hasslocher and D. K. Sinclair, Phys. Rev. D3, 1770 (1971).

10. G. Tiktopoulos and S. B. Treiman, Phys. Rev. D3, 1037 (1971).

11. H. Cheng and T. T. Wu, Phys. Rev. Lett. 24, 1456 (1970).

12. S. J. Chang and T. M. Yan, Phys. Rev. Lett. 25, 1586 (1970); Phys. Rev. D4, 537 (1971).

13. R. Blankenbecler and H. M. Fried, Phys. Rev. D, (to be published).

14. J. Botke, D. Scalapino, R. Sugar, Phys. Rev. D, (to be published).

15. J. A. Skard and J. R. Fulco, Phys. Rev. D (to be published).

16. In general the indices k and ℓ can be continuous.

17. B. J. Kirby and H. M. Fried (to be published).

18. R. C. Hwa, Phys. Rev. Lett. 26, 1143 (1971); M. Jacob and R. Slansky, Phys. Rev. D5, 1847 (1972).

19. V. N. Gribov, Zh. Eksp. Teor. Fiz. 53, 654 (1967) (Soviet Phys. JETP 26, 414 (1968). See also S. Mandelstam, Nuovo Cimento 30, 1127, 1143 (1963), and A. R. White, Nuclear Physics B37, 432, 461 (1968).

20. R. Blankenbecler, SLAC - PUB 1282.

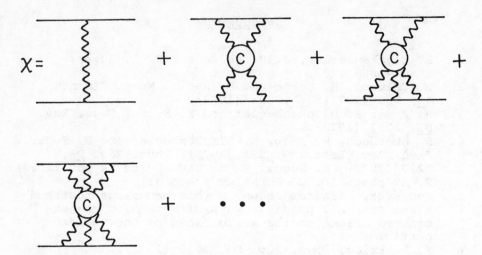

$\chi =$

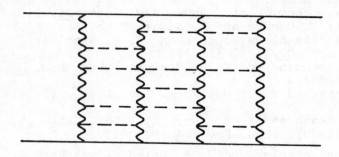

Fig. 1: The diagrams contributing to the eikonal phase. The circles represent connected t-channel amplitudes.

Fig. 2: A checkerboard diagram

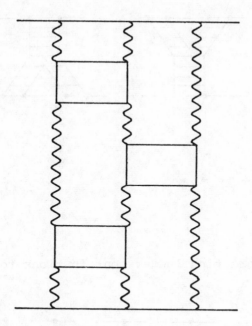

Fig. 3: A typical QED diagram involving the exchange of three interacting photons.

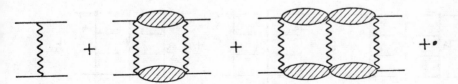

Fig. 4. Typical fragmentation graphs

606

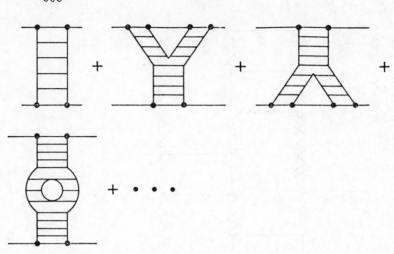

Fig. 5(a): Interacting ladder contributions to the eikonal phase.

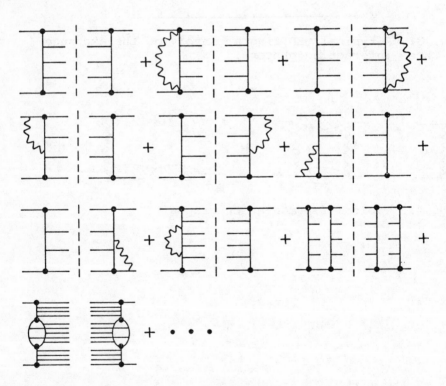

Fig. 5(b): Lowest order intermediate states with no large rapidity gaps.

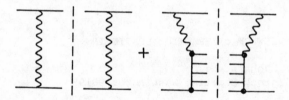

Fig. 5(c): Lowest order intermediate states with one
large gap.

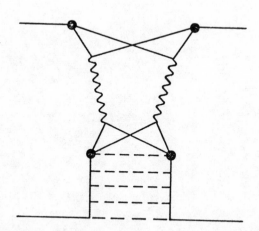

Fig. 6: An illustration of the close connection
between the triple Regge and Mandelstam.

608

REGGEON CALCULUS VIEW OF DIFFRACTION SCATTERING[*]

John N. Ng
University of Washington, Seattle, Washington 98195

ABSTRACT

Gribov's theory of the Pomeranchon is briefly reviewed. It is then demonstrated that the recent observed rise in
proton-proton total cross section at CERN ISR and the various
structures in the elastic cross section can be simultaneously
explained within the framework of this theory.

[*] Supported in part by the U. S. Atomic Energy Commission.

In this talk we assume the existence of a simple factorizable Regge pole (the Pomeranchukon) $\alpha(t)$ with intercept $\alpha(0)=1$. Associated with this pole are multi-Reggeon cuts required by t-channel unitarity. Such a j-plane structure leads to a $2 \to 2$ scattering amplitude $T(s,t)$ which for large s and small t can be expressed in a power series of $1/\xi$ where $\xi = \ln s/s_o$ and s_o is the Regge energy scale taken to be $1(\text{GeV/c})^2$. We begin by considering the two-body scattering process

$$P_a + P_b \longrightarrow P_c + P_d \tag{1}$$

If the amplitude is dominated by a Regge pole exchange in the t-channel as depicted in Fig. 1, the high energy behavior is given by

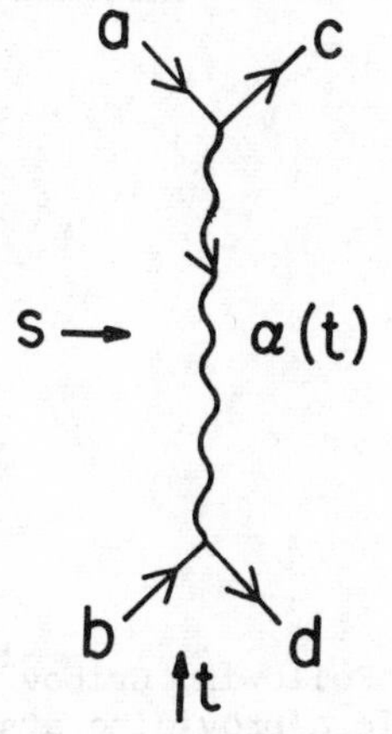

$$\frac{T(s,t)}{8\pi s} \xrightarrow[s \to \infty]{} g_a(t)\, g_b(t) \times \left(\frac{s}{s_o}\right)^{\alpha(t)-1} \eta(\alpha(t)) \tag{2}$$

Fig. 1
One Reggeon
exchange diagram

where $\alpha(t)$ is the trajectory exchanged and η is the signature factor given by

$$\eta(j) = -\frac{e^{-\frac{i\pi j}{2}}}{\sin\frac{\pi j}{2}} \tag{3}$$

for a positive signatured trajectory.

The partial wave amplitude $T(j,t)$ corresponding to Eq. (2) is

$$T(j,t) = \frac{g_a(t)\, g_b(t)}{j - \alpha(t)}$$

$$= \frac{g_a(t)\, g_b(t)}{\omega + \alpha' \vec{k}^2} \tag{4}$$

where $\omega \equiv j-1$ and we have assumed a linear trajectory for $\alpha(t)$ and $t \simeq -\vec{\kappa}^2$ with $\vec{\kappa}$ being a two-dimensional space-like vector perpendicular to the incident momenta. The two dimensional character of the momentum transfer vector can best be seen by expanding it in terms of two large Sudakov vectors p'_a and p'_b and a two-dimensional vector transverse to them. Explicitly,

$$P'_b = P_b - \frac{m^2}{s} P_a$$

and

$$P'_a = P_a - \frac{m^2}{s} P_b$$

Then, it is easily seen that

$$k \simeq \frac{t}{s}(P'_b - P'_a) + \vec{k}_\perp \tag{5}$$

and for small t and large s, $t \equiv -\kappa^2 \simeq \vec{\kappa}^2$. Following Gribov[1,2] we can interpret Eq. (7) as an external particle, a, providing a source $g_a(\kappa^2)$ for the production of a non-relativistic two-dimensional quasi-particle of energy $-\omega$ and momentum $\vec{\kappa}$ which subsequently decays into the sink $g_b(\kappa^2)$ provided by particle b.

The next order of diagram is depicted in Fig. 2. It corresponds to particle a emitting two virtual quasi-particles which propagate freely until they are absorbed by the sink at the other external particle b. Now we have a new vertex $N_{ac}(\vec{\kappa}_1, \vec{\kappa}_2)$ which describes the two particle-two Reggeon coupling.

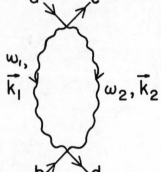

Fig. 2 Two Reggeon exchange diagram.

The partial wave amplitude corresponding to this diagram is given by[2]

$$T(\omega,\vec{k}) = \int \frac{d\omega_1}{2\pi i} \int d\omega_2 \int \frac{d^2\vec{k}_1}{\pi} \int d^2\vec{k}_2 \ \delta(\omega-\omega_1-\omega_2) \cdot$$

$$\frac{\gamma(\omega_1,\omega_2) \ \delta^2(\vec{k}-\vec{k}_1-\vec{k}_2) \ N_{ac}^{(2)}(\omega_1,\vec{k}_1;\omega_2,\vec{k}_2) \ N_{bd}^{(2)}(\omega_1,\vec{k}_1;\omega_2,\vec{k}_2)}{(\omega_1 + \alpha' \vec{k}_1^2)(\omega_2 + \alpha' \vec{k}_2^2)}$$

(6)

where

$$\gamma(\omega_1,\omega_2) = -\frac{\cos\frac{\pi}{2}(\omega_1+\omega_2)}{\cos\frac{\pi}{2}\omega_1 \ \cos\frac{\pi}{2}\omega_2}$$

(7)

The interpretation of Eq. (6) is clear. The integral runs over all energies ω_i consistent with energy-momentum conservation, and $D_0(\omega_i) = (\omega_i + \alpha'\vec{k}_i^2)^{-1}$ denotes the i-th Reggeon propagator and the N's give the amplitude for the production of two Reggeons from the external particles. The generalization of Eq. (6) to n-Reggeon exchanges is obvious. The n-Reggeons generated by particle a need not propagate freely. They can interact with each other via a vertex $\Gamma^{mn}(\omega_1',\vec{k}_1',\cdots\omega_n',\vec{k}_n';\omega_1,\vec{k}_1,\cdots\omega_m,\vec{k}_m)$ and m Reggeon results

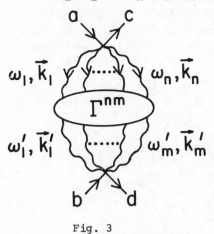

Fig. 3

General Reggeon exchange diagram including Reggeon interactions

from the interaction to be absorbed by particle b. The process is shown in Fig. 3. We shall restrict ourselves to the simplest example of Γ^{mn}; namely, the triple Regge vertex Γ shown in Fig. 4. Gribov and Migdal[3] have shown that if the full Reggeon propagator were to have a pole at $\omega = -\alpha'\vec{k}^2$ then the full triple Regge vertex $\Gamma(\omega_1,\vec{k}_1,\omega_2,\vec{k}_2,\omega,\vec{k})$ must vanish when ω_1,ω_2 and $\vec{k}_1$ and $\vec{k}_2$ are equal to zero. Hence, for small values of ω_i and κ_i we have

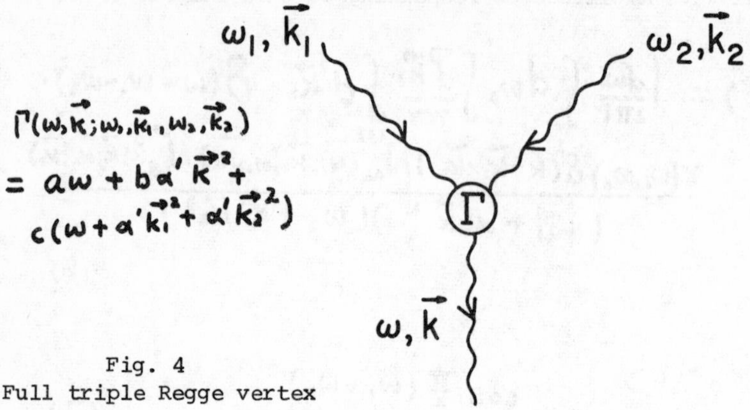

$$\omega_1, \vec{k}_1 \qquad \omega_2, \vec{k}_2$$

$$\Gamma(\omega,\vec{k};\omega_1,\vec{k}_1,\omega_2,\vec{k}_2)$$

$$= a\omega + b\alpha'\vec{k}^2 +$$
$$c(\omega + \alpha'\vec{k}_1^2 + \alpha'\vec{k}_2^2)$$

$$\boxed{\Gamma}$$

(8)

$$\omega, \vec{k}$$

Fig. 4
Full triple Regge vertex

The high energy ($s \to \infty$) and small fixed t behavior of the scattering amplitude T due to a particular Reggeon diagram is then obtained by first calculating the discontinuity $\Delta T(\omega, \vec{k}^2)$ corresponding to that diagram and then taking the Mellin transform, i.e.

$$\frac{T}{8\pi s} = \int \frac{d\omega}{2\pi i} e^{\omega\xi} (i + \tan\tfrac{\pi}{2}\omega) \Delta T(\omega, t)$$

(9)

The contour of integration encircles the singularities of $T(\omega, \vec{k})$ in left ω plane and $\Delta T(\omega, \vec{k})$ is taken across these singularities. To obtain $\Delta T(\omega, \vec{k})$ for a given Reggeon diagram, we just cut across all Reggeon lines in all possible ways and substitute $\delta(\omega_i + \alpha' \kappa_i^2)$ for each of the cut Reggeon propagators. The discontinuity across the two-Reggeon cut is depicted in Fig. 5. The two particle-two-Regge $N_{ac}(\kappa_1, \kappa_2)$ can be decomposed as in Fig. 6

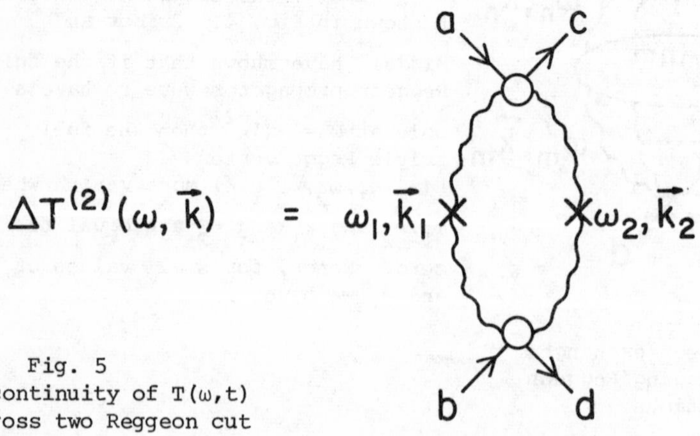

$$\Delta T^{(2)}(\omega, \vec{k}) = \omega_1, \vec{k}_1 \times \qquad \times \omega_2, \vec{k}_2$$

Fig. 5
Discontinuity of $T(\omega, t)$
across two Reggeon cut

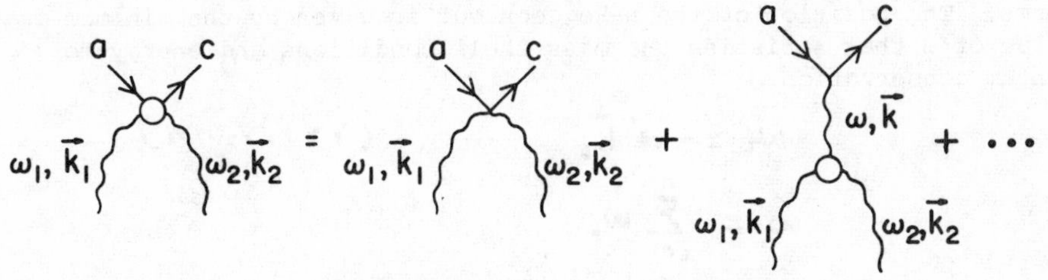

Fig. 6

Decomposition of two particle-two Reggeon amplitude

The first term if Fig. 6 corresponds to bare two Regge-two particle coupling N_o. Using Eqs. (6), (8), and (9) together with the cutting rule, we obtain

$$\text{Im} \frac{T^{(2)}}{8\pi s} = e^{-2z} g(t) \left[1 - \frac{b'z}{\alpha'_3} \left\{ b' + (a + b'z + \frac{N(t)}{g(t)})(\ln \gamma_3 + \int_0^z du \frac{e^u - 1}{u}) \right\} \right]$$
$$- \frac{e^2}{4\alpha'_3} \left[g^2(t) \{ a^2 - 4zb'^2 \} + N(t) \{ N(t) + 2ag(t) \} \right]$$

where $b' \equiv b - a$, $z = \frac{1}{2} \alpha'_3 \vec{k}^2$, $\ln \gamma = 0.5772$ (10)

and $\quad \Gamma(\omega, \vec{k}^2) = a\omega + b\alpha' \vec{k}^2$ (11)

corresponding to the contribution of the two Reggeon cut diagrams given in Fig. 7. a and b are defined by the triple Regge vertex

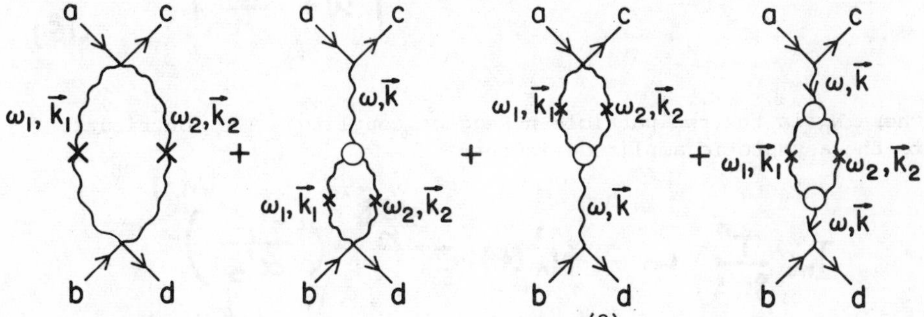

Fig 7.   Dominant contributions to $\Delta T^{(2)}(\omega, t)$

Including the pole term and using the optical theorem, we obtain the following result for the total cross section

$$\sigma_{tot}(s) = 8\pi \left\{ g^2(0) - \frac{1}{4\alpha'_3} \left[N + a g(0) \right]^2 + O(\frac{1}{3^2}) \right.$$

          ....(12)

In the same manner we can calculate the n-Reggeon exchange cut terms. The position of the n-Reggeon cut is given by the minimum value of ω that satisfies the mass-shell conditions and energy-momentum conservation

$$\omega_i = -\alpha' \vec{k}_i^2 \qquad (i = 1, \cdots n)$$

$$\omega = \sum_{i=1}^{n} \omega_i$$

$$\vec{k} = \sum_{i=1}^{n} k_i \tag{13}$$

This threshold occurs when the $\underline{\kappa}_i$'s share the momentum equally, i.e., $\underline{\kappa}_i = \underline{\kappa}/n$ and thus

$$\omega = \frac{\alpha' \vec{k}^2}{n} \tag{14}$$

Hence the discontinuity across the n-Reggeon cut is

$$\Delta T^{(n)}(\omega, \vec{k}) \cong \frac{(-1)^{n-1}}{\alpha'^{n-1}} N_n^2(\vec{k}) \, \theta\left(-\omega - \frac{\alpha' \vec{k}^2}{n}\right) \cdot \left| \omega + \frac{\alpha' \vec{k}^2}{n} \right|^{n-2} \tag{15}$$

where N_n is the two particle-n Reggeon coupling. The contribution to the asymptotic amplitude is then

$$\text{Im} \frac{T^n}{8\pi s} \sim N_n^2(t) \, e^{-\frac{\alpha' \vec{k}^2}{n}} \left(\frac{-1}{\alpha' \xi}\right)^{n-1} \tag{16}$$

The contribution to the total cross section is then of the order of $(-1/\alpha'\xi)^{n-1}$. The above formula is obtained from the approximation that $\alpha'\xi \gg 1$ and $\alpha'\kappa^2\xi < 1$ provided N_n does not contain Reggeon interactions such as in the second term of Fig. 6. Gribov and Migdal[3] have shown that including Reggeon interactions in N_n does not change the result if all the Γ^{nm} vanish when ω and $\vec{\kappa}$ approaches zero.[4] Hence we conclude that the dominant contribution to $T(s,t)$ comes from the pole term plus those given in Eq. (11). Now we have an amplitude of high energy scattering expressed in terms of the Regge residue function $g(t)$ and the two particle-two Reggeon coupling $N_o(\vec{\kappa})$ which cannot be determined in a model independent way, but must be parameterized.

Before we compare with the experiments, we note several general features of the theory independent of the parameters: a) the total cross section rises to a constant from below as given by Eq. (12). b) The imaginary part of the doubly scattered term, Fig. 2, is negative and hence interferes destructively with the single scattering term of Fig. 1 to produce a dip in the differential cross section. The exact location of the dip depends on the parameters. The branch cut in the angular momentum plane is logarithmic. c) The real part of the forward scattering amplitude approaches zero as $\xi \to \infty$ like B/ξ^2 where B is a positive constant. d) Equation (10) for the imaginary part of the scattering amplitude indicates clearly the existence of some structure in the angular distribution near the forward region. However, this structure depends on the particular parameterization of the triple Regge vertex and residue functions; and a break in the slope of $d\sigma/dt$ cannot be regarded as a prediction of the theory. e) The vanishing of the triple Regge vertex is required by consistency thus is a general feature of the theory. The recent experimental results[5] from CERN ISR on proton-proton collision show some of the above mentioned features. The total cross section is found to rise by about 4 mb from s = 548 to 2776 $(GeV/c)^2$. A pronounced dip appears at $|t| \stackrel{\sim}{\scriptstyle\wedge} 1.4$ and subsequent bump at $|t| \stackrel{\sim}{\scriptstyle\wedge} 2$ both of which show very little variation in s dependence. We show[6,7] that all these can be very well explained within the framework of Gribov's theory. In fitting the ISR data we have chosen the following forms for the two unknown functions $g(t)$ and $N_o(t)$:

$$g(t) = g(0) e^{R^2 t}$$

$$N(t) = N(0) e^{\beta R^2 t} \tag{17}$$

where R^2 corresponds to the Regge radius, β is chosen to be 1/2 in accordance with single-pole approximation for $N(t)$. The triple Regge vertex Γ used is given by (11) without further t-dependence given to a and b. The slope of the Pomerachukon is chosen to be $\alpha' = .37$ as given in (5). We find a good fit for all the ISR data $[s = 548, 932, 2005, 2776 (GeV/c)^2]$ with the following values of the parameters:

$$g^2(0) = 3.75 \ (mb)^{\frac{1}{2}} \ (GeV/c)^{-1}$$

$$N(0) = 4.72 \ (mb)^{\frac{1}{4}} \ (GeV/c)^{-3/2}$$

$$R^2 = 1.54 \ (GeV/c)^{-2}$$

$$a = -4.2 \ (GeV/c)^{-1}$$

$$b = 3.99 \ (GeV/c)^{-1}$$

Some examples of our fit are given in Figs. 8-10. For detailed com-

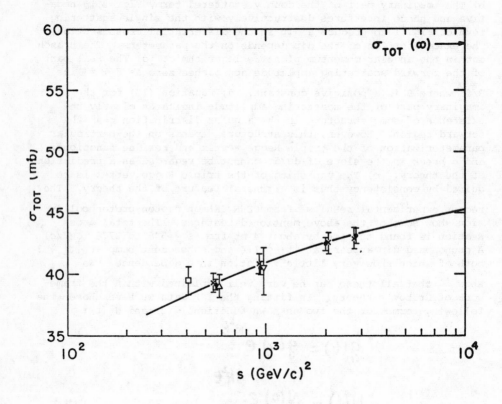

Fig. 8

Fit to pp total cross section
using Gribov's theory. Data obtained from Ref. 5.

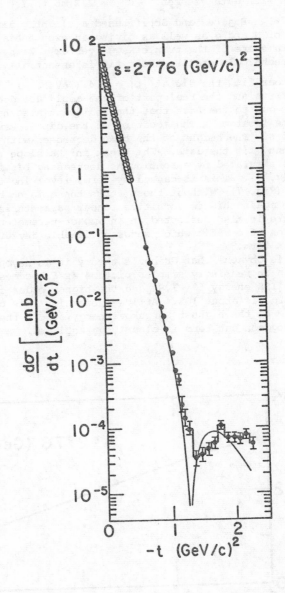

Fig. 9

pp differential cross section at s = 2776 $(GeV/c)^2$.
[Ref. 5]   The curve is given by Gribov's theory.

618

parison with data see ref. 5 σ_{el} = 7.2 mb to 7.6 mb (s = 548, s = 2776). Pajares and Schiff used a slightly different parameterization of N and g as well as giving an exponential t-dependence for the parameters of the triple Regge vertex. With the exception of these technical details, their fit is essentially the same as ours.

In our fit[6] the dip at $|t|$ = 1.4 $(GeV/c)^2$ is caused by a zero in Im T/8πs and the real part of the amplitude does not fill it up. This is due to the fact that the real part also has a zero near the same location. The location of the dip is essentially independent of s. The height of the bump decreases with increasing s in agreement with the data. The break in the slope of the diffraction peak is simulated by a continuous decreasing b(s,t) 13.1 to 11.8 (see Fig. 9). This is caused by terms involving the triple-Regge vertex (Fig. 7); without these terms there is no break. We emphasize again this is sensitive to our parameterization. This structure is also reflected in an impact-parameter (b-space) representation of our fit which shows noticeable deviation from a Gaussian form.[8]

It is obvious that Gribov's theory is an asymptotic theory that gives an increasingly simpler picture as ξ becomes large. At the highest ISR energy ξ = 7.92 and the higher order correction, i.e. $1/\xi^2$ term, is about 10%. At lower energies this correction is larger. At the highest Serpukov energy, ξ ≈ 5 the omission of the three-Reggeon cut term is clearly unjustified. A good fit of the

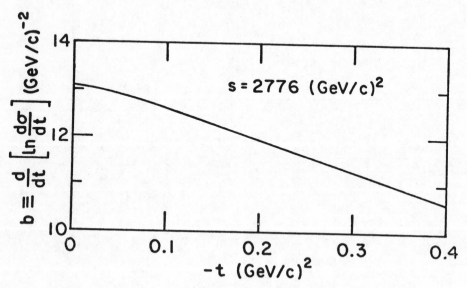

Fig. 10
The slope function b(s,t) is plotted
against −t at s = 2776 $(GeV/c)^2$

total cross section will take the form

$$\sigma_{tot} = 8\pi\left\{ \hat{g}^2(0) - \frac{1}{4\alpha'\xi}(N_0 + a\hat{g}(0))^2 + \frac{N_3}{(\alpha'\xi)^2} \right\}$$

where N_3 is some effective three-Reggeon cut term, just like the parameter N_0 should be regarded as an effective two Reggeon-two particle coupling. Furthermore, for $|t|$ near the region of the bump $\alpha'\xi\vec{\kappa}^2 \approx 6$ at $s = 2776$ (GeV/c)^2 and thus one is stretching Gribov's theory here. However, ISR gives the best data presently available to test out Gribov's theory. On the other hand, we can apply the same model to other reactions ($\kappa p, \pi p$, etc.). Many of the parameters (a, b, α', s_0) are reaction-independent. Thus measurements of reactions involving the Pomeranchuk exchange at highest NAL energy will provide important checks of the general features of Gribov's theory.

ACKNOWLEDGEMENT

I wish to thank Professor M. Baker and Dr. U. Sukhatme for many useful discussions and help in preparing this talk.

REFERENCES

1. V. N. Gribov, Zh. Eksp. Teor. Fiz. 53, 654 (1967) [Sov. Phys. JETP 26, 414 (1968)].

2. For a particularly lucid presentation of Reggeon calculus, see M. Baker, talk given at the VIII Recontre de Moriond, France, March 1973 (to be published).

3. V. N. Gribov and A. A. Migdal, Yad. Fiz. 8, 1002 (1968) [Sov. J. Nucl. Phys. 8, 583 (1969)].

4. The vertex Γ^{14} which corresponds to one Reggeon decaying into four identical Reggeons gives rise to a term of the order of $1/\xi$ and should be included in the calculation, see ref. 2. However, phenomenologically we have found no necessity of including such a term which introduces one extra parameter.

5. Data from Rubbia group presented at 16th International Conference on High Energy Physics, Chicago, Illinois, Sept. 1972. G. Barbiellini et al., Phys. Letters 39B, 663 (1972); U. Amaldi et al., Phys. Letters 44B, 112 (1973); and S. R. Amendolia et al., Phys. Letters 44B, 119 (1973).

620

6. U. P. Sukhatme and J. N. Ng, University of Washington preprint RLO-1388-654.

7. C. Pajares and D. Schiff, Orsay preprint (to be published).

8. C. Pajares and U. P. Sukhatme (private communication).

PERTURBATIVE APPROACH TO HIGH-ENERGY MULTIPARTICLE REACTIONS

William R. Frazer
University of California, San Diego
La Jolla, California 92037

ABSTRACT

Two-component models have been quite successful in fitting multiplicity distributions in high-energy hadronic collisions. The fact that the diffractive component is considerably smaller than the short-range-correlation component suggests the possibility of a perturbative expansion of the high-energy total cross section. The development of such an expansion is discussed, as well as some of its consequences.

Two-component models have been quite successful in fitting multiplicity distributions in high-energy hadronic collisions.[1-3] The fact that the diffractive component is considerably smaller than the short-range correlation (SRC) component suggests the possibility of a perturbative expansion of the high-energy total cross section. Although it is now easy to motivate a perturbative treatment by reference to two-component fits to data, in fact the idea was already present in the work of Chew and Pignotti,[4] and has been further developed by Chew and a series of collaborators.[5-7] The wealth of data from NAL and the ISR, which provide the prospect of measurement of the small parameter (or parameters) of the expansion and possibly of direct observation of some of the higher-order terms, has stimulated current developments by several authors which I shall review in this talk.[8-15]

In this brief talk I shall concentrate on the definition of the expansion, the description of a few of the low-order terms, and some estimates of their magnitude. I will not attempt to face the technical difficulties nor the celebrated paradoxes encountered when one attempts to sum the series and discuss its asymptotic behavior. Interesting and important as these problems are, they are probably not relevant to what is happening at NAL or ISR energies.[16]

Two-component models have used a variety of prescriptions for separating the SRC and diffractive components.[1-3] As measurements become more refined we must define terms such as "diffractive component" with more care if we are to avoid propagating confusion. A decomposition of the cross section which is conceptually simple and directly related to experimentally measurable quantities is the decomposition in terms of the number of large rapidity gaps.

Following Chew,[17] we decompose the total cross section according to the number of large rapidity gaps (larger than a specified Δ) observed in a given event. For example, Fig. 1 shows a three-gap event, provided that z_2, z_4, and z_6 are greater than Δ .

622

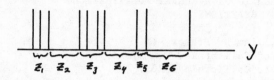

The total cross section can then be decomposed unambiguously according to the number of large gaps,

$$\sigma_{ab}(s) = \sigma_{ab}^{0,\Delta}(s) + \sigma_{ab}^{1,\Delta}(s) + \cdots . \tag{1}$$

Pictorially, we can represent this decomposition as follows:

$$\text{(2)}$$

where the symbol ⊖ represents the forward absorptive elastic amplitude $A(s) = s\sigma(s)$, and where the symbol ⊗ represents a cluster of particles produced with no large rapidity gaps. The wiggly line ∿ represents a Pomeron, the assumption being that Δ is chosen sufficiently large that Pomeron exchange dominates the production of such large rapidity gaps.

It is useful to make a further decomposition of the gapless clusters into those of high invariant mass, denoted by ▭▭▭ and those of low invariant mass, denoted by ‖ . Pictorially,

$$\otimes = \| + \text{▭▭▭} . \tag{3}$$

Equivalently, one can separate the clusters according to their spread in rapidity. For example, looking back at Fig. 1, one sees two high-mass and two low-mass clusters, provided that z_1 and z_3 are greater than some specified Δ_c , and that $z_5 < \Delta_c$.

Inserting Eq. (3) into Eq. (2) we then have the following decomposition, at high energies,

$$\text{(4)}$$

| SRC | elastic plus low-mass diff. dissoc. | diff. dissoc. into one high-mass and one low-mass cluster |

The three terms written explicitly on the r.h.s. of Eq. (4) correspond to those processes which have already been observed: the SRC component, elastic scattering, diffractive dissociation into low masses, and finally diffractive dissociation into high masses. The remaining terms are considerably smaller; some of them may nevertheless be detectable. I will return to this point later.

What is the utility of the decomposition in Eq. (4)? Three classes of applications have been made or attempted: a) Discussion of individual terms, their order of magnitude, their properties (I will specialize to these questions in the remainder of this talk); b) Attempts to sum the series, usually in simplified models (Koplik will discuss a factorizable model in the next talk); and c) Attempts at truly self-consistent calculations, in which the input Pomeron is equated to the asymptotic limit of the sum of the series.[18] This, too, has been accomplished only in simplified models, such as the Ball-Zachariasen model.[19]

Let us turn now to consideration of the terms in Eq. (4):

SRC component: In model calculations, and according to plausible general arguments, the asymptotic energy dependence of the no-gap component is governed by a simple Regge pole with intercept slightly below $J = 1$, the "bare" Pomeron.[20,21] Therefore, this component should remain constant, or decrease slightly with increasing energy. On the other hand, Gaisser and Tan have suggested that $N\bar{N}$ production through a multiperipheral mechanism could account for the rising pp cross section at the ISR energies.[21] In this case, the SRC component would rise in this range. At any rate, the energy dependence of the SRC component is an interesting question which can be settled experimentally in the near future.

I have been using the terms "SRC component" and "no-gap component" interchangeably. Their approximate equivalence is indeed implied by models, but again this should be checked experimentally.

Elastic scattering and low-mass diffraction dissociation: There is very little new that I can say concerning elastic scattering or low-mass dissociation. Perturbative calculations of elastic scattering await an adequate zeroth approximation about which to perturb.

Diffraction dissociation into high missing mass: Consider now the third term on the r.h.s. of Eq. (4), in the simplest case where the low-mass cluster is a single particle identical to the incoming particle; that is, single diffractive dissociation into high missing mass. If one assumes that the Pomeron is reasonably well represented by an effective Regge pole, one obtains for this process the usual triple-Regge formula,

$$\frac{d\sigma}{dM^2 dt} = \frac{G_P^0(t)}{16\pi s^2} \left(\frac{s}{M^2}\right)^{2\alpha_P(t)} (M^2)^{\alpha_0(0)} \tag{5}$$

where $\alpha_0(0)$ is the bare Pomeron intercept, and

$$G_P^0(t) \equiv \beta_{bbP}^2(t) \, \beta_{aa0}(0) \, |\xi_P(t)|^2 \, g_{PP0}(t) , \tag{6}$$

where $g_{PP0}(t)$ is the function describing the vertex of two Pomerons and one bare Pomeron.

From Eq. (5) one easily finds that the contribution to the total cross section of diffraction dissociation to high-mass states, $\sigma_{D,M > M_0}$, rises approximately proportional to ℓns over the energy range in which

$$2\alpha_p' \, \ell n(s/M_0^2) \ll d \, G_P^0(t)/d \, \ell nt . \tag{7}$$

Since the slope of the Pomeranchuk trajectory is small, this criterion should be approximately valid over the N.A.L.-I.S.R. energy range. In this case the rate of increase of the diffractive component is

$$\frac{d\sigma_{D,M > M_0}}{d \, \ell ns} \approx \frac{1}{16\pi} \int_{-\infty}^{0} dt \, G_P^0(t) \equiv \bar{G}_p/16\pi \tag{8}$$

Several authors have attempted to associate this increasing diffractive cross section with the observed rise in the total pp cross section.[8-15] This, of course, assumes that the SRC and low-mass diffractive contributions remain constant. Theorists can exhibit models in which (a) the rise in diffractive dissociation to high masses is indeed reflected in a logarithmically rising cross section (Ball-Zachariasen model[19]); (b) the SRC portion falls just enough to compensate for the rise, and results in a constant total cross section (classical multiperipheral model); and (c) the remainder of the cross section falls by twice as much as the diffractive part rises, resulting in a decreasing total cross section![22] Experimentalists can settle the issue by measuring the energy dependence of $\sigma^{0,\Delta}(s)$ and $\sigma^{1,\Delta}(s)$, the cross sections with no large rapidity gaps and with one (or more) large gap(s).

A second test of whether the rising total cross section is accounted for by high-mass diffraction is the independent measurement of the triple-Pomeron coupling. To account for the entire rising cross section one requires $\bar{G}_p/16\pi \approx 1mb$. Preliminary indications are that the triple-Pomeron coupling is in fact smaller by at least a factor 2.[24]

Another interesting property of high-mass diffraction in this picture is the multiplicity distribution of the dissociation products. At a function of missing mass M^2, the average multiplicity of particles produced in dissociation should rise proportional to ℓnM^2, with the same coefficient as the coefficient of ℓns in the total multiplicity.[10] More detailed predictions are made by specific multiperipheral-type models; generally speaking, they amount to saying that the "Pomeron-hadron cross section" should behave very similarly to an ordinary hadron-hadron cross section. This seems to be borne out by the results presented at this Conference by Winkelmann and by Whitmore.

Diffraction dissociation into high masses results in large multiplicity of dissociation products, which tend to fill in the dip in the multiplicity distribution expected by Wilson.[23] For example, Fig. 2 shows the multiplicity distribution which results in one specific model. The contribution of low-mass dissociation is not included, however.

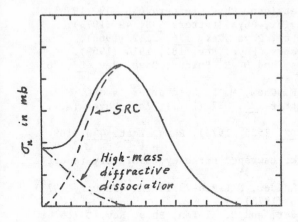

Fig. 2. Multiplicity distribution in model of Frazer and Snider.[10]

Higher-order terms: The expansion parameter in our perturbative approach can be identified as

$$\bar{\eta}_P \equiv \frac{1}{16\pi} \int_{-\infty}^{0} g_{PP0}^2(t) \ . \tag{9}$$

A generous estimate, obtained by associating the rising cross section with high-mass diffraction, gives $\bar{\eta}_p \approx .002$. Higher-order terms are therefore quite small even at ISR energies (they grow with powers of $\ell n s$, as long as Eq. (7) is valid). The next-largest term, after those we have already discussed, is probably the one with two large gaps, but no high-mass clusters produced; that is, ▭▭▭ . The largest singlet component of this is the one where there is a leading single particle on each end, ▭▭ . This diagram represents an inclusive process, in which two leading particles are observed; for example, in pp scattering one could look for events in which one proton has $x > 0.95$ and one proton has $x < -0.95$ (but excluding elastic events), thus guaranteeing rapidity gaps greater than 3 units on each end. My own generous estimate of this process is that it should be a fraction of a millibarn.[11] At this Conference a search for one particular exclusive channel of this type, $\pi^- p \to \pi^- \pi^+ \pi^- p$ with fast π^- and slow p , was reported by D. M. Chew. She found an upper limit of about 50µb for this channel.

I think it would be very interesting to observe this reaction, since it is an example of double Pomeron exchange, a process not contained in the optical picture of high-energy scattering. As evidence mounts that the Pomeron is at least in part a factorizable singularity of the S-matrix, it becomes increasingly difficult to avoid inferring that double (and multiple) Pomeron exchange processes exist. Nevertheless, direct observation of such a process would be a valuable stimulus toward further efforts to understand the Pomeron.

REFERENCES

1. W. Frazer, R. Peccei, S. Pinsky, and C. -I Tan, Phys. Rev. $\underline{D7}$, 2647 (1973).
2. K. Fiałkowski and H. Miettinen, Phys. Letters $\underline{43B}$, 49 (1973).
3. H. Harari and E. Rabinovici, Phys. Letters $\underline{43B}$, 49 (1973).
4. G. F. Chew and A. Pignotti, Phys. Rev. $\underline{176}$, 2112 (1968).
5. G. F. Chew and W. R. Frazer, Phys. Rev. $\underline{181}$, 1914 (1969).
6. G. F. Chew, T. W. Rogers, and D. R. Snider, Phys. Rev. $\underline{D2}$, 765 (1970).
7. H. D. I. Abarbanel, G. F. Chew, M. L. Goldberger, and L. M. Saunders, Phys. Rev. Letters $\underline{26}$, 937 (1971); Ann. Phys. (N.Y.) $\underline{73}$, 156 (1972).
8. G. F. Chew, Phys. Rev. $\underline{D7}$, 3525 (1973); Phys. Lett. $\underline{44B}$, 169 (1973).
9. M Bishari and J. Koplik, Lawrence Berkeley Laboratory report LBL-1702 (Feb. 1973).
10. W. R. Frazer and D. R. Snider, NAL-Pub-73/15/THY (January 1973) and Phys. Lett. $\underline{45B}$, 136 (1973).
11. W. R. Frazer, D. R. Snider, and C. -I Tan, Phys. Rev. $\underline{D}$ (to be published Nov. 1973).
12. A. Capella, SLAC-PUB-1198 (1973).
13. A. Capella, M.-S. Chen, M. Kugler, and R. Peccei, Phys. Rev. Lett. $\underline{31}$, 497 (1973).
14. Chih Kwan Chen, unpublished.
15. Jan Dash, Argonne preprint.
16. J. Finkelstein and K. Kajantie, Nuovo Cim. $\underline{56A}$, 659 (1968); R. C. Brower and J. H. Weis, Phys. Letters $\underline{41B}$, 631 (1972).
17. G. F. Chew, Phys. Rev. $\underline{D7}$, 934 (1973).
18. See the reviews by F. Zachariasen, Physics Reports $\underline{2C}$, 1 (1971) and Cal Tech preprint CALT-68-385 (March 1973).
19. J. S. Ball and F. Zachariasen, Phys. Lett. $\underline{40B}$, 411 (1972).
20. Joel Koplik, Phys. Rev. $\underline{D7}$, 558 (1973).
21. T. K. Gaisser and C. -I Tan, Brookhaven preprint BNL 18070.
22. R. Sugar, talk at this Conference; R. Blankenbecler, J. R. Fulco, and R. Sugar, SLAC-PUB-1281; R. Blankenbecler, SLAC-PUB-1282.
23. K. G. Wilson, unpublished.
24. See the review by Geoffrey Fox in the Proceedings of this year's Stony Brook Conference.

THRESHOLD EFFECTS AND OSCILLATIONS IN MODELS
WITH t-CHANNEL FACTORIZATION*†

Joel Koplik
Lawrence Berkeley Laboratory, University of California
Berkeley, California 94720

ABSTRACT

We review threshold effects and oscillating cross
sections in the context of models (such as the multiperipheral) which employ factorization and indefinite
repetition in the t-channel. The origin of logarithmic
energy thresholds is illustrated by the ABFST model and
applied to antibaryon production and rising cross
sections at high energy. We then discuss large-mass
diffraction dissociation and argue that this process is
not responsible for the increase in the p-p total
cross section at ISR energies.

I. INTRODUCTION

Recent experimental results from ISR have shown an unexpected
energy dependence in (at least) two quantities: the production of
antibaryons and the p-p total cross section. One interpretation
of these phenomena, suggested by Sivers and von Hippel,[1] Suzuki,[2]
and by Gaisser and Tan,[3] is to regard the former as a threshold
effect and the latter as its consequence. We will review the origin
of dynamical thresholds in multiperipheral models and their application to particle production and rising cross sections. A somewhat
similar idea concerns the "threshold" for large-mass diffraction
dissociation; we shall argue that such a mechanism does not involve
a genuine threshold and cannot account for the increasing p-p total
cross section. The unpublished work discussed here has been carried
out in collaboration with M. Bishari and G. F. Chew and will be
fully reported elsewhere.

II. MULTIPERIPHERAL THRESHOLDS

The origin of the threshold effects which concern us is clearly
exhibited by the pion-exchange multiperipheral model. The absorptive part of the elastic scattering amplitude is there given by the
sum indicated in Fig. 1, where the horizontal links on the right are
off-shell pions of squared-mass t_i and the circles represent $\pi\pi$
absorptive parts of subenergy s_i. Algebraically this can be

*Supported by the U.S. Atomic Energy Commission.
†Talk presented at the 1973 Berkeley meeting of the Division of
 Particles and Fields, APS.

628

written[4]

$$A(s,0) \quad \propto \quad \sum_N \int ds_A \, ds_1 \cdots ds_B \, dt_0 \cdots dt_N$$

$$\times \quad \frac{A_{\pi A}(s_A; t_0) \, A_{\pi\pi}(s_1; t_0, t_1) \cdots A_{\pi B}(s_B; t_N)}{(t_0 - m_\pi^2)^2 \cdots (t_N - m_\pi^2)^2}$$

$$\times \quad \frac{1}{N!}(Y - q_A - q_1 - \cdots - q_B)^N \, \Theta(Y - q_A - q_1 - \cdots - q_N - q_B)$$

$$(1)$$

after some internal integrations. The q_i and Y are Lorentz boosts defined by

$$\cosh Y \quad = \quad \frac{s - m_A^2 - m_B^2}{2m_A m_B}$$

$$\sinh q_{A,B} \quad = \quad \frac{s_{A,B} - m_{A,B}^2 - t_{0,N}}{2m_{A,B}\sqrt{-t_{0,N}}} \qquad (2)$$

$$\cosh q_i \quad = \quad \frac{s_i - t_{i-1} - t_i}{2\sqrt{t_{i-1}\, t_i}} \quad .$$

The step-function expresses energy conservation, and requires that the Lorentz boost Y from the rest frame of particle A to that of particle B be at least as large as the sum of the corresponding boosts q_i across each of the pion absorptive parts.

Since this is a multiperipheral model the t_i should be small, and we shall suppose that the combination of propagators and off-shell damping of the pion absorptive parts is such as to impose an effective cut-off

$$|t_i| \leq T \ll m^2 \quad .$$

In this expression m is the lowest important mass in the pion absorptive part; in the $\pi\pi$ case, for example, we have $m \approx m_\rho$.

This implies

$$\cosh q_i \gtrsim \frac{m^2}{2T} \quad ,$$

so that energy conservation requires

$$Y \gtrsim q_A + q_B + N \log \frac{m^2}{T} \quad , \tag{3}$$

and thus the increment in rapidity for adding another link is

$$\triangle \approx \log \frac{m^2}{T} \quad .$$

For future use, note that this threshold effect is more pronounced for large m. A similar argument can be made for any multiperipheral model,[5] which is essentially why these models give a logarithmic energy dependence of the multiplicity.

III. ANTIBARYON PRODUCTION

We will now apply these ideas to antibaryon production at high energy, showing how the threshold indicated by experiment can be understood in terms of our simple pion-exchange model. The experimental antibaryon cross section as a function of energy is shown in Fig. 2,[6,7] and may be roughly characterized as negligible below $s \approx 150$ GeV^2, and substantial and increasing approximately linearly in $\log s$ once the threshold is reached. A second important experimental fact[6] is that antibaryons are produced almost exclusively in the central region of rapidity, and not in association with the leading particles. Since antibaryons must be produced in $B\bar{B}$ pairs, whose mass is quite large in comparison with typical meson masses, the multiperipheral threshold mechanism just described immediately suggests itself. In the model above, antibaryon production is easily incorporated by assuming it occurs effectively through a $B\bar{B}$ resonance (or collection of resonances) near the kinematic threshold $(2m_B)$ in the $\pi\pi$ cross section, and that this resonance does not appear at the ends of the multiperipheral chain. The effective, dynamical threshold for $\bar{B}$ production in p-p collisions is then the threshold for the process shown in Fig. 3, which from Eq. (3) is

$$Y_{th} = 2q_{\pi p} + q_{B\bar{B}}$$

where

$$\sinh q_{\pi p} = \frac{\sqrt{T}}{2m_p} \quad ,$$

$$\cosh q_{B\overline{B}} = \frac{(2m_B)^2}{2T} \quad .$$

Using $T = 0.04$ GeV^2 (obtained from experimental measurements of n-p backward elastic scattering, which is controlled by pion exchange) we find $Y_{th} \approx 5.0$. This result corresponds nicely to

$\log \dfrac{150 \text{ GeV}^2}{m_p^2}$, so our simple model supports the proposal of Refs.

(2) and (3). The magnitude of the $\overline{B}$ production cross section is determined in the pion-exchange model by the cross section for the process $\pi\pi \to B\overline{B}$. We have verified[8] that the measured value of this latter cross section is indeed of the order of magnitude to account for the experimental results on $\overline{B}$ production in p-p collisions.

To estimate the effect of $\overline{B}$ production on the total cross section, it is convenient to use a further simplification of the multiperipheral model which approximates the sum over all partial cross sections which do not involve a $B\overline{B}$ pair by the leading Regge pole generated by the corresponding partial kernel. We assume this leading pole is located at $J = \alpha_0$, and it will be seen momentarily that consistency requires $\alpha_0 < 1$. Then the production of, e.g., two $B\overline{B}$ pairs, given by a sum of diagrams like those of Fig. 4a, is approximated by Fig. 4b. In addition we replace the integrated $\pi\pi \to B\overline{B}$ kernel by a coupling constant (g) and reduce the problem to the form of Ref. (5), by assuming the minimum rapidity intervals on the ends of the chain to be the same as the internal intervals (Δ). Then the N-$B\overline{B}$ pair absorptive part in A-B elastic scattering is

$$A^{(N)}(Y) = \int_\Delta^Y dy_1 \cdots \int_\Delta^Y dy_{N+1} \; \delta\left(Y - \sum_{i=1}^{N+1} y_i\right)$$

$$\times \; \beta_A \, e^{\alpha_0 y_1} \, g \, e^{\alpha_0 y_2} \, g \cdots g \, e^{\alpha_0 y_{N+1}} \, \beta_B \qquad (4)$$

$$= \; \beta_A \beta_B \, e^{\alpha_0 Y} \frac{1}{N!} \left[g\Big(Y - (N+1)\Delta\Big) \right]^N \Theta\Big(Y - (N+1)\Delta\Big) \; ,$$

where the y_i are rapidity differences and $\beta_{A,B}$ are Regge residues. The corresponding $\sigma^{(N)}(Y)$ are shown in Fig. 5.

To examine the asymptotic behavior of σ_{tot}, it is convenient to go to the J-plane. We have

$$A^{(N)}(J) \equiv \int_0^\infty dY \, e^{-JY} A^{(N)}(Y)$$

$$= \beta_A \beta_B \, g^N \left(\frac{e^{-\Delta(J-\alpha_0)}}{J - \alpha_0} \right)^{N+1} , \tag{5}$$

and the complete absorptive part is

$$A(J) \equiv \sum_{N=0}^\infty A^{(N)}(J)$$

$$= \frac{\beta_A \beta_B \, e^{-\Delta(J-\alpha_0)}}{J - \alpha_0 - g e^{-\Delta(J-\alpha_0)}} \tag{6}$$

The singularities of $A(J)$, which are the zeros of the denominator of (6), are a real pole above α_0 and an infinite sequence of complex poles to the left (see Fig. 6). The leading pole determines the asymptotic behavior of the total cross section (constant or decreasing power) and the complex poles reproduce the threshold behavior of Fig. 5, which appears as oscillations in σ_{tot}. The ratio of real to imaginary part of the amplitude also oscillates, roughly $90°$ out of phase with σ_{tot} (see Fig. 7). Note that the complex poles and resulting oscillations only arise if $\Delta \neq 0$; a genuine threshold is required. As shown in Ref. (3), if the parameters in Eqs. (4) - (6) are chosen to reproduce the B cross section and an asymptotically constant σ_{tot}, there results an increase in σ_{tot} of 5-10% above the first $\bar{B}$ threshold. One also finds a leading pair of complex poles at $J \sim \frac{1}{2} \pm i$, and this pair plus the leading real pole gives an excellent approximation for $Y \gtrsim 2$.

This result is in rough agreement with the rise in the p-p total cross section,[9] and if this mechanism is indeed the explanation the increase is seen as a transient effect and, barring new important thresholds (d$\bar{\text{d}}$ pairs?), the cross section should level off and gently oscillate to a nonincreasing asymptotic behavior.

For this to be a satisfactory explanation, one must ask why this particular threshold is so important. We suggest that there are two reasons:

1. The large mass of a B$\bar{\text{B}}$ system and the absence of $\bar{\text{B}}$'s as leading particles delays their appearance to a rather high energy when the total cross section has otherwise settled down.

2. The large magnitude of the $\pi\pi \to$ B$\bar{\text{B}}$ cross section near the B$\bar{\text{B}}$ threshold reflects an unusual concentration of resonances in this neighborhood.[8] These resonances are associated with the long-range pion exchange force that acts in the B$\bar{\text{B}}$ channel but which does not act in two-meson channels (such as $\pi\pi$, K$\bar{\text{K}}$, or $\rho\rho$). These resonances arise from the (nonrelativistic potential) mechanism that produces the low kinetic energy states of classical nuclear physics. Such a mechanism is usually ignored in high energy physics, but it has been shown to be responsible for the large B$\bar{\text{B}}$ cross sections at low kinetic energy.[10,11]

IV. TRIPLE-POMERON EFFECTS

A number of authors have argued recently that the rise in the p-p total cross section can be understood as the result of the appearance of large-mass diffraction dissociation.[12-15] This is based on the observation that the contribution of such processes to σ_{tot} is given by integrating the inclusive cross section corresponding to Fig. 8 over the region of phase space where both s and s/M^2 are large. Treating the pomeron trajectory as approximately flat and equal to 1, one finds a contribution proportional to $\langle g_p \rangle$ log s, where $\langle g_p \rangle$ is a certain average value of the triple-pomeron vertex. The measured value of $\langle g_p \rangle$ is about of the order of magnitude of the observed slope of σ_{tot}.

We would like to criticize this explanation on several different grounds. First, there are two numerical problems: (1) The predicted threshold for the increase seems to occur at too low an energy. Triple-pomeron behavior is, strictly speaking, the high-energy tail of the pomeron-particle total cross section, and the latter has the form shown in Fig. 9 [taken from Ref. (16)]. This gives $M_0^2 \approx 4$ GeV^2 as the threshold in fireball mass squared, and even taking $\Delta_p \approx 2$-3 units as the minimum rapidity gap between the proton and the fireball we would have a p-p total cross section which begins to rise at

$$Y = \Delta_p + \log M_0^2 \approx 3\text{-}4 \ .$$

Experimentally, the rise does not begin until $Y \approx 6$. (2) The measured magnitude of $\langle g_p \rangle$ corresponding to Fig. 9 is too low by about a factor 2 to account for the behavior of σ_{tot}.

A further difficulty is that Fig. 9 is really a smooth curve and contains no definite threshold. If σ_{P_p} is parametrized as a flat background with a low-M resonant effect superimposed, the "triple-pomeron threshold" is just Δ_P, which is much too low. It might be argued that this early rise is masked by other (decreasing) terms in σ_{tot}, but one must then consider a more complete model of the cross section.

If one does in fact look at σ_{tot} in more detail, a further objection arises within nonabsorbed perturbative models of the pomeron,[13,17] as described in Prof. Frazer's talk. In his notation, the total cross section is represented by the sum shown in Fig. 10. It is necessary to distinguish a bare pomeron (P_0) which is generated by events with no large rapidity gaps in the unitarity sum. The relation between the two different kinds of pomeron is that the physical pomeron intercept $\alpha_p(0)$ is the zero of a denominator function,

$$D(J) = J - \alpha_0 - e^{-(J-\alpha_0)\log M_0^2}$$

$$\times \int \frac{dt}{16\pi} \frac{G^2(t) \; e^{-\Delta_P(J - 2\alpha_p(t) + 1)}}{J - 2\alpha_p(t) + 1} \quad , \qquad (7)$$

where α_0 is the bare intercept and G is the P-P-P_0 triple-Regge coupling. The origin of this formula is formally the same as in the antibaryon model above; cf. the denominator of Eq. (6). The last term is a two-pomeron loop integral, with appropriate threshold factors.

The absence of a threshold within the pomeron-particle absorptive part, as described above, corresponds to setting $M_0 = 1$ in Eq. (7). In this case the remaining exponential factor, $e^{-\Delta_P J}$, is not sufficient to produce physically significant complex poles. The importance of this circumstance is that the only other Regge singularities of the model are the leading pole and a two-pomeron branch cut with a positive discontinuity, so if there are no complex poles the cross section must <u>fall</u>. This statement seems paradoxical, since one might think an arbitrarily large rise can be arranged by making G large enough. However, the form of $D(J)$ in (7) implies that the "renormalization" of pomeron pole intercept, $\alpha_P(0) - \alpha_0$, increases with G. Since $\alpha_P(0) \leq 1$, an increase in G necessarily lowers α_0, and makes the short-range correlation

634

component of σ_{tot} fall faster. Careful examination of the competing tendencies confirms the theorem that the only possible way to get (even a temporary) increase in σ_{tot} is via complex poles.

FOOTNOTES AND REFERENCES

1. D. Sivers and F. von Hippel, Argonne preprint ANL/HEP 7323 (1973).
2. M. Suzuki, University of California, Berkeley preprint (1973).
3. T K. Gaisser and C.-I Tan, Brookhaven preprint BNL 18070 (1973).
4. G. F. Chew, T. Rogers, and D. R. Snider, Phys. Rev. D2, 765 (1970).
5. G. F. Chew and D. R. Snider, Phys. Letters 31B, 75 (1970).
6. M. Antinucci et al., Nuovo Cimento Letters 8, 121 (1973). Note that the p̄ cross sections discussed in this paper include the decay products of antihyperons.
7. Figure 2, which is taken from Ref. 6, is really the integrated B̄ inclusive cross section, and is equal to $\sigma_{\bar{B}}$ provided we make the reasonable assumption that not more than one anti-baryon is produced per event.
8. G. F. Chew and J. Koplik, in preparation.
9. U. Amaldi et al., Phys. Letters 44B, 112 (1973); S. R. Amendolia et al., ibid. 44B, 119 (1973).
10. J. S. Ball and G. F. Chew, Phys. Rev. 109, 1385 (1957).
11. R. J. N. Phillips, Rev. Mod. Phys. 39, 681 (1967).
12. A. Capella, M.-S. Chen, M. Kugler, and R. D. Peccei, Phys. Rev. Letters 31, 497 (1973); A. Capella and M.-S. Chen, SLAC-PUB-1252 (1973).
13. W. R. Frazer, D. R. Snider, and C.-I Tan, La Jolla preprint UCSD-10P10-127 (1973).
14. D. Amati, L. Caneschi, and M. Ciafaloni, CERN TH.1676 (1973).
15. G. F. Chew, Phys. Letters 44B, 169 (1973); M. Bishari and J. Koplik, ibid. 44B, 175 (1973).
16. A. B. Kaidalov, V. A. Khoze, Yu. F. Pirogov, and N. L. Ter-Isaakyan, Phys. Letters 45B, 493 (1973).
17. M. Bishari, G. F. Chew, and J. Koplik, Lawrence Berkeley Laboratory reports LBL-2129 and LBL-2130 (1973).

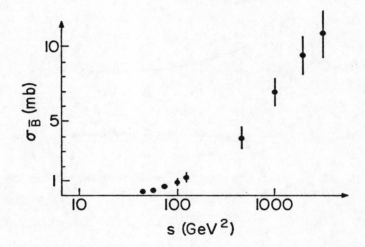

Fig. 1. The pion-exchange multiperipheral model.

Fig. 2. The antibaryon cross section as a function of energy.

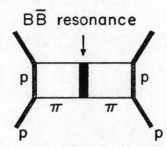

Fig. 3. Diagram controlling the $B\bar{B}$ threshold.

636

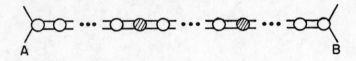

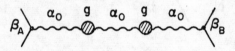

Fig. 4. Production of two $B\bar{B}$ pairs.

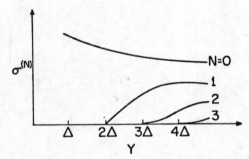

Fig. 5. The N-$B\bar{B}$ pair cross section as a function of energy.

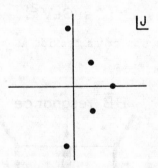

Fig. 6. Regge poles of the $B\bar{B}$ model.

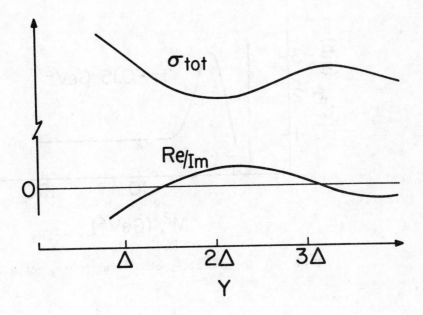

Fig. 7. Total cross section and ratio of real to imaginary part in the BB̄ model.

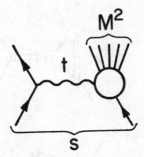

Fig. 8. Large-mass diffraction dissociation.

638

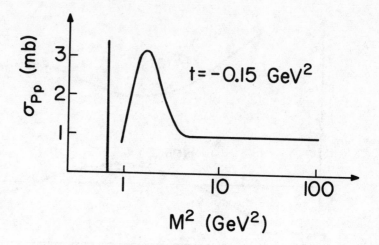

Fig. 9. The pomeron-proton total cross section.

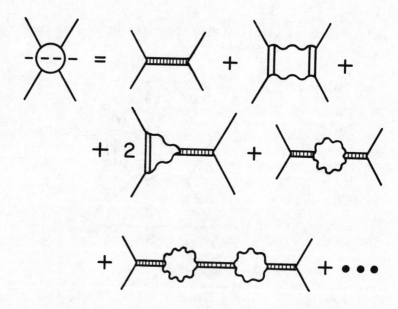

Fig. 10. Perturbative model of the pomeron.

PARTON MODELS AND DEEP
HADRON-HADRON SCATTERING*

Robert Savit
Stanford Linear Accelerator Center
Stanford University, Stanford, Calif. 94305

and

National Accelerator Laboratory†
Batavia, Illinois 60510

ABSTRACT

We review the recent applications of various parton models,
to the problem of hadron-hadron scattering at large momentum
transfers. Models which allow direct parton-parton interaction
as well as those that do not are considered. Predictions for the
structure of hadronic final states (whether or not transverse jets
exist), associated multiplities, and the s and t dependencies of
inclusive and exclusive cross-sections are described for the two
types of models and compared with available data. The relation
of the large momentum transfer (deep) region to the small momentum transfer (Regge) region is also discussed.

During the last couple of years, several attempts have been made to extend the intuitions about partons which have been developed in the study of
deep electroproduction to purely hadronic interactions at large momentum
transfers. In these applications, the hope has been that in this, the deep
hadronic region, some sort of impulse approximation is valid so that only the
simplest (in some sense) interactions have time to take place. Today I want
to discuss some of the major developments which have taken place along
these lines. I will describe, in a general way, the theoretical ideas behind
various approaches, and then discuss some of the experimental consequences
both for inclusive and exclusive (two-body) hadronic interactions. I will also
address myself to the question of providing a more precise definition of the
deep region. In physical terms this becomes the problem of determining the
kinematic region in which coherent (Regge) effects can be ignored.

In parton theories of deep hadron scattering one pictures the incident
hadrons as being composed of partonic constituents which mediate the basic
interaction between the hadrons. The constituents then recombine to produce
the final state hadrons. It is convenient to classify such theories according
to whether or not they allow direct parton-parton interactions between partons
belonging to different hadrons. A number of authors have described theories
which allow direct parton-parton scattering (type I).[1] While these models
differ in their details, they all share the common belief that some sort of

---

* Work supported in part by the U. S. Atomic Energy Commission.
† Present address.

640

gluon exchange is important in describing deep hadronic scattering. On the other hand, a theory which does not allow such direct parton-parton scattering (type II) has been developed by Blankenbecler, Brodsky and Gunion,[2] and has been discussed using a different formalism by Landshoff and Polkinghorne.[3]

Type I theories generally describe deep hadron-hadron scattering as shown in Fig. 1. Two partons, one from each hadron scatter off each other with some large momentum transfer, (in the example of Fig. 1 via single gluon exchange), and then by some, as yet unknown mechanism, turn back into hadrons.

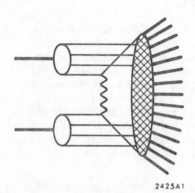

2425A1

FIG. 1--Contribution of direct parton-parton scattering (in this case, via gluon exchange) to deep hadron-hadron scattering.

On the basis of some very general arguments, one expects in this picture to see transverse jets of hadrons. Dynamically, these jets arise because the partons are supposed to like to radiate particles (in some sense) at lowish subenergies. Many hadrons will, therefore, be produced as the partons cascade step by step back to the origin of momentum space. Of course, a high subenergy event is required in the first place in order to produce a high transverse momentum parton. The gross structure of these jets can be inferred by extending Feynman's argument for ordinary hadron scattering to parton scattering. Feynman[4] argues that in ordinary (i.e, no large momentum transfers) hadron scattering at high energies the hadron wave functions become Lorentz contracted, so that the energy density looks like a delta-function along the collision axis in configuration space. Fourier transforming this leads to a constant energy density in momentum space along p_z, and therefore, a uniform population of hadron constituents in rapidity. (Logarithmic multiplicities of hadrons in ordinary hadron-hadron scattering then follows from assuming that the final hadron distribution is similar to the final parton distribution.) This argument can clearly be applied to the two exiting, widely scattered partons in a deep event,[5] and thus leads to logarithmic multiplicities in the transverse jets.

In these theories, one calculates inclusive cross sections in which the detected particle has a large $p_\perp$ by folding the differential cross section for parton-parton scattering into an integral with the distribution of partons in the initial hadrons and the distribution of hadrons in the struck parton. The detailed behavior of these cross sections is clearly dependent on the distribution functions for partons in hadrons and hadrons in partons.[6] However, for a wide class of theories, the energy dependence for the invariant cross sections does not depend on these details.[7] It is

$$E \frac{d^3\sigma}{dp^3} = s^{-2} F(x_1, x_2) \tag{1}$$

when $s \to \infty$, and $x_1 = -t/s$ and $x_2 = -u/s$ are fixed. This is an important, simple prediction of type I theories. Although present data do not seem to support Eq. (1), its theoretical range of validity is ambiguous, so it may not be fair to apply it to the present experimental situation. We shall have more to say about this later.

What do type I parton theories say about two body reactions at large $|t|$? The natural specialization of Fig. 1 to a $2 \to 2$ hadronic amplitude is shown in Fig. 2. Of course, one could replace the single gluon exchange with a more general parton-parton scattering amplitude, but in view of the popularity of single gluon exchange, let us consider just the present example. If the gluon is a vector, the contribution of this diagram to the differential cross section is

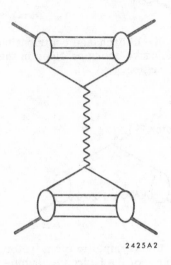

2425A2

$$\frac{d\sigma}{dt} \propto G^4(t) \left(\frac{d\sigma}{dt}\right)_{parton}$$

$$\propto \frac{G^4(t)}{t^2} \text{ (large } |t|) \qquad (2)$$

where G(t) is the electromagnetic form factor of the hadrons involved in the scattering. This is reminiscent of the Wu-Yang formula.[8] In fact, if we make the gluon infinitely heavy, we recover their expression. Unfortunately, the data for proton-proton scattering is not in agreement with this expression. Equation (2) has no s-dependence, and predicts a fall-off with large $|t|$ which is greater than what is observed. Furthermore, from Fig. 2 one

FIG. 2--Direct parton-parton scattering contribution to a deep hadron-hadron scattering event with a two-body final state.

would predict equal cross sections for pp $\to$ pp and $\bar{p}p \to \bar{p}p$ at large s and t. This does not seem to be substantiated by experiment.[9]

Once again, however, we must caution those who would crucify type I theories on the cross of experiment. The spirit of direct parton-parton scattering could be resurrected in a number of ways. First, it is possible that a single gluon exchange does not asymptotically dominate parton-parton scattering. Second, regardless of the correct asymptotic form of the direct constituent scattering, present experiments may not be probing the asymptotic region in the context of these models. We'll say more about this later.

Let us turn now to a brief description of type II parton theories — those in which direct parton-parton scattering is not allowed. In these models, the deep scattering region is assumed to be dominated by interchange of the parton constituents. Typical graphs for two-body and inclusive processes are shown in Figs. 3 and 4, respectively. The internal lines are partons (straight) and "cores" (wiggly). These latter represent the collective effects of the (hadron minus parton) system. The blobs are vertex functions whose

642

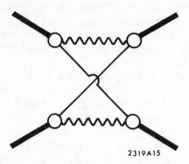

2319A15

FIG. 3--Interchange contribution (tu graph) to deep hadron-hadron scattering for two body reactions.

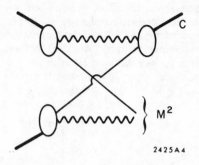

2425A4

FIG. 4--Interchange contribution to inclusive cross sections in the deep region.

asymptotic behavior is determined by calculating the form factor (Fig. 5), and choosing a vertex function which correctly reproduces the experimentally determined form factor. (In practice, meson form factors are assumed to behave like $(q^2)^{-1}$ and baryon form factors like $(q^2)^{-2}$ for large $|q^2|$.)

The topologies of the interchange graphs are determined by the quantum numbers of the constituents. If the partons are assumed to have quark quantum numbers then the topologies

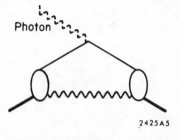

Photon

2425A5

FIG. 5--Asymptotic form factor in terms of the hadron's asymptotic wave function.

of the interchange graphs are the same as those found in the case of the Harari-Rosner duality diagrams.[10] For instance, Fig. 3 is a two body t-u diagram, and is the only one allowed for, say k$^+$p elastic scattering. (The relationship between duality diagrams and parton-interchange diagrams is rather interesting. See Refs. (11) and (12) for a discussion.) Notice that only the simplest components of the hadrons' wave functions are assumed to be important in these calculations: that is, the sea of parton-antiparton pairs is assumed to be an asymptotically unimportant component of the hadron.

What are the general features of deep scattering predicted by this theory? First, one should probably not expect two transverse jets of hadrons in a typical deep event. This can be seen by referring to Fig. 4. A jet of hadrons associated with particle C, which has a large transverse momentum is most likely to be produced by bremsstrahlung from that particle. Since C will lose some of its energy if it bremsstrahlungs a jet of hadrons, the interchange interaction which originally produced C will have to take place at a higher energy and with a larger momentum transfer than if a transverse jet were not produced. But since the interchange interaction falls (like inverse powers) with increasing s and t, such events will be suppressed. This argument is, of course, only heuristic. A more careful analysis of this problem within the spirit of the interchange model is clearly needed.

A number of single particle inclusive reactions have been calculated in this model. In the deep region the invariant cross section for detecting a particle with a large transverse momentum has the form

$$E \frac{d^3\sigma}{dp^3} = s^{-n} g(x_1, x_2) \tag{3}$$

Unlike type I theories, the power fall-off of s varies from reaction to reaction since it is dependent on the form factors of the particle involved in the scattering. For instance, for $pp \to pX$, $n = 8$, for $\pi p \to \pi X$, $n = 4$, and for $\pi p \to pX$, $n = 6$.

An important result of some of the work which has been done on the interchange model is a fairly clear idea of the range of validity of the predictions. In particular, the deep region in inclusive experiments may be defined as the region where x_1, x_2 and M^2/s all remain finite (non-zero) as s grows. (M^2 is the missing mass squared.) (As $M^2/s \to 0$, with x_1, x_2 fixed, we are still a deep region, but we are approaching the exclusive edge of phase space.) Note that since, in this region $p_\perp^2 \propto$ s Eq.(3) can be rewritten as a power of $p_\perp$ times as function of x_1 and x_2. As we move away from this kinematic domain, towards smaller $p_\perp$, other sorts of effects become important and change the character of the inclusive cross section. The reason is the following: as we mentioned before, the interchange process falls with increasing energy. Therefore, if we wish to detect a particle at a given, large $p_\perp$, the most important diagrams will be those that allow the interchange interaction to occur at the lowest possible energy consistent with the observation of a large $p_\perp$ secondary. Hence, for $p_\perp$ large, but significantly away from the edge of phase space, diagrams such as those of Fig. 6 become important. By allowing bremsstrahlung of hadrons from the incident particles, the effective energy of the interchange process is lowered. Furthermore, since the colliding particles can bremsstrahlung baryons, an incident proton can turn into a pion which then takes part in the interchange interaction. This is advantageous because the pion's form factor falls less rapidly for large q^2 than the proton's, thus leading to a less rapidly falling energy dependence in the near deep, or transition region. These effects become especially important near $x_F = 2p_\parallel/\sqrt{s} \sim 0$ (pionization region) when $s \sim M^2$, and $|t|$, $|u| \sim \sqrt{s}$ for large s. For example, the invariant cross section for $pp \to pX$

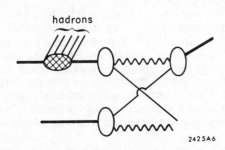

2425A6

FIG. 6--Bremsstrahlung diagrams which give rise to the transition region in type II theories of inclusive reactions.

in the transition region can still be written in the form (3), only now we have $n = 6$ rather than $n = 8$ as in the deep region. Furthermore, the invariant cross section generally falls less rapidly with $p_\perp$ for fixed s and $x_F \sim 0$ in this region than in the deep region.

For orientation, we have plotted in Fig. 7 the expected qualitative behavior of $E(d^3\sigma/dp^3)$ as a function of $p_\perp$ for $x_F \sim 0$, and a number of different values of s. Notice that there are three fairly distinct regions. For small $p_\perp$ the inclusive cross section is independent of s as required by Feynman scaling. In the transition region the fall off with $p_\perp$ is slower due to the occurrence of hadronic bremsstrahlung. As we move into the deep region, there is not enough energy for bremsstrahlung to occur and so the fall off with $p_\perp$ becomes sharper. Finally, at the very edge of phase space, the inclusive cross section matches smoothly on to exclusive one. The other regions of phase space can be discussed in a similar way, and are treated in detail in the third article in Ref. (2).

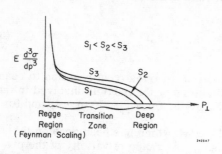

FIG. 7--Schematic representation of the behavior of inclusive cross sections predicted by type II theories.

Let us now turn to the predictions of the interchange theory for two body reactions. In the high energy fixed angle region, the differential cross section can be written in the form

$$\frac{d\sigma}{dt} = s^{-p}\, h(t/s) \tag{4}$$

p varies from reaction to reaction, depending on the number of baryons of mesons involved in the reaction. For $BB \to BB$ (or $B\bar{B} \to B\bar{B}$) reactions, p = 12, while for $MB \to MB$ or $B\bar{B} \to MM$, p = 8.

It seems reasonable to suppose that some sort of bremsstrahlung process also Reggeizes these two body reactions as we move in in t from the fixed angle region. This is, indeed, the case.[11,12] However, since we require a specific final state, the brem'ed hadrons must be caught by the exiting particles on their way out. This leads us to consider diagrams such as those shown in Fig. 8. Each blob is some Born term which we iterate in the t-channel to obtain graphs which become increasingly important at smaller and smaller $|t|$. By assuming a Born term which accurately describes fixed angle scattering, the first order corrections can be calculated by t-channel iteration.

Suppose, for instance, that we have a large angle scattering Born term of the form

$$M_0 = s^{-m} f(t)$$

The leading behavior of the first iterated graph (Fig. 8) is then

$$M_1 = s^{-m}\, \frac{f^2(t)}{|t|}\, \ln s \; .$$

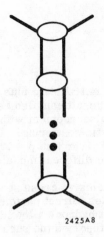

2425A8

FIG. 8--Generalized ladder graphs which Reggeize two body deep scattering in a wide class of theories (including type II parton theories).

The sum can be written, to this order in the couplings as

$$M = M_0 + M_1 = \beta(t) \, s^{\alpha(t)}$$

with $\beta(t) = f(t)$ and $\alpha(t) = -m + \beta(t)/|t|$. We see then, how we can build up moving Regge trajectories by summing generalized t-channel ladder graphs. This Reggeization procedure also provides us with a definition of the deep region in the case of $2 \rightarrow 2$ amplitudes. The deep region is that region where coherent Regge effects are unimportant, i.e., where $M_1 \ll M_0$. If, as predicted by type II theories, $f(t) \propto t^{-\ell}$, then for large s the deep region sets in when

$$|t| >> C \, [\ln s]^{\frac{1}{\ell+1}}$$

where C is a constant. Hence, the deep region is neither a fixed angle nor a fixed t region, but sets in someplace inbetween. [13]

There are two lessons to be learned from this. Phenomenologically, we learn that given a description of the deep scattering region, we can, by t-channel iteration learn how this behavior is extended in first order into the smaller t region. In a realistic analysis, it is necessary to deal with a coupled channel problem since, in M_1 the hadrons in the 2 particle intermediate t-channel state may be different from the external hadrons. This leads naturally to sets of Regge trajectories which become degenerate as $t \rightarrow -\infty$. Indeed, such degeneracies are expected and occur in a wide range of physical systems. [14] Second, we learn that since deep scattering is properly described by the large $|t|$ limit of the usual Regge expressions for hadronic amplitudes, it is in principle wrong to add parton dynamics to Regge exchange — they are two manifestations of the same thing, and one commits double counter errors by adding them together.

Before reviewing the experimental situation with regard to the two types of theories, I want to mention some recent work by Brodsky and Farrar. [7] They assume that hadron scattering is describable by a renormalizable field theory. Baryons are composed of three elementary (quark) fields, and mesons are composed of two. Two body reactions are considered in the kinematic domain $s \rightarrow \infty$, with t/s and u/s fixed. Writing the differential cross section in the form (4) these authors determine the power, p, by drawing the simplest connected Born diagrams and counting the propagators which must have large invariant mass ("hot propagators" in Brodsky's parlance). Using this rule, and assuming that higher order terms don't change the result (mod logs), Brodsky and Farrar find the same energy dependence as that found in the interchange theory, with one exception. Their result is conveniently summarized as

$$p = n - 2$$

where n is the number of elementary fields in the initial state plus the number of elementary fields in the final state. (This result can also be extended to photon induced processes.[7]) The one point of disagreement with the interchange model is in the case of baryon-baryon elastic scattering. The interchange theory predicts p = 12 while Brodsky and Farrar find p = 10. However, the difference is most likely traceable to the different models assumed for the baryon wave function.

The approach can also be used to calculate inclusive cross sections under the assumptions appropriate to type I theories (direct parton-parton interactions between partons belonging to different hadrons allowed), and also under the assumptions appropriate to type II theories (no such direct parton-parton interactions allowed). The results of these calculations are consistent with the predictions of the two types of theories as we have so far discussed.

What does experiment tell us about the merits of the two types of theories? As far as the general structure of deep reactions — especially transverse jet formation — is concerned, it is difficult to draw any definite conclusions. There is some slight indication from the Cern-Columbia-Rockefeller ISR collaboration that transverse jets may be formed in large $p_\perp$ events,[15] but neither the transverse momenta nor associated multiplicities are large enough to draw any firm conclusions. The ratios of various particles produced at large $p_\perp$ are certainly important quantities to study, but predictions of these ratios depend on fairly detailed aspects of the theories, and so are probably not appropriate as a first test of the general ideas.

Much more germain to the present discussion is the energy and, to some extent, the angular dependence of exclusive and inclusive processes. As far as the inclusive cross sections are concerned, we emphasize that the only high energy, large $p_\perp$ measurements which have been performed so far have been carried out in a range of $p_\perp$ which, at least in the context of type II theories, corresponds to the transition region. The results of these measurements[16] are consistent with the transition zone predictions of type II theories. However, it is difficult to compare type I theories with these measurements since, as we have stated before, there is no clear delineation of a transition zone, and so it is not clear over what range of $p_\perp$ the results are supposed to be valid. For this reason it is extremely important to measure inclusive cross sections at higher values of $p_\perp / \sqrt{s}$ either by increasing $p_\perp$ or decreasing s.

The situation for two body reactions is somewhat clearer. Type II theories appear to predict very well the energy and angular dependence around 90° in a variety of reactions. For instance, $d\sigma/dt \,|_{90^\circ}$ as a function of s for meson-baryon reactions is predicted to go like s^{-8}, and measurements of all the following reactions are consistent with this result:[17] $\bar{k}^0 p \to \pi \Sigma^0$, $k_L^0 p \to k_S^0 p$, $\bar{k}_p^0 \to \pi^+ \Lambda^0$, $\pi^\pm p \to \pi^\pm p$, $k^\pm p \to k^\pm p$, $p\bar{p} \to \pi^+ \pi^-$, and $p\bar{p} \to k^+ k^-$. It should furthermore be noted that this behavior persists in many of these reactions down to s of about 5 GeV^2. For pp and $\bar{p}p$ elastic scattering in the asymptotic fixed angle region, the interchange theory implies a differential cross section which behaves as s^{-12}. Brodsky and

Farrar find s^{-10} for the same quantity. At the present level of accuracy the data is consistent with both. [18] The simplest type I theories, on the other hand, such as the single gluon exchange pictured in Fig. (2) predict energy independent differential cross sections and, at least for the case of pp scattering, at fixed s a($d\sigma/dt$) which falls too rapidly with t. Of course, these predictions could be modified by using a more complicated parton-parton scattering amplitude, but this does not really seem to be in the spirit of type I models.

Let's conclude with a brief summary of what we've learned. Although the experimental situation is incomplete, type II theories seem to be in better shape in their description of the gross properties of both inclusive and exclusive hadronic reactions. For inclusive reactions, it is difficult to clearly compare type I theories to present data, since we do not really know their range of validity. On the other hand, there is a well-defined and necessary extension of type II theories which gives rise to a transition region, and which agrees well with the present data. Exclusive data near 90° is well described by type II theories, but not by type I theories. Again, however, the deep region predictions of type I theories may not be applicable to the present data — we do not know. Finally, the important question of the existence or nonexistence of transverse jets in the two types of theories has not really been settled theoretically (although there are some arguments which may be brought to bear) and has barely been asked experimentally.

ACKNOWLEDGMENTS

I am grateful to R. Blankenbecler, S. J. Brodsky, M. B. Einhorn and G. Farrar for helpful discussions while this talk was being prepared.

REFERENCES

1. Papers dealing with type I theories include S. M. Berman, J. D. Bjorken, and J. B. Kogut, Phys. Rev. D $\underline{4}$, 3388 (1971); S. D. Ellis and M. B. Kislinger, NAL-Pub-73/40-THY (1973); D. Horn and M. Moshe, Nucl. Phys. B $\underline{48}$, 557 (1972); and preprint CALT-68-382 (1973); (This model is a hybrid in that it attempts to incorporate both hard parton-parton scattering and wee parton exchange) and R. Savit, Phys. Rev. D $\underline{8}$, 274 (1973). While the last paper does not explicitly assume that the existence of direct parton-parton interactions, it is closer in spirit to type I theories than to type II theories.

2. R. Blankenbecler, S. J. Brodsky and J. F. Gunion, Phys. Letters $\underline{39}$ B, 649 (1972); Phys. Rev. D $\underline{6}$, 2652 (1972); Phys. Letters $\underline{42}$ B, 461 (1973); Phys. Rev. D $\underline{8}$, 187 (1973).

3. P. V. Landshoff and J. C. Polkinghorne, Cambridge University preprint Nos. DAMTP 72/43, DAMTP 72/48 and DAMTP 73/10; Phys. Letters $\underline{44}$ B, 293 (1973).

4. R. P. Feynman, Phys. Rev. Letters $\underline{23}$, 1415 (1969).

5. R. Savit, Ref. 1.

6. These points have been discussed by S. D. Ellis and M. Kislinger, Ref. 1.

7. S. J. Brodsky and G. R. Farrar, SLAC report no. SLAC-PUB-1290 (1973) have argued that Eq. (1) is valid generally in renormalizable field theories. See below for a discussion of their paper.

8. T. T. Wu and C. N. Yang, Phys. Rev. 137, 708 (1965); H. D. I. Abarbanel, S. D. Drell and F. J. Gilman, Phys. Rev. Letters 20, 208 (1968).

9. V. Chabaud, et al., Phys. Letters 38 B, 449 (1972). The experimental value for $(d\sigma/dt)_{pp}/(d\sigma/dt)_{\bar{p}p}$ at 90° is about 100. The type II interchange model predicts ~ 50 for this ratio.

10. H. Harari, Phys. Rev. Letters 22, 562 (1969); J. L. Rosner, Phys. Rev. Letters, 22, 689 (1969); P.G.O. Freund, Lett. Nuovo Cimento 4, 147 (1970). Because baryons are treated as effective two body states, there are certain duality diagrams which do not appear as interchange diagrams. Furthermore, interpretive problems arise in the context of dual models which incorporate essentially non-planar quark graphs. I thank M. B. Einhorn for comments on this point.

11. R. Blankenbecler, S. J. Brodsky, J. F. Gunion and R. Savit, SLAC report no. SLAC-PUB-1294 (1973), to be published.

12. R. Savit, "Multiplicities and Regge Poles in Deep Hadron-Hadron Scattering", Stanford Linear Accelerator report; Ph.D. thesis, Stanford University (1973).

13. Many of the results obtained by considering generalized ladder graphs actually follow from much more general assumptions. R. Savit and R. Blankenbecler, to be published.

14. Nearly degenerate energy levels usually occur in physical systems governed by a Hamiltonian with a large piece and a small (perturbative) piece. In the present case, (large $|t|$), the short range part of the Hamiltonian is large, and the long-range, coherent part is small. Near $t = 0$, on the other hand, the situation is reversed. This is similar to what happens in the case of an atom in a weak magnetic field (Zeeman effect) versus a strong magnetic field (Paschen-Back effect). For a further explanation, see Refs. 11 and 12.

15. B. J. Blumenfeld, et al., report presented at the International Conf. on New Results from Experiments on High-Energy Particle Collisions, Vanderbilt University, Nashville, Tenn., March 26-28, 1973.

16. B. J. Blumenfeld, et al., CERN Preprint August 1973. The inclusive production of all charged particles at the ISR has been reported by B. Alpen, et al., Phys. Letters 44 B, 521 (1973).

17. D. P. Owen, et al., Phys. Rev. 181, 1794 (1969); G.W. Brandenburg, et al., Phys. Letters 44 B, 305 (1973).

18. C. M. Ankenbrandt, et al., Phys. Rev. 170, 1223 (1968); J. V. Allaby, et al., Phys. Letters 23, 389 (1966); C. W. Akerlof, et al., Phys. Rev. 159, 1138 (1967); G. Cocconi, et al., Phys. Rev. 138, 165 (1965).

Chapter $\underline{V}$
<u>Astrophysics</u>

650

GALACTIC X-RAY SOURCES

E. J. Schreier
Center for Astrophysics, Harvard College Observatory/
Smithsonian Astrophysical Observatory, Cambridge, Ma. 02138

ABSTRACT

The relevance of galactic X-ray astronomy to the study
of compact stellar objects is discussed. After some general
remarks about X-ray astronomy, a brief picture of the X-ray
sky is presented. Finally, a more detailed discussion of two
specific galactic X-ray sources is presented. Observations
of Cygnus X-1 and Hercules X-1 are discussed in the light of
their possible identification with a black hole and a neutron
star respectively.

INTRODUCTION

The relevance of recent observations of galactic X-ray sources to
high energy physics lies not so much in the detailed emission mechanisms
for the X-rays as in the determination of the nature of the sources themselves. Some of the most significant and observationally exciting results
in X-ray astronomy in the past year or two have concerned objects which
are of great interest to other branches of physics: neutron stars and black
holes. These, along with white dwarfs, represent compact objects at the
endpoints of stellar evolution, where typically one or more solar masses
are concentrated in regions smaller than the earth.

Neutron star models, for example, embrace nearly all regimes of
physics[1]. Plasma physics is relevant to the magnetosphere, where fields
of 10^{12} gauss are involved with the radiation of 10^{37} to 10^{38} ergs/sec.
Solid state physics describes the outer crust. Nuclear physics describes
the bulk of the star, first heavy nucleii and then the main part of the star
which can be characterized as an enormous nucleus containing some 10^{57}
neutrons. Finally, the resonances and hadrons described by high energy
physics are generated at the center by the compression and ultra-
relativistic Fermi energies.

Black holes, representing the ultimate collapse of stellar objects
under gravitation, are simpler in that they are presumably described
only by general relativity. The difference between various compact
objects is a function primarily of the mass involved. When a star
exhausts its nuclear fuel and starts gravitational collapse, its mass to a
large extent governs its fate. A small star, of order one solar mass,
contracts until degenerate electron pressure balances gravitational force.

It then sits there as a white dwarf and slowly cools off. If more mass is contained, however, the collapse continues with two possible results. Either a supernova occurs, or gravitational collapse continues further until the Schwartzchild radius is reached and a black hole is formed.

Although the evolution of these objects is controversial (the above version being rather simplistic) it is relevant to describe the objects after the fact. In particular, theorists try to define a critical upper mass for a neutron star which can serve as a boundary between neutron stars and black holes. Depending upon what equation of state is used to describe the neutron star, the estimates vary but are close to one solar mass; there are arguments from general relativity for an absolute upper limit of about three solar masses[2].

The relevance of X-ray astronomy to these compact objects is thus not at a very sophisticated level, for the most important physical parameter we can measure is mass. Thus, although the physics involved in these objects is wide ranging, the physics dealt with directly in our observations is rather basic -- two body mechanics and Doppler effects. This is a corollary of the convenient and significant fact that a great many galactic X-ray sources are found to occur in binary systems.

The remainder of this talk will consist of a brief picture of the X-ray sky and a more detailed discussion of two specific sources: Cygnus X-1, a possible black hole, and Hercules X-1, a possible neutron star.

THE X-RAY SKY

X-ray astronomy covers the spectrum of photons with energies ranging from a few hundred electron volts to several hundred keV where it merges into γ-ray astronomy. It represents the next most energetic band of radiation above visible (and UV) light which does not get absorbed by the diffuse interstellar gas. The earth's atmosphere, however, is completely opaque to X-rays, and thus one must make observations from rockets, balloons, or satellites. The first detection of X-rays from beyond the solar system was made on a rocket flight in 1962[3]. After much pioneering work from rockets and balloons during that decade, the first true X-ray observatory, the satellite Uhuru, was launched on 12 December 1970. This satellite, containing two 800 cm^2 banks of proportional counters sensitive to X-rays from 2 to 20 keV was built by American Science and Engineering in Cambridge, and is still operating. Most of the X-ray data in the remainder of this talk was gathered with this instrument by the Uhuru group at AS&E, and currently at the Center for Astrophysics, Harvard College Observatory/Smithsonian Astrophysical Observatory, also in Cambridge.

The X-ray sky as seen from Uhuru is shown in Figure 1. There were 125 sources listed after the first year of operation as published in the 2U Catalog[4]. This can be compared to some 35 sources discovered in the previous decade. (The 3U Catalog, to be published, contains some

160 sources.) The apparent intensities range from about 2 counts/sec (2 - 6 keV) for M31 to 2×10^4 counts/sec for Sco X-1. The sources divide into two main groups. One is clustered along the galactic plane and is much more intense on the average. The other weaker group, containing about one-third of all sources, is uniformly spread over the sky and is identified with an extragalactic population. Some 14 of these sources are identified with known extragalactic objects, ranging from a "normal" galaxy (M31) to the rich galactic clusters.

The single most important feature of the galactic sources which has been discovered is the widespread time variability. In fact, with the exception of the identified supernova remnants, nearly all of the galactic sources show some variability. This variability manifests itself in two principle ways. One is short term variability of less than about a second which implies compact X-ray sources, and includes the periodic variations of the two known X-ray pulsars Cen X-3 and Her X-1. The second main type of variability involves eclipses and indicates the binary nature of certain sources. In fact, there is reason to believe that the class of X-ray binaries includes most galactic X-ray sources. We turn now to the two binary sources: Cygnus X-1 and Hercules X-1.

CYGNUS X-1

Cygnus X-1 was one of the first sources studied in detail from Uhuru. In fact, its variability[5] led to the search for other such sources which led in turn to the discovery of the X-ray pulsars and binaries. Figure 2 shows some early Uhuru scans over Cyg X-1. Statistically significant deviations of the intensity from the expected triangular response are seen (the collimator, which limits the angular acceptance of the detectors, produces a triangular intensity modulation as the satellite scans a constant, point source). In addition, regular pulsations were seen at times; figure 3 is a Fourier analysis of one observation showing a significant periodicity and first harmonic. However, different periods were seen at different times, and by different observers[6]. Although no single periodicity persisted, large fluctuations of intensity were seen on all time scales observed, as for example in figure 4. In one instance, a factor of two variability was seen on a time scale of 50 milliseconds[7]. This rapid coherent variability implies an emission region of less than about 15000 km; an X-ray source emitting 10^4 times the total luminosity of the sun coming from a region no larger than the earth.

As the position of the X-ray source was refined through further observations, a radio source was found at the same location[8, 9]. The identification of the radio source with the X-ray source was further confirmed by a correlated transition of both the X-ray and radio intensities[10], as shown in figure 5. The relatively precise radio location then led in turn to an unambiguous optical identification of the source with a 5.6 day spectroscopic binary[11]. This star was found to be a B0 supergiant -- a very massive star. Kepler's third law could then be used to infer a mass for the companion star, that is, the X-ray source. Conservative lower estimates for the mass of the companion have been set at significantly more than 3 solar masses.

Reviewing the chain of identifications, we find that Cyg X-1 is a compact object of less than 10^9 cm (from the fast fluctuations) with a mass greater than 3 solar masses (from the binary identification). These two facts together represent the operational definition of a black hole. Although further work is still being done, it appears very possible that the X-ray observations of Cygnus X-1 have led to the first discovery of a black hole.

HERCULES X-1

Hercules X-1 is one of two binary X-ray pulsars discovered by Uhuru. Extensive observations of the source with Uhuru, as well as with other X-ray experiments, together with an early unambiguous identification of an optical counterpart Hz Herculis, have made Her X-1 probably the most studied X-ray source in the sky.

The first main feature of the source, as shown in figure 6, is the presence of periodic eclipses, occurring every 1.7 days. These eclipses, during which the X-ray intensity drops by a factor of 10 or more, immediately suggest occultation by a binary companion. The binary periodicity, which has now been observed for more than a year and a half, also allowed the identification of the star Hz Herculis, an A or F-type star located in the X-ray error box which was found to undergo intensity fluctuations with the same period and phase as the X-ray source (figure 7)[12]. The accepted cause of the optical variation is heating of Hz Herculis by the X-ray source as it orbits.

The second main feature of Her X-1 is the regular pulsation. Some 90% of the intensity is modulated with a 1.24 second periodicity. A section of data is shown in figure 8, along with a minimum X^2 fit to the data of a sinusoid with harmonics. The presence of regular pulsations from an object in orbit about another star would lead one to expect Doppler variations of the period. This was, in fact, readily confirmed, as shown in the top half of figure 9. What is shown at each point is the difference between the observed time of arrival of a pulse, and the time which would be predicted by a constant trial period. If the true period were constant, a straight line would be obtained. As can be seen, the function follows a sine curve. The period and phase of this sine curve is very well correlated with the intensity occultations, also shown in the figure. What is seen are the pulses being alternately delayed and advanced by up to 13.2 seconds as the X-ray star goes behind and in front of the occulting star.

Thus, the amplitude of the curve gives the projected radius of the orbit (in our plane of view) directly in light seconds. This is rather impressive: a direct astronomical measurement of an orbital radius. It can also be noted that the derivative of the phase curve, a sine curve shifted by 90°, would be the usual Doppler variation of the period.

This analysis makes possible very precise determinations of a number of parameters, both directly observed and derived under the assumption of a circular orbit (this is justified by the low upper limit on orbital eccentricity). A typical set of such parameters is shown in the table. One of the most important parameters is the mass function, the

PARAMETERS OF HERCULES X-1

Observed Parameters

τ (average pulsation period in seconds)	1.237772 ± 0.000001
$\Delta\tau$ (half-amplitude of period variation in seconds)	0.0006986 ± 0.0000014
T (orbital period in days)	1.70016 ± 0.00001
ϕ_T (phase of eclipse: low center)	UT 1972 Jan. 13. 0772 ± 0.0003

Derived Parameters

ϵ (eccentricity)	≤ 0.05
$v \sin i = (\Delta\tau/\tau) c$ (km s^{-1})	169.2 ± 0.4
$r \sin i = (T/2\pi) v \sin i$ (cm)	$(3.95 \pm 0.01) \times 10^{11}$
$M_2^3 \sin^3 i/(M_1+M_2)^2 = (2\pi/T)^2 (r \sin i)^3/G$ (grams)	$(1.69 \pm 0.01) \times 10^{33}$

last item in the table. This relationship between the masses, the inclination i, and the known orbital elements, a restatement of Kepler's third law, is what leads to estimates for the individual masses. There are several approaches which can be followed to obtain the mass M_1 of the X-ray object. One is to study the visual star further to refine its spectral type (and thus mass), and to obtain a second mass function from the radial velocity variations of its spectral lines. Continuing observations of Hz Herculis are underway.

A second method uses the X-ray data and a reasonable model of the system. One can first relate the known separation of the stars and the duration of the X-ray eclipse to the size of the occulting object. One can then relate the occulting region to the equipotential surfaces (the Roche lobes) about the visible star; these are determined in turn by the masses and separation. The results are values for the two masses for each inclination. For a reasonable inclination angle of 85°, one finds that the X-ray star has a mass of 1.0 solar masses, the visual component being 2.0 solar masses. These numbers are consistent with the preliminary results from the optical studies.

There are various other features apparent in the detailed observations of Her X-1 which contribute to the overall model. Several of these are illustrated in figure 10. Each of the points is an independent Uhuru observation of the source. The main structure shows the existence of still a third recurring 3.5 day pattern of intensity variations. For 11 days or so, the source is intense and pulsing, and for some 24 days it is too weak to be observed. Three such high states are shown. It is seen that the source turns on abruptly, and then follows a rather smooth modulation, although significant point-to-point fluctuations are apparent. A rather important feature is the presence of intensity "dips" before the eclipses. These follow a regular pattern and furthermore, the X-ray data show a deficiency of low energy photons at these times. This is indicative of absorption of the X-rays, and is readily interpreted as due to gas streams between the two stars. A further phenomenon, not in this figure, involves small changes in the average pulsation period. These changes, on the order of microseconds, are predominantly speed-ups. Further details of the observations, as well as of the interpretations, can be found in the literature [13, 14, 15].

Although the observations are very complex, the basic data strongly suggest a consistent model. The 1.24 second time scale implies compactness, the stability of the pulsations over close to two years implies rotation as a clock, and the pulsations imply some beaming mechanism. Putting all this together with a 1 solar mass estimate, we obtain a magnetic rotating neutron star, in analogy with the radio pulsars. However, the presence of this object in a binary system ends the analogy. Whereas radio pulsars derive their energy from rotation and subsequently slow down, Her X-1 is speeding up. The obvious energy source for the X-rays turns out to be gravitation. Mass is transferred from Hz Herculis to Her X-1; as it falls into the deep potential well of the neutron star, it changes a large amount of gravitational energy into thermal energy, thereby allowing the generation of X-rays. It is hard, in fact, to think of another energy source; the distance to the source together with the observed intensity implies an intrinsic X-ray luminosity of some 10^{37} ergs/sec. But the accretion mechanism is very efficient -- an accretion rate of only 10^{-9} solar masses per year is necessary to power the X-rays, a number well in the regime of close binary mass transfer rates. Furthermore, we believe we actually see the mass stream between the two stars by way of the absorption dips. The beaming in this model is then due to the magnetic field holding out the mass which has come from the other star. Only at the magnetic poles, presumably inclined to the axis of rotation, will the matter be able to fall to the surface and emit the basically thermal X-rays which we observe.

CONCLUSION

We don't have such detailed models for the other galactic sources yet. But the overall picture is beginning to simplify a bit. There are four other sources in which we observe definite eclipses, with binary periods ranging up to 9 days. All of these have been identified with optical binaries. A fifth source shows a periodic intensity variation every 4.8 hours and a 4.8 hour infrared variable source has been seen. All of these sources show some short term variability, implying compactness. One of them, Cen X-3, is another X-ray pulsar with a 4.8 second period. If we go beyond these sources, there are over half a dozen other X-ray objects which show some characteristics of binary behavior, and which are being studied further. In addition, a survey of Uhuru sources currently underway is indicating that essentially all of the galactic X-ray sources are variable to some extent. Many of them vary in times shorter than a second, suggesting compact sources.

Since six X-ray sources are already identified with binary systems, and many others are showing similar behavior, it is not a far extrapolation to assert that a compact object in a binary system is a reasonable basic model for most galactic X-ray sources. The binary companion supplies mass, and the compact object, be it a white dwarf, a neutron star, or a black hole, supplies a deep potential well. The combination efficiently supplies the energy for the great luminosity seen in X-ray sources, solving one of the earliest puzzles in X-ray astronomy. Equally important, binary systems appear to be the closest things to astrophysical laboratories, and it is fortunate that such interesting physical objects as neutron stars and black holes are found in them.

REFERENCES

1. R. Ruffini, Lectures at the Summer School of Theoretical Physics at Les Houches, August 1972.
2. Ibid.
3. R. Giacconi, H. Gursky, F.R. Paolini, and B. Rossi, Phys. Rev. Letters 9, 439, 1962.
4. R. Giacconi, S. Murray, H. Gursky, E.M. Kellogg, E. Schreier, and H. Tananbaum, Ap. J. 178, 281, 1972.
5. M. Oda, P. Gorenstein, H. Gursky, E.M. Kellogg, E. Schreier, H. Tananbaum, and R. Giacconi, Ap. J. 166, L1, 1971.
6. E. Schreier, H. Gursky, E.M. Kellogg, H. Tananbaum, and R. Giacconi, Ap. J. 170, L21, 1971.
7. S. Rappaport, R. Doxsey, and W. Zaumen, Ap. J. 168, L43, 1971b.
8. L. Braes, and G.K. Miley, Nature 232, 246, 1971.
9. R.M. Hjellming, and C.M. Wade, Ap. J. 168, L21, 1971.
10. H. Tananbaum, H. Gursky, E.M. Kellogg, R. Giacconi, and C. Jones, Ap. J. 177, L5, 1972.
11. L. Webster, and P. Murdin, Nature 235, 37, 1972. Also, C.T. Bolton, Nature 235, 271, 1972.
12. W. Forman, C. Jones, and W. Liller, Ap. J. 177, L103, 1972.
13. H. Tananbaum, H. Gurksy, E.M. Kellogg, R. Levinson, E. Schreier, and R. Giacconi, Ap. J. 174, L143, 1972.
14. R. Giacconi, H. Gursky, E.M. Kellogg, R. Levinson, E. Schreier, and H. Tananbaum, Ap. J. 184, 227, 1973.
15. F. Lamb, C. Pethick, and D. Pines, Ap. J. 184, 271, 1973.

658

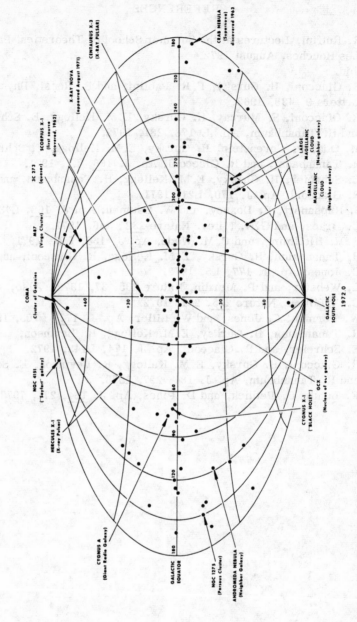

X-RAY SOURCES OBSERVED BY UHURU

CRAB NEBULA (Supernova) discovered 1963

CENTAURUS X-3 (X-RAY PULSAR)

X-RAY NOVA (appeared August 1971)

SCORPIUS X-1 (first source discovered, 1962)

3C 273 (quasar)

M87 (Virgo Cluster)

COMA Cluster of Galaxies

LARGE MAGELLANIC CLOUD (Neighbor galaxy)

SMALL MAGELLANIC CLOUD (Neighbor galaxy)

GALACTIC SOUTH POLE

NGC 4151 ("Seyfert" galaxy)

HERCULES X-1 (X-ray Pulsar)

GCX (Nucleus of our Galaxy)

CYGNUS X-1 ("BLACK HOLE?")

CYGNUS A (Giant Radio Galaxy)

GALACTIC EQUATOR

NGC 1275 (Perseus Cluster)

ANDROMEDA NEBULA (Neighbor Galaxy)

1972.0

Figure 1. The X-ray sky in galactic coordinates from the 2U Catalog.

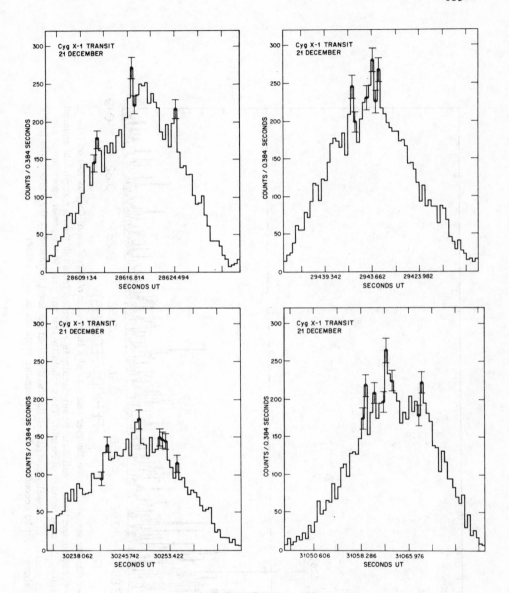

Fig. 2 Counts accumulated in the energy region 2.4 to 6.9 keV every .384 sec in the 5° x 5° FWHM detector during 4 transits of the Cyg X-1. Expected statistical fluctuations are shown in a few instances. The times shown are U. T. in seconds on December 21, 1970. Cyg X-1 was essentially in the center of the field of view during each pass.

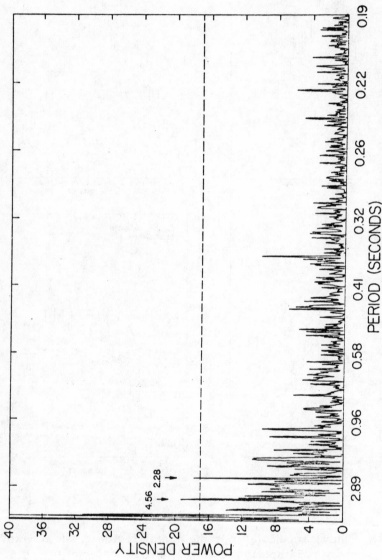

3. Power density spectrum from Fourier analysis of a 110 second observation of Cygnus X-1 on June 11, 1971 with 0.096 second time resolution. Power density is computed from the Fourier amplitude squared normalized by the total number of counts. The probability that any peak in the power spectrum of an equivalent interval of normally distributed data will exceed the level indicated by the dashed line is 10%. Periods above about 20 seconds are due to triangular response of collimator.

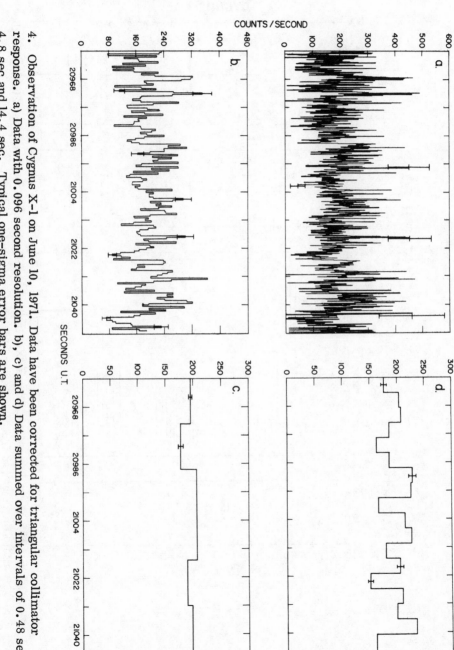

4. Observation of Cygnus X-1 on June 10, 1971. Data have been corrected for triangular collimator response. a) Data with 0.096 second resolution. b), c) and d) Data summed over intervals of 0.48 sec., 4.8 sec and 14.4 sec. Typical one-sigma error bars are shown.

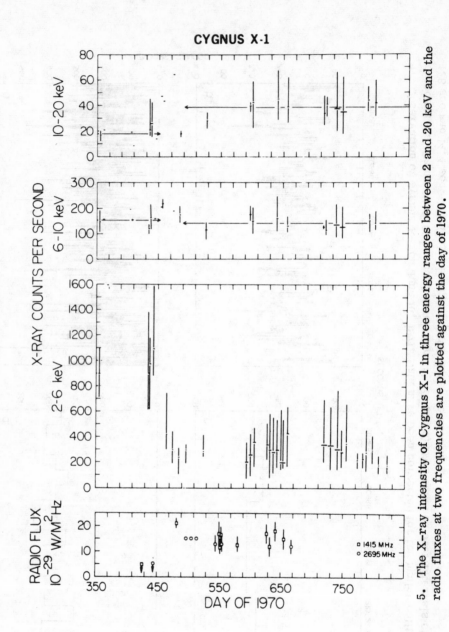

5. The X-ray intensity of Cygnus X-1 in three energy ranges between 2 and 20 keV and the radio fluxes at two frequencies are plotted against the day of 1970.

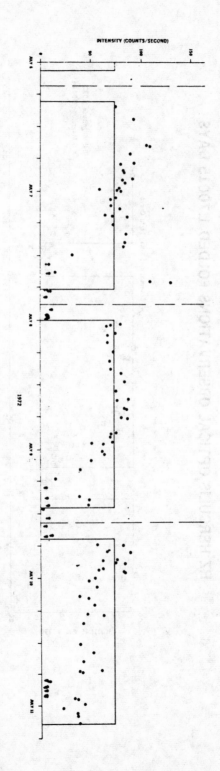

Figure 6. X-ray observations (2-6keV) of Her X-1 showing three orbital periods in July 1972.

664

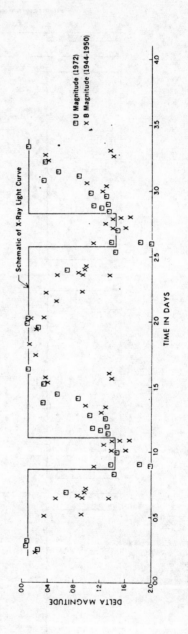

Figure 7.

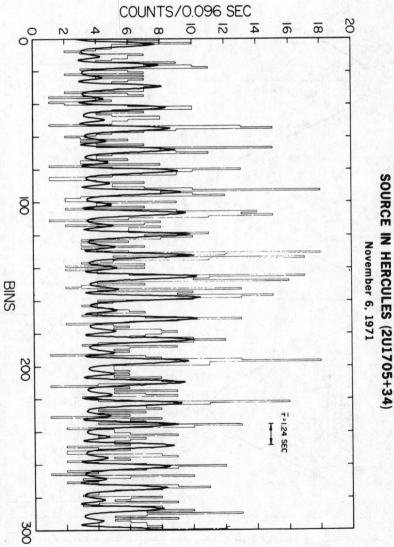

FIG. 8.—The counts accumulated in 0.096-second bins from Hercules X-1 during the central 30 seconds of a 100-second pass on 1971 November 6. The heavier curve is a minimum χ^2 fit to the pulsations of a sine function, its first and second harmonics plus a constant, modulated by the triangular response of the collimator. The functional fit is systematically below the peak counting rate partly due to the sharpness of the pulsing and partly due to the minimum χ^2 technique.

SOURCE IN HERCULES (2U1705+34)

November 6, 1971

COUNTS/0.096 SEC

BINS

$\tau = 1.24$ SEC

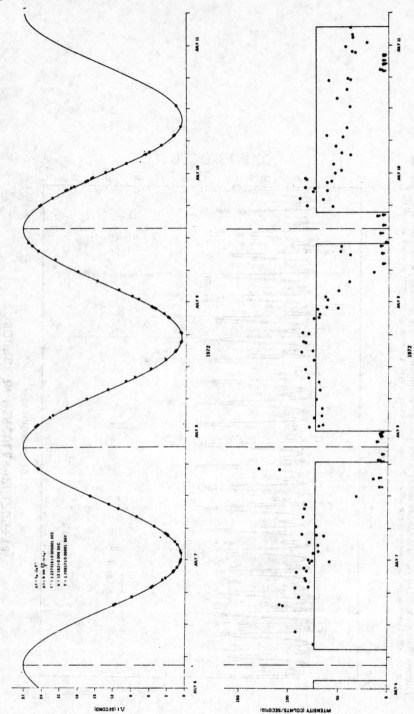

Figure 9. Hercules X-1 pulsation phasing showing sinusoidal Doppler effect, and corresponding intensity data.

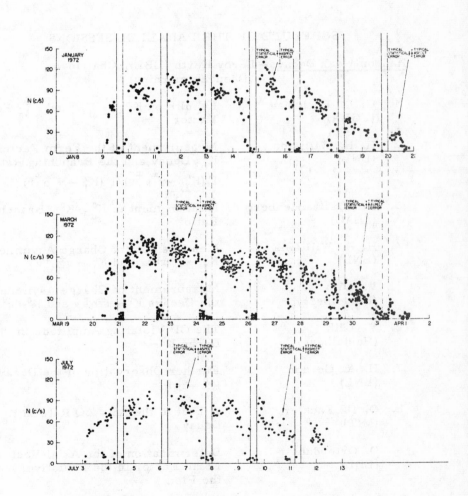

Figure 10. Three months of Her X-1 intensity data(2-6keV).

CONFERENCE PROGRAM

The 1973 Conference of the Division of Particles of the American Physical Society had morning and afternoon sessions of 3 to 4 hours in length for five days from Monday August 13 through Friday August 17. During the first two and one-half days there were parallel sessions, with three sessions being held at one time. Plenary sessions were held in the last half of the week. This program lists those people who spoke at each session. Asterisks to the left of speaker's names indicate those talks that are represented in these proceedings.

SCHEDULE OF THE PARALLEL SESSIONS

Hadron Weak Decays—Leroy Kerth (LBL), Chairman
(Monday morning)

1. C. D. Buchanan (UCLA) — Results on K^L_{e3}, $K^L_{\mu3}$, and $K^L_{3\pi}$ Form Factor

2. H. H. Williams (BNL) — Measurement of the Form Factor in $K^0_{\mu3}$ Decay and the Branching Ratio $\Gamma(K^0_L \to \pi^\pm \mu^\mp \nu)/\Gamma(K^0_L \to \pi^\pm e^\mp \nu)$

3. G. W. Brandenberg (SLAC) — Measurement of $K^0_{\mu3}/K^0_{e3}$ Branching Ratio

4. H. H. Williams (BNL) — Measurement of Charge Asymmetry in $K^0_L \to \pi^\pm \mu^\mp \nu$ and $K^0_L \to \pi^\pm e^\mp \nu$

5. V. Lüth (Heidelberg) — Measurement of Charge Asymmetry in the Decays $K^0 \to \pi^\pm e^\mp \nu$ and $\bar{K}^0 \to \pi^\pm \mu^\mp \nu$

6. V. Lüth (Heidelberg) — The CP Violating Amplitude in the Decay $K^0 \to \pi^+ \pi^-$

7. H. A. Gordon (BNL) — Further Observation of the Decay $K^0_L \to \mu^+ \mu^-$

8. O. D. Fackler (MIT) — A Test of the $\Delta S = \Delta Q$ Rate in K_{e3} Decay

9. D. Ortendahl (LBL) — Determination of the Axial Vector Form Factor in the Radiative Decay of the Pion

10. B. H. J. McKellar (Melbourne) — Theories of $\Delta S = 0$ Nonleptonic Weak Interactions

<u>Relativistic Heavy Ion Reactions</u>—Lee Schroeder (LBL), Chairman
(Monday morning)

1.	L. Goldzahl (Saclay)	Meson Production in dp and dd Collisions and High Energy Coherent Interaction of Deuterons on Protons
2.	T. Bowen (Arizona)	Production of Hypernuclei in a 2.1-GeV/Nucleon Oxygen Beam
3.	P. J. Lindstrom (LBL, Space Sciences - UCB)	Heavy Ion Inclusive Reactions at 2.1 GeV/Nucleon
4.	W. Schimmerling (LBL)	A Direct Measurement of Charged Pion Production by 520 MeV/amu Nitrogen Ions
5.	J. Papp (LBL)	Particle Production from Relativistic Proton, Deuteron, and Alpha Particle Bombardment of Various Nuclei
6.	H. J. Crawford (UCB)	Fragmentation of Au Bombarded with 2.1-GeV/Nucleon ^{16}O and ^{12}C Ions
7.	J. P. Wefel (NRL)	The Fragmentation of ^{14}N and ^{20}Ne Ions
8.	W. L. Wang (Carnegie-Mellon)	High Energy Heavy Ion Elastic Scattering
9.	A. C. Thompson (Carnegie-Mellon)	Measurement of dp Backward Elastic Scattering at Deuteron Beam Momenta of 3.43, 4.50, 5.75, and 6.60 GeV/c

<u>Diffraction Processes and Cross Sections at Very High Energies</u>—
Gerson Goldhaber (LBL), Chairman
(Monday morning)

1.	H. Lubatti (Washington)	Some Aspects of Pion and Nucleon Diffraction Dissociation Below 30 GeV
*2.	F. Winkelmann (LBL)	Diffraction Dissociation in 205-GeV/c π^-p Interactions
*3.	J. J. Whitmore (NAL)	Diffraction Dissociation in pp Interactions at NAL
*4.	A. A. Seidl (Michigan)	The Reaction pp $\rightarrow$ p + X at 405 GeV/c

5. S. Childress   Proton-Proton Inelastic Scattering in
   (Columbia)   the Diffractive Region As Observed
                     with Solid State Detector Array at
                     NAL

*6. F. Sannes   Measurement of $p+p \rightarrow p+X$ Between
    (Rutgers)   50 and 400 GeV

7. R. Cool   Elastic and Inelastic Proton-Proton
   (Rockefeller)   Scattering Data at Very Low t, from
                     the Internal H_2 Jet Target at NAL

(Monday afternoon)

*8. G. Goldhaber   Proton Diffraction Dissociation Data
    (UCB-LBL)   from the CERN ISR

9. U. Amaldi   Elastic Scattering and Diffraction
   (CERN)   Dissociation in the CERN ISR Energy
                     Range

10. P. Schreiner   Evidence for Double Pomeron Exchange
    (NAL)   in pp Reactions at 200 GeV

11. D. M. Chew   Evidence for Double Pomeron Exchange
    (UCB-LBL)   in the π^-p Reaction at 205 GeV

12. R. C. Hwa   Comparison with Theoretical Models
    (Oregon)

*Round table discussion on the agreement and discrepancies between
the experimental data. J. Lee-Franzini, J. Van der Velde,
F. Winkelmann, S. Childress, U. Amaldi, and others.

New Paths in High Energy Experiments — Lynn Stevenson (LBL),
Chairman
                 (Part of Monday afternoon)

*1. R. Settles   HYBUC and Preliminary Report on the
    (Vanderbilt) Σ^+ Magnetic Moment Experiment

*2. G. A. Smith   The NAL 30-inch Bubble Chamber-
    (Michigan State) Wide Gap Spark Chamber Hybrid
                     System

3. O. Piccioni   Nuclear Levels As Analyzers of High
   (UCSD)   Energy Interactions

4. E. F. Parker   Experimental Results with a Polarized
   (ANL)   Proton Beam and a Polarized Target

Particle Searches—Alfred Mann (Penn), Chairman
(Part of Monday afternoon following New Paths)

1. L. Leipuner (BNL) — Search for Quarks Produced in the Interactions of 300-GeV Protons

2. H. Bingham (UCB) — Quark Search in a Bubble Chamber Exposure to a 205-GeV/c Negative Particle Beam Produced by 300-GeV Protons

3. S. Frankel (Penn) — Search for Long-Lived Particles in Aluminum Targets Irradiated with 300- and 400-BeV Protons

Constituent Models and Light Cone Analysis—Geoffrey West (Stanford), Chairman
(Monday afternoon)

1. G. West (Stanford) — Deep Inelastic Electron Scattering from Atoms, Nuclei, and Nucleons

2. M. Kugler (Weizmann) — Current and Constituent Quarks

3. R. Cahn (SLAC) — Final States in Deep Inelastic Electron Scattering

4. Y. Frischman (Weizmann) — Topics in Light Cone and Scaling

*5. R. Savit (SLAC) — Parton Models and Deep Hadron-Hadron Scattering

6. M. Islam (Connecticut) — Bremsstrahlung Model and Bjorken Scaling

Gauge Theories—Helen Quinn (Harvard), Chairman
(Tuesday morning)

*1. M. Halpern (UCB) — Unified Gauge Theories of Spin ≤ 1

2. K. Lane (UCB) — Attempts to Calculate the Pion Mass

3. H. Quinn (Harvard) — Deep Inelastic Leptoproduction Predictions in Quark-Gauge Models

4. T. Appelquist (Harvard) — Gauge Theories for Strong Interactions

<u>Multi-Particle Production</u>—Richard Lander (UCD), Chairman
(Tuesday morning)

*1. D. Ljung   Experimental Inclusive γ, K^0, Λ, and
    (NAL) $\bar{\Lambda}$ Production

2. B. Y. Oh   Inclusive Spectra of Secondaries from
   (Michigan State)   200-GeV/c pp Interactions in the NAL
                           Hybrid System

3. R. Singer   Inclusive $\pi^{\pm}$ Spectra from pp Collisions
   (ANL)   at NAL

4. C. Bromberg   Study of $\pi^{\pm}$ Spectra and Correlations in
   (Rochester)   pp Collisions at NAL

5. D. Pellett   Charged-Particle Multiplicity in $\pi^+ p$
   (UCD)   and pp Collisions at 100 GeV/c

6. Z. Ming Ma   Semi-inclusive Scaling in pp Scattering
   (Michigan State)   Between 13 and 205 GeV/c

*7. J. Florian   Proton Interactions in Heavy Nuclei at
    (Washington)   200 GeV

*8. J. W. Elbert   Underground Muon Data Compared to
    (Utah)   Hadronic Scaling Predictions from 2
                           to 1000 TeV

9. R. Williams   Inclusive Reactions at 10 and 15.5
   (Washington)   GeV/c

10. A. Levy   Inclusive Study of Baryon-Meson and
    (MIT)   Meson Systems in $\pi^- p$ Interactions at
                         15 GeV/c

11. H. Neal   Polarization of Inclusively Produced
    (Indiana)   Particles

12. N. N. Biswas   Charged and Neutral Pion Multiplicity
    (Notre Dame)   in pp Interactions and a New
                           Parametrization of Inclusive Particle
                           Spectra

(Part of Tuesday afternoon)

*13. D. Sivers   Some Off-Beat Aspects of Proton-Proton
    (ANL)   Production Reactions

*14. G. H. Thomas   One-Dimensional Models and What Can
    (ANL)   be Learned About Them From NAL
                         and ISR Data

15. H. Bøggild   Production of Low P_T $\pi^{\pm}K^{\pm}p^{\pm}$ in the
    (Copenhagen)   Central Rapidity Region at the ISR

16. T. Ferbel   Multiplicity Distribution in 400-GeV
    (Rochester)   pp Collisions

<u>Large Transverse Momentum Phenomena</u>—Rodney Cool (Rockefeller),
Chairman
    (Part of Tuesday afternoon following Multi-Particle)

1. D. Theriot   Production of Large Transverse
    (NAL)   Momentum Gamma Rays at NAL

2. R. Cool   Observation at the ISR of π^0 Mesons
    (Rockefeller)   with Large Transverse Momenta

3. T. Ferbel   Energy Dependence of the Inclusive
    (Rochester)   Cross Section for the Reaction
     $\pi^+d \to \pi^-$ + Anything at Large
     Transverse Momenta

4. H. Neal   Recent Polarization Results in Large-
    (Indiana)   Angle Proton-Proton Scattering

<u>Two-Body Production Processes</u>—Michel Davier (SLAC), Chairman
    (Tuesday morning)

1. W. Dunwoodie   Experimental Results on Vector Meson
    (CERN)   Production

*2. J. A. J. Matthews   Inelastic Scattering Amplitudes
    (SLAC)

3. S. Kramer   Rho-Omega Interference
    (ANL)

*4. D. J. Quinn   Experimental Results on Pseudoscalar
    (Tufts)   Meson Photoproduction

*5. A. S. L. Parsons   Baryon Exchange Processes
    (Rutherford)

6. P. Nemethy   Hyperon Interactions
    (Yale)

(Part of Tuesday afternoon)

*7. R. D. Field   Predicting K^{*0} and $\overline{K}^{*0}$ Production
    (BNL)   from ρ^0 and ω^0 Production

Future Directions:

8. M. Davier　　　　　　Elastic Amplitudes
   (SLAC)

9. W. Meyer　　　　　　Charge Exchange and Resonance
   (ANL)　　　　　　　　Production

10. B. Sadoulet　　　　　Inelastic Amplitudes
    (LBL)

e^+e^- Experimental Results and Theory—Roy Schwitters (SLAC), Chairman
(Part of Tuesday afternoon)

1. G. Tarnopolsky　　　Electron-Positron Annihilation at
   (CEA-Technion)　　　5 GeV CM Energy

*2. C. D. Buchanan　　　Anti-Nucleon Production at SPEAR
    (UCLA)

*3. R. Cahn　　　　　　Electron-Positron Annihilation into
    (SLAC)　　　　　　　Hadrons

Neutrino Experiments—Harry Bingham (UCB), Chairman
(Part of Tuesday afternoon following e^+e^-)

4. D. Buchholz　　　　　Results from the Cal Tech-NAL
   (Cal Tech)　　　　　　Neutrino Experiment

5. H. Wachsmuth　　　　Possible Observation of Neutral
   (CERN)　　　　　　　Currents in the Gargamelle Neutrino
   　　　　　　　　　　Experiments

6. A. Mann　　　　　　Results from the Wisconsin-Penn-
   (Pennsylvania)　　　　Harvard-NAL Neutrino Experiment

Spectroscopy—Angela Barbaro-Galtieri (LBL), Chairman
(Part of Tuesday afternoon following Two-Body)

SU(3)-Inelastic Reactions and Higher Symmetries

1. M. D. Jones　　　　　Analysis of the $(70, 1^-)$ States Using the
   (Chicago)　　　　　　Symmetric Quark Model

2. R. Longacre　　　　　Partial Wave Analysis of SU(3)-
   (LBL)　　　　　　　　Inelastic Channels

3. R. G. Moorhouse　　　Resonance Formation Amplitudes in
   (Glasgow)　　　　　　$\pi N \rightarrow \pi\Delta$, ρN and the Quark Model

4. H. Oberlack　　　　　Resonance Formation Amplitudes in
   (LBL)　　　　　　　　Pion Photoproduction and the Quark
   　　　　　　　　　　Model

| 5. | H. J. Melosh (Chicago) | Relation Between Current Quarks and Constituent Quarks |
| 6. | M. Kugler (SLAC) | Signs of Resonant Amplitudes in a Theory Based on the Transformations Between Current Quarks and Constituent Quarks |

*Round table discussion on the "Comparison of Models for Resonance Decays." M. Kugler, H. J. Melosh, R. G. Moorhouse, and J. L. Rosner.

(Wednesday morning)

Mostly Baryon Resonances

1.	R. L. Kelly (LBL)	Partial Wave Analysis of K^+p Elastic Scattering
*2.	A. S. Carroll (BNL)	Precision Measurements of $K^{\pm}$ and $\bar{p}$ total Cross Sections on Hydrogen and Deuterium Below 1.1 GeV/c
3.	M. D. Jones (Chicago)	The Reaction $K^-p \quad \Sigma^0\eta$ near Threshold
4.	D. Merrill (Chicago)	Multi-channel Analysis of the Reactions $K^-p \to \bar{K}N, \Lambda\pi, \Sigma\pi$
*5.	R. D. Tripp (LBL)	Prospects for Y^* Experiments
6.	M. Pripstein (LBL)	New Results on the Reactions $\pi^-p \to n\eta$, $\pi^-p \to \pi^0n$ and the Polarization Parameter for $\pi^-p \to \pi^0n$

Meson Resonances

*7.	D. D. Carmony (Purdue)	Review of Evidence for High Mass K^* States
8.	G. Lynch (LBL)	Properties of the B Meson
9.	K. Moffeit (SLAC)	The ρ'
10.	G. Thompson (Purdue)	Partial Wave Analysis in the A_3 Region
*11.	G. A. Smith (Michigan State)	The R-S-T-U Mass Region

Theory of Strong Interactions—Geoffrey Chew (UCB), Chairman
(Wednesday morning)

*1. R. L. Sugar   The Eikonal Approach to High Energy
    (UCSB)   Scattering

2. J. Walker   Impact Picture of Strong Interactions
    (NAL)

3. F. Henyey   Impact Parameter Study of High Energy
    (Michigan)   Proton Scattering

*4. John Ng   Reggeon Calculus View of Diffraction
    (Washington)   Scattering

*5. W. R. Frazer   Perturbative Approach to High Energy
    (UCSD)   Multiparticle Reactions

*6. J. Koplik   Threshold Effects and Oscillations in
    (LBL)   Models with t-Channel Factorization

7. S. Auerbach   Froissart Bound on Weak Interaction
    (UCB)   Total Cross Sections

8. D. Lichtenberg   Veneziano Model and the Elasticities
    (Indiana)   of Pion-Nucleon Resonances

9. P. Finkler   Duality and Pseudoscalar Mesons
    (Nebraska)

Experimental Results on Leptoproduction—Hobey DeStaebler (SLAC),
Chairman
                    (Wednesday morning)

*1. A. Bodek   Experimental Results on Scaling and the
    (MIT)   Neutron-to-Proton Cross-Section
                      Ratio in Deep Inelastic Electron
                      Scattering

2. H. Meyer   Electroproduction of Hadrons
    (DESY)

3. A. Sadoff   Measurement of Charged Hadron
    (Ithaca College) Multiplicity in Electroproduction

4. G. Luxton   Pion Exchange in Inelastic
    (Stanford)   Electroproduction

5. A. Eisner   Measurements of Deep Inelastic Compton
    (UCSB)   Scattering

6. D. Buchholz   An Exploratory Study of High Energy
    (Cal Tech)   Neutrino Interactions at NAL

SCHEDULE OF THE PLENARY SESSIONS

Wednesday afternoon—R. Tripp (LBL) presiding

*J. L. Rosner (Minnesota)	Hadron Spectroscopy
*G. L. Kane (Michigan)	Phenomenology of High Energy Exchange Processes
*D. W. G. S. Leith (SLAC)	Diffractive Processes

Thursday morning—W. Fretter (UCB) presiding

*H. Bøggild (Copenhagen)	Inclusive Experiments at ISR-Energies
*T. Ferbel (Rochester)	Particle Multiplicities and Correlations at NAL Energies
*C. Quigg (Stony Brook)	What Have We Learned from High Energy Experiments?

Thursday afternoon—J. Bjorken (SLAC) presiding

*H. D. I. Abarbanel (NAL)	A Survey of Developments in Strong Interaction Theories
R. Cowsik (UCB)	The Role of Astrophysics in Understanding Elementary Particles
*E. J. Schreier (Smithsonian Astr. Obs.)	Galactic X-Ray Sources

Friday morning—B. Richter (SLAC) presiding

*H. L. Lynch (SLAC)	e^+e^- Experiments
*B. C. Barish (CalTech)	Experimental Results on Deep Inelastic Leptoproduction
*J. Kogut (Cornell)	Recent Progress in Theories of Deep Inelastic Phenomena

Friday afternoon—W. Wenzel (LBL) presiding

*H. Wachsmuth (CERN)	Review of Latest Results from High Energy Neutrino Experiments
*D. R. Nygren (LBL)	Review of K^0 Decays
T. Appelquist (Harvard)	Unified Field Theories

AUTHOR INDEX

AIP Conference Proceedings

	L.C. Number	ISBN
No. 1 Feedback and Dynamic Control of Plasmas (Princeton 1970)	70-141596	0-88318-100-2
No. 2 Particles and Fields - 1971 (Rochester 1971)	71-184662	0-88318-101-0
No. 3 Thermal Expansion - 1971 (Corning 1971)	72-76970	0-88318-102-9
No. 4 Superconductivity in d- and f-Band Metals (Rochester 1971)	74-188879	0-88318-103-7
No. 5 Magnetism and Magnetic Materials - 1971 (2 parts) (Chicago 1971)	59-2468	0-88318-104-5
No. 6 Particle Physics (Irvine 1971)	72-81239	0-88318-105-3
No. 7 Exploring the History of Nuclear Physics (Brookline 1967, 1969)	72-81883	0-88318-106-1
No. 8 Experimental Meson Spectroscopy - 1972 (Philadelphia 1972)	72-88226	0-88318-107-X
No. 9 Cyclotrons - 1972 (Vancouver 1972)	72-92798	0-88318-108-8
No.10 Magnetism and Magnetic Materials - 1972 (Denver 1972)	72-623469	0-88318-109-6
No.11 Transport Phenomena - 1973 (Brown University Conference)	73-80682	0-88318-110-X
No.12 Experiments on High Energy Particle Collisions - 1973 (Vanderbilt Conference)	73-81705	0-88318-111-8
No.13 π-π Scattering - 1973 (Tallahassee Conference)	73-81704	0-88318-112-6
No.14 Particles and Fields - 1973 (Berkeley Conference)	73-91923	0-88318-113-4
No.15 High Energy Collisions - 1973 (Stony Brook Conference)	73-92324	0-88318-114-2